An Introduction to

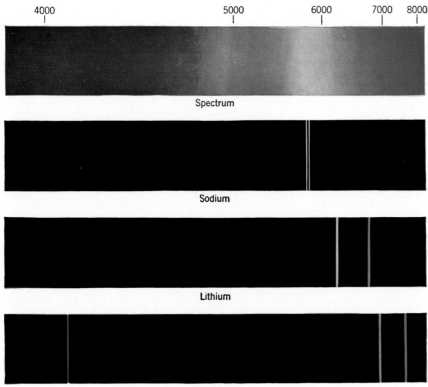

4000 5000 6000 7000 8000

Spectrum

Sodium

Lithium

Potassium

Continuous spectrum as from a body heated white hot (at top), and three bright-line spectra emitted by atoms, as indicated, in hot gases. The numbers at the top are wavelengths expressed in Ångstrom units. (From Dull, Brooks, and Metcalf, *Modern Chemistry*, Henry Holt and Company, Inc.)

FROM ATOMS TO STARS

An Introduction to the Physical Sciences

FROM
ATOMS
TO
STARS
the Physical Sciences

THEODORE ASKOUNES ASHFORD

Saint Louis University

Holt, Rinehart and Winston, Inc.
New York

TO MY WIFE AND SONS

(Without whose help the book might have been written many years earlier, but who have suffered the most during the period.)

PREFACE

This book is intended to give the student an understanding of the physical world as conceived by the scientists of our time. It is an extended discussion of some of the phenomena of our physical environment and their interpretation in terms of the ideas and theories of modern science. From the immense quantity of phenomena that occur or have been observed, a limited number have been selected to serve a two-fold purpose. On the one hand, they are representative of carefully observed nature, while on the other they form a basic pattern that can be interpreted by the ideas of science. The familiar phenomena are shown to take on new, and sometimes strange, appearances. The unfamiliar is then interpreted in terms of the familiar. All the phenomena, familiar and unfamiliar alike, are explained in terms of the same set of ideas—ideas that add up to a unified picture of the physical universe.

The discussion is addressed to the student whose primary interest is in a field other than science. All that is assumed is that he have an interest in the world around him. No special mathematical or scientific background is required. For the most part the discussion is carried on in pictorial terms using the arithmetic and geometry of ordinary experience. In few places is more than a knowledge of simple algebra required. The discussion is, however, quantitative and analytical and the student who has a natural or acquired facility for thinking in terms of numbers and quantities will follow the reasoning more easily.

A deliberate effort has been made to strip the subject matter of as much of its technical detail as possible and to ignore the distinctions between the sciences. Consequently, the treatment is integrated aiming at producing a unified picture of our environment without consciously recognizing the various branches of science. The discussion is generally developmental. It is historical in the sense of relating what ideas preceded other ideas, and what discoveries led to new ideas. The emphasis throughout is placed on the methods of science—both of discovery and of analysis.

The text is based on several courses that the author developed and taught in the college of the University of Chicago from 1936 to 1950. These courses were in the physical sciences, designed primarily for general education.

The text was used in manuscript form in a course for graduate students in philosophy, history, and religion at Saint Louis University. Part of the manuscript was used in a class given to high-school chemistry teachers in the Institute for the Teaching of Chemistry sponsored by the National Science Foundation at Saint Louis University.

The author is indebted to his colleagues and students for the development of the ideas and philosophy of the book. Special acknowledgment is due to the following, all former colleagues at the University of Chicago: Herman I. Schlesinger and Harvey B. Lemon, pioneers in the course; Walter Bartky, J. Harlen Bretz, Carey Croneis, Nancy Cross, Robert M. Garrels, William C. Krumbein, Lou Williams Page, Thornton L. Page, Zens L. Smith, Reginald J. Stephenson; members of the advisory committee of the course, James Franck, Maria Goeppert Mayer and Harrison Brown. To Dr. Nicholas D. Cheronis of Brooklyn College, for long discussions on science and science teaching. To Dr. Thornton L. Page for permission to reproduce an excerpt from the "Almagest." To Dr. Robert M. Garrels for the benefit of extended discussion in geology and help in obtaining illustrations.

The author further wishes to express his appreciation to all those who assisted in the writing of the book, especially to the late Dr. George W. Schaeffer at Saint Louis University for the strong interest and encouragement, also to Dr. Schaeffer and the administration of Saint Louis University for lightening the teaching load in the fall of 1957; to James Richter for suggestions in designing and executing the illustrations; and to Barbara L. Starkey for the assistance in editing, typing, and preparation of the manuscript.

T. A. A.

St. Louis, Missouri
February, 1960

CONTENTS

INTRODUCTION

1. SCIENCE IN MODERN SOCIETY

If one were to inquire what characteristic features distinguish the present civilization from the other civilizations in the past, he would find one element appearing again and again. This element is natural science. From its early beginnings in the sixteenth century, the development of science has influenced the course of western civilization more and more, until today it plays a most dominant role. It is not much of an exaggeration to say that we live in a world that, materially and intellectually, has been created by science.

This point is easy to illustrate on the material level. One merely needs to mention the telephone, the radio, the television, the automobile, and the airplane, or any of the countless devices invented by the application of science. Similarly, one may mention new materials, new plastics, new metals, new medicines, and, in short, point out the obvious fact that there is hardly an article used in the home, in the places of work, or in the places of enjoyment that has not been modified by technology based on science: the means of communication that bind this continent into a single community depend on scientific know-how; without modern sanitation it would be impossible to have large centers of population; without modern industry and agriculture it would be impossible to feed, to clothe, and to provide the "abundant life" to this large population. Scientific knowledge underlies the entire industrial and agricultural structure of modern life. Our immense industrial plant requires an army of highly trained men and women for its mere maintenance, to say nothing about its further development.

What does science mean in national defense and war? The atomic bomb and the hydrogen bomb come immediately to mind, because they have attracted, and rightly so, public attention throughout the world. More recently, satellites, space platforms, and intercontinental ballistic missiles have become the focus of attention. But there is much more involved than these developments. World War II was fought predominantly by machines. The battles were really won on the assembly line. For every man fighting on the front, there were 18 men under arms behind him manipulating machines and bringing up supplies; and behind these, 50 million workers forging the weapons of war, producing food, and safeguarding the health and welfare of the fighting men. Behind this formidable working force, there were scientists and engineers, inventing and perfecting radar, proximity bombs, new explosives, new drugs, and countless other devices and materials. This less-well-known story needs to be told and the average citizen should understand it. Nor has the picture altered since the war. If anything, it has become even more sharply defined. So long as the world remains hostile, science is necessary for our national survival.

Turning to the arts of peace, let us examine some facts. In the field of medicine the new wonder drugs have eliminated the dread of many a disease. With the discovery of penicillin and the other antibiotics, the pneumonia death rate has been reduced by 85 percent, that from streptococcus 60 percent, and all in all, 13 years have been added to the life expectancy of the average citizen. With the development of sanitation, typhus is virtually unknown, and epidemics no longer threaten the large centers of population. Indeed, our large cities would not be possible without modern sanitation methods. The Black Plague, which in the thirteenth century wiped out one third of the population of Europe, can no longer repeat the performance. And the battle goes on in the laboratory.

Take the instance of transportation and communication. Not so long ago the only travel on land was by foot or by means of horse or horse-drawn carriages; and on the sea by rowing or by sailboat. Then came the steamboat, the steam locomotive, the automobile, the airplane, the telephone, the radio, and the television. Whole populations can now move from place to place. It is now possible to travel by airplane to the furthest point on the earth in a matter of hours—in less time than it took to travel across a county by foot only a few generations ago. It is now possible to talk by telephone to the furthest point on earth. This is familiar enough, but it is not generally realized that all this is possible because some curious scientists in a laboratory, or in a shop, or in the kitchen wondered at the expansive power of steam (as James Watt did), or experimented with wires and magnets (as Faraday did), or mixed chemicals in a test tube (as Alfred Nobel did). Underlying all these developments is scientific knowledge.

Take the instance of soil productivity. Ordinary land, even the best land, yields about 25 bushels of corn per acre. With the understanding of the chemistry of the soil—the chemicals needed by a plant to grow and produce food, as studied by chemists—and with the development of hybrid varieties by the biologists and geneticists, it is now possible to produce 100 bushels of corn per acre. If this were done with every crop, it would mean nothing less than adding to the United States a continent one and one-half times its size, and this without war or conquest.

The story is similar in the case of energy and of power. The energy produced by a man is a few kilowatt-hours per day. A horse produces energy at a rate roughly six times that of a healthy man. But when this is compared with the energy of coal, oil, and the hydroelectric plant, it pales into insignificance. Few of us realize that when we drive to the gas station and say, "five gallons, please" we put in our tank the equivalent of a dam of 1,000,000 gallons of water, 50 feet high. Each person in the United States uses the equivalent of 30 horses in the form of electric power, coal, or gasoline. And what of the future? We are just entering the atomic age and have hardly begun to tap the prodigious sources of nuclear energy. The future, even more than the present, belongs to science.

This situation is also true in the case of chemicals. For example, a hundred years ago aluminum was a rare and very expensive metal. When the Washington monument was built, a German chemist was commissioned to prepare the aluminum for the lightning rods at a cost to the taxpayer of 10,000 dollars. Today it would cost only a few cents. How did this happen? An unassuming young man at Oberlin College was experimenting with batteries and compounds of aluminum. The result is the giant aluminum industry, producing hundreds of millions of tons per year for airplanes, for structural purposes, for cooking utensils, for nonrusting nails. Moreover, the source of aluminum is unlimited, over 8 percent of the crust of the earth being aluminum in combined form.

The same story can be told about magnesium or bromine, both of which are now obtained from sea water—again an unlimited source; or about nitrates, used for explosives and fertilizers, now obtained from the air; or about dyes and medicines, now obtained from petroleum. The list is endless. There is hardly an article of industry or commerce, in the shop, in the home, or in our food, that has not been touched by science. And in all these instances the pattern is similar. Some scientist has been experimenting quietly in the laboratory or in his study, because he was interested to know.

All this is impressive and familiar. There is, however, another part of the story less obvious and less well known, but far more important. It is the impact of science on the mind of man. Fundamentally, science is an intellectual enterprise, an attempt to understand the world in a particular way. All the developments mentioned above are but the results, the outcomes, of this intellectual activity. From the gropings of the past there has gradually emerged a clearer understanding of the working mysteries of nature and of the extent, in both time and space, of our physical universe.

The development of science is a story of expanding intellectual horizons. In terms of space, the concept of the universe as a valley bordered by the hilltops and enveloped by the dome of heaven perhaps only a few miles high has been expanded, first to include the whole Mediterranean basin, then the entire earth, and finally the vast cosmos in which the earth is but a tiny speck. The dome of heaven has been constantly receding: first to the moon and just beyond the planets, whose distances are measured in millions of miles; then to the stars and the limits of our galaxy, where light takes many years to reach even though traveling with the stupendous speed of nearly one fifth of a million miles per second; and more recently to galaxies and systems of galaxies, from which light takes hundreds of millions of years to reach the earth. The most daring and imaginative thinkers of the past could not even conceive of the vastness that the scientists of our day so confidently measure.

In terms of time, the story is similar. The memory of the individual extends to the time of his early childhood; from the accounts of living individuals time may be extended two or three generations; tradition extends it to several more generations; recorded history extends it to a few thousand years; archeologists add a few more thousand years; but when the geologist and the geophysicist enter the picture, they extend time first to hundreds of thousands of years, then to millions of years, and now they confidently speak of events that occurred 2 billion years ago or more. They consider problems such as the age of the earth, of the sun, of the stars, of our present universe. At the forefront of scientific thought, they now consider ways of investigating a prestellar age—the time when the elements were synthesized before the stars were formed. It is now possible to speculate intelligently on the possibility of a beginning of time!

In the direction opposite to the very large, human experience and human consciousness have been extended to the very small—into the microworld of molecules, atoms, and electrons. Not only the thin air and the fluid ocean, but even the solid earth and the strongest steel are conceived of as tenuous and porous—like swarms of bees—consisting of discrete particles, eternally moving or quivering and separated by empty space. These "molecules" are so small that 250 million of them could rest on the dot at the end of this sentence. The molecules, themselves, are complex, consisting of still smaller particles, the atoms, of which there are only about one hundred kinds. These atoms combine in one way to give aspirin; in another way to give a complex structure such as that of a vitamin; in still another to give strychnine, or the pigment of blue eyes, or the explosive, TNT, and so on—to give, in short, all the substances that make up the matter of the universe. Although inconceivably small, the atoms have been counted, weighed, and measured. The atoms themselves are nearly all empty space, consisting of still smaller particles—the protons, the electrons, and the neutrons—that are separated by distances thousands of times their own diameters. The atom seems to be built on a plan similar to that of the solar system. It has a small central nucleus around which electrons move in planetlike motion and it is, relatively, as "empty" as the solar system. More recently, these inconceivably small nuclei have been smashed, breaking up into nuclei of other elements and releasing the so-called "atomic" or "nuclear" energy.

In another direction, the orderly operation of the processes and forces of nature have been revealed. That baffling problem of the ages, motion and change, has been given at least a partial answer. The science of mechanics has been developed, in terms of which the motion of falling drops, of rolling stones, and of accelerating automobiles can be understood. This same set of laws of mechanics has been extended to describe the motions of planets, of stars, and of molecules. The whole of nature is revealed to be an orderly whole, a *uni*-verse, subject to law and order.

The success of science in the intellectual field and its applications in the practical field have had a tremendous influence on all departments of human thought and action. When James Watt invented the steam engine, he could not possibly imagine, even if he were inclined to do so, that he was introducing the industrial *revolution* with all that the word implies—a political, social, and economic upheaval. When von Bayer synthesized indigo from coal tar, 4 million acres of land in India were released for cultivation of grain, but only after dislocation, famine, and death to the millions who cultivated the indigo plant. Increasing life expectancy is transforming us into a nation of "oldsters" and many problems must be faced and solved. In our own day, the development of nuclear weapons makes wars of annihilation possible and forcibly thrusts upon us the necessity of coming to an understanding with the other nations. It is not merely a matter of peace and tranquillity, but, rather, poses the question of the very survival of the human race.

The impact on the arts is equally apparent. Millions can now see a first-rate performance of a Shakespearian play or hear a famous orchestra performing a Beethoven symphony. Very faithful reproductions of the masterpieces are now available and, for that matter, even the originals can be seen without too much trouble or expense. In politics we can now hear our representatives and the political candidates from our own living room. It is now possible for a large nation to have direct democracy for the first time in history. This creates new and bigger problems, but also greater opportunities, for the social scientists and the educators to work out.

The influence of science on philosophy and religion is just as significant, though more subtle and more difficult to describe or to evaluate. The intellectual framework of science is essentially that part of philosophy called "natural" philosophy. It began with the Ionian philosophers in the sixth century B.C. who asked fundamental questions about the nature of the heavens, the earth, life, and man. With the growth of scientific knowledge and increased understanding, better answers could be formulated and deeper questions asked. No modern natural philosopher can ignore the world revealed by the microscope, the test tube, and the telescope. Similarly, the methods of science are intimately bound with the branch of philosophy called epistemology, dealing with the theory of knowledge. The methods of investigation and the information that they reveal about the external world contributed to a deeper understanding of the nature of knowledge and truth. These influences in turn have affected religious conceptions and presuppositions.

It is not difficult to continue with other examples. But the point is clear. Science occupies a central position in our western society. It dominates our whole existence. No one can claim an all-around education without some understanding of it.

2. THE SCIENTIFIC METHOD

The unparalleled and ever-increasing success of science has led to the general belief that the scientists have developed and are employing a "method," which is extremely effective in gaining new knowledge, in organizing it, and in applying it. This has been variously called the "scientific method," the "scientific attitude," or "scientific thinking." Many persons, both scientists and nonscientists, have held strongly the opinion that the "invention" of the "scientific method" is the greatest achievement of modern science. In fact many educators and scientists have often said that science teaching can best serve the nonscientists (as well as the scientists) by giving them training in the "scientific method." However, there have been others who questioned these opinions. Volumes have been written on the subject—some sense and a good deal of nonsense. We shall probably add our share of both.

Difficulties and disagreements are encountered at the outset in deciding precisely what the "scientific method" is. So long as the discussion is carried on in general terms, there is not too much disagreement. There is no question that the scientists, by temperament and training, approach their problems in some systematic way. Nor is there much question that this systematic way has certain characteristic features which, taken together, define it and set it apart from the methods and procedures employed in other fields. And certainly there can be no doubt that the scientists, by these procedures, obtain results in their fields. If by "scientific method" one means the systematic way of the scientists, then all authors agree fairly well that there is a "method in their madness."

However, beyond this point there is wide disagreement and many questions arise. Is the scientific method a method of thinking, a method of discovery, a method of procedure, a technique, or is it essentially an attitude of mind? Is there *one method* used in all the sciences or are there many methods? Is the "method" to be considered broadly or narrowly? How is the method (or methods) related to the subject matter? How is it related to the kind of knowledge to which it leads? How does the method differ from common sense and from the methods used in other fields? Can the method be taught? Is the method applicable to other fields? To these and many similar questions there are no simple answers and no general agreement.

The difficulties and disagreements arise from many sources. In the first place, the activities of the scientists are very complex, varying from science to science, and from problem to problem within the same science. Other difficulties arise from the fact that different authors approach the subject from different points of view. The scientists attempt to understand and explain their method by analyzing their own processes of thought and their patterns of action. The nonscientists attempt to define the method by observing scientists in action, by listening to them describe what they do, or by analyzing their product—the resulting knowledge. As one might expect, conceptions vary widely as to what the method is. Another source of major difficulty is the lack of communication. The terms used in discussion of the method often have different meanings for the scientists and for the nonscientists in the several fields.

We cannot hope to avoid all these difficulties, but we do believe that the situation is not hopeless. We shall attempt to give the reader a reasonable understanding of the scientific method—what *we* understand the method to be—by doing three things. First, in the introduction we shall describe in general terms the attitudes and procedures of the scientists, and the nature of scientific knowledge. This may not give the reader precise notions, but at least it may avoid gross misconceptions and may set him thinking in the right direction. Second, and perhaps more effective, we shall use the scientific method throughout this book by approaching and solving the problems the way scientists do. Thus, by example we hope to illustrate the method. In addition, we shall make it a point to call attention to various characteristics of the method in the context in which they arise or are most prominently exhibited. Finally, we shall give a series of questions on methodology and a list of references at the end of this chapter. However, it is suggested that the reader return to the problems of method after he has mastered some of the facts and ideas of science.

The scientists have certain attitudes and predispositions, which they exhibit typically while they are engaged in their work. Of course, in their other activities as husbands, parents, citizens, or members of a social group, they are, by and large, no different from other people. But *as scientists,* they are intensely interested in the external world—in the phenomena that occur in nature, their description and interpretation. They accept, at least to begin with, the common-sense view that the external world is real and has an objective existence, independent of the individual. They take the external world to be consistent and not capricious; and to be neutral toward man—neither benevolent nor malevolent. Moreover, they believe that the world is orderly and can be known by examination and investigation. While they are convinced that the phenomena are innumerable, confusing, and sometimes even deceiving in complexity, they confidently believe that there is simplicity under this complexity. They conceive that their task is to take the multitude of confusing experiences from the external world and bring them into intelligible order, on the maxim that *"order alone is intelligible, disorder is unintelligible."*

The procedure of scientists has a certain general pattern in which the following steps can be recognized: Observation of phenomena and the establishment of facts; grouping of the phenomena into generalizations and laws of nature; and construction of theories which are used to interpret and correlate the phenomena and to predict new phenomena. Each of these steps is a complex procedure. The scientific method is not a "formula" that can be quickly learned and applied to all kinds of problems. We shall expand only slightly on these steps at this point.

Observations. A *phenomenon* is whatever is observed to occur in nature. A *fact* is a faithful description of a phenomenon or some aspect of the phenomenon. A fact is a *fact* only to the extent that it describes faithfully and accurately what happens. Certain facts thrust themselves upon us in the course of experience: the sun and the stars rise and set; the moon presents its phases in the course of a month; unsupported stones fall to the ground. By far the greater number of scientific facts, however, are obtained by purposeful observation and experimentation.

An important characteristic of the scientific method is the dominant role assigned to the phenomena. The phenomena are the ultimate source of all scientific knowledge. They are beyond appeal. Whatever happens, happens. This dominant role is transferred to the facts. For this reason great precautions are taken to establish the facts. They are subjected to the utmost and grueling scrutiny before they are admitted as facts—before they are accepted as faithfully representing what really happens.

Laws of Nature. Some facts have certain elements in common. Not only a particular stone fell at a particular time, and falls every time it is left unsupported, but other stones and other heavy objects fall as well. The fact is generalized into *all bodies fall*. Now this generalization, in a sense, goes beyond experience, for it includes an infinity of cases not yet observed. It is arrived at by ascribing a mode of behavior to nature. It is a *law of nature.* It is important to note that the law is *descriptive;* it describes a regularity found in nature. It is not *prescriptive;* it does not prescribe what *should* happen. Objects do not "obey" a law; the law is merely a description of their behavior.

Concepts. Although facts are ultimate, their significance may alter. Facts are not phenomena; they are *descriptions* of phenomena. They are abstractions from the phenomena. They depend upon the *concepts,* the *ideas,* with which one approaches the phenomena. For example, the description of falling bodies is made in terms of certain concepts such as time, distance, speed, etc. With different concepts, different facts are obtained. Facts are ultimate, but only in the sense that in terms of a given set of concepts, certain things can be described as happening. What we choose to describe and the terms in which we describe it are *not* in the phenomena. The development of science is in a large measure the development of concepts.

Theories. Let us assume that we have a group of verified facts, presumably descriptions of certain parts of experience. In searching for integration of experience, we look for relations between these facts and an explanation of "how" things happen. Already by grouping these facts we have selected them in terms of some idea. However, in formulating a *theory* to explain the phenomena, we go much further than this. We deliberately construct a mental picture, a unified structure, out of which the separate facts are necessary, logical consequences.

The elements of a theory are the *assumptions.* The proponent of a theory says, in effect, "Let me assume certain things, and I can interpret the phenomena. Let me assume that the earth rotates on its axis, revolves around the sun, and that its axis is inclined to the ecliptic, and I can explain the rising and setting of the sun and the stars and the succession of the seasons."

Out of the assumptions a logical structure is built which is the *theory*. All the statements of a theory are necessary, logical consequences of the assumptions. They are deductions and may be put in the form of a syllogism of the type:

If B always follows A
And A has occurred,
Then B will follow.

Numerous deductions may be drawn from the theory. The facts or phenomena must be among these deductions. It should be noted that in terms of the theory, the facts are no longer separate, but an integral part of the same logical structure.

A theory leads to further extension of experience. Many of the deductions from a theory correspond to facts not included in the original grouping. Thus other facts, not suspected to be related to those that originally suggested the theory, are now interpreted in terms of the same logical structure. Still other deductions may correspond to facts not yet observed. Experiments are then performed to see if the predictions can be verified. If they are verified, they lend support to the theory, but if they are not verified, they put a strain on the theory. The theory—that is, the set of assumptions—must be revised or discarded altogether.

At this point, the force of the statement, "Facts are the ultimate basis of science," may be felt. If the theory is not in accord with the facts, the theory must be discarded, not the facts. Facts are ultimate. In the laboratory the experimental material—say, a gas—is supreme; *it is divine*. Its behavior is beyond appeal. If the gas does not "obey" a "law," no attempt is made to "correct" the gas for its behavior. On the contrary, the result may be fatal to the "law." It is dramatic to witness a puny fact slay a giant theory.

There are, then, two essential characteristics of a theory: It *must be internally consistent,* and it *must correspond to experience.* If it is not consistent, it is not an orderly, logical instrument and cannot aid in obtaining rational understanding. If it does not correspond to experience, it has failed to perform the very function for which it was created.

This sketchy analysis of the scientific method is perhaps sufficient to bring out some basic characteristics of scientific knowledge. Scientific knowledge may be of two kinds: it may be a *description* of what is observed, or it may be an *explanation* of what is observed. There is, however, no absolute, sharp distinction between the two, although in a given situation and at a certain stage of the development of knowledge, the distinction is clear. There is a distinction between the statement, "The sun and the stars rise, cross the meridian, and set," and the statement, "The earth rotates on its axis and makes the heavenly bodies appear to rise and set." The former is a direct description; the latter is an explanation. The distinction, however, is relative. Even facts contain ideas, but the explanations contains more of our interpretation.

Related to this characteristic is the "degree of certainty" or "degree of truth" of scientific statements. Phenomena are ultimate: whatever

Nature of Scientific Knowledge. Degrees of Truth

happens is the "real" thing. Facts are closest to the phenomena and, hence, are most stable. They are least likely to change with time. Generalizations are a little farther removed from direct observation and, hence, are somewhat more uncertain. With more experience they may have to be altered or modified. Theories are the farthest removed from experience. They may have to be altered considerably or even abandoned. However, one must not get the misconception that all facts are more dependable (and "truer") than all theories. Some theories are more dependable, better established, than some facts. In each case the truth of a statement depends upon the amount of evidence supporting it. Each case has to be examined on its own merits at any given stage of development.

Another characteristic of scientific knowledge is its cumulative character. Facts are grouped into generalizations and lead to theories, which are then verified by further facts. Having verified the theories—to whatever extent they may have been verified at any given time—the theories are used as "facts" to develop more inclusive theories. The process is continued, with the apparent goal of explaining all natural phenomena in terms of a limited number of general and all-inclusive theories.

3. THE PATTERN OF THIS BOOK

This book is highly selective. From the immense amount of scientific knowledge that has been accumulated and now fills the libraries and to which the laboratories and research centers of the world are adding daily, we have selected a few central areas and problems. The areas so selected are basic and contain some of the great ideas around which this wealth of knowledge is organized. These ideas form a sort of framework, which can be grasped by the nontechnical person, and which, once grasped, form a picture of the world.

These areas are the following: The present conception of the solar system; the understanding of motion and energy; the basic ideas of electricity; the phenomena of light and radiation; the microworld of molecules, atoms, and electrons; the meaning of chemical reaction and the intimate structure of matter; atomic energy and its implication; the extent and structure of the stellar universe; and the age, past history, and possible origin of the earth and the universe.

Each chapter of the book begins with an introductory section which contains, in a sense, a part of the picture of the world. In this preliminary survey the presentation is authoritative or dogmatic—a fairy tale, if you wish—describing what the scientists conceive the world to be and stating their conclusions, without going into the evidence for these conclusions. Thus, ideas are presented in their main outline so that the reader may form the appropriate mental images in terms of his own experience. The remainder of each chapter, however, is analytical. There is an attempt to give reasons—either how the scientists came to believe what they believe, or on what evidence they so believe. With more information and more refined ideas, the mental images that the reader formed earlier will gain greater clarity and greater accuracy. This may appear repetitious, but it is intentional. It is not possible to give the whole story or the exact "truth" all at once. We shall have to give at first approximate truths. This, too, is characteristic of science. We do not have the final "truth." But scientists do believe that they are coming closer and closer to it. At any rate, science is not a finished product, but rather still growing and evolving.

If the reader merely wants to get some notion of the great ideas and areas of science, he may simply read the book in the sequence in which it is written. With an average memory, a not too distorted picture of the world will be obtained.

For a serious student who wants to get a deeper meaning, the entire text must be studied critically. It is designed to give "reasons" and justifications for what is presented. Sometimes the "reasons" are historical— on the principle that we have a better understanding of something if we know how it came to pass. At other times, the "reasons" are in the form of evidence—such as the observations of the scientists and their reasoning from these observations to the theories and then to the explanations. In still other cases, the "reasons" are relationships and their connections with other, sometimes more inclusive ideas.

If, however, the reader is one of those unusual individuals who wants to get an even greater understanding of the physical world and of science as an intellectual discipline, he will go even further than this. As he studies the book, he will find many questions arising and he will try to see if and how the development of the text answers some of them. He will find many good answers, but will also find new and more meaningful questions arising. He will then want to read the additional references in pursuit of these questions. The quest for knowledge, once started, never ends. The interested person will not want to stop with this book. At the end of the text there are references to other works. These references are annotated, with an indication of the area treated and the level of treatment. The serious reader will want to enhance his knowledge by reading some of these works. Everything he may read from now on will add to the basic picture—from a news item and the Sunday supplement to the more serious books. Nor need he stop with reading. Every experience hereafter will have a deeper meaning. If he happens to look at a rock, it will not be just a white rock or a gray rock, but an intricate pattern of atoms, with their whirling electrons, made of some of the same elements that make up our bodies, the other planets, or even the stars. The rock itself may have a story to tell; perhaps it was deposited when the dinosaurs roamed the earth, or when the entire North American continent was covered with the ocean, or perhaps during those gigantic convulsions of the earth when the mountains were born and continents emerged from the oceans.

If one continues, he will develop a rational attitude toward the world and be better prepared to understand it and the discoveries already made and those yet to come. The stars will not be merely points of light, but giant suns, many of them bigger than our sun. Interplanetary travel will not be a wild dream, but merely a matter of harnessing the forces of nature.

When some morning he may read of new discoveries, he will be able to fit them into the picture. The atomic bomb, the hydrogen bomb, radar, television, earth satellites were all startling when first announced, but only to those who did not have a basic understanding of science. Those who understood science could see that these discoveries and developments followed an orderly sequence. And what the developments of the future will be, who dares predict? However, we can feel quite sure of one thing. The new developments are most likely to follow from what is already known coupled with whatever new observations may be made, and all will most likely fit into the basic pattern of the ideas of science already developed.

NOTES AND EXERCISES

1. Contrast the method of procedure in several fields. How does a scientist proceed to determine the rust-resisting properties of a metal? How does he proceed to determine the distance of a star? The size of an atom? That molecules consist of atoms? How does an artist proceed to create a work of art? How does an artist (or critic) proceed to determine the value of a work of art? How does he decide that a painting "reveals a great truth"? How does an audience decide whether a speech is "good" or "bad"? How does a legislator decide what traffic laws to enact? How does a lawyer (or a judge) decide whether an accused person should be punished? What the punishment should be? Take similar examples from literature, music, foreign relations, philosophy, and religion.

2. Contrast the object or product of the activities in several fields. The product of the activities of a scientist is demonstrable knowledge. What is the object of the activities of an artist? a composer? a performer of music? an actor? an orator? a legislator? a lawyer? a philosopher? a theologian? a minister?

3. Distinguish between a phenomenon and a fact. Could the same phenomenon give rise to more than one fact? Suppose you are witnessing a tree on fire. How many statements of fact can you make, regarding this phenomenon? Make several.

4. The statement is made that the diameter of the earth is 8000 miles. Handbooks give the mean diameter of the earth as 7917.64 miles. Is the first statement false? In what sense is it false? In what sense is it true?

5. Facts alter depending on the conceptions held by the observer. Consider the statement "Unsupported stones fall downward." Is this statement true, if the earth is conceived of as flat? Is it true if the earth is conceived of as spherical? What is the meaning of "downward" in the conception of a flat earth? In the conception of a spherical earth?

6. On increasing the pressure on a sample of air, a physicist finds that the volume decreases to one half of the original volume. He makes a statement to that effect. After experimenting with several samples of air at various pressures he makes a second statement: The volume of air decreases in proportion to the pressure. Boyle's law states that the volume of any gas is inversely proportional to the pressure.

Is the first statement a fact? Is the second statement a fact? In what sense is the second statement different from the first? Is the third statement a fact? How different is it from the first? From the second? Why is it called a "law"?

7. On more extensive studies of gases at high pressures and low temperatures it is found that the volumes of gases do not decrease in proportion to the pressure. At very high pressures the deviations are very large. Moreover, on accurate measurement, no gas follows Boyle's law exactly. Is Boyle's law "false"? In what sense is it still "true"? Is the law still a statement of fact "based on observation"?

8. Distinguish between a statute law and a natural law. What happens if an individual does not obey the traffic laws? What happens if a gas does not obey the gas laws? Is it really possible for a gas to "break" a natural law? Can you "disobey" the law of gravity?

9. A person witnessing a tree on fire made the following statements: (a) The wood disappears, and only ashes remain. (b) The molecules of the wood combine with the molecules of oxygen to form molecules of the invisible carbon dioxide; the minerals in the wood form solid oxides.

Which of these statements is more nearly a description of what happens? Which of these statements is an explanation of what happens? Which statement depends on a theory for its meaning? Suppose you do not "believe" in atoms and molecules? Does the first statement make sense? Does the second statement make sense? With further knowledge, which is less likely to change? Which is more likely to change?

10. Distinguish between fact and theory. Distinguish between observation and explanation. What are assumptions in a theory? What are deductions in a theory?

11. The distinction between observation and theory is sometimes brought out forcibly in a courtroom. A witness relating an accident proceeds somewhat as follows: "The car was going on the left side of the street and I think that the driver had been dr—" At this point the lawyer interrupts, *"Never mind what you think, tell us what you saw!"* Why is the lawyer objecting?

12. What are the main characteristics of a theory? Discuss the function of a theory in explaining phenomena; in correlating phenomena; in integrating experience; in predicting new phenomena; in advancing knowledge. Why should a theory be a logical structure? Why should it correspond to the phenomena?

13. In what sense is a theory based on observations? In what sense does it go beyond observations? If the predictions from a theory do not correspond to the phenomena, is the theory true? Is it false? If the predictions do correspond to phenomena, is the theory necessarily "true"? Is it still useful?

On the theory that electricity consists of electrons, vacuum tubes are designed which work well. If in the future we come to the conclusion that electrons do not exist, should we stop using vacuum tubes? Will the vacuum tubes still work?

14. Certain statements in science are neither descriptions of phenomena nor explanations of them. They are mere definitions. Consider the statement: "The sun rises in the eastern horizon." Does the truth of the statement depend upon a theory? If so, on what theory? Does the truth depend on observation? If so, what observations would you make in order to prove or disprove it? How would you know where "east" is? If east is where the sun rises, where else can the sun rise?

15. Statements in science are accepted as true on the basis of one of three rather distinct types of reasons. The statements may be based on direct observation; they may derive their meaning from an accepted theory; or they may be true simply by definition.

Consider the following questions:

(a) In the United States is the sun lower or higher in summer than in winter?

(b) Does the sun go around the earth or does the earth go around the sun?

(c) Is a yard 3 feet or 9 feet long?

In question (a) which alternative is true? How do you know? If you did not know, how would you proceed to find out? Could a person not in the United States, and not knowing where the United States is, possibly know the answer? Does the correct answer tell us something about the external world? Is it a description of a part of the world?

In question (b), which alternative is true? Is it "really" true or is it accepted as true today? Was it always accepted as true? In terms of the earlier view (Ptolemy, p. 40), which statement is true? Is the correct alternative a description of what is observed or is it an explanation? Is it possible for the explanation to change in the future?

In question (c) which alternative is true? Do you need a theory to decide which alternative is true? Do you need a measurement to decide? Suppose you measured a yardstick and found it to be $3\frac{1}{4}$ feet long, what would you conclude?

Compare the three types of scientific knowledge exemplified by the three questions.

16. Does the truth (or falsity) of each of the following statements depend upon observation, theory, or definition?

(a) The distance to the sun is 93,000,000 miles.

(b) The solar system evolved from a nebula.

(c) Water consists of 89 percent oxygen and 11 percent hydrogen.

(d) A mile is 5280 feet.

(e) The freezing point of water is $0°$ C.

(f) A water molecule contains two hydrogen atoms and one oxygen atom.

17. Consider the statement: $2 + 2 = 4$. Is this true by theory? If so, what theory? Is it true by observation? If so, is it always true? Do two men plus two men equal four men? If you add two drops of water to two drops of water will you always get four drops? Might you get one drop? Does this mean $2 + 2$ is not equal to 4? Why is $2 + 2$ always equal to 4?

18. In Euclidean geometry the sum of the angles of a triangle is equal to 180 degrees. Does this mean that in a triangle made of ropes, or of light beams, the sums of the angles is equal to 180 degrees? In Lobachevskian geometry the sum is equal to or less than 180 degrees. In Riemannian geometry it is equal to or greater than 180 degrees. Which of the three statements is true? Poincaré, who considered the problem, came to the conclusion that the postulates of geometry are implicit definitions (see further Ref. 1.12b).

2

THE SYSTEM
OF THE WORLD

I. NEWTON'S CONCEPTION OF THE WORLD

The expansion of the Western World was in full swing when in 1687 Sir Isaac Newton (1642-1727) published his greatest work—perhaps the greatest scientific classic of all time—the *Mathematical Principles of Natural Philosophy*. In the third book, entitled "The System of the World," he gave us the conception that the sun and the planets with their satellites, including the earth with the moon, form a mechanical system, a giant but delicate and precise clock. The system is held together by a universal force—the force of gravity. The bodies of the system eternally move in relation to one another with clocklike regularity, obeying the same laws of motion as falling apples, rolling stones, curving baseballs, and speeding-up carriages. Outside this system, and in all directions, are the "fixed" stars of the firmament, but at such great distances that they have no perceptible influence on the motions of the bodies within the system.

At the center, or rather somewhere near the center of this system, lies the giant sun, a huge flaming ball of gas, dominating all other bodies with its enormous gravitational attraction, compelling them to move in nearly circular—but actually elliptical—orbits around it. Going outward from the central sun we encounter first the tiny planet Mercury, and then, in succession, brilliant Venus, the Earth, reddish Mars, the giant Jupiter, Saturn with its rings, and last (at that time) the then recently

Fig. 2-1. Isaac Newton. In his "Principia" (1687) he developed the modern concept of the system of the world. His laws of motions are the foundation of modern science. (The Bettmann Archive.)

15

discovered Uranus. All the orbits lie in roughly the same plane with the planets moving in them in the same direction but with different speeds. The further a planet from the sun, the lower its speed and, hence, the longer it takes to go around it. In fact at any given instant, the speed of a planet is completely determined by its distance from the sun, by the mass of the sun, and to a slight extent by the mass of the planet itself. Except for Mercury and Venus, each planet has one or more satellites, which revolves about it and accompanies it in the journey around the sun. The speeds and periods of the satellites, too, are completely determined by their distances from the parent planet and the combined mass of the planet and the satellite. The entire system continues to operate without further interference from any outside source.

Newton supported this conception with simple but faultless logic and mathematical rigor. So great was the impact of his work that lettered men everywhere read and discussed the theories of Newton. It even became fashionable for the society ladies, for whom simplified versions soon appeared, to discuss these ideas in the cultured salons of Paris. The effect was, of course, greatest on the scientists of the time and immediately following. Indeed, the effect became cumulative as time went on, so that today on looking back over the past two and a half centuries, we see the entire period dominated by the genius of Newton.

Newton's conception of the solar system is essentially the one we have today. To be sure, in the intervening time a great many details have been added. Two more planets and many satellites, planetoids, and comets have been discovered by means of more powerful telescopes. More accurate measurements have been made and a wealth of information, with new or improved instruments, has been gathered about the sun and the planets. With the development of the basic sciences—physics and chemistry—more meaningful interpretations have been made. However, the basic plan remains essentially as formulated by Newton. It is not without justice that Voltaire has said of Newton, "He was the wisest and most fortunate of all men, for there is but one world to discover."

Fig. 2-2. The solar system. Distances are drawn to scale

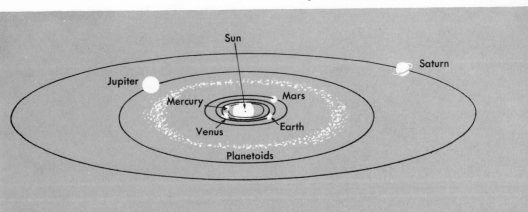

2. A ROCKET SHIP TOUR OF THE SOLAR SYSTEM

Adopting modern methods, let us take an imaginary tour through the solar system, using a rocket ship powered with atomic energy. The tour is highly imaginative, of course, since the human body and even the material from which the ship is made could not stand such a strain. Many engineering problems remain to be solved before space travel

TABLE 2-1
The Planets

Planet	Millions of miles from sun (mean)	Mean diameter, miles	Mass (earth = 1)	Time of rotation	Time of revolution	Number of satellites	Force of gravity at surface (earth = 100)
Mercury	36	3,000	0.054	88 da	88 da	0	38
Venus	67	7,700	0.81	?	225 da	0	88
Earth	93	7,900	1.00	24 hr	365 da	1	100
Mars	142	4,200	0.11	24.5 hr	687 da	2	39
Jupiter	483	88,000	318.3	10 hr	12 yr	12	265
Saturn	886	72,000	95.0	10.2 hr	29.5 da	9	117
Uranus	1,780	29,500	14.54	10.8 hr	84 yr	5	105
Neptune	2,790	28,000	17.2	15.8 hr	165 yr	2	123
Pluto	3,670	3,500	0.033?	?	248 yr	?	16?
Sun	——	860,000	330,000	25-35 da	——	—	2,730
Moon	93	2,160	0.0123	27.3 da	365	—	16.7

(Source: G. P. Kuiper, *The Atmospheres of the Earth and Planets.* Chicago: The University of Chicago Press, p. 308, 1951.)

ut sizes of sun and planets are highly exaggerated.

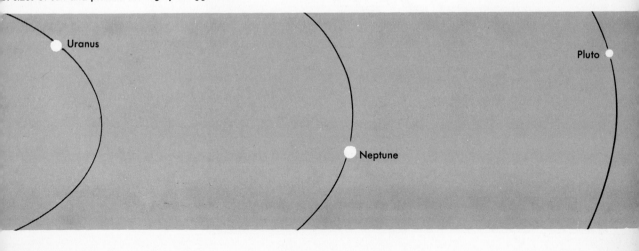

becomes a reality. However, disembodied imagination does not have physical limitations. We will be constrained only by reason, and what we are about to describe is scientifically accurate to the best of our present knowledge. The diagram (Fig. 2-2) and the data of Table 2-1 will aid in the trip.

The Universe as Seen from the Sun

We start at the surface of the sun. We may disregard the fact that our space ship with its contents would vaporize almost instantly at the temperature—nearly 11,000° F (6000° C)—and, being then completely atomized, mingle with the elements of the sun's atmosphere. All the elements that make up the universe are known. They are all here on the earth—we know of no materials that exist, or can exist, that would remain solid under the conditions of the sun's atmosphere. To avoid these difficulties our ship is made of imaginary material and is provided with perfect insulation.

Even granting this, problems still remain. The ship would have no solid ground on which to rest, for the surface of the sun is gaseous. Nor is its surface still. Tremendous storms rage—so large that not only our ship but the entire earth could be engulfed and beaten up like a leaf in a tornado. The ship might be thrown upward in a prominence to a height of half a million miles in a matter of minutes, or it might be caught in a vortex of a sunspot and drawn into the interior of the sun, where the temperature rises rapidly to *millions* of degrees.

Another thing to reckon with is the tremendous gravitational pull. We cannot lift anything, and our feet cannot carry our own weight. Each passenger would weigh 2 tons or more—twenty-seven times his weight on the earth. No bone could stand such a force; a man would literally collapse.

Fig. 2-3. Large active prominence, 140,000 miles high, photographed in the light of calcium, July 9, 1917. Note relative size of the earth shown by circle at lower right. *(Mount Wilson and Palomar Observatories.)*

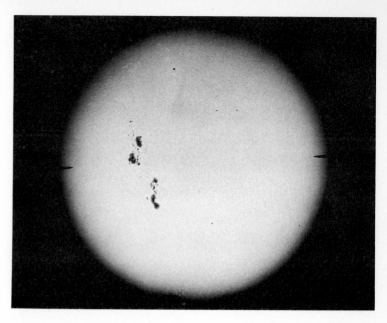

Fig. 2-4. Photograph of sun taken under excellent conditions, showing large sunspots and grain structure of sun's surface, July 31, 1949. The movement of the sunspots from west to east proves rotation of the sun. *(Mount Wilson and Palomar Observatories.)*

Nevertheless, let us imagine that we stand in our space ship on a quiet surface on the sun and make observations. If the dazzling light surrounding us could be blotted out, we would be surprised to see that the sky appears much the same as it does from the earth. There is no sun in the sky, of course, and the moon with its familiar phases has practically disappeared. Otherwise, the constellations appear the same as from the earth, the stars forming the familiar patterns. We can still recognize the Big Dipper, the Square of Pegasus, the Z of Orion, the W of Cassiopeia, the V of Taurus, the Northern Cross.

Among the stars we see the planets, including a bright new one, the earth, accompanied by the moon. The planets slowly change their positions among the stars, along a belt of twelve constellations known as the *zodiac*. With some exceptions to be noted presently, they all appear about as bright as from the earth. From the sun, all the planets appear as full discs at all times, for they are observed from their source of illumination.

The brightest object in the sky is Mercury. This is not surprising, for although it has a small surface, it is near the source of illumination and also near the point of observation. We know it is the nearest planet because its motion is the swiftest against the unchanging background of stars, making a complete cycle (and thus returning to the same constellation) in about 88 days. Even if no other means of measuring the distance were available, we could still tell the relative distances to the planets by observing their periods—that is, the time they take to return to the same constellation. The longer the period, the farther out the planet.

Next in brightness and in distance is Venus, making a complete revolution in about seven and one half months. Despite its greater distance, it appears almost as bright as Mercury, because of its greater surface and the high reflecting power of its thick atmosphere.

Next we see the earth, accompanied by the fainter moon, the two

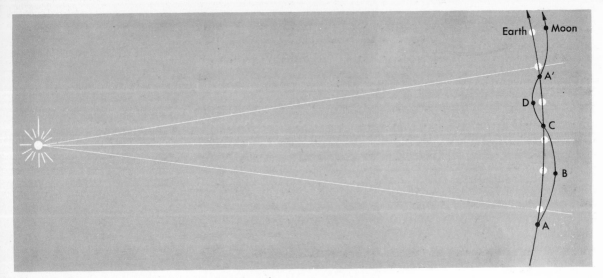

Fig. 2-5. Motion of earth and moon as observed from the sun.

giving the appearance of a twin planet. We do not see the moon encircling the earth once a month. Actually, from our vantage point on the sun we observe the two bodies circling us in a counterclockwise direction, although not always in step with one another. The moon is seen now behind the earth, then a week later in line with it, and then ahead of it, again in line with it, and then again behind it. In each of these positions, our friends on the earth see the moon in the various phrases. When it is trailing the earth in position A, the moon is in the first quarter. A week later in position B, the moon is full. In position C it is in the last quarter and in position D it is a new moon. As seen from the earth, the moon in this position appears close to the sun, and hence difficult or impossible to see. However, from the sun the moon always appears full.

Occasionally, when in position D, the moon comes exactly between the sun and the earth, and we know that those on the earth, directly under the shadow of the moon, are witnessing a solar eclipse. At other times, when the moon is in position B, it disappears behind the earth, and the earthlings are witnessing a lunar eclipse. But these events do not happen very often. Usually the moon passes the earth either a little above or a little below our line of sight. Technically the astronomers describe this by saying that the plane of revolution of the moon around the earth is inclined by about 5 degrees to the plane of revolution of the earth around the sun.

Beyond the earth we see Mars, making its cycle around the sun in nearly two years. It is never as bright as when seen from the earth at its brightest; nor, on the other hand, as faint as at its faintest. We recall that Mars changes greatly in brightness as seen from the earth. But from the sun, it always appears of medium brightness. A telescope is necessary to see its two satellites.

A telescope is necessary, too, to see the hundreds of little planets, or planetoids, that lie beyond Mars. So let us pass on to Jupiter, which next to Venus is the brightest object in the sky. It moves along the zodiac about one constellation per year, making a revolution in 12 years. With a small telescope, we should be able to see its four largest satellites, which are about as big as the earth's moon. These are the satellites first seen by Galileo in 1610. A larger telescope is necessary to see the remaining eight satellites.

Next we see Saturn, slowly making the cycle in nearly 30 years. With a small telescope, the rings and two of its satellites can be seen. Beyond Saturn is Uranus, making the cycle in 84 years, and beyond it is Neptune, requiring 165 years for the annual journey. A powerful telescope is needed to see Pluto, forty times farther out than the earth, making the journey in 250 years. But Pluto would be faint indeed. If the earth were removed to the distance of Pluto, it would become $1/(40)^4$ or about 2,500,000 times fainter than in its present position.

We note one more interesting thing. The sun is rotating. If we happen to be in the sun's equator, we would turn once in about 25 days, but on going either north or south of the solar equator, the period increases to about 35 days near the poles. Obviously then, the sun rotates as a fluid and not as a rigid body. As a consequence of this rotation, we see the stars rise and set. The direction of rotation is the same as that of the revolution of the planets—that is, counterclockwise as seen from the North Star. However, the revolution of the planets is slower than the rotation of the sun, creating the impression that the planets are trying to follow the turning of the sun.

A Visit to the Planets

We are now ready to leave the sun to visit the planets. If we had thought of using a single thrust, like the early V-2 bomb, we might as well not attempt it. A simple calculation shows that a speed of 383 miles per second or 1,400,000 miles per hour is necessary to overcome the gravitational pull of the sun. With a speed less than that, the space ship would fall back into the sun, much as a bullet fired upward on the earth falls back to the earth. But by using a steady thrust, like a jet plane, we can steadily gain height and speed. We will not try to calculate the amount of nuclear energy necessary for this, nor the amount of material that must be thrown backward in order to move forward.

Let us circle the sun before leaving it. On rising above the outer portions of the atmosphere the ship moves through tremendous storms. The atmosphere itself is mostly hot hydrogen gas with about 17 percent helium. Small amounts of most of the other elements have been detected and probably all are present. We move through the chromosphere (color sphere), so-called because of the beautiful colors it shows when seen from the earth through a spectroscope, and soon find ourselves in the tenuous regions of the corona.

By this time the ship should have developed a fairly high speed. It is necessary to continue to use energy constantly in order to overcome the attraction of the sun. In order to reach the planets in a reasonable time we might adopt a speed of 1,000,000 miles per hour and keep it constant. That in itself would be quite difficult because of the constant pull of the sun, which tends to slow us down and even pull us backward.

At a million miles per hour we would reach Mercury in about 35 hours. At such a speed we would loop the planet in a fraction of a

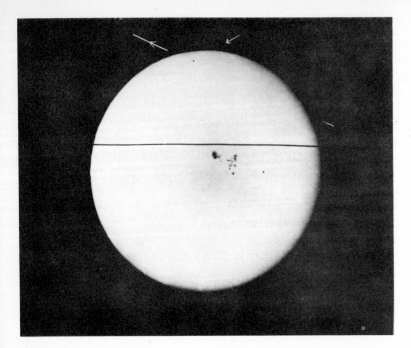

Fig. 2-6. Transit of Mercury, November 14, 1901. The black dot (white arrows) is Mercury moving across the disk of the sun. (Yerkes Observatory.)

second and pass beyond. Consequently, we slow down to 1000 miles an hour and circle the planet in about 10 hours. We travel over the desolate and probably rocky surface, and land on the dark side. There is no atmosphere and probably there are no ice ponds, for the force of gravity is too weak to hold gases or to have ever held any amount of water vapor. The sky is black and the stars shine sharply without twinkling. The planets, too, appear much as they appeared from the sun. However, their motions are now more complicated since they are observed from a moving planet. By staying a couple of months we can be sure to see all the planets. Since it takes Mercury 88 days to revolve around the sun, the zodiac constellations would rise and set in succession and the planets would be somewhere among them, slowly drifting eastward among the fixed pattern of the stars.

Since Mercury rotates at the same rate as it revolves, its dark side always remains dark; that is, it always keeps the same side toward the sun. Interestingly enough, the moon, too, always keeps the same side toward the earth in going around it. It is the sun's force of tidal friction on Mercury that resulted in the planet's turning at the same rate it is revolving. The earth's tidal friction similarly caused the moon to keep the same face toward the earth. Since this side of Mercury never sees the sun, the cold is bitter—a temperature of $-250°$ C has been measured.

As we travel toward the lighted side, the sun appears quite suddenly. There is no dawn or reddening of the sky as known on the earth, but a brightness due to the corona followed almost without warning by the dazzling disc of the sun. In the Mercurian sky, the sun's disc covers nearly nine times the area in our sky. Directly under the sun the heat would be unbearable. The intensity of sunlight would be seven times as strong as it is on the earth, without taking into account the fact that on Mercury there is no atmosphere to tone down the sun's rays. The temperature reaches over 400° C. If there were any large bodies of metallic lead on the planet (which is not very likely), we could sail on oceans of molten lead.

We return to the dark side to take off from this inhospitable place, and travel toward Venus. It is wisest to time the take-off when Venus is above us, in a direction opposite to that of the sun, for then the journey would be shortest. It would not be a difficult task to overcome the gravity of Mercury, which is only about two fifths that of the earth and weakens very rapidly as we move away from it. But the force of the sun, which diminishes only slightly over great distances, still has to be overcome. A mere 3 miles per second is sufficient to escape from Mercury, but 43 miles per second is necessary to overcome the sun's gravitational field at the distance of Mercury.

With our standard speed of a million miles per hour, we reach the vicinity of Venus in about 30 hours. Approaching the planet we see heavy blankets of clouds in the atmosphere. These clouds are not water vapor, but some solid material in the form of fine dust. Unless our space ship is slowed down to very low speed, we will burn up in the atmosphere from friction, like a meteor or an artificial earth satellite. We pass through the thick atmosphere and land on the surface of Venus. It is probably solid but could be covered by a universal ocean.

It is not easy to imagine what we would experience here, for our knowledge of the surface conditions on this planet is very limited. We would be the first human beings to see the surface, since from the earth the thick clouds completely obscure it. On the dark side, we may not be able to see anything. The stars and planets would probably be completely invisible through the perpetual clouds. Even on the bright side the sun would probably be invisible, although there would be some light diffusing to the depths.

Would we see any living creatures? The probabilities are strongly against it. An analysis of the atmosphere from the earth shows it to be nearly all carbon dioxide. At most there are only traces of oxygen or water vapor—we have not been able to detect any from the earth. With its thick blanket of carbon dioxide and dust particles and its nearness to the sun, the temperature of Venus at its equator must be near the boiling point of water. Any oceans? Possibly, but they would be hot oceans. Under these conditions, life as we know it on the earth is not possible.

More energy will be needed to take off from Venus than was used when the ship left Mercury, for gravity on Venus is more than four fifths that of the earth. Moving toward the earth we see a truly beautiful sight. The earth is the brightest object in the sky and near it the moon looks like a very bright star. The earth itself changes in brightness as it turns and presents now more of the highly reflecting ocean, now more of the land. As we get nearer it grows brighter and we begin to see the outline of the oceans and the continents and gradually some of the larger features of the landscape. We reach the vicinity of the earth in about 30 hours. Postponing a landing on the earth, we land near the middle of the dark side of the moon.

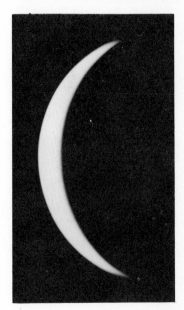

Fig. 2-7. Venus in crescent phase, photographed in blue light with the 200-inch Hale telescope. *(Mount Wilson and Palomar Observatories.)*

Fig. 2-8. Moon at the full phase. The dark "seas" and the rays are most prominent when the moon is full; the crater and mountains are difficult to discern due to lack of shadows. Lunic II landed almost halfway between the crater Tycho (bright spot near top of the disk) and the crater Copernicus (bright spot in dark area, a little to the lower right). *(Mount Wilson Observatory.)*

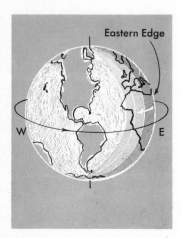

Fig. 2-9. The earth observed from the moon, during three days past "full earth." While the earth turns from west to east (black arrow), once a day, the shadow creeps westward (white arrow), darkening about one quarter of the disk per day.

If it happens to be a new moon, we shall reach the moon first, for in this phase it is between the sun and the earth. We may choose to land on the flat bottom of a crater, which has steep walls as high as any mountain on the earth. These depressions are called craters although there is good reason to believe that they were formed by falling giant meteorites in the early stages of the creation of the moon. They are not unlike the meteor crater in the Arizona desert or the much larger Chubb Crater in Northern Quebec. The ground is probably fine powder, formed from the rapid heating and cooling of the rock. There is no motion of any kind, no rivers and no wind, for there is no atmosphere. The moon probably never had any water vapor; its gravity is much too weak to hold any substance that can become a gas at the prevailing temperatures. At this time the temperature is 200 degrees below zero Fahrenheit, but will rise above the boiling point of water 2 weeks later.

It is "midnight" on the moon, but we can see plainly by the light reflected by the "full earth" above. The full earth presents a lighted area fourteen times larger than the area of the full moon as seen from the earth. On the full earth above we recognize the main features of its landscape. The outlines of the oceans, the continents, the Great Lakes, and the larger islands are clearly visible.

In the course of a week, we would see the earth turn seven times. By focusing our attention on some feature—say the Panama Canal— we would see it come up from the western edge into the sunlight, move across the center and disappear behind the eastern edge in the darkness.

The people on the Canal experience sunrise and sunset, respectively. But one more interesting thing is happening. The sunset line, which started from the eastern edge, gradually moves toward the center so that one full week later it is dividing the face of the earth into a lighted half and a dark half. We would then say that the earth is in the "last quarter."

At this time we are also witnessing sunrise on the moon. We first see the summits of the craters reflecting the glaring sunlight, which gradually comes lower into the bottom of the crater. Finally the sun hits us directly. The shadows are sharp, and the temperature rises rapidly. The sun rises higher and higher. In one week it has reached its zenith. It is midday on the moon. The temperature has risen to 250° F. The sky is still black and the stars are shining on this fearfully hot day. Somewhere near the sun in the sky is the earth—dark and barely visible. It is "new earth."

We could wait for sunset, another seven days from "midday," but it is best to move to the dark side and take off once again. Incidentally, we shall now see the side of the moon which is not visible from the earth. It is quite easy to overcome the moon's gravity—only one sixth that of the earth. We can jump on the moon twenty or more feet without much effort. If there were buildings on the moon, staircases would hardly be necessary. A step down from the second story would be no more jarring than if we stepped down 2 feet on the earth. We take off for Mars from the darkened side of the moon. We are glad when we realize that in the last two weeks we have been carried across the moon's orbit nearly half a million miles and saved fuel for about one half hour. We reach Mars in about 50 hours.

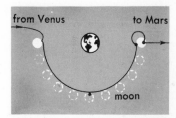

Fig. 2-10. Path of trip from Venus to Mars, by riding on the moon.

Fig. 2-11. Meteor Crater in Arizona was formed by large meteor in recent geologic past. Moon's craters are believed to have been formed similarly in the remote past, but have survived due to absence of erosion on the moon. *(U. S. Geological Survey.)*

Mars is in many respects similar to the earth. It turns on its axis in about 25 hours, and the axis itself is tilted about 24 degrees from the perpendicular to the plane of the orbit. Here a year is a little less than two earth-years. Consequently, Mars has seasons like the earth, but twice as long. The diameter of Mars is a little over half and its mass about 0.1 that of the earth. Hence the gravity on the surface is only 0.4 as strong. This, however, is sufficient to hold an atmosphere about 1000 times thinner than our own. Both oxygen and water vapor are present. The latter deposits as frost in the winter on each pole, forming the characteristic ice caps seen through a telescope. We may land on the ice caps, for the frost is probably very thin. The so-called "canals" are probably optical illusions seen by Schiaparelli and Lowell some decades ago at the limits of visibility. If these are canals, they probably could not carry the small amount of water that might form from the melting of ice. The water would soon evaporate in the low pressure of the thin atmosphere.

The astronomical phenomena observed from Mars are similar to those observed from the earth. There are sunrise and sunset, winter and summer. But the sunlight is considerably weaker—about a third as intense as on the earth. The constellations are similar and in about the same positions from comparable latitudes. We would be blessed with two moons, both, however, much smaller than our own. Interestingly enough, the nearer satellite, Phobos, circles the planet faster than the latter rotates and consequently rises in the west and sets in the east.

The existence of life on Mars is still an unsettled question. The existence of intelligent beings is most unlikely—the "Martians" of science fiction are pure imagination. It is too far-fetched to attribute to intelligent beings the construction of the "canals"—if they are *canals*. However, the presence of oxygen and moisture makes some simple forms of life possible. Recently, changes in color have been observed at various times of the martian year, suggesting the growth of some type of vegetation. It is not settled whether the changes in color are due to vegetation or to changes in the color of the rocks, from variation in humidity and temperature. (For the recent status of the question see Ref. 2.4.)

We leave Mars, heading in the direction of Jupiter. In the vast space between the two planets, we encounter thousands of little planets or planetoids. From the spacing of the other planets we may feel that there should be another planet here. According to some theories there was another planet that broke up, perhaps from the gravitational pull of Jupiter, and these planetoids are the fragments. According to other theories the planetoids are made from the material destined for a planet that never formed. We are not quite sure which theory is nearer the truth (see p. 583).

Ceres, the largest planetoid, would be interesting to visit. With a diameter of only 480 miles, the gravity on the surface cannot be very strong. If Ceres is made up of average earth materials, the gravity would be one sixteenth that of the earth at the surface. A 6-foot jumper could soar to over 100 feet, and alight as gently as he would from a 6-foot jump on the earth—and all in eerie slow motion.

Or we might choose to visit another little planetoid, Eros. This

Fig. 2-12. Mars photographed in blue (top) and red (bottom) light with the 200-inch Hale telescope. The white caps are believed to be ice; they appear at the pole during the winter in that particular martian hemisphere and disappear during the summer. *(Mount Wilson and Palomar Observatories.)*

tiny planet, a few miles in diameter, is at most 24 hours (24 million miles) beyond Mars. A stay on it of a few years might be disturbing, for the planetoid moves in a highly elliptical orbit and would carry us back toward the earth. If the timing was right, it would carry us to within 16 million miles of the earth. In fact, if we had thought of it sooner we could have boarded Eros near the earth and thus had a free ride to beyond Mars. This, however, would not have saved any fuel (Ex. 11).

The visit to Eros will repay us in two ways. It is the heavenly body which, next to the moon, comes nearest the earth. (More recently other planetoids have been discovered, one of them coming to within 3 million miles of the earth.) We can measure its distance from the earth quite accurately and from that calculate just as accurately all other distances in the solar system (Ex. 13). Because of its low gravity a man can jump to almost any height; in fact, if not careful, he might jump off the planetoid altogether. And this planetoid is not the smallest by any means. There are some only a fraction of a mile in diameter and chunks of rock down to the size of pebbles.

If we had not stopped for the diversion of the planetoids, the trip from Mars to Jupiter would take about 340 hours, or about 14 days. The distances are indeed getting greater, but we are rewarded by a visit to the largest planet by far. This giant ball is ten times the earth's diameter, or 1000 times its volume. Incidentally, it is intermediate between the earth and the sun in diameter.

Great difficulty is encountered as we attempt to land the ship on the surface of Jupiter. Its dense atmosphere, probably made of hydrogen and helium, carries extremely thick clouds. These clouds are not droplets of water or crystals of ice, but droplets and crystals of ammonia and methane. Below the atmosphere there is probably a universal ocean

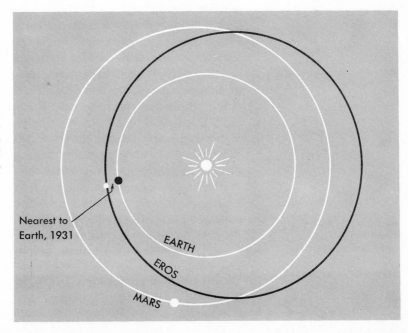

Fig. 2-13. The orbit of Eros is an ellipse, looping the orbit of Mars. On February 1, 1931 Eros came to within 16 million miles from the earth. A space ship might board Eros near the earth and ride to beyond the orbit of Mars.

Nearest to Earth, 1931

EARTH

EROS

MARS

Fig. 2-14. Jupiter, in blue light, showing large red spot, satellite Ganymede and shadow above. Photographed with the 200-inch Hale telescope. *(Mount Wilson and Palomar Observatories.)*

Fig. 2-15. Saturn and its ring. Photographed in blue light with the 200-inch Hale telescope. *(Mount Wilson and Palomar Observatories.)*

of liquid ammonia and methane. This fluid envelope causes the planet to rotate, much like the sun, faster at the equator than near the poles. And Jupiter does indeed rotate rapidly. At the equator, it makes a complete rotation in less than 10 hours, the speed corresponding to about 25,000 miles per hour. The rapid rotation causes the planet to be markedly flattened at the poles.

Down below the thick atmosphere and the cold, but liquid, ocean there must be a solid surface. How far below is not definitely known, but probably about half-way down. There is some evidence that there is a solid surface of ice that extends perhaps 15,000 miles downward. This explains why Jupiter taken as a whole is quite light, having an average density only a little greater than that of heavy wood. In all probability we would not be able to land on a solid surface.

By traveling above the thick clouds, we can see the four Galilean moons, all about the size of the earth's moon, as well as the eight smaller ones. They are rising and setting at different times and traveling at different speeds, depending on their distance from the planet. Indeed, here is a miniature solar system. The two outer satellites are of interest since they travel backward—that is, in a direction opposite to that in which the planet rotates or the other satellites revolve. Some astronomers think that these were planetoids that came too close to Jupiter and were captured in its strong gravitational field. (See p. 584 for the implications on the possible origin of the solar system.)

By remaining on Jupiter until Saturn is directly above us in the opposite direction from the sun, the enormous distance between the two planets can be covered by the space ship in about 400 hours—nearly 17 days. We may have to wait as long as 20 years for this to occur, however. In 12 years we on Jupiter will make a complete revolution around the sun, while Saturn will barely move through one third of a revolution.

From the distance of Jupiter, Saturn must be a beautiful sight, nearly twice as bright as when seen from the earth. On coming nearer, the impressive ring appears larger and then clearly separates into three rings, which, in turn, also become more and more tenuous. The stars can be seen through them, and we realize that they are not a solid sheet, but a swarm of particles, all moving like tiny satellites with speeds depending on their distances from the planet. With care and unusual luck, it should be possible to sail right through the rings without damage to the ship.

As on Jupiter, finding a surface on which to land would present a problem. The outer envelope is gaseous hydrogen and helium. Below that must be a universal ocean of liquid methane and ammonia. Far down is the solid surface. The planet is not unlike a peach with a soft light envelope and a solid dense core. This makes the overall density of the planet three fourths that of water. If an ocean of water could be found that was sufficiently large, this planet would float on it.

The trip from Saturn to Uranus will take us 900 hours under the most favorable conditions when both planets are on the same side of the sun. Although it may be nearly 30 years before the two planets are in this position, we decide to wait; for Uranus might be in its orbit on the opposite side of the sun and the trip would then take much longer.

Conditions on Uranus are not too different from those on Saturn. We find a thick atmosphere of hydrogen and helium and clouds of solid ammonia and methane. The solid surface below is probably also frozen ammonia and methane. The sunlight is very feeble. In fact, at this distance it has decreased in intensity to about 1/400 that on the earth.

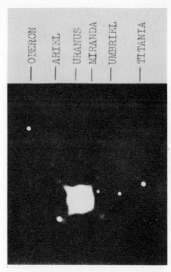

Fig. 2-16. Uranus and its five satellites. Miranda (barely visible in the photograph) discovered by Kuiper on February 15, 1948 with the 82-inch reflector. *(McDonald Observatory.)*

Fig. 2-17. Neptune and its two satellites (white arrows). Photographed by Kuiper on March 29, 1949 with the 82-inch reflector. *(McDonald Observatory.)*

Fig. 2-18. The discovery of Pluto, shown on two successive dates (white arrows), on March 10 and 11, 1934. *(Yerkes Observatory.)*

The apparent size of the sun and its gravitational attraction have also decreased in the same proportion. All three quantities decrease as the square of the distance.

It may be necessary to remain on Uranus nearly 90 years before taking off for the next planet, Neptune. However, the time can be spent observing the planet's five satellites and the motions of the sun in the Neptunian sky. It is interesting that the sun appears at times overhead at the pole of this planet. In fact, the axis of Uranus is tilted 98 degrees from the plane of its orbit, resulting in the planet revolving from east to west.

The journey to Neptune would take a full 1000 hours—41 days nonstop. We may stop at Neptune to observe its nearer satellite, not too bright because it is smaller than the earth's moon. This satellite is further from Neptune than our moon is from the earth, and receives but feeble sunlight to reflect. The other satellite, discovered recently by Kuiper (Fig. 2-17), is much smaller and farther from the planet. The itinerary of our long trip through space calls for one more stop. So under favorable conditions we take off for Pluto, a journey requiring another 40 days.

Here in the depth of space is a planet not much larger than Mercury in size and much less in weight. The sun appears less than 1/1600 as bright and also 1/1600 as large as from the earth. Yet it appears far brighter than any other star. The temperatures, even in direct sunlight, are 350 degrees below zero, Fahrenheit—not much above absolute zero. The gravitational attraction of the sun has decreased in the same proportion. All the other planets are somewhere between us and the sun or beyond it. All would show the phases of the moon, but only through a telescope. We have traveled to the end of the solar system.

A computation of actual traveling time would show that no less than five months were necessary to cover this distance, even at the extraordinary speed of a million miles an hour, and this without counting stopping time or waiting time. Of all the strange experiences, two impressions probably stand out above all others. The first is the immensity of empty space, punctuated only here and there by the presence of bodies of matter. The second is the overpowering presence of gravity compelling these bodies to move in precise regularities.

Our trip through space is over and all that remains is the journey back to the earth. However, two strong temptations could easily beset the adventurous traveler from our vantage point on Pluto. Since we have come so far, why not continue even further and search for other planets? It is very reasonable, even very likely, that there are such planets. But the possibilities of finding them in this vast waste of space are so extremely remote that after a little reflection, we should have no difficulty in suppressing this ambition.

The other temptation may be to take off for the stars—say, the nearest star. We have already overcome nearly all of the attraction of the sun so that by developing a speed greater than 15,000 miles per hour, we can go on forever. Perhaps there is even enough fuel left to develop a speed of a million miles per hour.

A little calculation would soon dissuade us from this attempt, too. The nearest star is 27 trillion miles still further out in space. Even at

Fig. 2-19 *(top left).* Launching of Juno II. This rocket put Explorer II into orbit. Progress toward making the imaginary trip described in the text a reality. *(U. S. Air Force.)*

Fig. 2-20 *(top right).* The 91.5-pound Explorer VII composite radiation satellite is mounted on top of the fourth stage of a Juno II vehicle prior to launch into orbit from Atlantic Missile Range, Cape Canaveral, Florida. *(National Aeronautics and Space Administration.)*

Fig. 2-21 *(bottom right).* A model of a manned satellite capsule is positioned in the Full Scale Tunnel of the Langley Research Center—part of the "Project Mercury" effort. *(National Aeronautics and Space Administration.)*

the speed of a million miles per hour it would take 3000 years to reach it. We begin to appreciate fully that even though the distances in the solar system are vast, the distances between the stars are far vaster.

So we decide to return home. At first thought the return trip may appear easier, since we can take advantage of the pull of the sun. On second thought, however, we find that energy must be used in reverse. If we aim at the earth when it is situated between us and the sun, even at a very low speed, the gravitational pull of the sun will speed the ship tremendously. By the time we reach the earth, the ship would attain a speed of 100,000 miles per hour and, unless slowed down, would rush past it into the sun. Accordingly we adjust the ship's speed as it nears the earth and pass at very low speeds, in succession, the outer portions of the atmosphere, the ionosphere, the stratosphere, the troposhere, and finally land on the surface.

Though the trip was imaginary, the observations and experiences of the would-be travelers are substantially correct, to the best of our present knowledge. With the rapid development in rocketry and nuclear engines, the day of an actual trip may not be far off. However, one point is worth making. All the knowledge related above has been obtained by man without his leaving the earth. The conception of the solar system has been arrived at from observation and reasoning. In the next chapter we shall relate how, in the course of history, the ideas and conceptions of the solar system have been developed.

3. FROM PTOLEMY TO NEWTON

The conception of the solar system presented in the previous section and the evidence for the reality of this conception were developed from observations arrived at by careful reasoning throughout the centuries. The complete story is long and complicated, but the main outline and the essence of the argument are simple enough to be grasped by the average nontechnical person. Many of the observations are accessible to anyone without the use of instruments. Even when instruments are used, what is observed with their aid can be described in terms that can be easily visualized.

The Conception of the Celestial Sphere

If we stand on an open space anywhere in the United States on a clear moonless night soon after sunset, we see stars in all directions. These appear to be located on a dome above, resting on the horizon. We further note, as the ancient shepherds must have noted long before the dawn of history, that the stars are not regularly distributed, but grouped in certain patterns which are called constellations. Thus, we recognize the Big Dipper, the Little Dipper, the W of Cassiopeia, the

Fig. 2-22. Photographic evidence of the apparent rotation of the sky, about a point near the North Star. Exposure 6 hours. The bright streak nearest the center was produced by the North Star. (Photo by Anthony Wausnock.)

V of Taurus, the Square of Pegasus, the brilliant Z of Orion, and so on. These groupings appear permanent for many generations and form the geography of the sky, much like the continents, oceans, islands, mountain ranges, and rivers form the geography of the earth.

After observing the sky for a few hours, we note that the stars move westward, rising in the East and setting in the West. This statement, while true as a first approximation, is seriously inaccurate. More precisely, we observe the stars rising somewhere in the eastern horizon—all the way from the south point to the north point—crossing the meridian and setting in corresponding points on the western horizon. Moreover, a group of stars in the northern sky does not actually rise or set, but moves around a point near the North Star, Polaris. A better way of describing what we see is as follows: All the stars appear to move in parallel circles whose common center is near Polaris in the Northern sky. On further observation, we see that these circles have another common center in the southern sky, but below the south point. We gradually develop the conception that the spherical sky with the stars on it moves as a single body around these two points. These are called the poles of the sky.

This is the conception of the celestial sphere. It is a shell enveloping all space and we are in the middle of it. At any time our horizon divides it into an upper half, which is visible, and a lower half below the horizon, which is, of course, invisible. As this sphere, with the stars on it, turns throughout the night, a part of it comes up in the eastern horizon, while at the same time a part of it disappears in the western horizon. At dawn, the stars fade from the intense light of the sun, which is scattered by our atmosphere. We have no reason to believe that the stars are not still there. We shall take up later how the stars, too near the sun to be visible in daytime, can be located.

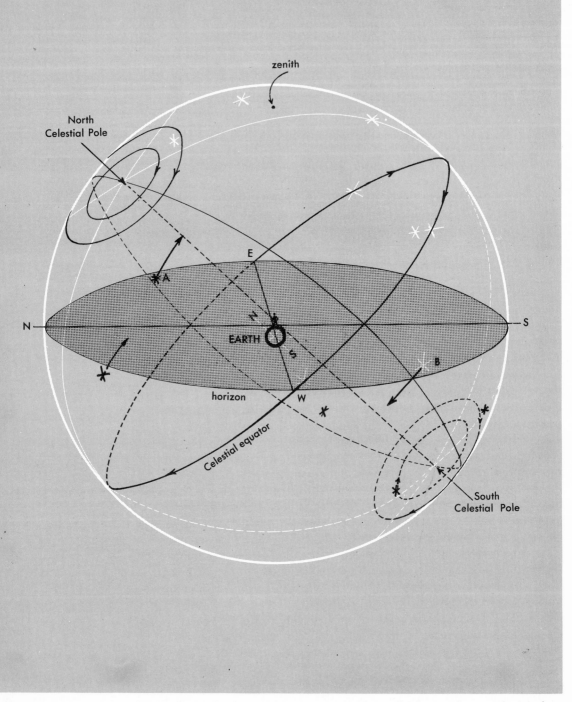

Fig. 2-23. Concept of the celestial sphere. The sky appears as a giant sphere of infinite radius, enveloping the observer on the earth. At any time, half of the sphere is visible above the plane of the horizon, the other half is invisible, below the horizon. The sky appears to turn about two points: the north celestial pole (directly above the North Pole of the earth) and the south celestial pole. The stars are carried on this sphere and rise (star A) or set (star B) as they cross the plane of the horizon. The celestial equator is a circle, directly over the earth's equator.

It might seem strange at first, but it is nevertheless true historically that this conception of the celestial sphere led to the concept that the earth which we inhabit is likewise a sphere, and later that it rotates. Since the celestial sphere moves unobstructed under the earth, the surface on which we stand could hardly be a platform whose support extends to infinite depth. Rather, the earth must be suspended somewhere in the middle of the celestial sphere. But what shape is it? We might guess it is a sphere, and even argue with Aristotle that since all parts of the earth are attracting one another, the only shape it could have is spherical. However, the conception that the earth might be a sphere is one thing. To demonstrate scientifically that it is indeed a sphere is another matter. Let us follow the evidence.

Contrary to popular belief, Columbus was not the first man to proclaim that the earth is spherical. Two thousand years earlier Aristotle taught the same thing, and a full fourteen centuries earlier than Columbus, Ptolemy gave nearly all the lines of evidence used today. Let us quote from his Almagest, written about 150 A.D.

The Evidence that the Earth Is a Sphere

"We are best led to the concept that the earth is sensibly of spherical form by the following considerations. We observe that the sun, the moon, and the other heavenly bodies do not rise and set at the same time for all the inhabitants of the earth, but rather first for those to the east and later for those to the west. For we find that the phenomena of the eclipses, particularly those of the moon, which always occur at the same absolute time for all people, are not, for all that, seen at the same hour relative to noon; that is, at an hour equally distant from the middle of the day; but that, in every case, the times are later for eastern observers and earlier for those further to the west. Now since the difference between the times when one observer and another see these eclipses is proportional to the [east-west] distances between their respective locations, one can conclude that the surface of the earth is certainly spherical, and that the uniformity of its curvature extends to the whole; it results that each of its parts makes an obstacle to the following parts, and limits the view in a similar manner for all. This would not happen if the earth had any other shape as can be seen from the following reasoning.

If the terrestial surface were concave the inhabitants of the western part would be the first to see the heavenly bodies rise; if it were a plane, all its inhabitants would see them rise and set together; if it were composed of triangles, quadrilaterals or polygons of any shape, all the inhabitants of the same plane face would see the phenomena at the same time; things which are not observed to occur. It is also evident that the earth is not a cylinder whose surface views the rising and setting and whose bases face the poles of the sky, an assumption which one might judge more probable; for if such were the case, there would be no stars which are always visible, but on the contrary, some stars would rise and set for everyone on the earth, and certain stars up to an equal distance from each pole would be invisible to everyone. However, the further we go toward the north, the more stars we discover which never set, and at the same time, southern stars disappear from

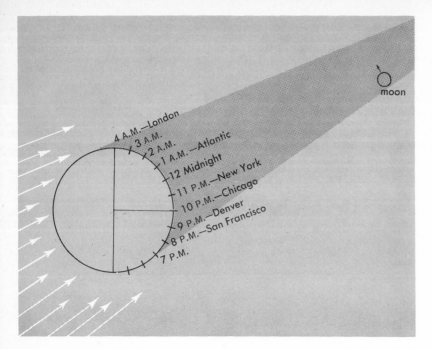

Fig. 2-24. Eclipse of the moon observed at different local times. Cited by Ptolemy as direct evidence that the earth's surface is spherical in the east-west direction.

view in the same proportion. Therefore, it is evident that here too, along the north-south direction, by an effect of the uniform curvature of the earth, each part forms an obstacle to the adjacent parts due to uniform curvature of the earth, which proves that the earth has in every direction a spherical curvature. Finally, on the sea, if at any point and in any direction, one travels towards mountains or other elevated places, one sees these objects as if coming out of the sea where they were apparently hidden by the curvature of the surface of the sea." *

Let us examine in some detail two of Ptolemy's arguments in a modern setting. Suppose an eclipse of the moon takes place and the beginning is observed from Chicago to be at 10 P.M. The same event is also observed from New York at practically the same instant, but the time in New York is 11 P.M. Ships out in the Atlantic would report that the eclipse began at midnight or even later, depending on how far east of New York they were. Similarly, observers from San Francisco would report that the eclipse occurred at 8 P.M. This clearly argues that the east-west surface of the earth is spherical.

Similarly, for the north-south direction we can start at Chicago, and observe any star—let us say the North Star, for the sake of simplicity. It is about 42 degrees above the northern horizon. Driving directly north, we note that the elevation of the North Star increases, and in proportion to the distance traveled. If we travel 400 miles to Marquette, Michigan, we find that the elevation has risen by about 5½ degrees, and is now 47½ degrees. As we drive southward, the elevation decreases, again in proportion to the distance traveled. Thus,

* Translated from the Greek and the French by T. A. Ashford and T. L. Page (1946).

from New Orleans, roughly 830 miles south of Chicago, the elevation of the North Star is only 30 degrees.

Similar observations are obtained, no matter from what point we start. If the stars were not moving, this would be true of any star regardless of the direction we traveled. Since we know how the stars are moving, we can correct for their motion. We conclude, therefore, that the earth is everywhere spherical.

The observations that led to the conclusion that the earth is spherical also give us a method of measuring its circumference. By accurate measurement, we find that for every 69.5 miles we move over the surface of the earth, a star overhead changes in elevation by 1 degree. For 90 degrees the distance would be 90 × 69.5; and for 360 degrees, we would have to encircle the globe, or a distance of 360 × 69.5 or 25,220 miles. Dividing 25,220 by $\pi(3.14)$, we get about 8000 miles for the diameter.

The Shape, Size, and Rotation of the Earth

Eratosthenes, in the third century B.C., used this method and obtained a value within 1 percent of the modern value. He observed that on the summer solstice the noon sun was directly overhead at Syene, on the upper Nile. On the same day, the sun was 7 degrees south of the zenith at Alexandria. Estimating that Syene is about 500 miles due south from Alexandria, he obtained about 70 miles per degree. Columbus would not have maintained that he could find a shorter route to India by sailing westward, if he had read Ptolemy.

Using the same method, but with more accurate measurements, we find that the earth is slightly flatter at the poles and slightly more curved, north-south, at the equator. Calculations from these measurements show that the diameter of the earth is 27 miles shorter from pole to pole than across the equator.

The fact that the earth is flattened at the poles suggests that it is rotating, the centrifugal force of rotation causing the bulge at the equator. Several other lines of evidence lead to the same conclusion.

Convincing evidence of the earth's rotation is given by the behavior of a swinging pendulum, freely suspended from the ceiling. If the experi-

Fig. 2-25. Modern direct evidence for sphericity of the earth. The photograph on the left was taken by a camera on a V-2 rocket at an altitude of 100 miles above the earth. The diagram at the right will help identify the important landmarks in the photograph. (*Official U. S. Navy Photograph.*)

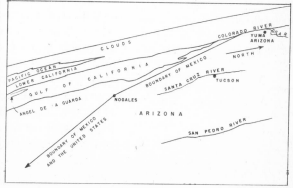

ment is carried out on the north pole of the earth, the evidence is more obvious. A heavy weight is suspended from the ceiling with a flexible cord and set swinging back and forth in the direction of a star visible through the window. We mark the point on the window that is in line between the pendulum and the star. After some time, we note that the pendulum is no longer pointing toward the mark on the window but it is still pointing to the star, which by this time has moved westward. The pendulum continues to follow the star, the plane of swing turning through 15 degrees each hour, thus making a complete rotation in 24 hours with respect to the room. Actually, the plane of swing does not change, but the room—that is, the earth upon which the room is resting—is turning under the swinging pendulum. If the sky turned and the earth stood still there would be no reason for the pendulum to change the plane of swing with respect to the room.

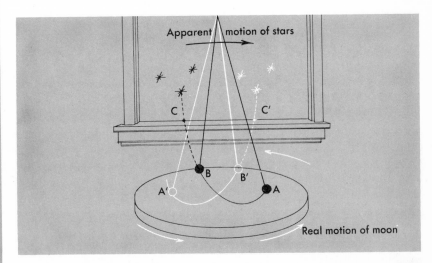

Fig. 2-27. Foucault pendulum, proving the rotation of the earth. The pendulum is set swinging along AB, in line with the point on the window C, and also in line with the stars. Slowly the plane of swing turns, and the pendulum is swinging along A'B', in line with C', a different point on the window, but still in line with the stars. Hence it is the window (earth) which is turning and not the stars (sky).

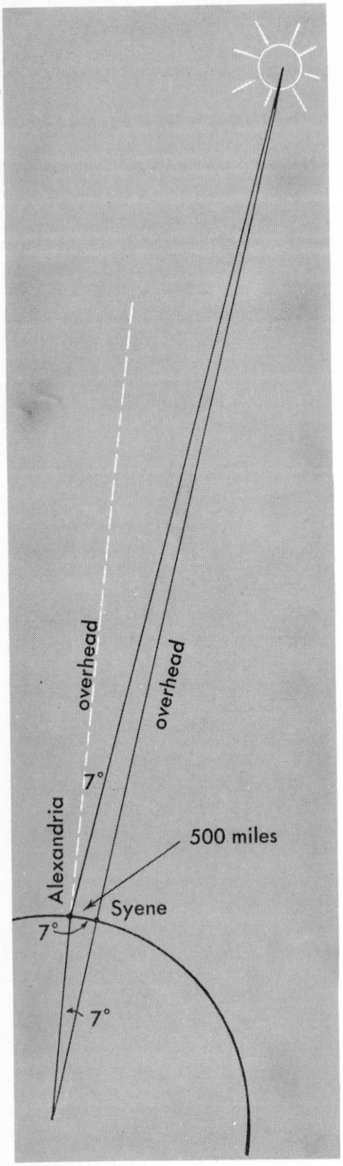

Fig. 2-26. Method of Eratosthenes for measuring the diameter of the earth. The sun's rays are essentially parallel. The sun is overhead at Syene but 7 degrees from zenith at Alexandria. Hence the arc of the earth's circumference between the two cities is 7 degrees. The distance is 500 miles, making a distance of about 70 miles per degree.

The experiment can, of course, be carried out wherever we happen to be, but it may require a little complicated geometric reasoning to follow the results. If we are at the equator the plane of swing does not, and should not, turn. At all points between the equator and the pole, the plane will turn by an amount dependent on how near we are to the pole. Analyzing the problem geometrically, we see that the amount of turn should be proportional to the sine of the angle of latitude. Jean Foucault first carried out the experiment at the Pantheon of Paris in 1859. He found that the amount of turn is about 10 degrees per hour, just as predicted for the latitude of Paris.

This illustrates one of the great advantages of mathematical reasoning. We perform the experiments under convenient or possible conditions, and use mathematical reasoning to analyze the results.

So far we have expounded the idea that the earth is a sphere rotating from west to east, thus making every object in outer space appear to be located on a sphere turning from east to west. The sun, the moon, and the five planets also appear somewhere among the stars on this sphere, and hence partake of (share in) the apparent daily motion of the sphere. The seven celestial bodies, however, also have other motions: while all the stars move in unison, retaining their relative positions, the sun, the moon, and the planets change their positions among the stars.

The eastward motion of the moon is the easiest to watch. We locate the moon among a certain group of stars on a clear night. As the hours pass, the moon slowly moves *eastward* among the stars about one degree every two hours; thus if it rose with a group of stars, it will be lagging behind them when they are about to set. The moon drifts eastward about 13 degrees per day and in approximately 27 days is back to the same group of stars. This slow eastward motion is opposite to the daily westward motion, and is superimposed upon it.

The moon does not drift directly eastward. It moves in a circle inclined to the celestial equator (Fig. 2-29) by an angle that varies from 18 to 28 degrees. (The celestial equator is a great circle, everywhere 90 degrees from the north or south pole, dividing a northern and southern hemisphere. We may think of it as a giant wire ring over the earth's equator.) The moon, therefore, moves in a circle oblique to the celestial equator, along a group of constellations known as the Zodiac. Half of the time the moon moves northeast and the other half it moves southeast.

In the same belt of the Zodiac are five "wandering stars" or planets, drifting eastward like the moon, only more slowly. Mars moves eastward about 15 degrees per month, requiring nearly two years to return to the same constellation. Jupiter takes twelve years to make the cycle, and Saturn nearly thirty.

The three planets, however, have a more complicated motion than the moon. At certain times Mars slows down in its eastward

The Apparent Motion of the Sun, Moon, and Planets, in the Background of the Stars

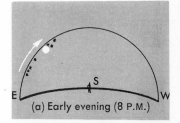

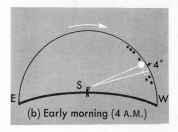

Fig. 2-28. The eastward drift of the moon among the stars. In the 8 hours between 8 p.m. and 4 a.m. the moon has drifted eastward by about 4 degrees.

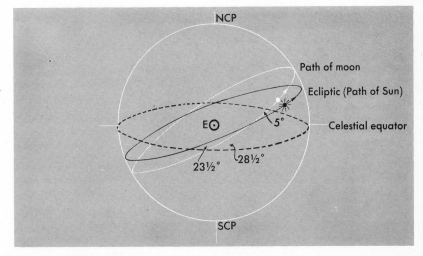

Fig. 2-29. As observed from the earth (center of diagram), the apparent path of the moon in the sky is oblique to both the celestial equator and the ecliptic. The ecliptic is the apparent path of the sun in the belt of the zodiac constellations. Eclipses can occur only when both sun and moon are at intersections of their paths.

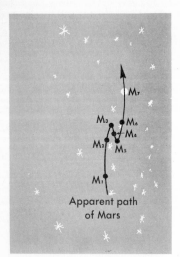

Fig. 2-30. Retrograde motion of Mars. While its general motion is eastward, Mars at times (about every 2 years) drifts westward for a while.

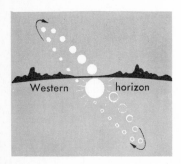

Fig. 2-31. Successive positions of Venus with respect to the setting sun. When above the western horizon Venus is an evening star. When below the horizon, it precedes the sun and is visible in the eastern horizon, as a morning star.

The Ptolemaic Concept of the World

movement, stops, drifts *westward* for a time, stops once again, and then resumes its eastward motion. Jupiter and Saturn follow the same pattern but in a less pronounced manner. It is significant that this phenomenon occurs every time the planet appears on the opposite side of the sky from the sun—that is, 180 degrees from the sun. When they retrograde the planets are observed near the meridian at midnight, or in the eastern horizon soon after sunset.

The motion of the sun is simpler than that of the planets, but more difficult to observe, the background of stars not being visible when the sun is in the sky. However, by noting which stars follow the sun soon after sunset, and which stars are ahead of it before sunrise, we can easily locate the position of the sun among the stars. If these observations are made night after night, we will realize that the sun, too, drifts eastward about 1 degree per day, or 30 degrees per month, taking a year to return to the same constellation.

The annual path of the sun is almost a perfect circle, and its motion is almost, but not quite, steady and uniform. From its southmost advance on December 21, the sun moves northeast to cross the celestial equator on March 21, and continues northeast until June 21, when it has made its most northerly advance. At this time it begins to move southeast, crosses the celestial equator on September 21, and continues southeast until December 21. Thus it traces a complete circle in the sky in the course of one year. This circle is called the *ecliptic,* because eclipses can occur only when the moon is crossing this circle.

The most complicated motions are exhibited by Mercury and Venus. These planets are always found near the sun. Mercury is never more than 27 degrees and Venus never more than 47 degrees from the sun.

When Venus is 47 degrees west of the sun, it rises in the eastern horizon about 3 hours before sunrise as a brilliant "morning star." Morning after morning it can be seen drifting eastward faster than the sun. After about 4 months Venus is too near the sun to be visible; several weeks later, however, now being east of the sun, it appears shortly after sunset as the "evening star." The planet continues on this path until it is 47 degrees east of the sun, setting at this time about 3 hours after sunset. The motion is then reversed; Venus retraces its path, becomes invisible, and then reappears once again west of the sun as the "morning star."

Mercury swings east and west of the sun in the same pattern as Venus, only more swiftly. The planet was named after Mercury, the wing-footed and swift messenger of the Roman gods, and also has the same name as the quick-running metal, quicksilver.

From the basic observations just described and many more details we have not mentioned, the ancients developed the geocentric concept of the world, which Copernicus and Newton finally overthrew.

According to the older system formulated in fairly final form by Ptolemy in the "Almagest," the earth, spherical and immovable, lay at the center of the universe. The earth was also the center of gravity.

At the very center were the dense materials of the earth. On the surface was the lighter water, above it was the air, extending almost indefinitely upward, but gradually replaced by fire and ether that reached to the firm shell of heaven. On the sphere of heaven were the fixed stars. According to some views, these were luminous bodies made of fire and pressing against the dome of heaven by their lightness much as helium balloons press on the ceiling of a room. (There followed a medieval conception that the stars were "holes" in the sky through which we could see glimpses of the heavenly light, the infinite heaven, outside the finite celestial sphere.)

Between the earth and the celestial sphere were the sun, the moon, and the five planets. They moved in crystalline, transparent spheres, concentric with the earth. The moon occupied the first sphere, and, in succession, Mercury, Venus, the sun, Mars, Jupiter, and Saturn occupied the other spheres. The planets were not on these spheres but on secondary spheres whose centers were on the primary spheres. For example, Mars was moving on a cycle upon a cycle (epicycle) as shown in Figure 2-32.

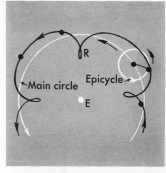

Fig. 2-32. Motion of a planet according to the Ptolemaic view. The planet moves in an epicycle whose center is carried on a circle around the earth. When in position R, the planet retrogrades.

It is easy to dismiss this conception as primitive. It is easier still to say that it was a mere speculation not based on observation. Nothing could be further from the truth. This conception was developed from observations and required the highest mathematical skills both to understand and to present it. It combined the basic ideas of physics, chemistry, astronomy, and mathematics that were held at that time. In physics, for example, it explained why heavy bodies go downward and light bodies move upward. Heavy or "earthly" materials move in straight lines downward, heavenly bodies move in circles. It conformed with the idea of the four elements—earth, water, air, and fire—and the quintessence, considered by some as the substance of the stars. Moreover, it was a picture of direct human experience as observed from the surface of the earth. Even today the planetarium, which reproduces the phenomena of the sky by projecting images on a fixed dome, is constructed on the geocentric scheme. The geocentric view further conformed with theological views of the times, and gave the comforting feeling that man is important and is at the center of Creation. This was the conception held by the greatest minds of the ages down to three or so centuries ago.

Yet the system had to go. It had to go not for one "reason" but for many and different reasons. For one thing the system became complicated with the passage of time and the collection of additional and more accurate data. In order to explain the motion of the planets and to predict their future positions accurately, it became necessary to add epicycles upon epicycles. By 1450 no less than 19 epicycles were necessary to explain the motion of Mars. Thinkers began to wonder if something were not basically wrong with the geocentric view. Thus, Alphonso the Wise in 1550 remarked meaningfully that if he were present at the time of Creation he could give a hint or two to the Creator.

This does not mean that the whole system was thrown out in summary fashion. All the observations, of course, had to be retained but had to be seen in a new perspective. As we have seen, the sphericity of the earth was retained. So was the idea that the moon is nearest the earth and travels around it. The other ideas were replaced and altered one at a time.

The Copernican Revolution

The first blow against the old-world view was dealt by Nicolaus Copernicus (1473-1543). In order to reduce the immense complexity of the Ptolemaic system, Copernicus first proposed that it is the earth rather than the sky that is turning on its axis daily. Then he made the more daring suggestion that the remaining phenomena could be explained much more simply by interchanging the position of the sun and the earth, thus making the sun the center of the world, and the earth just another planet. With the sun, he carried Mercury and Venus into the center, these planets going around the sun in primary circles and not in epicycles. The earth then became the third planet from the sun, with the moon going around the earth in an epicycle. However, he still allowed the earth to be the center of gravity.

Thus, Copernicus argued that the eastward motion of the sun is only apparent. As we move around the sun, we see the sun against a different background of stars. Since we move in a circle around it, the sun appears to move in a circle about us (Ex. 20). When the constellation of Capricorn is overhead, the sun appears in the constellation of Cancer (Fig. 2-34).

All the phenomena were tremendously simplified by these changes. According to Copernicus, the phenomena appear complicated because we observe them from a moving earth. Mars retrogrades, because we move faster than Mars. As we overtake it, it appears to move backward, against the background of the more distant stars. Jupiter retrogrades

Fig. 2-33. Copernicus revised the heliocentric theory, with the sun at the center and the earth rotating in a great circle around the sun. *(The Bettmann Archive.)*

Fig. 2-34. Sun's motion among the stars only apparent. When the earth, at E, is moving under the constellation of Capricorn, the sun appears in the constellations of Cancer, moving eastward.

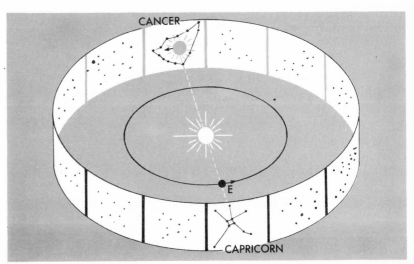

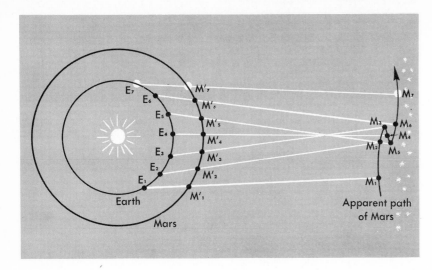

Fig. 2-35. Retrograde motion of Mars, according to the heliocentric view. E_1-E_7 successive positions of the earth; M'_1-M'_7 successive positions of Mars at corresponding times. M_1-M_7 successive positions of Mars in the sky as seen from the earth.

by a lesser amount, because it is further out. Each of these planets retrogrades precisely at the time the earth is between it and the sun. Similarly when either Mercury or Venus retrogrades, it overtakes the earth. This view also explains, in a simple way, that Mercury and Venus are never observed far from the sun since they must always be somewhere in their orbits which are within the orbit of the earth.

While this simple Copernican theory explained all phenomena, the explanations were only approximate. Over the centuries, accurate observations have been made on the position of the planets. To explain more closely the past positions and to predict the future ones, Copernicus had to assume that each planet moved about a center that was a little off the sun. To complicate matters further, each planet moved about a different center so the sun could not be the one center of the solar system. Soon more cycles had to be added to explain the observations, and the more accurate observations the more complications in the theory. Nevertheless the basic idea seemed sound.

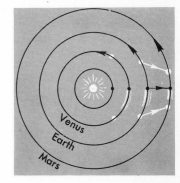

Fig. 2-36. Retrograde motion of planets. Mars retrogrades when the earth overtakes the planet. Venus retrogrades when it overtakes the earth.

Observations of Tycho Brahe

What embarrassed the defenders of the Copernican theory most were the accurate observations of Tycho Brahe (1546-1601). In the history of astronomy he is the outstanding example of a scientist who collects data. As an astronomer royal and astrologer to the King of Denmark, he had at his disposal an excellent astrolab by which he recorded accurately the positions of the planets. Night after night for many years he patiently recorded the elevation of the planets as they crossed the meridian. He did some theorizing of his own, but his outstanding contributions to science were his measurements. Had he lived longer, he probably would have collected more data. Yet we must not underestimate his type of work. It is first necessary to know what it is we are trying to explain before we attempt to explain it.

Kepler's Laws of Planetary Motion

Fig. 2-37. Johannes Kepler. His laws of planetary motion provided the foundation for Newton's system of the world.

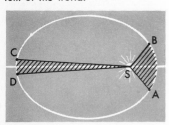

Fig. 2-38. Kepler's Law of Areas. A planet traveling faster when nearer the sun covers the distance AB in the same time as it covers the distance CD. However, the area ASB is equal to the area CSD.

The Newtonian Synthesis

It took a genius of a different sort to interpret the data of Tycho Brahe. Having inherited Tycho's two volumes of observations, Johannes Kepler (1571-1630) set for himself the task of determining the true and exact path of Mars. Accepting the Copernican scheme, his problem was to find the center of the orbit, the distance of the planet relative to the earth-to-sun distance, and the inclination of the plane of the orbit relative to that of the earth, from which Tycho's observation had been made. He tried one center after another, one distance after another, and one inclination after another. For each trial an incredible amount of calculation was involved. After fourteen years of labor he came to the conclusion that the path of Mars is not a circle.

Anyone else would have given up after this, but not Kepler. He then tried an ellipse, placing the sun at the center, and repeated the now more complicated calculations. Still Mars was not at the positions observed by Tycho. Finally, he put the sun at one focus of the ellipse; and, after many trials, at long last the predicted position of Mars coincided with the observations.

The results of his twenty years of labor were crystallized in his laws of planetary motion, three of which contain the essence of his findings. We may restate these as follows:

(1) *Elliptical Orbit Law.* A planet moves in an ellipse around the sun, which occupies one of the foci. So far as we know, there is nothing at the other focus.

(2) *The Law of Areas.* A planet moves fastest when nearest the sun and slowest when furthest from it. If a line is drawn between the planet and the sun, the line sweeps equal areas in equal intervals of time (Fig. 2-38).

(3) *The Harmonic Law.* Comparing any two planets, the further a planet is from the sun, the longer it takes to go around it. More precisely, the square of the periods are proportional to the cube of the average distance from the sun. Thus Jupiter, which is about five times as far from the sun as the earth, takes $\sqrt{5^3}$, or $\sqrt{125}$, or over 11 years to go around it.

Kepler's laws describe with a high degree of accuracy the motions of the planets. Thus Copernicus was right in his fundamental idea. The plan of the solar system, though more complicated than was thought at first, is nevertheless relatively simple.

The great success of Kepler convinced most thinkers of the soundness of the Copernican view. However, the overthrow of the Ptolemaic system involved much more than the matter of complexity. It could still be argued that Kepler's laws were in reality merely a neat mathematical scheme that permitted one to calculate the positions of the planets, much as a time-table permits the prediction of the motions of trains. The train does not move from one line of the table to the next; it moves on tracks on the ground. Physically, these people argued, the earth does not move. What was needed for the overthrow of the old view was a new physics and a new chemistry. Further, no "reason" was given for the regularities which Kepler's laws described.

It was the genius of Newton that supplied the new mechanics and showed that planets obey a fundamental law and must move in the way they do. The full significance of Newton's contribution cannot be appreciated until we study in the next chapter his laws of motion. Nonetheless, we can give at this point some idea of his achievement and his reasoning, without, however, implying that this is the exact order in which he reasoned.

According to Newton's first law of motion, every material body, whether on the earth or in the heavens, possesses the fundamental property of movement in a straight line, unless acted on by a force. Seeing that a planet does not travel in a straight line, but in a curved path around the sun, Newton theorized that the sun must exert a force of attraction on the planet. Moreover, this force must decrease with distance, since the farther the planet is from the sun, the slower it moves and the less it is bent (that is, it moves over a circle of lesser curvature— see p. 85). By relatively simple but mathematical reasoning, he argued that since the path is an ellipse, the force must decrease as the *square* of the distance increases. That is, if a planet is twice as far from the sun as another planet, the force must be one fourth as great (per pound of the planet). Finally, since at any distance a planet bends by just the right amount to move in an ellipse, this force must be proportional to the mass of the planet and, by symmetry, it must also be proportional to the mass of the sun.

This is a sketchy outline of difficult reasoning and we shall return to it in Chapter 3. The point to be made now is that Newton was led to enunciate his famous law of gravitation, which may be stated as follows:

Every body in the universe attracts every other body with a force that is proportional to the product of the masses and inversely proportional to the square of the distance.

In mathematical form the force, f, is given by the equation:

$$f = G\,\frac{m_1 m_2}{r^2}$$

where m_1 is the mass of one body, m_2 the mass of the other body, and r is the distance between them. The constant, G, is a number which can be determined in the laboratory.

Newton showed, though we shall not attempt to explain it here, that Kepler's laws are consequences of the law of gravitation. Thus, in a single law Newton synthesized all the motions and regularities of the solar system. The mass of the sun and the masses of the planets can be calculated by making appropriate observations. Likewise, all the relative distances of all the planetary bodies can be calculated. More significantly, he showed that the world is a rational system, subject to law and order.

Newton's synthesis goes even deeper than this. He showed that the heavenly bodies obey the same laws of motion as bodies here on the earth. He destroyed the distinction between the "earthly" and the "heavenly." The substance of the heavenly bodies is not different from the material of the rocks. All are endowed with the fundamental properties of inertia and gravity. Thus, a false distinction that dominated the minds of men was shattered.

It is not difficult to relate other triumphs of the law of gravitation. Careful study tells us that Kepler's laws should not hold exactly, since each planet also attracts all other planets and is in turn attracted by them. Therefore, a planet does not follow the path of an exact ellipse, but one with small irregularities. However, from the known masses and the distances of the other planets we can calculate exactly what the path should be.

In two instances, however, the observed path was not exactly as calculated. When Uranus, a sixth planet, was discovered in 1781 by William Herschel, the path was calculated using the law and taking into account all the known planets, Uranus deviated from the predicted path. If the law still held, this discrepancy could only mean that there must be another planet outside Uranus causing the unaccounted-for perturbations. Two mathematicians, John Couch Adams and Urbain Leverrier, independently calculated where the unknown planet should be. In 1846, on the explicit directions of Leverrier, the astronomer Johann Galle looked and, in less than half an hour, found a new planet—Neptune—near the predicted position. In 1931 Pluto was discovered in part by similar calculations.

Since the time of Newton, the law of gravitation has been found to hold in the remote regions of space. Stars have been observed which revolve about one another or rather around their common center of gravity, much as an oversized planet larger than Jupiter would revolve around the center of gravity between it and the sun. The law has been found to hold for groups of stars and indeed for entire galaxies, consisting of millions of stars. We reserve a part of this story for Chapter 15. The point here is that the law is truly universal.

Limits of the Newtonian System—Relativity

It was stated earlier that the law of gravitation predicts with absolute accuracy the motion of any object in the solar system. This statement could be made until the beginning of this century. However, about that time it was realized that for Mercury the point of closest approach to the sun shifts by a very small amount not predicted by this law. The difference is only a few seconds of arc per century—but nonetheless is real. In 1915, Einstein proposed the general theory of relativity, which modified the laws of motion of Newton and also gave a different interpretation to his law of universal gravitation. It is beyond the scope of this book to attempt to present this theory. The interested reader is referred to an excellent book that gives an understandable treatment of the subject (Ref. 3.2; see also 3.6 and 3.11g).

Suffice it to say that both the laws of motion and the law of gravitation describe with extraordinary precision all motions we are likely to encounter. Indeed, the laws of motion and the system of mechanics developed by Newton are the model on which all science up until recently and most of science even today is built. We shall take up this story in the next chapter.

NOTES AND EXERCISES

1. Sunspots persist for several days or weeks. How can we use the sunspots to determine the rotation of the sun? In what direction do the sunspots move over the surface of the sun? Why do sunspots appear dark?

2. If we stood on the earth's equator and saw Orion overhead, how long would it be before it set? Where would it set?

3. Westward is defined as clockwise as seen from the North Star. How would it be, as seen from the south? Why do the hands of the clock move in the direction they do? (Remember the early clocks were sundials.) Had clocks been developed in the southern hemisphere, which way would the hands probably go?

4. Why do we not have eclipses of the moon every month? Why do the planets not eclipse one another?

5. Mars as seen from the earth varies a great deal in brightness, but from the sun it always appears of medium brightness. Draw a diagram to explain this. How much variation in brightness do you expect for Mars as seen from the earth?

6. Why should the earth decrease so tremendously in brightness if carried to the distance of Pluto? How much total light would it receive from the sun at 40 times the present distance? How faint would the total light it reflects become if observed from 40 times the distance?

7a. In going from Mercury to Venus why would the overcoming the force of the sun be a greater problem than overcoming the force of Mercury?

b. What would a 200-pound man weight with respect to the sun— that is, attracted by the sun—at the distance of Mercury, which is about 80 times further from the center of the sun than it is at the surface of the sun? What would he weigh with respect to Mercury at the surface of Mercury? If you move 1,000,000 times further into space, what would these weights be?

8. How do we know from the earth that the moon has no atmosphere? Why would the stars be visible and the sky black in the daytime on the moon? Would you expect to see the stars in the daytime from a satellite 200 miles high?

9. Describe the course of a full "day" on the moon from sunrise to sunrise, giving times, temperatures, appearance of the earth, etc.

10. Why does Venus show phases like the moon as seen from the earth? In what phase does Venus appear largest? Would the earth show a crescent phase as seen from Mars? Galileo was the first to observe the phases of Venus. Does this "prove" the heliocentric theory?

11. Can we take advantage of the elliptical orbit of Eros and travel to Mars? Can you show by means of diagrams how this can be accomplished? Would this save a space ship any fuel? Why not?

12. How do we explain the low density of the larger planets? What has probably happened to the hydrogen and helium for the earth and the other small planets? (See also p. 588.)

13. How can Eros be used to measure accurately the distances in the solar system? What do we know from Kepler's laws of motion. (See also p. 474.)

14. Another good way of getting a proper conception of the solar system is to construct an imaginary model to scale. Let 1 foot represent 1 million miles, so that the sun is a ball about 10 inches in diameter in the center of the room. How large and where would Mercury be? Continue the model for the rest of the solar system. Where would the nearest star be?

15. What is the nightly path of a star only 40 degrees from the North Star? Would this star ever set for an observer in Chicago, latitude 42 degrees? How many degrees must a star be to touch just the horizon at its lowest point? What would its path be if it is 70 degrees from the North Star? What would it be if it was 90 degrees from the pole, that is, on the celestial equator? What if it was 120 degrees from the north pole, that is, 60 degrees from the south pole? What if it was 30 degrees from the south pole?

16. On March 21 the sun is on the celestial equator and rises on the east point. How long is it above the horizon? Is this true for any point on the earth? Do you see why they call this day "equinox"?

17. At its northernmost point on June 21 the sun is 23½ degrees north of the celestial equator—that is, 66½ degrees from the north pole. For an observer in the northern hemisphere, where does the sun rise with respect to the east point? How many hours is it above the horizon? Where is the sun on December 21 and where does it rise? Can you now explain the variation of daylight throughout the year?

18. If we go northward in the United States, the North Star rises higher by one degree for every 69.5 miles of travel. Where would it be if we went clear to the north pole of the earth? Where would the North Star be if we traveled southward to the equator? Where would the south pole of the sky be? Where would the celestial equator be?

19. Describe how the stars would appear to move for an observer at the equator. Would there be any stars that never rise or set? Describe how the sun would appear to rise and set at the various times of the year.

20. Place a light in the middle of the room. Note the part of the wall that is in the background. Now move around it. Note how the light appears to move in the background of the various parts of the room.

21. Place two balls near the light. One nearer to represent the earth and one farther to represent Mars. Move both of them in the same direction, but the inner, the earth, faster than the outer. Do you observe that as the earth overtakes Mars, the latter appears to move backward with respect to the background of the room?

22. Observe a chair which is near the wall—that is, nearer to the light than to the wall. As the earth goes around the sun, do you observe the edge of the chair moving back and forth with respect to points on the wall behind? This is parallax. In the course of the year, the nearer stars appear to shift back and forth with respect to the farther background of stars. The shift is extremely small. For the nearest star, it is barely 1½ seconds of arc. A second of arc is the angle a dime would subtend at a distance of 12 miles. We can measure fairly accurately angles down to 0.01 second. How far should a dime be to subtend an angle of 0.01 second? (See also p. 469.)

23. "The annual path of the sun in the sky is almost a perfect circle, and its motion almost, but not quite, steady and uniform." The earth moves in an ellipse, and is nearest the sun January 3 and farthest on July 3. Since the sun appears almost the same size during the year, what can we say about the distance from the sun during the year? When more accurate measurements are made, when does the sun appear largest? When is its eastward drift the fastest? Why is the path not a perfect circle? Can you explain it by the effect of the moon on the earth?

24. An ellipse may be drawn by taking a string and two pins and placing the pins some distance apart to form the foci. With the string rather loose one runs a pencil describing an oval. By varying the distance of the pins and the length of the string, ellipses of various eccentricities may be drawn. Where is the sun in the ellipse? What is on the other focus? What planets vary most in speed, those whose path is more nearly circular, or those whose path is most eccentric?

25. Calculate the period of Pluto from the fact that its distance from the sun is 40 times the earth-to-sun distance.

26. Calculate the mass of the earth given the radius as 6.4×10^8 cm, the force of attraction between it and a gram of mass as 980 dynes, and the value of G in the same units as 6.67×10^{-8}. How does the value compare with that obtained from the distance and period of revolutions of the moon?

27. The rotation of the earth (or the apparent daily motion of the sun) makes time of a particular place depend on longitude. If it is 6 P.M. Monday in St. Louis, what time and day is it in New York? In London? In Calcutta, India (90 degrees E)? In Tokyo (135 degrees E)? In Honolulu (155 degrees W)?

28. If you are circling the earth westward, in general you will change the date *twice*—once at midnight, and again at the international dateline. There are two different reasons for it; can you explain each? The second of these was noticed for the first time by the sailors of Magellan, who first circumnavigated the earth. They arrived in Spain on Wednesday according to their log. What day was it in Spain?

3

MOTION

I. TWO SYSTEMS OF MECHANICS

When Newton published his *Principia,* he did much more than overthrow the Ptolemaic view that the earth is the center of the world. In the process he replaced the Aristotelian system of mechanics by establishing a new physics and prepared the way for the development of a new chemistry. He created a system of mechanics by which the motions of all bodies, whether on the earth or in the heavens, can be understood or at least described and predicted. At the foundation of this system lay three simple principles—his three laws of motion. All modern science is based, directly or indirectly, upon these laws.

It is not obvious how an understanding of motion can have so profound an effect on the thinking of men until we realize that motion is a part of a greater idea—the idea of *change* in general. Change is a universal phenomenon—a fundamental fact of existence. Nothing seems to remain the same. The stars change their positions, the rivers flow, the stones roll, the animals run, the pond freezes, thaws, and disappears on evaporation; the fire consumes the fuel; the structures deform and crumble; the trees, the animals, and men are born, grow, age, die, and disintegrate. On the common-sense level, we adjust to this fact of change and manage to survive. On the philosophic level, it led Heraclitus to proclaim his motto, "Everything flows." Nothing remains the same.

When, however, we attempt to analyze change intelligently, we encounter great difficulties. In man's struggle to understand the world, nothing has given him more trouble than change. A very basic difficulty probably springs from the fact that the human mind is constructed to think in stationary pictures. We grasp only that which retains its form

50

long enough for us to perceive it. We try to understand change in terms of a succession of still pictures. Intimately bound with *change* is the idea of *time*. Time is one aspect of change, in the sense that one stationary mental image succeeds another *in time*. Out of this comes the idea of cause and effect. When one event precedes another under certain specified conditions, the first event is said to be the cause of the second.

Aristotle, in the fourth century B.C., made a forward step when he analysed change into *locomotion,* or change of position; *augmentation* and *diminution,* or change in quantity; *alteration,* or change in quality, and *generation* and *corruption*. By the last three he meant, roughly, but not quite, the kind of changes that take place in the melting of ice, in the burning of fuel, and in the life processes. Philosopher-scientists before him, and after, put forth the idea—really a hope—that if we can understand *loco*motion, we may eventually understand all other changes as involving motions of the atoms of matter. This idea will be elaborated on more fully in the discussion of chemical changes and the atoms in Chapter 8.

Even locomotion—the mere change of position—was difficult to understand. How does a body change its position as it moves? How many positions does it take in going from one place to another? At any instant does it occupy a definite position? If so, is it standing still at that instant? If it is standing still, how does it acquire motion in the next instant? The ancients never gave satisfactory answers to such questions. We may mention in passing that we also have difficulties of our own.

A clearer appreciation of these difficulties may be obtained by examining one of Zeno's famous paradoxes. Zeno stated that the fast runner, Achilles, could not overtake a slow-moving tortoise in a race if the tortoise had started earlier. Suppose, said Zeno, that the tortoise, moving 1000 feet an hour, started 10 hours earlier than Achilles, who is capable to 10,000 feet an hour. It will take Achilles 1 hour to cover the 10,000 feet that the tortoise is ahead, but meanwhile the slower tortoise will have gone another 1000 feet. True, Achilles will make this 1000 feet in 1/10 hour, but by this time the tortoise will have gone another 100 feet. Achilles would now have to cover this distance, but the tortoise would again be ahead by 10 feet. This argument can be continued indefinitely, with the tortoise always staying ahead.

Now Zeno was no fool, nor were the other philosophers who struggled with the problem. They knew perfectly well that Achilles would overtake the tortoise. The point is, *where is the catch in this argument?* Is there something wrong with the human mind that it cannot grasp such things? Or is motion an illusion, since human reason finds contradictions in it? Some philosophers thought so, and asserted that motion is impossible, since the *inconceivable cannot exist*. This led to the equally famous motto, "Nothing is new under the sun"—exactly opposite to the motto of Heraclitus.

Another example may bring out a different difficulty in conceiving motion. Imagine a ring falling, and a bullet shot horizontally and so aimed as to pass through the center of the ring. Let us consider the instant at which the center (of gravity) of the ring occupies the same point as the center of the bullet. At this instant, the bullet and the ring

Fig. 3-1. Heraclitus. His motto: πάντα ρεῖ- everything flows. (*The Bettmann Archive.*)

Fig. 3-2. Aristotle. The greatest natural philosophy of antiquity. His system of mechanics dominated western science until challenged by Galileo and Newton. (*The Bettmann Archive.*)

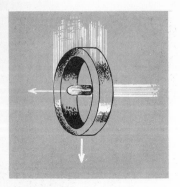

Fig. 3-3. Ring and bullet in motion. Centers of mass occupy the same point.

occupy the same point. Why then, in the next instant will the ring and the bullet occupy different points? What is different about the ring and the bullet? We say it is velocity. But what is velocity? Is it *intention?* Do the ring and the bullet at this instant have different "intentions," of occupying different positions in the next instant? We have to postpone resolving this difficulty.

Difficulties of a different sort arose in the attempt to find the causes of motion and how bodies move under these causes. Aristotle gave us the first system of mechanics. He began by distinguishing between natural and forced or "constrained" motion. In natural motion, bodies move toward their "proper" place. Thus, heavy bodies move downward seeking the center of heaviness; light bodies, such as fire, move upward seeking the place of lightness. The way they move is also according to their nature. Earthly bodies, light or heavy, move up or down in straight lines; celestial bodies move in circles. Moreover, heavy bodies move in proportion to their heaviness. A heavy weight falls faster than a light weight.

Constrained motion was also disposed of rather simply by this system. A heavy body, of itself, would move downward but an outside force can make it move on the floor horizontally, by forcing it. The body can be made to move in a straight line, in triangles, or even in circles. But continued pushing is necessary if it is to move in any direction other than down. After the outside force is removed, the body continues to move a little longer because the air behind it forms eddies and pushes it on for a while. If the push stops, the object stops moving.

A heavy object can even be pushed upward, against its natural tendency. If it is thrown upward, the eddies of the air push it upward for a while longer. But soon the push of the eddies stops, the body stops, and the natural tendency reasserts itself so the body returns, falling downward. If a body is thrown sideward, the natural tendency again asserts itself so the body falls downward in a curve.

These are some of the essential parts of the Aristotelian system. Three points in his system are important to remember: The distinction between natural and forced motion; the principle that a body would move in forced motion only so long as a force is acting on it; and the statement that the natural fall of a heavy body is faster than that of a light body.

We have given the Aristotelian system in some detail for two important reasons: this system dominated the best minds for over two thousand years; moreover, the system seems sound and appears to be derived from direct experience—the untutored mind adopts it intuitively. Without special instruction, this is the system the average person has more or less hazily in the back of his mind. Against this background it will be easier to understand and appreciate the Newtonian system.

It is not easy to point out what is wrong with Aristotelian mechanics. True, the statement that heavy bodies fall faster than light bodies can be checked by experiment and found false. But the main trouble with the system is that it missed the point. The points emphasized turned out to be of no importance. For example, the distinction between natural and constrained motion turned out to be of no significance. The system also failed to emphasize what *was* important. It failed to develop the concepts that ultimately describe and explain motion.

Galileo was the first to challenge the Aristotelian system effectively. He said the distinction between natural and constrained motion is not real. At least it is not significant and merely confuses the issue. He went further and flatly denied the basic principle of Aristotle; that a body needs a force to keep it moving. According to Galileo, if there is no interference with a moving body, it will keep on moving in a straight line forever—no force is necessary. He developed the idea of *acceleration* and argued that a heavy and a light ball, if released from the same height, will reach the ground at the same time. There may be some question as to whether he actually dropped the balls from the leaning tower of Pisa, but there is no question about his argument or his conclusions. We shall take up his concept of acceleration in a later section.

Newton's contribution is the subject of the remainder of this chapter. Newton accepted and further developed Galileo's ideas. Galileo's principle of natural straight-line motion became Newton's first law. Newton developed two more laws, and the three together form a complete and all-inclusive system by which all motion can be understood and described.

Fig. 3-4. Galileo emphasized the necessity of experiment in gaining knowledge of nature and developed the idea of acceleration and inertia.

2. NEWTON'S LAWS OF MOTION

The easiest way to understand the modern concept of motion is to develop first, step by step, the ideas that describe it. The more important questions concerning the causes of motion and how bodies move under the influence of forces will be taken up afterwards.

The most characteristic property of a moving body is *speed*. By virtue of its motion, a body travels a certain distance in a given time. Speed is defined as the ratio of distance to time. To begin with we may take the idea of distance and of time from common sense and everyday experience, measuring distance by ordinary methods, such as a yardstick, and time with a clock. Speed, therefore, is distance divided by time. That is,

Speed

$$\text{speed} = \frac{\text{distance}}{\text{time}}$$

or mathematically,

$$v = \frac{s}{t}$$

where *v* stands for speed (velocity), *s* for distance (space), and *t* for time.

Thus, if we motor from Chicago to St. Louis, a distance of 300 miles, in 6 hours, our speed is 300 miles divided by 6 hours, or 50 miles per hour. Note that in order to express speed, both "miles" and "hours" are required. Speed may be expressed in feet per second, yards per minute, inches per century, centimeters per second, and so on. In all cases it is necessary to have some unit of distance per (divided by) some unit of time.

Further, there are several kinds of speed. The speed just calculated for the Chicago to St. Louis trip is the *average* speed. To find it, the total distance is divided by the total elapsed time. This does not mean, however, that 2 hours after starting we had gone 100 miles or that our speed was 50 miles per hour. Two hours after starting we might be going 70 miles per hour, or have stopped for gas.

To understand this, the concept of *constant* speed is necessary. Constant speed means *equal distances* traveled in *equal intervals* of time. The average speed calculated above is a fictitious speed. The statement that the average speed is 50 miles per hour means that if we had traveled with the constant speed of 50 miles per hour, we would get to St. Louis at the same time as in the actual trip. Like many other averages, average speed may not be real. Consider, for example, the statement that the "average" family has 2.7 children. Nevertheless, the idea of average is useful. The total distance is obtained by multiplying the average speed by the total time.

Still another kind of speed must be distinguished—*instantaneous* speed. It is the speed a body has at any one instant. The speedometer of a car registers the instantaneous speed. We should try to avoid the difficulties mentioned above in conceiving the meaning of instantaneous speed. However, we must try to think of instantaneous speed as having a real existence. At any instant a moving body has some definite speed. If the body is moving uniformly, its instantaneous speed is the same as the constant speed. But even if the speed is changing and may be different in the next instant, it has some definite value at any given instant. We urge the reader to try to understand the meaning of this paragraph. The ancients had great difficulty with the idea of instantaneous speed.

It might help to look at speed in still another way. Speed is a *rate,* describing how rapidly distance is covered as time goes on. The statement that we are going 30 miles per hour does not necessarily mean that we shall go 30 miles in the next hour. This speed is possible even if we go for only 10 seconds more. Speed is the rate at which distance is covered at that particular instant (see Ex. 2).

Accelerated Motion   When a body changes its speed, it is *accelerated*. Note that in such a case not only the position of the body changes (since it is moving), but the *speed itself* is changing. We must concentrate on the second point.

Suppose we are traveling at 30 miles per hour. We step on the accelerator as steadily as possible and notice the speedometer going up to 35, 40, 45, and then 50 miles per hour. We are moving all the while, of course, but that is not the point to note. The point is that the speed is going up. Suppose it took 10 seconds to speed up from 30 to 50 miles an hour. Altogether, 20 miles per hour have been gained in 10 seconds, or on the average 2 miles per hour have been gained *each second*. This last quantity is called the *acceleration*. It tells how many miles per hour we speed up per second. It is the rate at which the speed itself is changing.

Thus, acceleration is the rapidity with which speed is changing. It is that hard-to-define something called the "pickup." If in the previous example our speed had increased from 30 to 50 miles per hour in 5 seconds, the change in speed would be the same, but it would have taken place *faster*. The acceleration would have been 4 miles per hour each second.

Galileo Galilei (1564-1642) was the first to develop the idea of acceleration. The ancients never had it. It is a difficult concept—probably the most difficult encountered in this book. What makes it so difficult is that it is *a rate of a rate*. It is often confused with speed, which is itself a rate. Acceleration is not speed, or even change in speed; it is the *rate* at which speed itself is changing.

It is necessary to understand the concept of acceleration; for without it the subtlest points of Newton's mechanics will be missed. We will now introduce one more concept—the idea of velocity and its distinction from *speed*.

Velocity is an idea that contains both speed and direction of motion. In saying that a body moves at 30 miles per hour, we have specified its speed. But when we say that it moves at 30 miles per hour northwest we have specified its velocity. Constant velocity implies constant speed and in a constant direction—that is, in a straight line. When we say constant velocity, we need say no more—constant velocity implies both. On the other hand, constant speed may or may not mean constant velocity. For example, a body moving in a circle with a constant speed of 30 miles per hour, does *not* have constant velocity, because the direction of motion is changing every instant.

The point for the distinction is that a body can be accelerated by speeding it up, by slowing it down, or by deflecting it—that is, by changing the direction of its motion. In other words, by changing the *velocity* of a body, it is accelerated. This point will be clarified further in the discussion of Newton's laws of motion.

Before going further it is important to emphasize the meaning of speed, constant speed, average speed, instantaneous speed, the distinction between speed and velocity, and the meaning of acceleration. It is not necessary to work numerical problems to get these ideas, although it might help to get the clear meaning of the concepts if some problems are practiced. The Exercises 1 through 12 at the end of the chapter may help in this connection.

Galileo and Falling Bodies

It was a milestone in the history of science when Galileo used the concepts developed above to explain the motion of bodies freely falling on the earth. Of particular importance is the idea of acceleration. In

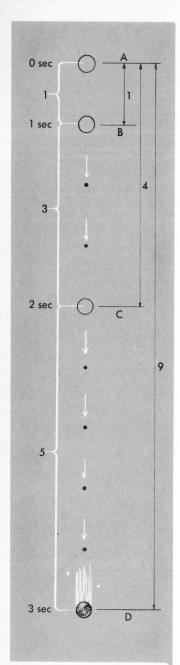

Fig. 3-5. Body freely falling from rest. Distances fallen during successive seconds are in ratios 1, 3, 5, 7 . . . ; total distances in ratios 1, 4, 9, 16 . . . .

fact, he developed the idea because he guessed that bodies fall with uniformly accelerated motion.

That a body speeds up as it falls had been known for a long time from even casual observation. Bodies falling from great heights acquired higher speeds than those falling only a few feet. What Galileo wanted to know is the exact relation. If a body falls from twice the height, would it acquire twice the speed? The answer seemed to be a "no," but he had great difficulty in measuring the rapid speeds of falling bodies. Although he invented the pendulum clock, he still had experimental difficulties in measuring such short time intervals. Thus he resorted to reasoning as well as to invention and experimentation.

Suppose, he reasoned, a body increases steadily in speed, as the time of fall increases: that is, suppose a falling body is uniformly accelerated. This implies that the body falling for 2 seconds acquires twice the speed, and in falling 3 seconds acquires three times the speed, it would acquire in falling 1 second. Then what are the consequences? Galileo continued as follows: If a body falls for 1 second, it will acquire a certain speed (we now know it to be about 32 feet per second). Before the end of the second the speed was less than that, and in fact during the entire second, except at the very end, the speed was less than that. If the speed was increasing steadily the *average* speed was half of that, or 16 feet per second. With an average speed of 16 feet per second, in 1 second the body would fall 16 feet. Thus, while at the *end* of the first second the speed is 32 feet per second, the body falls a distance of only 16 feet during the entire second.

Suppose the body falls for 2 seconds. It will acquire a final speed of 64 feet per second. The average speed for this 2-second interval is 32 feet per second, and since it is falling for 2 seconds, it will fall a distance of 64 feet.

Thus Galileo reasoned that if a body falls for twice the time, it will be falling with *twice the average speed,* and (since it will be falling for *twice* as long) it will fall *four* times as far. If the body falls for *three* times as long, it will have an average speed *three* times as great, and (since it will be falling *three* times as long) it will go *nine* times as far. Thus, the total distance fallen should be proportional to the *square* of the time.

It might be well to stop for a moment and consider a point in the method of science. So far, Galileo has not proved that the distance a body falls is proportional to the square of the time. What he said is that *if* a body increases uniformly in speed in proportion to the time it falls, then the distance fallen is proportional to the square of the time. Conversely, *if* the distance fallen is proportional to the square of the time of the fall, then the speed must increase uniformly with time. But whether bodies actually fall in this way or not can only be decided by an experiment. No amount of logic or even complicated mathematical reasoning can decide that. Bodies fall whichever way they fall. They are under no compulsion to fit into our concept or to follow our reasoning. The only way to find out how bodies fall is by experiment and observation. Though Galileo was not the first man to experiment, he was

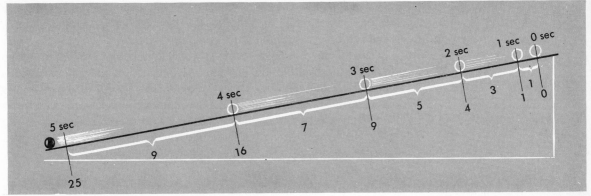

Fig. 3-6. The speed of a ball rolling downhill increases uniformly with time. Starting from rest the ball covers distances in the ratio of 1, 3, 5, 7, 9 . . . in successive seconds. The total distances are in the ratio of 1, 4, 9, 16 . . . .

the most influential figure to appreciate and point out the role of the experiment in science.

Galileo dropped weights from various heights and measured the height and the times of fall. As best he could tell from his measurements, a body four times as high falls in twice the time. But the time intervals were short and his measurements were not very accurate. He resorted to invention and more analysis.

He experimented extensively with inclined planes. He took a long plank and made a straight and smooth groove in it. He inclined the plane at a gentle slope and let a ball, as smooth and round as he could make it, roll down the groove. With a pendulum clock, which he invented, he measured the distances that the ball rolled downhill in successive swings of the clock. He found that in two swings the ball rolled four times as far as in the one swing, in three swings nine times as far, and so on. Here, he argued, is the ball "falling" downhill, and so slowly that its fall can be measured.

Galileo then increased the steepness of the plane and repeated the experiment. The ball now rolled faster, but still the distances covered were proportional to the square of the time. As he continued to increase the steepness, the ball rolled faster and faster and became more difficult to measure but, in so far as he could measure, the distances continued to be proportional to the square of the time. From this point on, he reasoned, "If I had a very long plank and increased the steepness more and more, the distance should continue to be proportional to the square of the time. If, finally, I increased the steepness until the plank is

Fig. 3-7. Galileo's extrapolation to free fall. The ball covers distances proportional to the square of the time, regardless of the steepness. The relation should hold for a vertical plane, which is free fall.

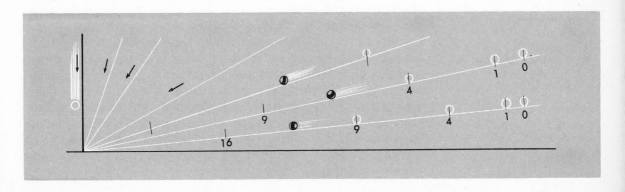

vertical, the ball would hardly touch the plank at all, but rather fall freely alongside of it. I shall then have a freely falling body, and the distances should still be proportional to the square of the time."

Thus Galileo discovered the law of falling bodies. We need not go into all the intricacies of the problem. His method of analysis and experiment carried him very far. However, he never quite grasped why bodies on the earth are uniformly accelerated, although he made great strides toward it. It was reserved for Newton to answer that question. To Newton he bequeathed all of these ideas. He also contributed the idea of inertia, which will be discussed in the next section.

Newton's First Law of Motion

Newton was a young man barely 20 years old when he developed his system of mechanics. In one master stroke he solved the riddle of motion. Not only did he add to the ideas of his predecessors, but he integrated all these ideas into a single whole. At the foundation of his system lie three simple principles.

As stated earlier, the first law is a clear statement of Galileo's idea of inertia. We quote from Newton's *Principia:*

> **Law 1. Every body perseveres in its state of rest or of uniform motion in a right line, unless it is compelled to change that state by forces impressed thereon.**

Here Newton says that it is the nature of a material body to retain its state of motion. It will do so unless it is "interfered with." If the body is at rest, it will remain at rest; if it happens to be in motion, it will continue to move in a straight (right) line with undiminished speed.

There are three distinct points in this law. First, that a body at rest tends to remain at rest is a universal lesson of experience. Things stay put. They do not start moving without a cause. If we see a chair start moving about without anyone pushing or pulling it, we know there is something "wrong." Material objects do not behave that way.

Second, it is also a matter of experience that the natural tendency of a body is to move in a straight line. If we throw a ball across the room, or roll it across a level floor, we expect it to go straight. If we see the ball suddenly changing its course, obviously something is wrong. It is the nature of material objects to move in a straight line.

However, the third point of Newton's first law—that a body continues to move with constant speed—seems contrary to experience. True, a moving body may continue on its course for a time, but it always slows down and eventually stops. How could Newton make such a statement, and use it as the very foundation of his system?

It was really Galileo who developed and justified the idea. He admitted that all moving bodies on the earth slow down and eventually stop, but he maintained that this happens because there is always interference from friction. He experimented with balls rolling on smooth level planes. The smoother he made the planes, the more nearly perfect the balls—the further they went before stopping. He reasoned that if the planes could be made perfectly smooth and level, a perfect ball should roll on them forever. True, he went beyond experience, but not without reasoning.

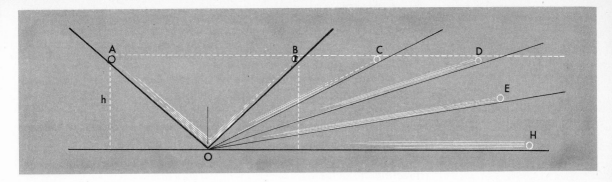

Fig. 3-8. Galileo's argument for the law of inertia. On a smooth horizontal surface, OH, a perfectly smooth ball should go on forever without slowing down.

One of his arguments seems to convince even the most skeptical. He took two very smooth planks AO and OB and made a V as shown in Figure 3-8. He let a ball roll from A and found that having descended to O, it rolled up OB to B, almost the same height from the table as A. The smoother the plank, the more nearly the ball rose to the same height. Then he replaced OB with a longer plank OC. Now the ball went further, but again it tended to rise to the same height at C. If there were no friction, he argued, the ball, having descended from A, should go to C in order to reach the same height. He tried longer and longer planks always with the same result. The ball had to go further each time to reach the same height. He then asked this question, "If I have a long horizontal plane, OM, how far must the ball go to reach the same height?" The obvious answer would be, "Forever—it will never reach that height."

Galileo made a still deeper analysis. The ball, having descended from A, has a certain speed at O. If it moves up along OB it loses its speed rather rapidly. Along OC it must lose the speed more slowly since it keeps rolling for a longer time. The less the slope, the more slowly it loses the speed. If there is no slope at all—that is, if the plank is horizontal—the ball should not lose any speed. In other words the ball should move not only *forever* but with *undiminished* speed.

Newton's second law answers the very question that the first law raises. Suppose we grant that a body tends to keep its state of motion if it meets with no interference. What happens when we *do* interfere with it? Newton's answer would be very simple but emphatic: "Then *the body will be accelerated*." It will be either speeded up, slowed down, or deflected from its straight course, depending on the way we interfere with the body. In other words it will suffer a change in its *velocity*. Incidentally, it is for this reason that velocity has been defined to include both speed and direction. A change in velocity means a change in either speed or direction of motion and, according to Newton, a force is required to do either.

The idea of "interference" needs further and precise clarification. What we call "interference," Newton called a "force" exerted on a body. We are familiar with forces in a general way. The muscular sense of push or pull, connected with effort, gives the most primitive notion. We are also familiar with forces of weights, forces of stretched or compressed springs, forces exerted by magnets or by electric charges, forces

Newton's Second Law of Motion

exerted by motors and moving bodies in general, and so on. In the second law Newton gives a more precise idea of force and a new definition. *A force is anything that can accelerate a material body.*

Newton said that the body will always be accelerated in the direction of the force acting on it. If the force acts in the direction in which the body is already moving, the body will be speeded up; if in the opposite direction, the body will be slowed down; if at right angles, the body will be deflected; if at any other angle, the body will be partly deflected and partly speeded up or slowed down depending on the direction of the force.

Newton went further than this in his second law. He said that the amount of acceleration the body would suffer will depend on two things: first, on how big the force is, and second, on how much matter there is in the body. For a given body, the bigger the force, the greater the acceleration. More precisely, double the force, double the acceleration. Thus, if we let one spring act on a ball, we will observe a given acceleration; if we let two identical springs act on the same ball, we will observe double the speeding up. If we put *two* motors in a car (keeping everything else the same), we will have *double* the pickup. This means that with two motors we can get double the final speed in a given time; or, if we prefer, the same final speed in half the time. Thus the acceleration is directly proportional to the force.

The amount of matter in the body has the opposite effect. The bigger the body—that is, the more mass in the body—the less the acceleration. Again, and more precisely, double the mass, half the acceleration. Thus, if we hitched a car to another car of the same weight (mass), the motor of the first car would produce only half the pickup on the combined mass it would produce if the car were speeding up alone (again other things being equal). Thus the acceleration is inversely proportional to the mass.

Combining the two ideas into a single statement, we get Newton's second law: The acceleration produced is directly proportional to the force and inversely proportional to the mass; or mathematically,

$$a \propto \frac{f}{m}$$

Newton himself expressed it as follows:

Law 2. The alteration of motion is ever proportional to the motive force impressed; and is made in the direction of the right line in which that force is impressed.

(By "motion" Newton means "quantity of motion," which he clearly defines as the product of the mass and the velocity. This quantity, now called "momentum," will be explained presently.)

Some of the implications of Newton's first two laws of motion are far-reaching and subtle. One of them is the idea of *inertia* or *mass*. According to Newton, every material body possesses the fundamental property of resisting any change in its state of motion. It resists or "rebels against" being accelerated. If it is at rest, it resists being set in motion; if in motion, it resists being stopped. It resists the forces speeding it up, slowing it down, or deflecting it from a straight path. It is this "rebellion" or "reluctance" that is called "inertia."

This property of inertia is so characteristic of a material body that it may be used as its definition. *A material body is anything that requires a force to accelerate it.* We might even say that it is this property of inertia that distinguishes a material body from a ghost, an idea, a form, a concept, or an emotion. These other things may have real existence, but they are not material. The idea of a material body is used throughout science. Thus, as discussed later, we know that an electron is a particle of *matter* precisely because it resists accelerating forces, and in fact we measure its mass that way.

The amount of resistance to accelerating forces is a measure of the *inertia* or *mass* of the body. Thus we say that 2 gallons of water has twice the mass (or inertia) of 1 gallon, because twice the force is needed to speed up the 2 gallons by the same amount in the same time. We say that it has twice the mass of 1 gallon, *not* because it would quench the thirst of twice as many people, though that might be true; *or* because it would wet twice the surface, *or* because it has twice the volume, *or even* because it has twice the weight, though all these things are true. We say this *only* because twice the force must be used to shake it about. All these other properties are true, but they are incidental to the idea of mass, as we shall proceed to show.

Quenching power is obviously not inertia. A gallon of lemon juice might quench more thirst, but has hardly more mass than a gallon of water. Wetting power is not mass. A gallon of soap water wets more surface than a gallon of plain water, but has no more mass. Volume as such is not mass. A gallon of mercury has the same volume as a gallon of water, yet it has $13\frac{1}{2}$ times the mass. Finally, weight is not mass. A gallon of water weighs $8\frac{1}{4}$ pounds on the earth but barely $1\frac{1}{2}$ pounds on the moon, and in interstellar space it is almost weightless. Yet it would require just as much force to shake (that is, to accelerate by a given amount) a gallon of water on the earth, on the moon, or in interstellar space.

The distinction between mass and weight requires further explanation. It is difficult not to confuse the two ideas. Both weight and mass are expressed in pounds. Thus if a brick *weighs* a pound on the surface of the earth, we say that it has a *mass* of 1 pound. In other words, in considering a pound brick we can be thinking of two distinct things. One is the weight of the brick. The *weight* is the *force* with which the earth is pulling it downward. The other is the resistance the brick would offer to our effort to shake it about—that is, to accelerate it. The first, the weight, is variable. If the brick is moved away from the earth, its weight decreases. If it is taken to the moon, it weighs only $\frac{1}{6}$ pound. But the other property, mass or inertia, is always the same. The brick offers the same resistance to speeding up, whether the earth is attracting it or not.

A very interesting property of forces is that they add algebraically. (As a matter of fact they add geometrically, but we will consider this complication later.) Thus, if John pushes on a car with a force of

25 pounds and Bob pushes in the same direction with a force of 40 pounds, the result is the same as if only one of them pushed with a force of 65 pounds. On the other hand if John pushes forward with a force of 25 pounds and Bob pushes backward with a force of 40 pounds, the result is the same as if Bob alone pushed backward with a force of 15 pounds. The automobile will accelerate backward in response to this force, provided there is no friction. Thus forces can add up as well as cancel one another. We said earlier that a force is anything that can accelerate a body. The statement is still true, but the force must be unbalanced. It is the *net* force that accelerates bodies.

We can now take up the case of friction more intelligently. Galileo asserted that there must be friction present during motions of bodies around us. In fact he argued ingeniously about the impossibility of making a perfectly smooth surface. There are always some irregularities that act as obstructions. Even in air there is friction, since a body moving through it must push aside some of the air.

However, with Newton's ideas, the nature of friction can be taken up more directly. Since all moving bodies on the earth slow down and eventually stop, there must be a force slowing them down, for only a force can reduce the speed of a body. This force can even be measured by measuring the mass of the body and the rate at which it slows down. Since friction is a force, it can be overcome with another force in the opposite direction. It is interesting to consider the special case in which the frictional force tends to slow down a moving body. If a force equal to the opposing force of friction is applied so as to act on the body in the direction of its motion, the two forces will exactly cancel one another, and the result is the same as if no force acts on the body at all. Consequently the body will keep the speed it happens to have and continue to move with it. The body will not stop, as we may be inclined to think, nor will it speed up or slow down, but will continue with the speed it has.

Perhaps the most surprising implication of Newton's first two laws of motion is that a force is not necessary to *move* a body. A force is necessary *only to accelerate* it. If a body is moving, however slowly, it will of its own accord cover any distance, however great, given sufficient time. "Very well," one may say, "this is obvious enough, if there is no friction. But what if there *is* friction? Is it not necessary to use a force to *move* a body if there is friction?" The answer is *no*. To be sure, a force is necessary to *counterbalance* the force of friction, but beyond that force, no additional force is necessary to keep it moving. Once friction is counterbalanced, the body will move of itself, by virtue of its own velocity.

"Still," one may object further, "suppose a body is lying motionless, on a frictionless floor. Is it not necessary to use a force to *move* it to another point on the floor?" The answer is still *"no."* To be sure a force is necessary to set it in motion, to accelerate it, to give it speed. But once the body has acquired speed, it will move of its own accord— it needs no force to move it. A force is necessary to accelerate a body but not to move it. Unless the reader sees these subtle points, he has not grasped the essence of Newton's first two laws of motion.

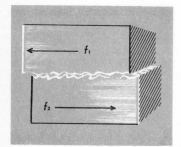

Fig. 3-9. Galileo's idea of friction.

One of the most important properties of forces is that they always appear in pairs. There is never just one force in any given situation. For every force there is always an equal and opposite force. This simple statement is Newton's third law of motion. Newton stated it as follows:

> Law 3. To every action there is always opposed an equal reaction; or the mutual actions of two bodies upon each other are always equal, and directed to contrary parts.

The truth of this statement is rather obvious in most instances. If you push on the wall with a force of 25 pounds, the wall resists your push and pushes you back with a force of 25 pounds. If you pull on a spring with a force of 30 pounds, the spring stretches and pulls you with the same force. If you increase the pull to 35 pounds, the spring stretches further until it develops a force of 35 pounds, and pulls you with that force. If you attach a rope to a wall and pull on the rope with a given force, the wall pulls you back with that force. As you increase the force pulling on the rope, the wall increases the backward pull. This can continue until the strength of the rope—that is, the forces that hold the rope together—are exceeded, and the rope breaks. At that instant both forces suddenly disappear. You are no longer pulling on the wall, and the wall is no longer pulling on you.

A similar situation is observed when a book is placed on a table. The book presses on the table with the force of its weight. The table is depressed slightly and deforms until it creates a force equal to the weight of the book and pushes upward. A greater weight produces a greater deformation and a greater upward force, exactly equal to the weight upon it. As we increase the weight on the table, ultimately the strength of the legs will be exceeded, and the table begins to accelerate—it comes crashing down.

It is instructive to analyze the case further. The book is exerting a force on the table top, and the table top is exerting an upward force on the book. Now the table is resting on the floor, and therefore its legs are pressing down on the floor with this additional force. The floor, then, exerts an equal and upward force on the legs. But the floor is resting on the beams, and the beams on the wall, and the walls on the earth. At all these points of contact—wherever we choose to analyze the problem—we find that wherever there is a force, there is always an equal and opposite force.

There is a subtle distinction between these two opposite forces which must be kept clearly in mind. It is the distinction between "by the body" and "on the body." The downward force, the *action*, is *by* the book *on* the table. The upward force, the *reaction*, is *by* the table *on* the book. The two forces—action and reaction—are never on the same body. (In the analysis, we can choose, of course, to consider the whole building as one body, but then the analysis is meaningless and impossible until we begin to talk of different parts of the building, thus in effect reintroducing the two different bodies.)

Of further interest is the case of the table crashing down. When the force exerted by the weight of the load exceeds the force that the cohesive forces of the legs can exert, the difference in force can be made up only by the table accelerating—crashing down. A simpler illustration may help explain this. With a rope we pull on an object weighing 50 pounds, which is lying on a table. Since there is friction, the object is resisting our pull without moving. But how? Through the protrusions of its rough surface on the rough surface of the table, the object is pushing the table in our direction. The table then is pushing on the object in the opposite direction. The object therefore is reacting to our pull, by pushing *on* and in turn being pushed back *by* the surface of the table. This is what we call friction.

What happens if we now pull with a force greater than that of friction? The object will then begin to accelerate in our direction. If we pull with a force of 20 pounds and the frictional force is only 15 pounds, the object will accelerate toward us, the accelerating force being 5 pounds. When calculated, the acceleration is found to be about 4 inches per second per second.

At this point a serious misconception is likely to arise. We are pulling with a force of 20 pounds, but the frictional force is only 15 pounds. These forces are not equal, though they are opposite. What happened to Newton's third law? Is it not valid when there is acceleration? But Newton insists that the law always holds. If we understood him correctly, the forces should be equal. According to Newton what happens is that the body, by virtue of its inertia, resists our acceleration, and in so doing *develops* a resisting force of 5 pounds, exactly equal to the accelerating force. Thus our pulling force of 20 pounds is "resisted" by 15 pounds of friction and 5 pounds of force necessary to accelerate the object. If we increase our pull by another 5 pounds, the body will accelerate faster and develop 10 pounds of resistance.

The question may arise how much force a 50-pound body can develop in resisting acceleration. The answer is, *any force whatever*. If it is speeded up slowly, it will develop only a small force. If it is speeded up rapidly, it will develop a greater force, always equal to the accelerating force. This 50-pound body can develop a force of a million pounds, a billion pounds, or any amount if it is accelerated fast enough. There is no upper limit.

Perhaps the idea can become more meaningful in a different situation. If a 50-pound body falls from a height, say 1 foot, how much force could it exert on stopping? The answer is "*Any force,* depending on how fast it is stopped." If the body is stopped very slowly, a very small force is sufficient. If it is stopped very rapidly, a greater force is needed. There is no upper limit—a thousand pounds, a million pounds, a billion pounds—it depends on how rapidly the body is stopped. If you want to stop it *instantly*—well, you *cannot*. You would need an infinite force.

Newton's third law applies to countless interesting instances. In walking, we push the floor or the earth backward, if we are to go forward. As it speeds up, a car pushes the road backward, and as it comes to a stop, forward. If there is little friction, as on ice, the car cannot get started, or if moving, cannot stop. The oars push the water backward, in order that a boat can go forward. An airplane pushes the air backward on moving through it. A rocket ship in interplanetary space

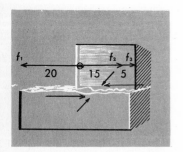

Fig. 3-10. Newton's third law of motion. At any point the forces are always equal and opposite. $f_1 = f_2 + f_3$

must throw gases or other materials backward in order to go forward. A gun recoils on firing a bullet. We cannot lift ourselves by pulling on our bootstraps, no matter how hard we pull. Thus, the innocent-looking statement that forces are always equal and opposite has far-reaching consequences.

Further implications of the meaning of Newton's third law emerge when it is restated in terms of momentum. Momentum, too, is an innocent-looking concept until it is examined. It is simply defined as the product of the *mass multiplied by the velocity* of a body. Thus a body having a mass of 5 pounds and moving with a velocity of 6 feet per second has a momentum of 30 foot-pounds per second. A 20-gram body moving with a speed of 30 centimeters per second has a momentum of 600 gram-centimeters per second.

When a force acts on a body and accelerates it, the momentum of the body is invariably changed, since the velocity is changed, although the mass remains the same. A given force, acting on a body for a given time, will produce a certain change in the velocity, and hence a certain change in the momentum. Now the same force acting for the same time on a body of twice the mass will produce half the acceleration, and hence half the change in the velocity. But the change in the momentum is still the same since it is the product of double the mass *times* half the velocity-change. Thus the interesting conclusion emerges: *A given force will produce the same change in momentum in a given time regardless of whether it acts on a large body or on a small one.*

When two bodies collide, no matter how they are moving, the forces that act between them are equal and opposite. Since they remain in contact with each other for the same time, it follows that each body suffers the same change in momentum, but in opposite directions. Regardless of what the masses of the bodies are, this statement is true. If we add the two changes in the momenta algebraically, calling one positive in one direction and the other negative in the opposite direction, we see that there has been no change in the total momentum as the result of the collision. Whatever total momentum the two bodies had before the collision, they will have after the collision. The momentum of one body may increase and that of the other body may decrease, but when we add the two algebraically, we find that the sum remains the same both before and after the collision.

Carried to its logical conclusion, this analysis has universal implications. If there is no change in the momentum in one collision, there is no change in two collisions, or in any number of collisions. In other words, if all the bodies in the universe collide, or otherwise exert forces on one another, there can be no change in the total momentum as the result of the action of these forces. Consequently, *the total momentum of the universe remains constant.* This statement is completely equivalent to the statement that the forces are equal and opposite. For this reason, Newton's third law of motion is sometimes called the law of conservation of momentum.

One final word about momentum. It is a quantity that persists. If we take the mass of every body in the universe, multiply it by its velocity, and add all the products, we will get a number representing the total momentum of all the bodies in the universe with respect to some reference system. Suppose that a million years from now we could repeat the calculations with the bodies that may exist then. If we were to take the mass of each of these, multiply by its velocity (with respect to the same reference system), and add all the numbers, we would get the *same number* as now. This mysterious quantity called momentum has a kind of transcendent existence. It persists through time. It cannot be created; it cannot be destroyed. No exception to the law of conservation of momentum has been found so far.

The implications of the universal conservation of momentum had far-reaching effects in fields outside of science. Some writers have interpreted the law to imply complete determinism in all motion and activity, including human action. Other writers have made the further interpretation that complete determinism implies the *denial of free will*. The interested reader is referred to Exercise 21.

Application of Newton's Laws to Gravity

Galileo gave no reason why bodies fall with uniformly accelerated motion. With Newton's laws of motion a clearer understanding of gravity is possible. Since all bodies on the earth are universally accelerated toward it, there must be a force of attraction between the earth and the bodies on it. Moreover this force must be quite constant, since it produces a constant acceleration. This force is called the weight of bodies.

This force of attraction must be proportional to the mass of the attracted body. Thus two bricks, having twice the mass of one brick, have also twice the weight. By actual measurement the force of gravity is found to be sufficient to speed up a falling body 32 feet per second for every second it is falling.

It is also easy to see why all bodies on the earth, light or heavy, fall with the same acceleration (if air resistance is neglected). Consider one brick as the light object and let a two-brick package tied together represent the heavier body. The weight of the brick is the force that speeds it downward. This force is sufficient to give the brick a speed of 32 feet per second in 1 second. In the two-brick package we have twice the weight, or twice the force, which in itself would produce twice the speed if it acted on a single brick. But this double force must speed up the two-brick package, which has twice the mass and hence twice the resistance to acceleration. Therefore, the two-brick package will also reach a speed of 32 feet per second in 1 second.

As a further illustration consider a car with a motor capable of giving to the car a certain pick-up. Now put a second motor in the car. Neglecting the extra weight of the added motor, the pick-up will double. Now having a car with two motors, load the car until the total mass is twice that of the empty car. Two motors on a loaded car will produce the same pick-up as one motor on the empty car. In the first example above, the weight of the two bricks represents the two motors and the total mass of the two bricks represents the car with its load.

Bodies accelerate toward the earth not only when they fall freely, but at all times they are not supported, as, for example, when they are in flight. Thus if we throw a ball upward, the instant it leaves our hand, the ever-present gravity acts on a ball to reduce its upward speed. The

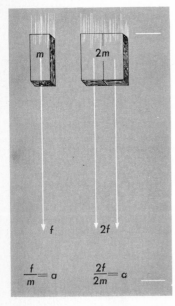

Fig. 3-11. Why a heavy and a light object fall at the same rate. A two-brick package has twice the weight (2*f*) but also twice the mass (2*m*). Hence, acceleration is the same as in one brick.

Fig. 3-12. Projectiles fall in flight. Projectiles B and C reach the ground at the same time as a freely falling body A.

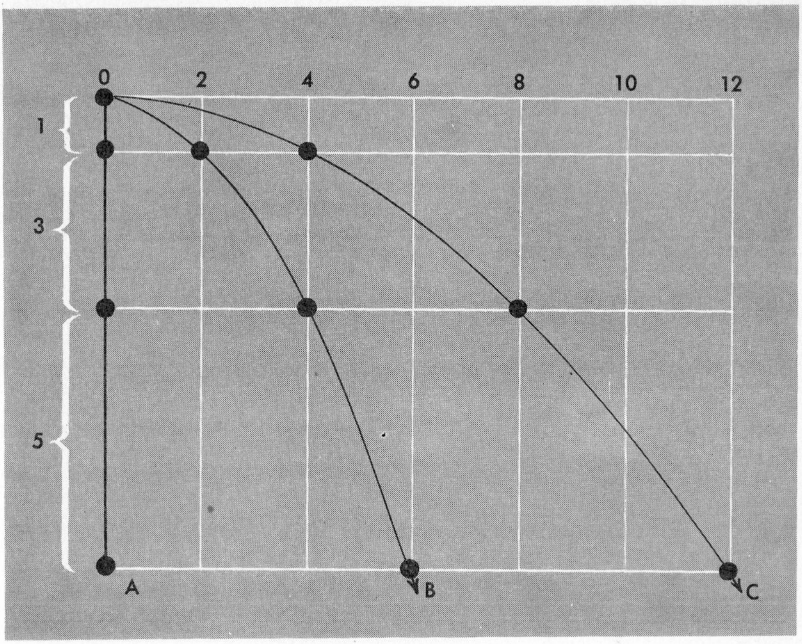

ball continues to move upward but with ever-decreasing speed, until the speed is reduced to zero. At this instant the ball stops, but only for an instant. Relentless gravity proceeds to speed it downward, and the ball descends with ever-increasing speed. During the entire flight the ball is accelerated downward. It is slowed down in the upward flight, and speeded up in the downward flight.

Of special interest is the motion of a projectile shot horizontally. According to Newton's first law, if there were no gravity, the body should continue in a straight line and should cover equal distances in equal intervals of time. But gravity acts on it simultaneously and bends it in a curved path. We saw earlier that bending it from a straight course is acceleration. In this instance the body obviously *falls* at the same time it moves forward. It is this "fall" that is due to the acceleration of the earth's gravity. Incidentally, it is quite clear that a body shot horizontally would reach the ground at the same time as another body released at the same instant. The amount of "fall" is the same in both cases. This statement is strictly true if we neglect air resistance and consider the earth's surface as flat.

The principle of putting an artificial satellite into orbit by continuing to increase the horizontal speed (Fig. 3-13) is an extension of this reasoning. As the speed of the projectile is increased it lands further and further out. And if the speed is sufficiently increased, the curvature of the earth becomes perceptible. If the speed is sufficient (about 7 miles per second), the projectile will fall just enough to remain always the same distance from the earth's surface and move parallel to it. The projectile then would become a moon circling the earth.

Newton was, of course, aware of all these ideas when he explained the moon's motion. He reasoned that in going around the earth, the moon is accelerated; that is, it falls toward the earth. By simple geometry, knowing the distance to the moon and the period the moon takes to go

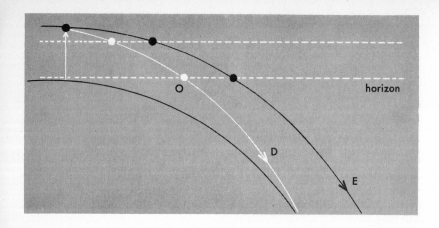

Fig. 3-13. A projectile becomes a moon. Projectile D would have reached the ground at O. Projectile E, at 7 miles per second, falls at the same rate as the curvature of the earth recedes.

around the earth, he could calculate the amount of fall (or acceleration) the moon suffers per second. He found that the moon falls .0045 feet per second. If gravity deflects the moon, then it is much weaker there than on the surface of the earth where a body falls 16 feet the first second.

Then he guessed that gravity is weakened as the square of the distance. Since the moon is 240,000 miles away, or 60 times as far from the earth's center as the surface of the earth is from the center, the force of gravity should be $1/60^2$ or 1/3600 as strong. Now 1/3600 or 16 feet per second is very close to 0.0045 feet per second. From this he concluded that the force that accelerates the moon toward the earth is gravity. It is the same force that causes the apple to fall and the projectiles to follow a curved path. Elated, he wrote to Robert Hook on July 16, 1685, "On this day I conceived of gravity as extending to the moon." You will recall that Copernicus, who placed the sun at the center of the solar system, left the earth as the center of the moon's

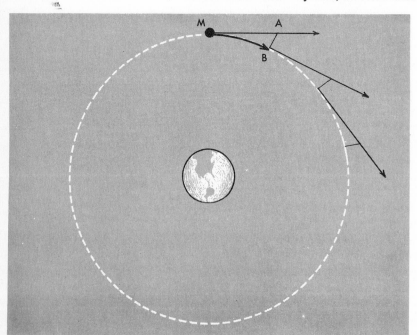

Fig. 3-14. The moon is constantly "falling" toward the earth. Instead of moving in a straight line MA, the moon follows path MB due to the earth's attraction. The distance AB represents the "fall" toward the earth.

motion and also as the center of gravity. Copernicus thought of gravity as a local phenomena on the surface of the earth.

Newton proceeded to extend the idea of gravity to the entire solar system and to the formulation of his famous law of gravitation. First he solved the mathematical problem of how gravity weakens with distance. He had already solved the problem in reverse. He had asked the question, "If a body is attracted by a central force, and if the force varies inversely as the square of the distance, what path would the body take?" We shall not attempt to present here his mathematical reasoning but his answer was clear and definite, "The path will be an *ellipse* with the central force at one of the foci."

From here on Newton proceeded with beautiful mathematical reasoning to show that all the bodies of the solar system follow the laws of motion and the law of gravitation. As a side project he invented the calculus to help him in his calculations. Unfortunately the mathematics involved is more than we can attempt to explain here. At this point the reader may wish to reread the last two pages of the preceding chapter. The interested reader may want to go further and study the third book of *Principia,* and get the reasoning from the master himself (Ref. 3.7 and 3.11b).

3. THE CONCEPT OF ENERGY

A primitive idea of energy is a part of ordinary language and everyday experience. We speak of the energy of an active person, the energy of foods, the energy of coal, the energy of a moving train, the energy of sunlight, the energy of a dam, the energy of the electric current, the heat energy of steam under pressure. We even speak of atomic energy and glibly repeat that matter itself is a form of energy. We have a vague concept of the idea, but as often as not we confuse energy with power, or with force, or with momentum.

If we are asked to clarify further our hazy notion of energy, we may say that energy is something that enables us to do things. A hard-working man needs energy to do his work, and indeed a laborer needs more energy than a person doing easy work. With electric energy we run our machines, we sweep floors, and run our elevators. The energy of gasoline runs our automobiles. A fast-moving bullet has enough energy to penetrate the floorboard, which a stationary bullet cannot. With the idea of energy we always associate the idea of accomplishment or work. Prompted sufficiently, we may go so far as to say that energy is the ability to do work.

It was a happy inspiration when it was realized that the idea of energy can be defined by first clarifying the idea of "work." But how can work be defined? To begin with, it is reasonable to say that if we carry two chairs upstairs we do twice the work of carrying only one. Similarly we do twice the work in pushing a chair across the floor 20 feet that we do if we push it only 10 feet. But how are we to compare the work done in pushing a chair 20 feet with the work done in carrying it upstairs or with the work of washing a car? And does it matter whether we carry the chair upstairs slowly or fast? Does it matter whether the bullet in piercing a board moves slowly or fast? We need a precise definition of "work" to answer such questions.

A clear concept of both work and energy can be obtained from Newton's mechanics. Although Newton himself never developed the idea, other great men after him did so by using his ideas and extending them. The road is long and tortuous, but now that we have arrived at the concepts, we can side-step most of the difficulties by taking liberties with history and presenting some of the concepts out of the historical order of their development.

The Concept of Work

The beginning point is a definition of "work." After many trials it was decided to define work only in terms of force and distance. *Work* is to be measured by the force multiplied by the distance.

$$\text{work} = \text{force} \times \text{distance}$$

or in symbols,

$$W = f \times s$$

Let us analyze the meaning of this definition. If we lift a chair two stories, we do twice as much work as lifting it one, because the *distance* is twice as great. Similarly, if we lift two chairs instead of one to the top of the stairs, we do twice as much work because the weight, the *force,* is twice as great. To compare the work of carrying a chair upstairs to that of pushing it across the floor, we measure the force and the distance in the first case and multiply the two; we then repeat the process for the other case and finally compare the two products.

However, there is more meaning to this definition. For any work to be done, both a force *and* a distance are necessary. We may be pushing on a wall for hours, and get really tired, but if the wall does not move—if the distance the force moves is zero—we have done no work. Similarly, a body moving without friction with constant speed across a pond of ice does no work, because while there is distance covered, there is no force. Further, neither time nor speed, as such, nor anything else matters. We do the same amount of work in carrying a chair upstairs whether we do it fast or slowly, whether we lift it straight up or along the stairs. (This is strictly true if there is no friction.)

It may run against the grain to restrict the meaning of work in this particular way. To justify this, many so-called arguments, some of them quite complicated, have been presented. In the final analysis, however, there is only one real argument. Only by defining work as the product of force and distance and *nothing else* is it feasible to develop the concepts that describe the world simply, clearly, and without contradictions.

The units of measurement in which work is to be expressed should be obvious. They must contain the units of distance and the units of force. Work may be expressed in foot-pounds or pound-feet, foot-inches, ton-yards, ton-kilometers, gram-centimeters, and so on. But there must always be a unit of force and a unit of distance. Thus in lifting a weight of 10 pounds 6 feet we do 60 foot-pounds of work, or 20 foot-yards. In the metric system, a common unit of energy is the dyne centimeter, called the *erg* (Ex. 17). It is the work done when a force of 1 dyne is lifted through a height of 1 centimeter. Thus if you lift a mosquito the thickness of your finger, you have done about 1 erg of work. Since this unit is so small, 10,000,000 ergs are designated as a *joule.*

We are now in a position to give a definition of energy. *Energy is whatever it takes to do work.* Or from a slightly different point of view, *energy is the ability to do work.* When we do work we spend energy; if we have energy, we can do work. This idea will take on more meaning as the forms of energy are discussed one by one. We may point out, however, that energy is expressed in the same units as work, because it is measured by the *work it can do.*

A common form of energy, and perhaps the easiest to understand, is the energy of lifted bodies. If we lift a body of 10 pounds to a height of 6 feet from the floor, we do 60 foot-pounds of work. We have spent 60 foot-pounds of energy. But now a curious thing happens. The lifted body now has energy, because it can now do work. For example, the lifted body can be attached to a pulley or to a lever, and on falling back to the floor it can lift an equal weight to the same height, or half of the weight to twice the height. By a different arrangement the lifted body can be made to drag a weight across the floor, sweep the floor, open the door, and so on. In other words the lifted body now has energy because it can do work; that is, it can exert a *force* for a *distance.*

The only difference between the body on the floor and the body 6 feet from the floor is its position. Yet by virtue of this position it has energy. This form of energy is called *potential energy.* It might have been better to call it "positional" energy. It is not the position as such, however, that gives the body the energy. It is the position of the body in the earth's field of force. The force of gravity permits us to do work on the body in lifting it, and thereby store energy in the lifted body. This force pulls it toward the floor, and gives the body the energy so that the body in turn can do work on falling. It is possible, of course, to have potential energy under different circumstances provided forces are present. Thus a body attached to the end of a stretched spring (or a compressed spring) has energy of position with respect to an unstretched spring. Similarly, a magnet near another magnet has energy of position because it is attracted or repelled by magnetic forces. However, since the relations are easiest to visualize in lifted weights, most of our examples will be taken from this field.

From this discussion it is clear that the potential energy of a body in a given position has a definite meaning and a definite value only with respect to a reference point. Thus in the example given above, the body has 60 foot-pounds of potential energy with respect to the floor. It has

The Concept of Potential Energy

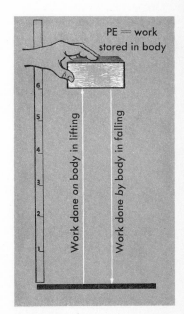

Fig. 3-15. Potential energy is stored work. At the height of 6 feet, the 10-pound body has 60 foot-pounds of potential energy. Sixty foot-pounds was done on the body in lifting it; 60 foot-pounds can be done by the body in falling.

more energy with respect to the basement, still more with respect to sea level, and still more with respect to the center of the earth. In practically all experiments only *differences* in potential energy between one position and another are measured.

It is instructive to re-examine how potential energy is measured. It can be done in two rather distinct ways. We can always measure the potential energy of a body by the amount of work the body can do in going from one position to the other—for that is our definition. But if there is no friction, it can also be measured by the amount of energy necessary to put the body in its present position; that is, to move it from the floor to the height of 6 feet as in the example. In other words, the potential energy a body possesses at a height of 6 feet is the amount of energy we put into it in lifting it from the floor. Thus, the significant point emerges; this thing called energy is not lost or diminished, but remains the same provided there is no friction. This property of persistence or indestructibility is what gives the concept of energy its great importance.

The Concept of Kinetic Energy   Another form of energy, quite different from potential, is the energy of moving bodies. It is called *kinetic energy*. A ball rolling on the table top has no potential energy with respect to the table top, yet it has energy because it is moving. What gives it this energy? Obviously the energy comes from motion, for the ball has no energy when it is standing still. But what aspect of its motion? A little analysis, or experimentation reveals that one of the factors is the *speed*. Thus, a bullet thrown leisurely would not worry us, but the bullet coming toward us with a speed of 2000 feet per second would be another matter. The difference between the two cases is speed. The other factor in the kinetic energy is the *mass* of the moving body. If a toy train is coming toward us with a speed of 3 feet per second (about 2 miles per hour), it would cause no concern. But if a real locomotive is coming toward us with the same speed, we had better step aside. What is the difference? The real locomotive has a much greater mass. Thus, the kinetic energy of a moving body depends on the *mass* and on the *speed*.

Further analysis is necessary to find the exact relation. Let us consider balls thrown upward. After a ball leaves our hand, it rises, and therefore does work. It raises itself against the force of gravity. The amount of work it does is equal to the force (that is, its weight) times the distance it rises. If we give to a 1-pound brick a speed of 32 feet per second, it will rise to a distance of 16 feet. Therefore in throwing the brick we do 16 foot-pounds of work. If we give the same speed (32 feet per second) to a 2-pound brick it will rise to the same height. But since the weight of the 2-pound brick is twice as much and rises to the same height, twice as much work is done. Thus if the two bodies have the same speed, the 2-pound body has twice the kinetic energy of a 1-pound brick; that is, the *kinetic energy* is strictly proportional to the *mass*.

The speed, however, enters the relation differently. If a pound brick leaves our hand with a speed of 64 feet per second, it will rise to 64 feet, or four times as high (compared to a pound brick with 32 feet per second rising only 16 feet). This is so because the faster brick has twice the speed, and continues rising for twice as long. Thus with twice the speed it can do four times as much work. With three times the speed, it will rise to nine times the height and, therefore, do nine times the work. In other words, the kinetic energy of a moving body is proportional to the *square of the speed*. Summarizing the two relations we find that the kinetic energy is proportional to the *mass* (*m*) times the *speed* (velocity, *v*) *squared*. Further analysis shows that the exact relation (in symbols) is

$$KE = \tfrac{1}{2}mv^2$$

If the reader is interested in the mathematical derivation he may examine Exercise 24.

A deeper insight into the concept of kinetic energy is obtained by raising the more basic question: Why should a moving body possess energy? The answer is quite direct. According to Newton's laws a material object in motion exerts a force on being stopped, and since it cannot be stopped instantly, it must exert this *force* over some *distance*. But if a moving object can exert a force over some distance, it can do work, and hence, by definition, it has energy. Indeed, by measuring the work it does on stopping we find the energy to be equal to $\tfrac{1}{2}mv^2$. It does not matter whether the object is stopped slowly or fast. A large force will stop it over a short distance, a small force over a larger distance, but in both (and all) cases the product of the force times the distance is the same.

The same answer is obtained by approaching the question from the opposite direction. The amount of kinetic energy a moving body possesses must be equal to the amount of work necessary to give it the speed that it has. Since a force is necessary to speed it up from rest, and this force must act over the speeding-up distance, the product of the force and the distance is the amount of work that went into the body. Therefore, this must be the amount of kinetic energy that it has. On going through the analysis mathematically we find it again to be equal to $\tfrac{1}{2}mv^2$ (see Ex. 24).

Transformation of Energy

One of the interesting characteristics of energy is that under suitable conditions one form may change into the other. Thus a body rising against the force of gravity changes its kinetic energy into potential energy. If we throw a body upward, it leaves our hand with a certain speed and as a consequence has a certain amount of kinetic energy— equal to $\tfrac{1}{2}mv^2$. With respect to the level of our hand, the object has zero potential energy and after being thrown receives no more energy from our hand. However, as it rises it loses speed and hence loses kinetic energy. *But,* and *this is the important point,* on rising it gains height, which means that it gains potential energy. Obviously it *cannot lose speed unless it gains height,* and it cannot gain height unless it loses speed. In other words, it cannot gain potential energy unless it loses kinetic energy.

As we observe a rubber ball, or better, a steel ball bouncing up and

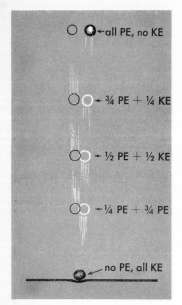

Fig. 3-16. Transformations of energy exhibited by steel balls bouncing on steel plate. At all times PE + KE is a constant, equal to the total energy.

down on a steel plate, we witness transformations of energy. As the ball rises, the kinetic energy is transformed into potential energy. As the ball descends, the potential energy is transformed into kinetic energy. As the ball strikes the steel plate, the steel plate and the ball are compressed and deformed. We can think of the particles of the steel as tiny springs being compressed. The kinetic energy of the ball now becomes potential energy of compressed springs. As these springs rebound they kick the ball upward, giving to the ball kinetic energy, while they themselves relax.

If there is no friction, a far more important principle emerges. *The total amount of energy remains constant.* A ball bouncing upward clearly illustrates this. As it leaves the steel plate, the ball has a certain speed and a certain amount of kinetic energy—enough to carry it to a specific height. At the highest point the ball stops; it has no more kinetic energy. But it now has potential energy. How much? Just the amount needed to speed the ball downward, so that as it is about to strike the steel plate it has the same speed it had going upward. Therefore, the ball has the same kinetic energy it had before. At the top of the bounce the ball must have had as much potential energy as it had kinetic at the bottom. At all intermediate points it has some kinetic and some potential. What it loses in kinetic it gains in potential. The total energy is the same. The ball neither loses nor gains any. This is always true when there is no friction.

We can point to an interesting case where frictionless transformation of energy is taking place and at the same time gain a greater insight into one of Kepler's laws of planetary motion. The earth is furthest from the sun on July 3 and nearest on January 3. On July 3, it has a certain kinetic energy and a certain potential energy with respect to the sun. From July 3 to January 3, the earth moves halfway around the sun, and what is important to us at the moment is that it comes closer to the sun. It loses "height" with respect to the sun, and hence it loses potential energy. What happens to its potential energy? It becomes kinetic energy, so that the earth speeds up, attaining the maximum speed on January 3. From then on, the kinetic energy is transformed into potential. At any time during the year the total energy of the earth (the sum of the potential and kinetic) is the same. If the earth lost any

Fig. 3-17. Conservation of PE and KE of the earth in going around the sun. In January the earth is nearest the sun (PE is minimum), but moves the fastest (KE is maximum). Note the law of areas.

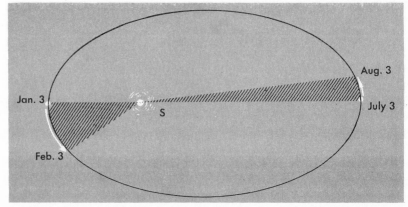

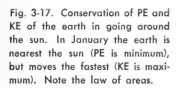

of the total energy during these transformations, it would get closer to the sun with every revolution and ultimately fall in. This analysis reassures us that the solar system is stable. No energy from an outside source is necessary to keep it going.

Unfortunately, in all real systems on the earth, the sum of the potential and kinetic energy (known collectively as mechanical energy) is not conserved. Ever-present friction exerts its forces and exacts its toll. In the example of steel balls bouncing on steel plates, the ball does not return to quite the same height from which it was dropped. On the way down, the force of gravity encounters the resisting forces of the air. Only the difference between the force of gravity and friction accelerates the body. Consequently, the body does not have all the speed it would have in the absence of friction. The kinetic energy gained up to the moment the ball is about to strike the plate is less than the potential energy it had at the top. On the way up, frictional forces are encountered in the opposite direction, so that some of its kinetic energy is not converted into potential energy. An even greater amount of energy is lost at the impact. The ball, therefore, rises to lower and lower heights after each bounce and soon lies motionless on the steel plate, having neither potential nor kinetic energy.

What becomes of the mechanical energy thus destroyed? After a long search, experimentation, and analysis, the answer finally came that it is converted into *heat,* and that heat is itself a form of energy. The main points of the argument are as follows: By actual observation we find that whenever mechanical energy disappears heat is invariably produced. For example, motors become hot on running, and an automobile tire spinning on sand may get hot enough to melt the rubber. Conversely, we know that heat is a form of energy, because it can be made to do work. A steam engine, for instance, moves a train by using the heat of the fire to produce motion.

Further experiments show that whenever a definite quantity of mechanical energy disappears, a definite quantity of heat appears. Conversely, whenever a given quantity of mechanical energy is produced, a definite quantity of heat disappears. The quantity of mechanical energy disappearing is always proportional to the quantity of energy appearing and *vice versa.*

From these observations the principle emerges that mechanical energy and heat are different forms of the same entity, namely, energy. What is lost in one form reappears in the other. Neither form is conserved separately, but taken together they are. This is the principle of conservation of energy. If we measure the potential energy, the kinetic energy, and the heat of a system, the sum has a certain value, which remains constant. Transformations of energy may change the amount of each, but the total amount is constant. Mathematically,

$$PE + KE + heat = constant$$

This is the law of conservation of energy. However, to understand the argument sketched above, it becomes necessary to study the phenomena of heat in some detail, to learn how to measure quantity of heat, and to see how the actual measurements demonstrate this law. This will be discussed in the next section.

4. HEAT AS A FORM OF ENERGY

It is not difficult to show that heat is a form of energy. In the first place, whenever work is done against frictional forces, heat invariably appears. We expend energy against the frictional forces and instead of storing potential or kinetic energy, we obtain heat. Conversely, under the proper conditions, heat can do work. A steam engine, using the heat of the firebox can move a train, and hence do work. Similarly, a steam boiler may explode, giving kinetic energy to the fragments. Since energy is defined as the ability to do work, heat must be energy.

Considerable difficulty is experienced, however, in attempting to state clearly what is meant by heat. It is difficult to say precisely what aspect of the firebox is to be called heat—that is, to *define* heat. Heat phenomena are common enough. In fact, herein lies the difficulty. In everyday language so many words are used to describe heat phenomena that the terms are often confused in meaning. Thus, we have terms such as heat, amount of heat, warmth, warm, hot, burning, boiling, incandescent, degree of heat, fever, temperature as well as opposite pairs such as heating and cooling, hot and cold, heat and cold, to mention only a few. We must, therefore, establish clear definitions and distinguish between these terms. In particular, it is necessary to distinguish between *amount* of heat and *degree* of heat, which is called temperature.

We may start with the primitive physiological sensation of "hot" and "cold," and provisionally define *hot* as the sensation we receive when we put our hand near a fire, and *cold* as the sensation we get when we touch ice. The definition can now be extended to the "hotter" and the "colder," and the terms arranged in the order: very cold, cold, cool, neutral (neither cool nor warm), warm, hot, very hot. Thus we have a rough scale for expressing the *degree of heat*. The degree of heat is called "temperature," and is a measure of the "hotness" or "coldness" of objects. The hotter the body, the higher the temperature; the colder the body, the lower the temperature.

Next we must distinguish between the *degree* of heat (temperature) and the *amount* of heat. A gallon of boiling water is no hotter than a cup of boiling water. The "hotness" or temperature is the same in both cases. Yet a gallon of boiling water has a *greater quantity* of heat than a cup of boiling water. Further, a cup of boiling water is hotter than a bathtub of warm water, yet it does not have as much heat. The temperature is higher for the cup of water but the total amount of heat is smaller. We may take another example. A gas stove in burning produces a flame of a certain degree of "hotness," but also produces heat. The longer the flame burns the *greater* the quantity of heat it produces, but the flame does not attain any higher temperature. Two burners burning separately produce twice as much heat, but the flames are equally hot. From this situation we see that degree of heat and quantity of heat are different. We may define (provisionally) heat as *whatever the burner produces as it burns*. The longer it burns the greater the *quantity* of heat it produces.

While temperature and quantity of heat are distinct ideas, they are nevertheless related. In order to raise the temperature of a given body, heat must be added, and the higher the desired temperature, the more heat must be added. The converse is also true in most, although not all, cases. (Let us disregard for the present the situations in which this is not true.) Further, when we touch a hot object, the object cools and our hand becomes warmer. We say that heat "flows" from the hot object into our hand. Similarly, if we touch a cold object, heat flows from our hand and warms up the object. Obviously, heat flows from a hotter body to a colder body. In fact we can say that *temperature is that property of a body which determines whether heat will flow into the body or out of the body when in contact with a second body*. When the temperatures of the two bodies are the same, there is no heat flow either way. In this way we also understand the *sensation* of temperature. When heat flows from an object into our hand, we say the object is hot, or has a higher temperature than our hand; when heat flows from our hand into the object, we say the object is cold, or has a lower temperature than our hand.

With these basic ideas we can proceed to refine them and ultimately define and measure temperature and quantity of heat. The sensation of "hot" and "cold," while convenient and perhaps necessary for the preliminary notion of temperature, is not capable of precise measurement. In fact the sensation is quite unreliable, for it depends on the temperature of our skin. The reader may want to try an interesting experiment. We take three buckets—one containing cold water, another lukewarm water, and a third hot water. We put our left hand in the cold water and the right hand in the hot water. If, after a minute or so, we put both hands in the lukewarm water, the left hand feels warm and the right hand cold, and yet the lukewarm water is the same. We need a more objective means of measuring temperature.

In principle any property of materials that changes with the "hot" and the "cold" (that is, is *different* in ice and in boiling water) can be used for the definition and measurement of temperature. Air expands with heat and contracts with cold. By using this property of air, Galileo constructed the first thermometer. He took a flask, fitted it with a long glass tube, and inverted the tube in water. By submerging the tube in a deep jar before corking it, he adjusted the level of the water so that it stood at some intermediate height above the outside level. When he poured ice water over the flask, the air contracted and the level of the water in the tube rose. When he poured hot water over the flask, the air expanded and the level dropped. As expected, he noticed that on a

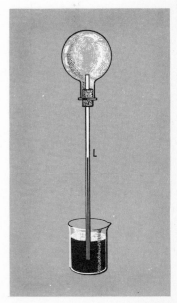

Fig. 3-18. The first thermometer. The level, L, rises with cold and falls with heat.

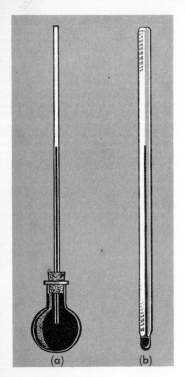

Fig. 3-19. Evolution of liquid-in-glass thermometers: (a) water-in-glass (b) mercury-in-glass. On heating, both liquids expand by a greater amount than glass.

cold morning, the water level stood higher than on a hot day. With a flask of large volume and a tube of small diameter, very small changes in "hotness" and "coldness" can be detected. Thus, we have an instrument that records small changes in "hotness" and "coldness." Moreover it is objective—a definite height of the water level represents a definite degree of hotness and coldness independent of our subjective feeling, or the condition of our skin.

Galileo's thermometer has one serious drawback. The volume of air (and all gases as we shall see later) depends also on the pressure of the atmosphere. On the other hand, the volume of a liquid or a solid remains practically constant at almost any pressure. Consequently, the thermometer was modified by filling the flask with water up to about the middle of the tube, and inverting the apparatus. When this water thermometer was placed in hot water, the level stood higher; in ice water, the level stood lower. Apparently the water expands and contracts more than the glass. Hence we can measure temperature by the differential expansion of water and glass by merely noting the height of the liquid. Soon other liquids were tried. In particular, Fahrenheit found that mercury in glass is a good combination, because mercury expands much more than glass on heating, and it permits the construction of less bulky instruments. This resulted in the invention of the familiar mercury-in-glass thermometer.

Having a convenient instrument to measure "hotness" and "coldness," we may proceed to define more clearly the idea of temperature. If the mercury thread is high, the temperature of the thermometer is high; if the thread is low, the temperature is low. When the thermometer is put in contact with an object, heat either flows from the object to the thermometer or from the thermometer to the object, until the temperatures of the object and the thermometer are the same. Thus, the height of the thread is a measure of the temperature of the object. The higher the thread, the higher the temperature, for a given instrument. However, the height of the thread will vary from instrument to instrument depending on the volume of the bulb relative to the thickness of the thread. In comparing two instruments we cannot say that the one with the longer thread represents the higher temperature. We do not have, as yet, a *temperature scale*.

To establish a temperature scale it is first necessary to investigate two groups of phenomena using an unmarked thermometer. We have already discussed the first phenomenon. As we add heat to an object from a burner, the temperature rises, as shown by the rise in the thread of our thermometer. This, however, is true only so long as the object does not melt or boil. If we take some very cold ice and add heat from a burner, we observe at first a rise in the height of the thread of the thermometer in contact with the ice. The rise continues but not indefinitely. At a certain point, the thread ceases to rise, and precisely at this instant we observe a new phenomenon. The ice melts. As we continue to add heat, the ice does not get any hotter but melts. Moreover, the temperature of the resulting water is the same as that of the melting ice; for the thread is at the same height whether the thermometer is in contact with the water or the ice. With good stirring, only after the last speck of the ice has melted does the mercury thread begin to rise.

A phenomenon similar to melting is observed on boiling. On continuing to heat the melted ice water, the thread of the thermometer continues to rise, but again, not indefinitely. Sooner or later the thread again stops rising and at this instant the water begins to boil. Continuing the heating merely causes more water to boil. Further, the thread stands at the same height, whether the thermometer is immersed in the water or in the steam above the water. Steam and water under these conditions are at the same temperature. Not until the last drop of water has evaporated does the steam begin to rise in temperature.

The constancy of the temperature during melting and boiling provides a reliable and convenient means of defining a temperature scale. We mark on the thermometer the point at which the mercury thread stands during the melting of ice and call it (define it) 0 degrees. Similarly we mark the point at which water boils and call it 100 degrees (Exercise 28). We divide the interval into 100 equal divisions and call each a degree. By extending the divisions above the boiling point and below the freezing point of water we obtain the centigrade scale.

In the English-speaking world another scale, called the Fahrenheit scale, is commonly used. The phenomena and the procedure for defining the Fahrenheit scale are exactly the same as for the centigrade scale, except that the freezing point of water is called 32 degrees and the boiling point 212 degrees, so that the same temperature interval is marked off into 180-degree divisions. The temperature or degree of "hotness" of boiling water is, of course, the same in both scales but different numbers are used in the two scales. The same is true for melting ice. Actually, we could construct any number of scales and in fact, need not limit them to water. With other substances such as mercury, alcohol, or iron the melting and boiling points could similarly be used for the definition of temperature scales. This analysis may serve to point out the arbitrariness of the scales in measuring temperature or degree of "hotness."

It is relatively easy to translate temperature readings from one scale to another. Since the interval between the melting of ice and the boiling of water is 100 degrees on the centigrade scale and 180 degrees on the Fahrenheit scale, a centigrade degree is larger than the Fahrenheit degree by a factor of 180/100 or 9/5, and conversely. Thus, 20° C is 20 × 9/5 or 36 Fahrenheit degrees above freezing, so that it corresponds to 36° + 32° or 68° F. Similarly, 86° F is 86 − 32 or 54 Fahrenheit degrees above freezing. This is 54 × 5/9 or 30 centigrade degrees above freezing, or 30° C. These relations may be summarized in the formula:

$$°F = \frac{5}{9}(°C + 32)$$

or

$$°C = \frac{9}{5}(°F - 32)$$

and can be shown graphically as in Figure 3-20.

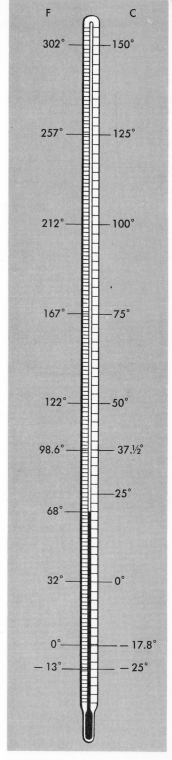

Fig. 3-20. The Centigrade and Fahrenheit scales. The same instrument can be graduated to read in either scale.

Quantity of Heat— the Calorie

Having defined the temperature and the centigrade degree, we can proceed to define quantity of heat and the unit of heat. The unit of heat is the "calorie" and is defined as the amount of heat necessary to raise the temperature of 1 gram of water by 1 centigrade degree (more precisely from 15.5° C to 16.5° C, as explained below and in Exercise 36). Thus, to raise the temperature of 30 grams of water from 20° to 70° C, a burner must supply 50 calories for each gram, or 30 × 50 altogether.

With this definition we can measure the quantity of heat in any given process and express it in calories by merely noting how many grams of water this quantity of heat will raise by one centigrade degree. In this way we can measure the amount of heat produced by a burner, released by a chemical reaction, or given up by a hot body as it cools when placed in water. For example, by actual measurements, we find that 1 gram of ice on melting will cool 1 gram of water from 80° C down to 0, or 80 grams of water from 1° C down to 0. Thus to melt 1 gram of ice, 80 calories are necessary. Similarly we find that 1 gram of steam, on condensation, will raise the temperature of 540 grams of water from, say 20° C to 21° C. This, of course, means that 540 calories are necessary to boil 1 gram of water.

When we measure the amount of heat given up by hot bodies when placed in water, we find an interesting and perhaps unexpected phenomenon. If we mix 100 grams of water at 80° C with 100 grams of water at 20° C, we get a mixture with a temperature of 50° C, as expected. But if we add 100 grams of iron at 80° C to 100 grams of water at 20° C, we find that the final temperature is only about 26° C. If we repeat the experiment with lead, the final temperature is about 22° C.

There is no difficulty in understanding the case of mixing hot and cold water. The hot water in cooling from 80° C to 50° C gave up 30 calories per gram, or a total of 3000 calories. The cold water in warming up from 20° C to 50° C absorbed also 30 calories per gram, or 3000 calories. Obviously, the amount of heat given up by the hot water is the same as that absorbed by the cold water.

However, to understand the case of hot iron and water we need the idea of *specific heat*. In the experiment mentioned above, the water was heated by 6 degrees (from 20 degrees to 26 degrees), while the iron was cooled by 54 degrees (from 80 degrees to 26 degrees). Now the amount of heat absorbed by the water is the amount given up by the iron. This means that the same amount of heat that changed the temperature of water by 6 degrees changed the temperature of the same weight of iron by 54 degrees, or about *nine times as much*. Thus while 1 calorie will raise the temperature of water 1° C, it will raise the temperature of iron 9 degrees. To put it differently, to raise the temperature of 1 gram of iron by 1° C, only 1/9 of a calorie is necessary.

The number of calories required to heat 1 gram of a substance 1° C is called the *specific heat*. Thus the specific heat of water is 1 calorie per gram per degree, that of iron 1/9 of a calorie per gram per degree, and that of lead 0.03 calories per gram per degree. Different substances have different specific heats as shown in Table 3-1 (Exercise 35).

TABLE 3:1
Specific Heats

Water	1.000
Ice	0.500
Steam	0.400
Iron	0.11
Lead	0.032
Silver	0.058
Copper	0.095

By starting with the idea of the "hot" and the "cold," we have defined temperature, temperature scales, quantity of heat, and units of heat. It is particularly important to keep in mind the distinction between temperature and quantity of heat. Temperature is the "degree" or "intensity" of heat and is measured in degrees on an appropriate scale. Quantity of heat is measured in calories. Heat itself is something that the burner produces as it burns. It is that "something" that is contained in hot bodies, or rather that a body contains more of when hot than when cold. It is something that "flows" from bodies at higher temperature to bodies at lower temperature. Moreover, this "something" is an entity that persists. As we measure it, we find that the same quantity of it passes from one body to the other. This "something," which we call heat, is a form of energy as we shall proceed to show.

Law of Conservation of Energy

We are indebted to Count Rumford for recognizing the correspondence between heat and mechanical energy. Up to his time, heat was regarded as some sort of "weightless" fluid that passes from one body to another, is released on burning, and is squeezed out of substances on friction. While supervising the boring of cannons, he noticed that the amount of heat "squeezed out" of the metal was inexhaustible. So long as the drill operated, heat was developed. He therefore came to the conclusion that heat is "motion." In his own words, "It . . . appears difficult, if not quite impossible, for me to imagine heat to be anything else than that, which in this experiment was supplied continuously to the metal, as the heat appeared, namely motion." He measured the amount of heat developed by measuring the temperature rise of a bucket of water, and established the correspondence between heat developed and amount of work done by the horses operating the drill. What Count Rumford called "motion" we have defined as mechanical energy. We shall continue his argument and that of his successors in the terms that we have already clearly defined.

We have already established that heat is a form of energy. Under the proper conditions heat can do work and it can be transformed into potential or kinetic energy of bodies. We can now measure the quantity of heat and express it in calories, and we can, of course, measure the quantity of mechanical energy and express it in ergs, joules, or foot-pounds. With additional experiments we find that, whenever a definite quantity of mechanical energy disappears on encountering frictional forces, a definite quantity of heat appears. The amount of heat is always proportional to the quantity of mechanical energy disappearing. Conversely, whenever mechanical energy is produced, a definite quantity of heat disappears (Ex. 38).

To illustrate how the relationship between heat and mechanical energy is established, we shall describe an experiment that is simple to visualize and to perform even though not very accurate. If we drop some stones from a certain height into a bucket of water, the temperature of the water rises. We can determine the number of calories produced by measuring the temperature rise and by weighing the water. We can also determine the number of joules (or ergs or foot-pounds) of mechanical energy of the stones by measuring the height and weighing the stones. We can then calculate how many joules disappear for every calorie produced (Exs. 38 and 39).

In countless such experiments, performed with necessary precautions so as to insure accuracy, we find that whenever 4.18 joules (about 3 foot-pounds) of mechanical energy disappears, 1 calorie of heat is always produced. Thus, if we drop a book weighing 1 pound from a height of about 3 feet onto a table, the table and the book are warmer by about 1 calorie. Conversely, whenever a steam engine produces 3 foot-pounds of mechanical energy, 1 calorie of heat disappears (we mean *disappears;* we do not mean is given to the surroundings).

It is these experimental facts that establish the principle that mechanical energy and heat are different forms of the same entity, namely, energy. What is lost in one form reappears in the other. For every calorie lost in a process, 4.18 joules appear and *vice versa*. If in a given system the kinetic energy, the potential energy, and the heat are measured and expressed in the same units, we get a number representing the total energy of the system. If the bodies in the system now collide or otherwise interact, and after some time we again measure the kinetic energy, the potential, and the heat and express these in the same units, we get the same number as before. The total energy is the same. For a closed system,

$$\text{PE (ergs)} + \text{KE (ergs)} + \text{heat (in ergs)} = \text{constant number (representing the total energy)}$$

This is the famous law of *conservation of energy*. If the universe is a finite closed system, this law applies to the whole universe. The total energy of the universe is constant.

In terms of the principle of the conservation of energy we can understand the operation and function of machines. A machine is a device that transforms energy from one form into another. In a water mill, the potential energy of the water in the reservoir is transformed into the kinetic energy of the water running down the pipe from the reservoir. The water then imparts the energy to the grinding wheels, which turn and grind the grain. In a train, the heat of the boiler is transformed into the motion of the piston, which then imparts kinetic energy to the wheels and to the whole train. In an automobile, the heat produced by the exploding gasoline in the cylinders is transformed into the kinetic energy of the moving car.

In all these instances, the total amount of energy remains the same. However, an unfortunate fact about these transformations must be mentioned. Because of the presence of friction, mechanical energy is always transformed into heat, sooner or later. However, the converse is not always true. Only with special machinery is it possible to convert *some* of the heat into mechanical energy. Thus, a good steam engine barely converts more than 15 percent of the heat into kinetic energy of the train; the rest goes to warm up the countryside. But even the fraction that is converted into the motion of the train is soon transformed into heat by friction elsewhere, mostly to warm up the tracks, the wheels, and the brakes.

One of the most far-reaching conclusions of the law of conservation of energy is that a perpetual motion machine is impossible to construct. Strictly speaking a perpetual motion machine is one that runs forever without slowing down. However, the would-be inventors imply further that such a machine would continue to do work without any fuel or other source of energy. But any running machine to which no further energy is added slows down and stops, because ever-present friction changes the mechanical energy into heat. It is possible to reduce friction but not to eliminate it entirely. And even if friction could be completely eliminated, we would still be no better off. The moment the machine is put to work—the moment energy is drawn out of such a machine—it would slow down and eventually stop.

The thoughtful reader may still raise some questions about the impossibility of a "perpetual motion" machine. Since, by the very principle of conservation of energy, all the energy is there, why could we not use the heat produced by friction to run the machine or another machine? Or why could we not cool the ocean by 1 degree and use the enormous heat it contains to run our machines? The answer to these questions lies in another principle implied above. Heat, of itself, always flows from a higher temperature to a lower temperature.

The principles of operation of heat engines are too involved for a detailed discussion here, but we can indicate the fundamental ideas. Heat engines operate on the principle of taking heat from a hot body and transferring it to a colder body. In the process, a fraction of the heat is transformed into mechanical energy, the remainder is given to the colder body. The greater the difference in temperature, the greater the fraction of heat transformed into mechanical energy. Thus we cannot cool the ocean and derive a fraction of that heat unless we have a body colder than the ocean to receive the heat. For any *efficient* process, we need a *much* colder body. Similarly, we cannot use the heat developed by the friction of machines, because the heat is at low temperatures. Besides these difficulties in principle, there are practical difficulties. In the case of a train, all the heat from the wheels, the brakes, and the miles of track would have to be collected and put into the steam engine. But even if this could be done, the temperature of the collected heat would be too low to be of much value in heating the steam engine.

The reader has probably also noticed an interesting correspondence between temperature and height. Heat flows from a higher temperature to a lower temperature. Water flows downhill, from a higher level to a lower level. In a waterfall high up in the mountain feeding into a reservoir, the only potential energy available for use is the *difference* between the upper and lower level of the reservoir. The rest of the potential energy is still retained by the water, as it flows down on its way to the ocean. In a hot body, such as the firebox, the only usable heat is that corresponding to the temperature *differential* between which the heat engine operates. Thus, temperature corresponds to height in some sense, and the temperature as well as the temperature difference determine what fraction of the heat will be converted into work.

The fact that heat is a form of energy, and the many correspondences found between heat phenomena and mechanical phenomena, suggested early that heat is a form of "motion." But "motion" of what? We shall return to this question in Chapter 7 and show that heat and temperature are related to the motion and energy of the molecules of materials. Meanwhile, we shall leave heat as we have defined it and reiterate the basic principle, that heat and mechanical energy are forms of the same basic entity—namely, energy—which is indestructible.

Since the law of conservation of energy was formulated a hundred years ago, other forms of energy have been recognized. Chemical energy, electric energy, magnetic energy, radiant energy, and more recently nuclear energy were added one by one. The most radical addition was the recognition that even matter itself is a form of energy. Each time that a new form of energy was recognized, it was shown experimentally that it can be incorporated into the law of conservation of energy. In each case, whatever amount of the new form of energy was produced, a proportional amount of the other forms of energy disappeared, and *vice versa*. The sum of all forms of energy in the universe is a constant. Energy, therefore, is a fundamental reality of the world. It is immortal. It changes but never dies.

NOTES AND EXERCISES

1. An airplane travels from New York to San Francisco, a distance of 3000 miles in 6 hours. What is the average speed of the plane? Is this a constant speed? Is the motion of the plane uniform? Is it accelerated? Why do we say, in general, average speed is a fictitious speed?

2. The difficulty in obtaining a clear idea of instantaneous speed is inherent to the idea of "rate" in general. The most common idea of rate is "price." It is the "rate" of "money *per pound*." It is independent of quantity. Suppose the price of sugar is constant, for any quantity. If 100 lb of sugar costs $10.00, what is the price (rate) per pound? If we buy 50 lb, how much must we pay? If we buy only 1/2 lb, what is the total bill? What is the price? What is the price, if we buy only 1/100 lb? 1/1,000,000 lb? What is the price if we do not buy any sugar? At constant speed, the speed is the same for 1 hour, 10 sec, 1/1,000,000 sec, or for an instant (no time duration at all).

3. A mile is 5280 feet and an hour is 3600 sec. How many feet per second is 1 mile per hour? If an automobile travels 60 miles per hour, how far does it go in 1 sec?

4. Light travels the enormous speed of 186,000 miles per second. How many miles does it travel in a minute? In an hour? In a day? In a year? This last distance is called the *light year*.

5. How long does it take light to reach the earth from the sun, a distance of 93,000,000 miles? How long does it take to reach Pluto? If it takes light 4½ years to reach the nearest star, how far is the star, in miles?

6. A meter is 100 centimeters and 1000 meters is a kilometer. A kilometer is very nearly 5/8 mile. What is the speed of light in kilometers per second? In centimeters per second? According to Einstein this is the fastest speed any object can attain.

7. A car turns a corner at a constant speed of 30 miles per hour. Does it have constant velocity? Does it have acceleration?

8. *Acceleration in a circle.* It is difficult to see that deflecting a body without altering its speed is called acceleration, implying that it is essentially the same as speeding it up in a straight line. Yet both are acceleration, and can be measured in the same units—say feet per second per second. Consider a body moving in a circle at constant speed. At A it is moving in the direction of AX, with a speed V_i. An instant later it is moving in the direction of the curved arrow AY. It has not changed its speed, but has changed its direction. Its velocity is V_f, which is different because the direction is different. If we draw these velocities, we see that the change in velocity, V_c, is equal to at. We now have three similar triangles, AOY and XAY in the circle and the triangle of velocities, on top. Therefore,

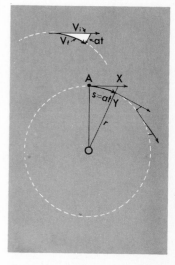

Fig. 3-21. Acceleration in a circle.

$$\frac{XY}{AY} = \frac{AX}{AO} \quad \text{or} \quad \frac{at}{v} = \frac{vt}{r} \quad \text{or} \quad a = \frac{v^2}{r}$$

where r is the radius of the circle and $v = V_i = V_f$. What is the acceleration of a satellite moving with the speed of 18,000 miles per hour (27,000 ft per sec) at about 200 miles above the surface of the earth (a distance of 4200 × 5280 ft from the center)? [Ans.: about 32 ft per sec²; is this surprising?]

9. The planets are moving in ellipses around the sun. Why do we say that they are accelerated? Is Mercury accelerated more or Venus? Explain. There are two reasons.

10. A car travels on a straight, level road at 40 miles per hour (about 60 ft per sec). The brakes are applied and the car stops in 8 sec. What speed (in miles per hour) does it lose per second? What is the (negative) acceleration in miles per hour per second? What speed does it lose in feet per second? What speed in feet per second does it lose per second? What is the negative acceleration in feet per second per second?

11. In the previous problem, what is the average speed in feet per second? How many feet does the car go before stopping?

12. If the car in Problem 10 were going 80 miles per hour, how many seconds would it take the same brakes to stop it? What would its average speed be in feet per second? With this average speed and time required to stop it, how far would the car go before stopping? How does this distance compare with that at 40 miles per hour?

13. A falling body increases its speed at the rate of 32 ft per sec for each second it falls. What speed does it have 1 second after it starts falling? 5 seconds after it starts falling? 10 seconds after it starts falling?

14. What is the average speed of a falling body during the first second of fall? How far does it fall in 1 second? What is the average speed of a body falling for 10 seconds? How far does it fall in 10 seconds? Do you now see why the distance of fall is proportional to the square of the time—that is, to the time *multiplied* by the time?

15. We defined a material body as anything that requires a force to accelerate it. We have defined a force as anything that can accelerate a material body. Do you notice any circularity in these definitions? In what sense, and how can we break the "vicious circle"?

16. Curiously, we can use Newton's laws of motion to define a straight line. Can you do it?

17. In the metric system the ultimate unit of force is the dyne. It is the force necessary to speed up a body of 1 gram of mass by 1 cm per second, every second it acts on it. It is approximately the weight of a mosquito. If you have a mass of 1 gram, and you let a (constant) force of 1 dyne act on it, what speed would it gain at the end of 1 second? If this 1-gram body is acted on by an unknown force, and at the end of 1 sec the speed is 400 cm per sec, how many dynes are there in this force?

18. If this 1 gram is acted on by a force so that at the end of a second it has a speed of 980 cm per sec, how large is the force? Now 1 gram of mass is actually pulled toward the earth with a force which we define as 1 gram. But this gram of force is capable of accelerating a body of 1-gram mass by 980 cm per sec^2. How many dynes, therefore, is a 1-gram weight?

19. The engineer does not start a train as a unit. He first pushes all the cars backward for a short distance and then proceeds to speed up forward. Can you explain why he does this?

20. A very interesting application of Newton's laws arose in the development of the atomic bomb. As the bomb begins to explode, it expands and soon the reaction stops before even a small fraction of the precious material has reacted. The problem is to keep the material from expanding until more of it reacts. It was calculated that a shell of the strongest steel will do some good, but that a similar shell of lead, even though it has no tensile strength, would do much better. Can you give a reason for this?

21. A simplified argument for complete determinism is as follows. At any one instant, the universe (if finite) consists of a certain number of bodies (stars, planets, human beings, molecules, atoms, electrons) each moving with a certain velocity. These bodies collide or in general exert forces on one another. Therefore, the state of the universe in the present instant completely determines the state in the next instant and in all subsequent instants. When a hand is raised (for good or evil), it is not raised by the "free will" of the person, but is merely the necessary result of the previous configurations and motions of the bodies involved—ultimately, of the previous state of the universe. Consequently, so the argument goes, the person has no free will and no responsibility for his actions. Many objections have been raised to this, and to the more sophisticated arguments. The interested reader is referred to Ref. 3.10).

22. Suppose a chair has a mass of 12 lb. How much work do we do in lifting it to the second story, a height of 10 ft? In pushing it across the floor, we might encounter a force of 3 lb. How much work do we do in pushing it 10 ft across the floor?

23. Do you do any work in holding up a chair weighing 12 lb? In lifting it 3 ft? In throwing it, imparting to it a speed of 10 ft per sec? In pushing against it while it is nailed to the floor?

24. Let us see how we get the relation KE $= \frac{1}{2}mv^2$. Let us take a body of mass, *m*, at rest, and give it a certain amount of kinetic energy, KE. We speed the body by exerting a force *f* (which may be constant) for a given distance *s*, thus doing on the body a certain amount of work *W*.

Now the amount of work we do on the body is the force times the distance.

$$W = f \cdot s$$

The force will produce an acceleration *a*, over a time *t*, and since

$$f = m \cdot a$$

we have

$$W = m \cdot a \cdot s$$

But an acceleration *a* will produce a final speed *at*, and an average velocity ½*at*. Since the distance *s* is equal to the average speed times the time:

$$s = \bar{v} \cdot t = \tfrac{1}{2}at \cdot t$$

we have

$$W = m \cdot a \cdot \tfrac{1}{2}at^2$$

or

$$W = \tfrac{1}{2}m \cdot a^2 t^2$$

But now, since

$$at = v$$

then

$$a^2 t^2 = v^2$$

and therefore $W = \tfrac{1}{2}mv^2$

That is, the work we put into the body is ½*mv*² and that is the kinetic energy it has.

Therefore,

$$\text{KE} = \tfrac{1}{2}mv^2$$

Problem: Suppose we use a smaller (constant) force *f′* to give the body the same velocity *v*. By going through the analysis, show that the body will acquire the same kinetic energy as with force *f*.

25. The relation of KE = ½*mv*² permits us to get another idea of an erg. A 2-gram mass going with a speed of 1 cm per sec has 1 erg of KE. How much KE does a 6-gram bullet have if moving with a speed of 1000 meters (about 3300 ft) per sec?

26. Suppose you have a 10-lb steel ball bouncing up and down a steel pavement to a height of 64 ft. Assume that there is no friction—that is, that the collisions on the pavement are elastic and that there is no air resistance. Calculate the PE and the KE at the height of 64 ft and add the two. Repeat the calculation, after it has fallen 16 ft. Repeat the calculations after the body has fallen 64 ft, just as it is ready to strike the plate. How does the total KE and PE compare in the three cases? How much KE does the ball have at a height of 32 ft?

27. A swinging pendulum is an instance of transformation of energy. Assuming no friction, at what point is the speed the lowest? At what point is the pendulum moving fastest? At what point is the KE greatest? Lowest?

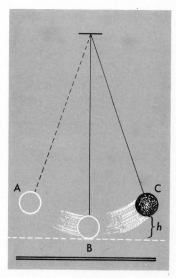

Fig. 3-22. Transformations of mechanical energy.

At what point is the PE greatest? Lowest? How does the sum of KE and PE at *B* compare with that at *A?* With that at *C?*

28. *Note:* In the more precise definition of 100° C, the pressure must be kept at 76 cm of mercury. This precaution is necessary, because the boiling points of liquids depend on the pressure, as we shall see later (Chap. 7). Unless extremely high precision is desired, this precaution is not necessary for the melting point.

29. Room temperature is about 68° F. To what temperature on the centigrade scale does this correspond?

30. Normal blood temperature is 98.6° F. What is the normal blood temperature on the centigrade scale?

31. A cold wave hitting Europe sent the thermometer down to −20° C. What is this temperature on the Fahrenheit scale?

32. As we shall see later, the lowest possible temperature on the centigrade scale is −273° C. This is called absolute zero. What is the lowest possible temperature on the Fahrenheit scale?

33. How much heat is required to heat a pound of water (453 grams) from 20° C to boiling?

34. Calculate the heat required to start with a kilogram of ice at −20° C, and heat it until it finally boils to steam at 100° C. Do it stepwise.

(a) How many calories are necessary to heat the ice to 0° C? (The specific heat of ice is 0.5 calories per gram per degree.)

(b) How many calories are necessary to melt the ice?

(c) How many calories are necessary to heat the water from 0° C to 100° C?

(d) How many calories are necessary to boil the water at 100° C?

(e) What is the total heat necessary?

35. The specific heat of aluminum is 0.214 calories per gram per degree. If you have 6 calories, how many grams of aluminum can you heat by 1 degree? Looking up the specific heats of copper, silver, and lead (p. 81) calculate how many grams of each of these metals you can heat by 1 degree if you add 6.2 calories to each. Do you recognize these numbers? As we shall see later, these are approximately the gram-atomic weights of the elements.

36. The discussion on page 80 implies that the specific heat of water is defined as 1, and that it is the same for water at all temperatures. This is not exactly true. The specific heat of water (as that of all other substances) is slightly different at different temperatures. If you mix exactly 100 grams of water at 80° C with exactly 100 grams at 20° C, the resulting temperature is about 50.03° C, or slightly above 50° C. What does this mean about the specific heat of water from 20° C to 50° C, as compared to that from 50° C to 80° C? For these reasons a calorie is defined precisely as the quantity of heat necessary to raise the temperature of air-free water from 15.5° C to 16.5° C.

37. Curiously, calories have become a household word in connection with food and diet. They are units of energy, one large Calorie being equal to 1000 calories as we have defined the latter. However, they express not the amount of heat a food contains, but the amount of energy the food will give when it is burned in the body. Thus, 1 gram of sugar will give about 4.0 Calories, 1 gram of protein about 4.5 Calories, and 1 gram of fat about 9.0 Calories. If a daily ration contains 400 grams of sugars, 200 grams of proteins, and 50 grams of fats, how many Calories does this represent?

38. It may be interesting to calculate how much warmer Niagara Falls is at the bottom than at the top, as the result of conversion of potential energy into heat. The height is 245 meters. What is the potential energy of 1 kg of water at the top of the fall? How much potential energy is converted into heat? Express this in joules. If one calorie is 4.18 joules, how many calories of heat is developed? What is the temperature rise of the water?

39. According to modern theories, a star is formed by the condensation of a cool gaseous nebula. The temperature of the resulting star rises to thousands of degrees. Can you explain how this happens?

40. Power is often confused with energy, but it is distinct from it. *Power* is defined as the rate of doing work, or what amounts to the same thing, power is the rate of expending energy. If you run upstairs in 10 sec, you do a certain amount of work in a given time, by lifting your weight to the second story. If now you ran up the stairs in 5 sec, you do the same amount of work, but in half of the time. Your power is double the amount.

One joule of work done per second is 1 *watt*. Lifting 10 million mosquitoes a height of 1 cm in 1 sec is about a watt. A 60-watt lamp draws from the electric line 60 joules of electric energy per second. A horsepower is 746 watts.

What is your power if you run upstairs a height of 12 ft in 10 sec? In 5 sec? Take your weight as 50 kilograms or 110 lb and express your power in watts and in horsepowers. How fast must you run upstairs to develop 1 horsepower?

41. The periods and heights from the earth of the artificial satellites can be calculated by direct comparison with the natural moon. The moon is 239,000 miles from the center of the earth, and its period is 27.3 days. Calculate the period in minutes.

Vanguard I, launched on March 17, 1958, had a period of 133 min. Calculate its average distance from the center of the earth, using Kepler's Harmonic law (round off figures for approximate results). If the radius of the earth is 3960 miles, what is the average height of Vanguard I above the earth's surface? The minimum height (perigee) is reported as 404 miles. What is the maximum height (apogee)? [Reported apogee distance 2465 miles.]

42. *Weighing the earth.* Using Newton's law of gravitation, the mass of the earth can be calculated. Cavendish, around 1800, was the first to determine the value of the constant G. The present value is 6.67×10^{-8} meaning that if two spheres 1 gram each are 1 cm apart, they attract one another with a force of 6.67×10^{-8} dynes. The mass of the earth can then be calculated from the force of the earth on 1 gram of mass, which is 980 dynes. Taking the radius of the earth as 6400 km, calculate the mass of the earth in grams. What is it in pounds? In tons? The mass of the earth can also be calculated from the period of revolution of the moon around the earth. Can you do it?

4

ELECTRICITY

INTRODUCTION

The phenomena of electricity are as universal as those of gravity. We are familiar, of course, with electric currents and electric power. It is difficult to conceive of modern living without them. With the turn of the switch the lights go on and the countless electric appliances operate. Silent and invisible, this mysterious fluid runs through the wires, heats the filaments of the lamps, or produces the force necessary to operate a sweeper. It carries the human voice with the speed of light through the telephone wires or transoceanic cables, operates the radio and television, and even produces the electromagnetic waves that carry the signal through space without the benefit of a conductor.

Electrical phenomena are widespread in nature, and have been observed long before the dawn of the electrical age, though not understood as such. During thunderstorms they are exhibited on a large scale, particularly in the form of lightning. The beautiful displays of the northern lights are essentially electrical in character. Less well known is the fact that several electric layers surround the earth and reflect radio waves, thus making possible the transmission of short-wave radio signals over the curvature of the earth's surface.

In the living world there are electric eels and other organisms capable of producing electric currents. The nerve current of the human body is essentially electric, and the functioning of the brain with the mysterious brain waves that it emits during normal or strenuous mental activity are essentially electric in nature.

Not so well known is the fact that electricity is used on a large scale to carry out chemical reactions. Niagara Falls is a center of industry by virtue of the abundant electric power available; it is also the site of a large chemical industry. This function of the electric current is not to be confused with the power associated with it. The electric current is capable of directly causing chemical reactions. For example, ordinary salt (sodium chloride) can thus be decomposed into the elements chlorine and sodium. In Niagara Falls, salt solutions are electrolysed to produce chlorine and sodium hydroxide in large tonnages. Another example is the decomposition of aluminum ore to give metallic aluminum, which now has countless uses. A third example is electroplating, during which compounds of metals in solution are decomposed and the free element is deposited on other metals, as in the case of chrome or silver plating. Interesting in this connection also is the fact that in a battery, a current is generated by means of chemical reactions. In fact there is a close relationship between electricity and chemical reactions. According to modern concepts, all chemical reactions involve electric charges.

The relationship between electricity and chemistry is not merely incidental but, on the contrary, is most fundamental. Matter itself is basically electrical in character. All matter is a composite of electricity, of which there are two kinds, positive and negative. Every material object is made up of an immense number of tiny packages of electricity. A ton of rock, for example, consists of about $\frac{1}{2}$ pound of negative electricity and $1999\frac{1}{2}$ pounds of positive electricity, and of course the same is true of a ton of water or any other material.

Electricity is also responsible for the production of light. By this we do not mean that electricity is necessary to heat the wire to produce light, but that the light emitted by the hot wire is produced by the electric charges *in the atoms* of the wire. Even in two such diverse objects as a bonfire or a firefly, the light is produced by electric charges—moving and accelerating within the atoms and molecules of the hot material, in the case of the fire; or in the cold material in the case of the firefly.

The surprising thing is that electricity, with all its immense complexity, can be understood fairly well in terms of less than a dozen rather simple ideas, each derived from relatively simple observations.

2. ELECTRIC CHARGES AND MAGNETS

The story of electricity begins about 600 B.C. when the Ionian philosopher Thales of Miletus noticed a curious property of amber. When a piece of amber is rubbed on a cat, it acquires the interesting property of attracting small pieces of dry grass or other light objects. Rather intriguing is the fact that the amber attracts these objects on coming near, and even before touching, them. This property of the

Simple Phenomena of Static Charges

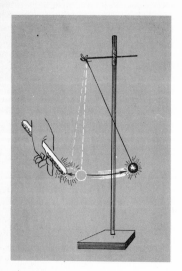

Fig. 4-1. Attraction, followed by repulsion.

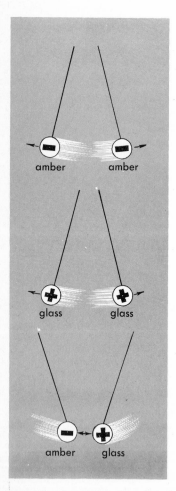

Fig. 4-2. Like repel; unlike attract.

amber disappears after a few minutes, and instantly if the amber rod is touched with the hand. Through the centuries, others performed this experiment for amusement and the phenomenon came to be known as "electricity" from the Greek word *electron,* for amber. Translated literally, electricity would be called "ambericity."

Very little was added to this knowledge until the time of William Gilbert (1540-1603), a court physician of Queen Elizabeth. By this time it was known that several other substances besides amber exhibited this property, notably sealing wax and sulfur, and that the cat was not necessary—only its fur. Nowadays a number of plastics can be used—say in the form of a comb on ordinary human hair attached or unattached to the scalp. An important variation is to rub a glass rod with a silk cloth.

Gilbert hung with a silk thread a light ball made of dried pith. He then electrified an amber rod in the usual way by rubbing it with a cat's fur, and brought it near the pith ball. As expected, the pith ball was attracted and touched the rod. But now Gilbert noticed something unexpected. After touching the rod, the ball was vigorously repelled by it. The ball was no longer an ordinary pith ball. However, if he merely touched it with his hand, the ball once again became normal. He repeated this experiment with electrified rods of sulfur, sealing wax, and glass, and in each case the pith ball behaved in a similar way.

Gilbert then tried another experiment. He first touched the pith ball with an amber rod. As expected, the amber rod repelled it. He then brought near an electrified wax rod and it repelled the ball, too. An electrified sulfur rod produced the same effect. But when he brought near an electrified glass rod, the pith ball was *attracted.* Apparently the electrification of glass was different from that of amber. He tried as many electrified substances as he had available and found that they either repelled the pith ball or else attracted it. In other words they acted either like an amber rod or like a glass rod. From this he concluded that there are two kinds of electrification.

We reach the same conclusion more convincingly from the following experiment. If we suspend with a silk thread an electrified amber rod, another electrified amber rod repels it, but an electrified glass rod attracts it. On the other hand if we suspend an electrified glass rod, another glass rod repels it, but an amber rod attracts it. The conclusion reached after extensive experimentation is that all other electrified substances behave *either like glass or like amber.* If the electrified object attracts the amber, it invariably repels the glass; and if it repels the amber, it invariably attracts the glass. In other words, there are *two and only two* kinds of electrification.

By convention, we call the glasslike electricity *positive* and the amberlike *negative.* This is the most fundamental definition of positive and negative electricity. When later we say that the copper-end of the battery is "positive" or that the nucleus of the atom has "positive electricity," we mean that it has the same kind of electricity as an electrified glass rod, and would be repelled by it. In all cases the final proof for such statements is to perform a series of experiments and relate them to either the glass rod or the amber rod.

From these experiments and these definitions comes the first *law* of electricity. *Like kinds of electricity repel—unlike kinds attract.* This statement is a natural law, for it summarizes a regularity observed in nature.

From these experiments, too, comes our first idea of an *electric charge*. Since an amber rod behaves in this unusual manner after being rubbed with fur, we could say that it is in an electrified *condition*. However, we can also say that the rod has *something on it* giving it this peculiar property, and this something we call an *electric charge*. We are inclined to the second view because this "something" is apparently movable. It can be transferred on the pith ball and on other objects under suitable conditions. This means that once a charge has been produced by rubbing the right substances together, it can then be transferred to other objects. Any kind of object (under suitable conditions to be described more fully later) can be charged either positively or negatively. For example, a small metal ball, or a pith ball covered with a metal foil and suspended with a silk thread, can be charged negatively or positively by simply touching it with an electrified amber rod or glass rod, respectively.

The idea that an electric charge resides on the electrified body is further strengthened by the fact that the charge is exhaustible—in any given instance, there is a definite amount of it. Thus, if we have an electrified amber rod and touch a sufficient number of pith balls with it, this peculiar property of the rod weakens and soon becomes too weak to be detected.

The movability of the charge, and a few more simple experiments, lead to the idea of conductors and insulators. If a charged metallic ball is connected to a neutral metallic ball with a silk thread, the charge is not transferred. But if the balls are connected with a metallic wire, the charge *is* transferred. Thus, some materials such as metals, many solutions, and wet objects generally are conductors of charges, while other materials such as dry amber, silk, wool, wood, sulfur, plastics, rubber, glass, wax, or oil are nonconductors or "insulators." Likewise air is a nonconductor; for if it were a conductor, it would not be possible to isolate any charge in its presence.

Another very interesting observation is that during rubbing, both kinds of electricity are produced. Thus, if an amber rod is rubbed with a cat's fur, the amber rod acquires a negative charge but the cat's fur also acquires a charge which is positive. This can be shown by the fact that the fur attracts a suspended electrified amber rod. Similarly, when glass and silk are rubbed together the glass acquires a positive charge and the silk a negative charge.

A Theory of Electricity

We now have sufficient background to attempt our first theory of electricity. From the facts already established, it seems obvious and reasonable to *assume* that all material objects contain both positive and negative electricity. Ordinarily, the amounts of positive and negative charges are equal and therefore the objects are neutral. During rubbing, however, one kind of electricity or the other leaves one of the rubbed objects and attaches itself to the other object. For example, in rubbing an amber rod with cat's fur, negative charges leave the fur and attach themselves to the amber rod. The cat's fur, therefore, exhibits a positive charge and the amber rod a negative.

From this point of view, a negatively charged body contains an excess of negative charge or a deficiency of positive. Similarly, a positively charged body contains a deficiency of negative or an excess of positive.

It is not possible from these experiments alone to decide whether the negative charges are transferred from the fur to the rod, or whether the positive charges are transferred from the rod to the fur, or for that matter, whether both of these things happen to some extent. Nor is it possible to decide in conduction experiments whether the negative charges, or the positive, or both, move. From other experiments and more complicated reasoning (Chapt. 12), we come to the conclusion that, in solid objects, only the negative charges move. However, in fluids, such as pure liquids (other than molten metals), in solutions, in gases, and in free space, sometimes the positive, sometimes the negative, and sometimes both kinds of charges move. Let us therefore accept these conclusions provisionally, postponing the evidence until later.

As a consequence of the mutual repulsion and mobility of the negative charges in solids, we would expect that in a conductor the charges would move to the outer surface. If we have a hollow sphere and put a charge inside on a wire connected to the sphere, the charge quickly goes to the outer surface. The most delicate electrical experiments could be performed inside a wire cage while outside or on the wire wall of the cage the most violent electric storms rage. Similarly, the occupants of an automobile are quite safe from lightning, but, of course, not from any fire that might be started by the lightning.

The distribution of the charges on the surface of the conductor depends on the shape of the conductor. On a sphere the distribution is, of course, uniform because the curvature is uniform. But on a pointed conductor the charges concentrate on the point, for in this way they get on the average as far from each other as possible. If the conductor has a very sharp point then a very high concentration of charges may result. Indeed, the concentration of the charge may be so high that the molecules of the air, acting like tiny pith balls, pick up the charge and are then violently repelled, thus discharging the conductor. Lightning rods act on this principle (Ex. 3).

Besides mobility and transferability of the charges, a very important property is their ability to exert forces on other charges through empty space. An electrified glass rod attracts an electrified amber rod at a distance. True, the experiments are usually carried out in air, but then the reader will recall that air is a nonconductor and no charges move through the air from the amber rod to the glass rod. The experiments work as well (in fact, a little better) in vacuum. The charges, therefore, have the ability to exert forces through empty space.

These properties of charge explain another phenomenon known as *induction*. Taking two neutral metal spheres, with insulated bases and in contact with one another, we bring an electrified amber rod near one

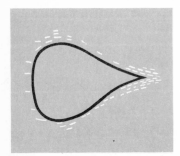

Fig. 4-3. Concentration of charge at points.

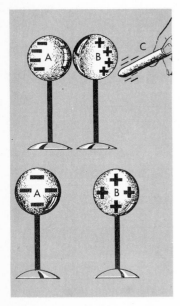

Fig. 4-4. Charging by induction. In (a) the negative charge, C, attracts positive charges from A into B (or repels negative charges from B into A). In (b) separation of the spheres in the presence of C results in permanent positive charge on B and negative charge on A.

of them as shown in Figure 4-4. On separating the two spheres, while the amber rod is near *B,* we find that sphere *B,* which is nearer the rod, has acquired a positive charge, and that sphere *A,* the further one, has acquired a negative charge.

The explanation of this phenomenon is very simple. While the amber rod was near *B,* it repelled some of the movable negative charges from *B* into *A.* When the spheres were separated, sphere *A* remained with an excess of negative charges and sphere *B* with a deficiency (Ex. 4). This method of charging a body by the proximity of another charged body, but without contact, is called *induction.*

Induction explains why an electrified rod attracts a *neutral* pith ball in the first place. On coming near the pith ball the amber rod *induces* a positive charge on the near side, and a negative on the far side. Because the attraction for the near side is greater than the repulsion for the far side, a net force of attraction results.

Electroscope

From these fundamental ideas, we can build a simple instrument which will detect charges and indicate whether they are positive or negative. This instrument is called the electroscope. We take an ordinary glass bottle with a plastic cap or rubber stopper, and through it run a metal wire terminating in a knob above the stopper. At the other end of the wire, inside the bottle, we suspend two metal leaves. If now we touch the knob with an electrified amber rod, the leaves will diverge.

The explanation of the divergence of the leaves is as follows: Some of the negative charges are transferred from the rod to the knob of the electroscope. These charges being on the metal—which is a conductor—and repelling each other, distribute throughout the surface, some of them getting to the leaves. Since both leaves now have a negative charge, they repel one another and hence diverge. If we repeat the experiment touching the neutral electroscope with an electrified glass rod, the result will be similar; but now the charge will be positive, since there will be a deficiency of negative charges on both leaves.

We can also charge an electroscope by induction. On bringing an amber rod near the knob of the electroscope (but without touching it), we notice the leaves will diverge. According to our theory, the negative charges of the rod repel, from this distance, the negative charges on the knob, which repel in succession their neighboring charges, until some of them get to the leaves of the electroscope. Hence the leaves diverge. If we remove the amber rod without at any time touching the knob, the charges redistribute themselves and the leaves collapse. The electroscope is still neutral.

A different result is observed if we touch the knob with our hand while the amber rod is near, and the leaves are diverging as a consequence. On touching, the leaves will collapse at once. Again according to theory, the negative charges at the knob are under the tension of repulsion from the charges on the amber rod and from the charges down the leaves. But they are under no such tension from our neutral finger. Consequently some of the charges leave the knob and enter our body, where they distribute themselves to reduce the mutual tension (Ex. 5).

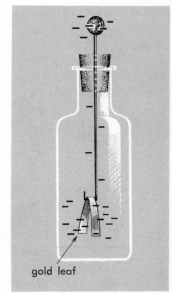

gold leaf

Fig. 4-5. Electroscope. The leaves having like charges diverge.

When our finger is removed a deficiency of negative charges is left on the electroscope. This becomes evident if the amber rod is taken away, for then the leaves diverge, indicating a positive charge.

With this wonderful little instrument it is possible not only to detect very small charges but also to determine whether they are positive or negative. If we suspect that a body is charged, all we need do is touch the knob of a neutral electroscope with it. If the leaves diverge, the body was charged, and the same charge was placed on the electroscope. If now we want to know whether the charge is negative or positive, we comb our hair and bring the (plastic) comb near the knob of the electroscope. If the leaves diverge further, the charge is negative; if they collapse, the charge is positive (Ex. 6).

Coulomb and the Measurement of Charge

A significant advance in this field was made by Charles Coulomb (1736-1806), who placed these phenomena on a quantitative basis. We have already developed on a semiquantitative basis the notion of quantity of charge and the dependence of the force on the quantity of charge and on the distance. If the electroscope leaves diverge a little, the charge is small; they diverge further, the charge is greater, for it exerts a greater force. Similarly, the force becomes greater as the charges are brought nearer one another, but weakens as they separate.

To place these ideas on a quantitative basis, Coulomb first developed the so-called quartz torsion balance, utilizing the remarkable elastic properties of fine quartz fibers. These fibers can be made by melting a piece of quartz glass and drawing it out. Coulomb took a rod of insulator material and attached a metal sphere at each end (Fig. 4-6). He then suspended the rod from the center, with a quartz fiber which he fixed firmly at D. This system swings about an equilibrium position until it comes to rest. It is so delicate that very small forces will twist it, the angle of twist being proportional to the force. In effect, this system is a delicate balance.

Coulomb first investigated the effect of distance. He placed a charge on sphere B. On bringing B near A, the force of repulsion twisted the suspension, and the rod assumed some position A'. On bringing B nearer, the twist was greater. At the rest position, the twist was *four* times as great as when the distance was half as far; nine times as great if the distance was one third as far; and similarly for other values. Thus he discovered that the force is *inversely* proportional to the *square* of the distance.

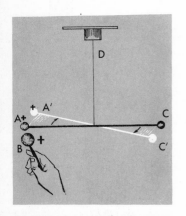

Fig. 4-6. Coulomb's balance by which he discovered his famous law. The angle of twist is proportional to the force.

The dependence of the force on the quantity of the charge was more difficult to establish, because he had no good way, as yet, of measuring charges—and worse, he had not yet defined a unit charge. He resorted to the following experiments and reasoning. Taking two metal spheres of identical size and construction, he put a charge on one of them. He did not know, of course, the quantity of the charge, but he called it Q. He then brought the charged sphere into contact with the other sphere. Each sphere now contained half of the original charge, or $Q/2$. By again discharging one of the spheres and repeating he obtained a charge of one fourth of the original, then one eighth, and so on.

With this beginning, Coulomb now carried out the following series of experiments. He put a charge, Q_1, on the sphere A of his balance, and another charge Q_2 on sphere B. On bringing sphere B near A he noted the amount of twist. He then touched sphere B with a similar neutral sphere and brought it to the same distance from A as before. The deflection was now one half of the original. He repeated with other fractions of the original charge and found that for the same distance, the deflection was proportional to the charge on sphere B. By keeping the same charge on B and repeating the experiments on A, he found that the force is also proportional to the charge on sphere A. In other words, the force is proportional to the *product* of the two charges.

Coulomb expressed these relations mathematically in his now famous law:

$$f = \frac{Q_1 \; Q_2}{r^2}$$

In words, the law states that the force is proportional to the product of the charges and inversely proportional to the square of the distance between them.

Coulomb's law is used to *define* a unit charge. If there are two equal charges 1 centimeter from each other, and they exert a force of 1 dyne on each other, then each is defined as an electrostatic unit of charge. This is often abbreviated as esu. (A dyne is a force about equal to the weight of a mosquito, as explained in Chap. 3, Ex. 17.)

The similarity between Coulomb's law and Newton's law of gravitation has probably already been noticed by the reader. In both cases the force varies inversely as the square of the distance. In both cases the force depends on the *product* of the charges or the masses, respectively. There are, however, some important differences. In the case of gravitation, the force is always one of attraction. In the case of electricity, it may be either attraction or repulsion.

Another important difference is that in the case of electricity the force depends also on the medium between the charges. When two charges are in vacuum, at a certain distance between them they exert a certain force on each other. If air is substituted between them, the force becomes slightly less. If a carton of oil is placed between them, care being taken not to touch either charge, the force becomes 1/81 as great. Such experiments show that all material media decrease the force between the charges and thus have a *shielding* effect. The amount of reduction is characteristic of the dielectric medium between the charges and is known as the dielectric constant of that medium. Thus, for water the dielectric constant is 81. This factor of reduction is usually included in the Coulomb equation and symbolized by D.

$$f = \frac{Q_1 \; Q_2}{D \cdot r^2}$$

There is no such shielding effect in gravitation, as is shown by the most accurate astronomical observations. For example, in going around the earth, the moon is attracted by both the earth and the sun. If at the time of a lunar eclipse the attraction of the sun were shielded by the

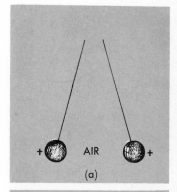
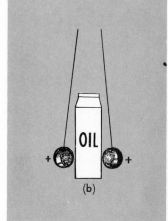

Fig. 4-7. Dielectric medium. A medium between the charges decreases the force.

earth, the moon would follow a somewhat different curve. The effect, no matter how slight, would accumulate in a period of years and would make future eclipses impossible to predict on the simple law of gravitation. The fact that future or past eclipses can be calculated with a high degree of accuracy is convincing evidence that there is no shielding effect in gravitation.

**The Smallest Charge—
The Electron**

In the preceding discussions we have used the idea that a body, charged or uncharged, contains a large number of small positive and negative charges. Without justification we have implied that these charges are discrete and separate. Unwittingly, we have by-passed and settled the fundamental question of whether electricity is a perfectly continuous fluid or consists of discrete packages. Without going into the whole problem of continuity and corpuscularity at this point (see Chap. 6), we may raise some direct questions. Is there a limit to the smallest charge that can be put on a pith ball? If so, how small is this charge?

Nearly a century of discussion and experiment has pointed to the conclusion that electricity consists of packages of the same size, and estimates of the size have been made. Around 1910, Robert Millikan (1868-1953) perfected a method by which he measured accurately the magnitude of minute charges and gave strong evidence that the smallest of these are all of the same size. He received the Nobel prize for this work.

Millikan made a round box about the size of a snuffbox. The side was of cardboard, into which he cut two small windows—one for the purpose of shining light into the box and the other for viewing the inside with a small laboratory telescope. The top and bottom of the box were metallic, and were connected to a high-voltage source, with switches to turn on, off, or reverse the charges of the upper and lower plates, and with a rheostat by which he could increase or decrease the voltage. At the center of the top plate he made a small pinhole.

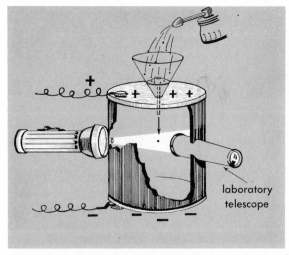

Fig. 4-8. Millikan's oil-drop experiment. The illuminated drop appears as a star in the field of the telescope.

With the plates uncharged, he sprayed some oil from an atomizer over the top and looked into the box through the telescope. After waiting patiently, he saw a drop of oil which had found its way through the pinhole and was slowly settling. The illumination made the drop appear as a bright star in the field of the little telescope. By carefully measuring the rate of settling, and knowing the density of the oil, he calculated the size and the mass of the oil drop.

Suspecting that the drop of oil had been charged by friction in the process of spraying, he turned the switch charging the upper plate positive and the lower plate negative. The drop was, in fact, charged, for it suddenly began to settle faster. Evidently the charge was positive, for in addition to the weight, the drop was repelled by the upper plate and attracted by the lower plate. On increasing the voltage, the drop settled still faster. On reversing the charge on the plates, the drop slowed down and, as he increased the voltage, even moved upward. He could make the drop go up or down with any speed, and by delicately adjusting the voltage he could make it stand still, thus balancing the weight of the drop with the electric forces on its charge.

Knowing the voltage, and the weight of the drop, Millikan could calculate the force on the drop and the quantity of charge on it. He and his associates over a period of many years observed thousands of drops, large and small, made of many kinds of oil and other liquids. Some drops were positively charged, others negatively. Some drops had small charges, others larger. Millikan even found a way of charging drops in flight, by shining x-rays on them, or by putting radioactive substances into the box. For each experiment, the charge was calculated from the measurements of the voltage and the rate of settling.

The significant point here is that in all these measurements, the charges on the oil drops were either 4.8×10^{-10} electrostatic units, or twice that, or three times that up to almost two hundred times that; never a charge smaller than this value, never a charge other than a whole-number multiple of it. This smallest charge that exists, and which may be either positive or negative, is called the *electronic* charge. A better way of realizing the smallness of this charge is to say that one electrostatic unit of negative electricity consists of a little over 2 billion (2,090,000,000) of these smallest charges, which are sometimes called *electrons*.

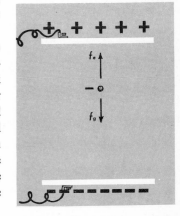

Fig. 4-9. Oil drop suspended. The downward force of gravity (f_g) is balanced by the upward electrical force, f_e.

Magnetism

Magnetic phenomena bear resemblance to the electric phenomena and have been known from time immemorial. Long ago it was discovered by many races independently that the mineral magnetite, Fe_3O_4, has the peculiar property of attracting other pieces of the same mineral as well as pieces of soft iron. It was also known very early that the strength of attraction in a given specimen is localized in certain regions or "poles." In ancient China, someone discovered that by shaping the mineral in the form of a bar, with the regions of strong attraction near the ends, and suspending it by a thread, the bar orients itself in a north-south position. Another Chinese before the eleventh century had the inspiration to use these "leading stones" or "lodestones" for direction finding. When the discovery reached western Europe, it gave rise to the magnetic compass, a device very useful in navigation during the period of expansion of western Europe. The usefulness of the compass spurred the discovery that a magnet can be made very conveniently by stroking a steel bar with a natural magnet, or with another steel magnet.

The magnetic phenomena are in many respects similar to the electrical phenomena. North-seeking poles repel one another, and south-seeking poles repel one another, but north-seeking poles attract south-seeking poles. In magnetism, too, there is attraction at a distance. Similarly there is the phenomenon of induction. A magnet attracts a piece of unmagnetized iron, such as an iron nail. On bringing the magnet near the nail, an opposite pole is induced on the nail, and then attraction follows. A iron nail near a magnet becomes itself temporarily a magnet and can attract other nails. On removal of the magnet, however, the nail loses its magnetism almost instantly. However, if a steel nail or a steel bar is used it retains the magnetism much longer, becoming a "permanent" magnet.

Coulomb investigated the law of attraction-repulsion between magnets and found it to be similar to that of electric charges. The force between two poles is proportional to the product of the strength of the poles and inversely proportional to the square of the distance between them. As in the case of electricity, the medium between the poles alters the force. However, in this case, the medium may *increase* or *decrease* the force as compared to a vacuum. Substances such as iron or nickel *decrease* the force, while substances like bismuth *increase* the force. The amount of increase or decrease is a characteristic of the medium and is called magnetic permeability and symbolized by the Greek letter μ. The entire relation may be stated in Coulomb's law of magnetic attraction-repulsion:

$$f = \frac{P_1 P_2}{\mu \cdot r^2}$$

As in the case of electricity, a unit pole is defined as the pole of such strength that, if placed 1 cm from a second pole of equal strength, it repels or attracts this second pole with the force of 1 dyne.

While the similarities between magnets and charges are striking, there are some very important differences. In the first place charges are *separable,* poles are not. It is easy to separate a negative charge from a positive one (as by rubbing an amber rod with fur) and move either kind any distance and study it separately. When an attempt is made to isolate a north pole by cutting the magnet, however, the piece cut off (as well as the remaining part) becomes a full magnet with both a north end and a south end. No matter how thin a section is cut, it always has a north end and a south end.

Coulomb was aware of this difficulty when he developed the law of magnetic force. He overcame the difficulty in part by using long bar magnets, so that the effect of the other and more distant poles was negligible, although still there. His results were at best approximate and his law is a bold idealization from experience. He overcame the difficulty only mathematically, by correcting for the presence of the other pole.

Another difference is that the amount of magnetism of a bar is inexhaustible. We can make as many magnets as we please from a given magnet by stroking unmagnetized bars, without diminishing the strength of the original in the slightest. This is not so with electricity. Moreover, there is no such thing as "neutralization" in a magnet. Both the S (South-seeking) end and the N (North-seeking) end are on the same body; yet they do not "neutralize" one another. Nor is the phenomenon of conduction found in magnetism. Still another difference lies in the fact that while all bodies can be electrified under suitable conditions, only a few show clearly magnetic properties.

These and other considerations lead to the conclusion that magnetism is not as fundamental a phenomenon as electricity. In fact, as we shall see in the next section, magnetism is but one aspect of electricity, though a very important one.

Magnetic Fields of Force

Before leaving this topic we would like to introduce the idea of magnetic field, which will help us visualize many of the phenomena. From the previous discussions we realize that the space around a magnet, in air or even in a vacuum, is not just ordinary empty space but a region where magnetic forces are present. This region is called a magnetic field. By definition a magnetic field is a region of space in which another magnet—placed in that space—would experience a force of attraction or repulsion.

The field of force surrounding a large magnet is best investigated by using the north pole of a tiny but long magnet—long enough so that the south pole does not interfere appreciably. With this tiny magnet we can explore the space around the large magnet in order to determine where the field is strong and where it is weak, and also to find in which direction the force is exerted at any point. We can then plot the field of force.

We get the idea of a field even more directly from the following experiment. We place a glass plate over a magnet and sprinkle some iron filings. When the glass is tapped, the iron filings line up along certain streamers (as shown in Fig. 4-10), which concentrate near the poles and spread out as they move away from them. Some of the streamers go all the way from one pole to the other. The whole effect resembles a cucumber. The iron filings, becoming tiny magnets by induction, line up to give this pattern. A small compass placed anywhere in the field will line up along these streamers.

This experiment, more than any other, gives rise to the idea of "lines of force." We can represent a field by drawing these lines of force. Where the field is strong we draw many lines; where it is weak, we draw a few. By lines of force we simply mean the direction of magnetic forces. Thus, a field is represented by the direction and distribution of the lines. In a sense these lines are a fiction. In the absence of iron filings, there are no material filaments—no lines of any material. But the *forces* are still there and are real.

The idea of a field can be applied equally well to any region of space where forces act. Thus around electric charges there is an electric field: that is, another charge in that region would experience a force.

Fig. 4-10. Visualization of a magnetic field. The iron filings line along the invisible "lines of force."

The electric field is strong, if the force is large, as it would be near a large charge and becomes weaker at greater distances from it. Similarly the space around material bodies is called a gravitational field, meaning that a material object in that space would be attracted. We already had occasion to speak of the strong gravitational field of the sun and how it weakens in the region of the outer planets. It is also of interest to realize that a given region of space may be simply free space, or it may be a magnetic field, an electric field, or a gravitational field. It may be any and all three fields at the same time. The strength and direction of each of these fields at any point of the region would be measured by the force experienced at that point by an electric charge, a magnetic pole, or a material object, respectively.

3. CHARGES IN MOTION— ELECTRIC CURRENTS

This complex subject may be introduced by a simple definition: *Electric currents are charges in motion.*

Analyzing the implications of this definition—and it is important to do so—we conclude that there is an electric current every time a negatively charged body is connected to a positively charged body; for then the negative charges move through the conductor from one body to the other. Similarly, there is an electric current when an electrified body is discharged. The spark of lightning is an electric current. Strictly speaking, we can have an electric current by taking an electrified glass rod and moving it about, waving it with our hand or mounting it on a moving automobile. All of these are instances of electric currents which have the characteristic properties we are about to discuss. However, electric currents of any consequences are produced either by electric batteries or by generators. Each of these involves a different principle and each will be discussed at some length.

Galvanic Current

In 1780 Luigi Galvani (1737-1798), professor of anatomy at the University of Bologna, noticed that a frog's leg, suspended by a copper hook on an iron fence, twitched every time it touched the fence. Without much evidence, he considered the phenomenon electrical, chiefly because the frog's legs showed similar contraction in the vicinity of an electrostatic machine. Pursuing the studies further he established the fact that many pairs of dissimilar metals produced this effect, if a paper moistened with salt solution or an acid was placed between them and one of the metals touched the nerve while the other metal touched the muscle.

Alessandro Volta (1745-1827) increased the effect many times by using a series of plates of the dissimilar metals, alternating the plates and placing moistened paper between them (Fig. 4-12). This is the voltaic pile from which modern batteries have been developed. The current produced became known as the "Galvani current."

Many experiments were carried out with the Galvani current. The ability of the current to decompose solutions was soon discovered. In 1811 Humphrey Davy (1778-1829) discovered two new metallic elements, sodium and potassium, by passing the current through their molten hydroxides.

By far the most important property of the galvanic current is the effect it has on a magnet. This was discovered accidentally by Hans Oersted (1777-1851) in 1824. While holding a wire over a compass he noticed a deflection when the circuit was completed. Subsequently, it was found that if a wire leading from the copper terminal of the battery to the zinc terminal is held over a compass whose north pole is pointing toward the zinc battery, the north pole turns counterclockwise (Fig. 4-13). We may visualize these relations best by holding the wire in the right hand with the stretched thumb pointing in the direction from copper to zinc. The magnet is below the hand with the north pole pointing in the same direction as the thumb. When the current passes, the north pole turns toward the left, in the direction of the half-closed fingers.

We shall not dwell on these relations except to emphasize two significant points. *A galvanic current has magnetic properties.* Indeed, *it is a magnet;* for nothing but a magnet can affect another magnet. Perhaps a more graphic description would be that a wire carrying the current is surrounded by a magnetic field. Moreover, this magnetic field has no north or south pole. It is *circular,* surrounding the wire, as if an invisible bar magnet has been bent around the wire to form a ring. The plane of the ring—that is, the plane of the magnetic field—is at right angles to the wire carrying the current. Moreover, this magnetic field appears suddenly on making the current and disappears just as suddenly on breaking the current.

The discovery of the magnetic properties of currents was a "break" in the problem. Up to this time electrostatic phenomena and magnetic

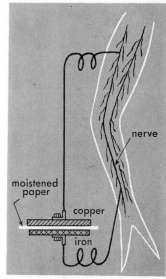

Fig. 4-11. Contraction of muscle by galvanic current.

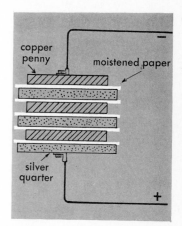

Fig. 4-12. A voltaic pile—the first battery.

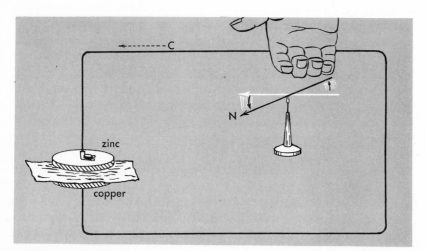

Fig. 4-13. The magnetic effect of the galvanic current. The magnetic needle originally parallel to the wire turns at right angles to the direction of the current, C.

phenomena were separate. Only charges affected charges; only magnets affected magnets. The similarity between the phenomena were suggestive but as yet no connection between them had been found. Here was the galvanic current which on the one hand was similar to charges in that it contracted muscles, and on the other hand had magnetic properties. A fundamental principle began to emerge; namely, that charges *in motion* have magnetic properties and that magnets *in motion* have effect on charges.

The magnetic properties of the galvanic current were soon firmly established. In fact, galvanic currents of any size, kind, or origin were detected by their effects on magnets and were even measured by the force they produce on magnets (see below).

Charges in Motion

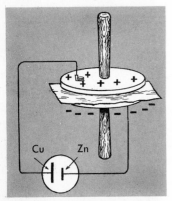

Fig. 4-14. Condenser. Large quantities of charge accumulate on each plate.

However, there was still considerable doubt that a galvanic current was, in fact, an *electric charge* in motion. No relation between the "Galvani" current and the charges produced on amber rods and glass rods had been established. Early attempts to charge the electroscope with the terminals of a battery had failed. Suspecting that the charge was there, but too small to be detected, Volta, in 1800, magnified the effect by his device of placing several batteries in a series. A more convenient way of increasing the effect is the following. We take two large metal plates with insulated handles and, placing wax paper between them, touch the upper plate with the copper terminal of the battery and the lower with the zinc terminal. On breaking contact and separating the two plates, we find a very large charge on each plate. On bringing the upper plate to an electroscope, we can now charge it easily; the charge coming from the copper end of the battery is positive—that is, is repelled by an electrified glass rod.

The explanation of this device, known as the condenser, is very simple. The *small* positive charge in the copper terminal is added to the upper plate, but this instantly draws a negative charge on the lower plate from the zinc terminal. The two plates as a whole are practically neutral, for they are separated by a small distance. The chemical action of the battery produces more charge on the upper plate, which is instantly neutralized almost completely by the negative charge on the lower plate. In this way a very large charge can be put on each plate. As long as the plates are very close together, no charge is evident. If the plates are separated, however, the charges on each plate become apparent, and a very loud discharge takes place on bringing them near one another without an insulator between them.

Incidentally, condensers are widely used in radios and televisions, their function being to accumulate large quantities of charge. Users of television are warned never to touch the inside of the set. Anyone not heeding the warning, may get quite a shock, literally as well as figuratively.

That charges in motion have magnetic properties was established in the most direct way by Henry A. Rowland (1848-1901) in 1890. He attached a wooden disk on an axle of a motor and placed separate strips of metal near the rim. With a static machine he charged the metal strips positive and placed the apparatus in a glass case. Outside the case

Fig. 4-15. Rowland's experiment. The motion of the positive charges on the disk had the identical effect on the magnet as the galvanic current from copper to zinc.

he had a compass. On rotating the disk rapidly he noticed a deflection of the magnetic compass. The effect was that of a wire whose direction from copper to zinc was the same as the direction of the motion of the metal strips (Ex. 19 and 20). This experiment demonstrated that a Galvani current is the same as a charge in motion.

The complex phenomena of electric currents can be understood most directly by considering some of the concepts that describe them. These concepts are: current, quantity of charge, voltage, electric energy, resistance, and power; they can best be developed in terms of the methods of their measurement. Indeed, the meaning of these concepts becomes sharpest in terms of the units of their measurement.

Strength of Current—the Ampere. Let us first clarify the idea of *current* generally. "Current" implies motion and is measured by the quantity of material passing through a point per unit time. Thus the current of a river may be expressed in cubic feet per second, gallons per hour, and so forth. The current of traffic may be expressed as the number of cars per minute, the number of passengers per hour, or the amount of steel per day passing a given point. From the meaning of "current," it is evident that the current of a pipe, for example, may be increased in two ways: by increasing the size of the pipe, without changing the speed of the flow; or by keeping the size the same, and increasing the speed; and, of course, by a combination of the two. Similarly, the current of traffic may be increased by adding more lanes, or by increasing the speed of the cars.

In electricity, current implies quantity of charge flowing per unit time. A high current may mean either a large charge moving slowly or a small charge moving rapidly. In either case, a given current will produce the same effect on a magnet: that is, it will have a magnetic field of the same strength. Long before it was known that currents were electric charges in motion, the strength of a current was measured by the force it produced on a magnet.

A unit of electric current is defined as follows: We take a section of a conductor 1 cm in length, bend it into an arc of a circle, whose radius is also 1 cm, and place in the center of this uncompleted circle a unit magnetic pole. If the current will now produce a force of 1 dyne on the unit pole, we say (define) it is a unit current. This unit is called the *absolute ampere.* However, since most of the currents encountered under ordinary conditions are smaller than this unit, a new unit, the *practical ampere,* is used and is defined as 1/10 of the absolute ampere. It is well to think of the ordinary ampere as that current that will produce 1/10 dyne on the unit magnetic pole in the system described above.

Quantity of Charge—the Coulomb. An ampere implies a certain quantity of electric charge flowing per unit time. It is clear that an ampere is not a quantity of charge, but it is the *rate* at which the charge is flowing. In the flow of ordinary materials, liquids, and the like, there is no name for the unit of current. The flow is simply expressed as so-many gallons per hour or so-many pounds per minute. But in electricity the one word "ampere" stands for a certain quantity of electricity

Fundamental Concepts of Current Electricity

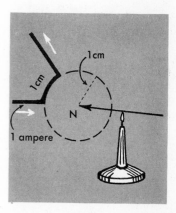

Fig. 4-16. Definition of unit current. One ampere exerts a force of 0.1 dyne on a unit pole at the center of the circle.

flowing per second. If the current is 1 ampere, the quantity of electricity flowing per second is called (defined as) the *coulomb*. The coulomb, then, is a unit of charge such that if it flows through a given point per second, it will produce a force of 1/10 dyne in the system described above (Fig. 4.16).

It is interesting to compare this new unit of charge, the coulomb, with the electrostatic unit and with the charge on the electron. By actual measurement it is found that 1 coulomb is equal to nearly 3 billion (3×10^9) electrostatic units. Since an electrostatic unit is about 2 billion (2×10^9) electrons, a coulomb is 6×10^{18} electrons. This is a very large number indeed. In an ordinary 100-watt lamp which carries about 1 ampere, 6 billion-billion electrons flow each second (Ex. 14 and 15).

Potential Difference—the Volt. Although the volt is a household word, we venture to say that very few persons have a clear understanding of the concept. The usual analogies with fluid pressure or the designation of voltage as "electromotive force" may have some merit, but are likely to give the wrong idea. Yet the correct idea is not difficult, if it is approached the right way.

Let us consider a large body *C,* charged positively. Another positive charge, Q^+, at any nearby point such as *A* or *B,* will experience a force of repulsion. If the charge is at *A* and we want to move it to *B,* then we must do *work* against the repulsive forces. In other words, there is a *potential energy difference* between the charge being at *B* and the charge being at *A,* because work must be done in moving the charge from *A* to *B.* The *potential difference* between point *A* and point *B* is the difference in potential energy of a unit charge when it is at *A* and when it is at *B.* If, in carrying a coulomb of electricity from *A* to *B,* 1 joule of work must be done, then we say (define) the difference in potential as 1 volt.

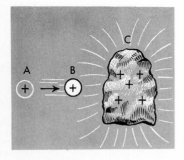

Fig. 4-17. The potential difference between A and B is the potential energy difference between the two points, per unit charge.

Thus, in saying that an automobile battery has 6 volts, we mean that in order to carry 1 coulomb of negative electricity from the positive pole and force it onto the negative pole, work equal to 6 joules must be done. Conversely, when the battery operates, it gives 6 joules of work for every 1 coulomb of charge it forces through the starter or the radio of the car.

It is important to note that voltage has no meaning unless we specify, or clearly imply, the two points (or more generally the levels) we are talking about. It should also be noted that distance as such between the two points does not matter—it does not enter into the definition. Thus, in Figure 4-17 the same distance between *A* and *B* would represent smaller voltage if both were further from body *C* but at the same distance from one another. Similarly, in the case of the battery, the voltage is the same whether the positive and negative terminals are near each other or far. In all cases, voltage is measured by the amount of *work done in carrying a unit charge* (1 coulomb) between the two points under consideration.

Electric Power and Electric Energy—the Watt; the Kilowatt Hour. The watt is a unit of power and is a measure of the rate of doing work. It is not specific to electric power, although it is used most often in this connection. As defined in Chapter 3 (p. 89, Ex. 40) 1 watt is 1 joule per second.

$$\text{watt} = \frac{\text{joule}}{\text{sec}}$$

From this definition it is clear that a watt-second is a joule. Similarly 1 watt-minute is 60 joules and 1 watt-hour is 3600 joules. A kilowatt hour is 1000 times that. All these units are units of energy or work —so many joules. Quite properly we pay the power company for the number of kilowatt hours we use, for this represents the amount of work done by the generators in pushing the electricity through our wires and appliances. We do not pay the company for its "electricity." The electric charges are in our wires all the time and either surge back and forth, in alternating currents, or run back into the power lines in one direction, in direct currents.

Relations between Electrical Units. A very simple relation exists between watts, volts, and amperes. The relation follows from the definitions of these quantities and the definition of a coulomb. We can see these relations most directly by mathematical reasoning as follows:

Since 1 volt is 1 joule per coulomb	$\text{volts} = \dfrac{\text{joules}}{\text{coulombs}}$
then 1 joule is 1 volt times a coulomb	$\text{joules} = \text{volts} \times \text{coulombs}$
But 1 watt is 1 joule per second	$\text{watts} = \dfrac{\text{joules}}{\text{seconds}}$
That is, 1 watt is 1 volt times 1 coulomb per second	$\text{watts} = \text{volts} \times \dfrac{\text{coulombs}}{\text{seconds}}$
Now, 1 coulomb per second is 1 ampere	$\dfrac{\text{coulombs}}{\text{seconds}} = \text{amperes}$
Therefore 1 watt is equal to 1 volt times 1 ampere	$\text{watts} = \text{volts} \times \text{amperes}$

This result may appear of technical significance only, but it permits the calculations of the power of any device on which the voltage of the line and the current going through the device is known. Often the information is available the other way around. The manufacturer usually stamps on the device its rating as so many watts or so many horsepowers. (A horse power is simply 746 watts.) Thus if a toaster is rated at 550 watts, and is intended for 110-volt line, it will draw $\dfrac{550 \text{ watts}}{110 \text{ volts}}$ or 5 amperes.

Resistance—Ohm's Law—Conductivity. If a wire of a given length is connected between the terminals of a 110-volt line, a certain amount of current will go through. Now take an identical wire of twice the length. We find by actual measurement that the current is only half as great. The relation is general, and in all cases the amount of the current is inversely proportional to the length of the wire. Apparently the wire offers a certain amount of *resistance* to the passage of current, much as a pipe offers resistance to the passage of a fluid.

Continuing the analogy, a thick wire carries more current than a thin one across a given voltage, much as a pipe of large diameter carries more fluid per second than one of small diameter for the same pressure. In fact, the current is proportional to the cross sectional area of the wire, which means that it is proportional to the *square* of the diameter.

The analogy can be carried one step further. In a pipe, the greater the pressure drop, the greater the flow. Similarly, the same piece of wire connected across a 220-voltage drop has twice the current that would result from connecting it to a 110-volt line. Georg Ohm (1787-1854), who investigated this relation, found that for a given conductor the current is proportional to the voltage drop, or mathematically

$$\text{voltage} = \text{constant} \times \text{current}$$

or,

$$\frac{\text{voltage}}{\text{current}} = \text{constant}$$

In other words, for a given conductor the ratio of the voltage to the current is constant. This constant ratio is a property of the wire and is called the *resistance* of the conductor. If the voltage is given in volts and the current in amperes, then the resistance of the wire is given in *ohms*.

Thus the potential difference or voltage drop is analogous to pressure drop in fluids. However, the analogy must not be carried any further. As explained earlier (p. 106), potential difference is not pressure. The former is energy per unit charge, the latter is force per unit area. They are *not* the same.

The analogy fails in another way. Wires of the same cross section and length offer different amounts of resistance if they are made of different materials. In fact, the specific resistance of a material is a characteristic property of the material. Thus silver has a low specific resistance while nichrome wire has a high one.

It is perhaps more meaningful to think of the reciprocal property of resistance called *conductivity,* or more properly, *conductance.* Thus silver has a high conductance and nichrome low conductance. Apparently some materials hold the charges very loosely and have high conductance, while others hold them very firmly and hence have low conductance. The so-called *insulators* must be substances that hold the electrons with extreme firmness and hence have extremely low conductance or very high resistance.

Electric Motors and Generators   The immense importance of electric motors and generators impels us to consider two additional principles that underlie their operations. All the bewildering variety of motors and generators depend on two related principles: currents can exert a magnetic force; and moving magnets can produce currents. However, these two principles also have far-reaching theoretical implications, and their understanding is a tool toward the understanding of the nature of electricity, light, and matter.

Electric Motors. All electric motors are based on the simple principle that an electric current has magnetic properties and exerts a force on a magnet. This force under proper conditions can produce motion. The actual construction of any motor may be complicated, and literally thousands of gadgets have been designed and are constantly being designed. All are based, however, on this fundamental principle. Let us consider some simple devices.

If we hold a wire carrying a current over a compass, the compass is deflected. If we hold the compass firmly, and the wire loosely, the wire is deflected. One or the other will move—it does not matter which, since the forces are mutual.

In the simplest situation, a conductor carrying a current is placed between two magnets. This must be visualized in three dimensions (Fig. 4-18). At point *A* between the two magnets, a pin runs through the paper at right angles to the plane of the paper, so that the head of the pin is above the paper and the point of the pin below. The head of the pin connects to the positive end of the battery and the point to the negative. As contact is established the pin will begin to move toward the bottom of the page, tearing through the paper if there is enough current. If the current is reversed the pin will move in the opposite direction. Here we have the essentials of an electric motor.

This effect can be visualized by drawing the lines of force of the magnetic fields. The field of the stationary magnets may be represented by the (roughly) parallel lines of force from the north pole to the south pole (Fig. 4-19). The magnetic field of the current may be represented by concentric circular lines running clockwise around the pin. It is clear that the lines concentrate at *B* and "neutralize" at *C*. Consequently there is repulsion on the pin at *B* and attraction at *C*. As a consequence the pin moves in the direction of the large arrow. This is the simplest motor conceivable, resulting in motion in a straight line.

In the next step we obtain rotatory motion, using an ordinary wire, instead of a pin. By bending the wire into the form of a loop, placing it in a magnetic field, and sending a current through it, the loop will now rotate. Segment *B* will be forced in one direction and segment *A* in the opposite direction, since the current is going *in* through *B* and coming *out* through *A* (Fig. 4.20).

Continuous rotation in the same direction is accomplished by a simple device called the commutator. At the top of the loop is a divided ring separated by an insulator. Half of the ring is in contact with one side of the wire and the other half with the other. As the loop turns, the left side is always in contact with the positive and the right side with the negative, so that the current in the loop always goes in the same direction with respect to the magnetic field. Therefore the forces are always in the same direction and the rotation is continuous. This is a complete direct-current motor.

The motor may now be improved in many ways. The force may be increased by increasing the current, or by increasing the number of loops, or by increasing the number or the strength of the magnets. The strength of the magnets may also be increased by winding some of the wire carrying the current around the magnets, thus making them into

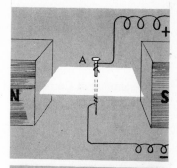

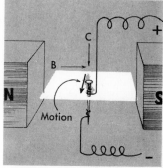

Fig. 4-18. Force on a conductor in a magnetic field. The pin carrying the current moves at right angles to both the direction of the field *B* and the direction of the current *C*.

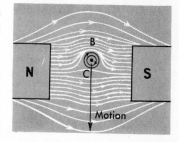

Fig. 4-19. Motion due to interaction of the permanent field of the magnets and the circular magnetic field of the current.

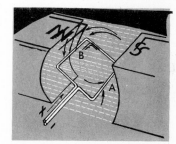

Fig. 4-20. Rotation of a loop conductor in a magnetic field.

strong electromagnets. We shall leave such things to the engineers and the technicians to work out. The fundamental principle is that a current in a magnetic field produces a *force,* which under the proper arrangements will cause motion.

Generation of Currents— Electromagnetic Induction

Soon after the discovery that electric currents produce magnetic fields, many scientists wondered if the converse were not possible— namely, that magnetic fields could produce electric currents. In retrospect, the idea sounds very simple. If charges in motion produce a force on a magnet, then a magnet in motion should produce a force on a charge, and under suitable conditions cause the charge to move, thus producing a current.

The "suitable conditions" were discovered by Michael Farraday (1791-1867) after many trials. He took a coil of wire and connected each end to a galvanometer, in order to detect the current, if he had one. The circuit was now completely closed but, of course, there was no current. He then thrust the north end of a magnet through the coil. Instantly, a momentary current was registered on the galvanometer. While the magnet was stationary in the coil, no current registered. But as he was pulling out the magnet, a current was again registered, but in the opposite direction. Apparently a current is *induced* in a wire only when the magnetic field around the wire is *changing.* Indeed, the more rapidly the magnetic field changes, the more current is induced. Of course, it does not matter whether the magnet moves or the coil moves, so long as there is relative motion between the magnetic field and the electric charges in the coil of wire.

Fig. 4-21. Induction of current in a closed circuit by the motion of a magnet. Current is induced only while the magnet is moving.

This is the principle of *electromagnetic induction* upon which all generators of electricity depend. Once the principle was discovered, all kinds of devices were designed to produce currents of any magnitude. It is no longer necessary to depend on the feeble currents produced by batteries.

A generator, therefore, may be thought of as a device by which electrons within the wires are pushed around by means of magnetic fields. A generator does not "generate" electric charge, in any sense; but it does generate a current—it makes the charges flow. Since energy is necessary to push the electrons around, a generator, in a very real sense, transforms mechanical energy into the energy of the moving charges.

It is instructive to compare a generator with a motor. Actually, the same device can function as either. If a current is sent through the device, electric energy is used to produce motion and do work. This is a *motor.* On the other hand, if the device is rotated by hand, or mechanical energy is put into it by some other means, a current is produced which has electric energy. Then the device is a *generator.*

There are two types of generators—those that generate direct current (d-c) and those that generate alternating current (a-c). The simplest type to imagine and to construct is the a-c type. If a coil is rotated in a magnetic field, the current will flow in one direction during half of the turn and in the opposite direction in the other half of the turn. This is so because the direction of the induced current depends on the direction of the magnetic field and on the direction of the motion of the coil.

The result is an alternating current. In order to get d-c current it is necessary to have a commutator similar to that of a d-c motor so that pulses in the same direction will be obtained from each outlet of the coil. Apart from the ease of construction, a-c generators are more widely used because alternating currents can be transformed from one voltage to another by a device known as the transformer.

Incidentally, the transformer also depends on the principle of electromagnetic induction. We said earlier (p. 110) that a current is induced whenever a magnetic field changes around a conductor. To have a change in the magnetic field it is not even necessary to have "motion" in the ordinary sense of the word. A coil (A) to be connected to a battery is placed alongside another coil (B), and the latter is connected to a galvanometer making a closed circuit (Fig. 4.22). The instant the first coil is connected to the battery and the current begins to flow, a current flows in the second coil, even though there is no material connection between the two coils. On breaking the contacts in the first coil (and at the instant of breaking), a current is again registered in the second coil, but in the opposite direction.

The explanation is: A magnetic field builds up around the first (primary) coil when the current begins to flow through the coil. This means that the magnetic field is growing (that is, *changing*) in the space surrounding the first coil. But since the coils are near, the magnetic field around the second coil is changing also. This changing magnetic field induces a current in the second coil. When the switch is turned off, the current in the first coil collapses, but *while it is collapsing,* a current is again induced in the second coil. Thus a current is induced whenever a magnetic field is *changing* around the conductor, regardless of the reason.

Figure 4-23 illustrates one of the fundamental mysteries of nature. A charged body has only an electric field around it. A bar magnet nearby has only a magnetic field around it. The charge ignores the

Transformer

Fig. 4-22. Induction of a current in the secondary coil B, during making or breaking of the current in the primary coil A.

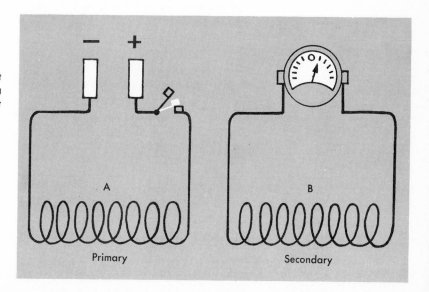

Primary

Secondary

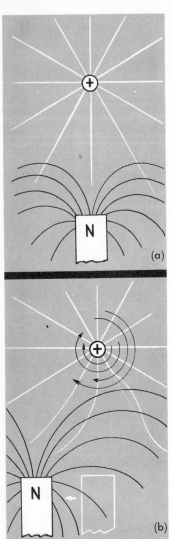

Fig. 4-23. Dual personality of an electric charge. In (a) the charge and the magnet are at rest relative to one another. In (b) the motion of the magnet causes the charge to exhibit a magnetic field as well as an electric field.

magnet and the magnet ignores the charge. There is no effect of one upon the other. But let the charge move, and it is no longer only a charge but also a *magnet*. For nothing but a magnet can affect another magnet. It has a magnetic field along its path, at right angles to it. If the bar magnet is still nearby, it will be affected in the direction shown.

Even more curious perhaps is the fact that even if the charge does not move, it shows its magnetic personality when the magnet moves. We leave the charge at rest, but move the magnet near it. Just as soon as the magnet begins to move, the charge shows its magnetic properties by producing a force on the magnet. The important thing is the *relative* motion between the magnet and the charge. Even more generally the charge exhibits its magnetic properties whenever a magnetic field *changes* around the charge.

SUMMARY

In this chapter we have attempted to describe the very complex world of electricity. Yet the fundamental phenomena, the basic concepts, and the principles are really very few. All the materials of the world contain an immense number of tiny negative and positive charges of electricity. The positive charges are associated with the weight and kind of material and ordinarily do not move unless the material itself moves. The negative charges, on the other hand, are light weight and can easily be detached from the positive charges and from the material in which they are found. Ordinarily, a material object has an equal number of positive and negative charges. But if some negative charges are detached from one body and placed on another body, the former is charged positively and the latter negatively.

These charges have three fundamental properties: They repel one another but have attraction for the opposite kind; they exert this force at a distance, through empty space or through other media, and the force diminishes as the square of the distance; when in motion, they have magnetic properties. All the electrical phenomena can be explained in terms of these properties.

We reserve for later (Chap. 11) the story of how these charges enter into the composition of all the elements and how they are responsible for the chemical reactions and the physical properties of all materials. However, in the next chapter we shall show how these charges under certain conditions produce light and other radiations.

NOTES AND EXERCISES

1. Can you explain why static charges were first produced by rubbing amber and other insulators? Why a metal rod cannot be electrified by rubbing while holding it in the hand? Why electrified objects become neutral on touching them? Why Gilbert's experiments are difficult or impossible to carry out on a very humid day? Why it is dangerous to turn on the light while in a bathtub, or while stepping on the wet ground? Can you suggest a way for electrifying a metal rod by rubbing it with a silk cloth?

2. What is the evidence that there are two and *only two kinds* of electrification? In the absence of definite knowledge from experimentation, how many kinds are possible? Name some possibilities.

3. The explanation of lightning and the function of the lightning rod is as follows: In a thunderstorm the raindrops falling through the cloud become charged (usually positive) by friction. Consequently the upper part of the cloud becomes negative and the lower positive. If there is wind, and there usually is, the two parts of the cloud are separated, each having enormous quantities of charges. Under proper conditions, a discharge occurs between the clouds, the spark itself being an oversize electric spark. In a single spark something like 10 to 50 coulombs are discharged. The thundering is a result of the rapid heating of the path and the subsequent collapsing of the vacuum created, like any ordinary "explosion."

If the upper part of the cloud is dissipated without discharge, the lower part induces the opposite charge in the earth. A discharge may follow between the cloud and the earth. The charges are concentrated on any protrusions such as trees or high buildings, particularly if they are wet or the buildings have a conducting metal structure. The trees, even if dry, are always conductors due to their sap.

Lightning rods are in good contact with the earth, and concentrate high charges at the points. The charges dissipate themselves gradually by charging the molecules of the air and repelling them into the cloud. Thus the charge is usually neutralized before it reaches the proportions of a violent discharge. Even if a small discharge takes place, it is usually conducted to the ground without too much damage.

Are lightning rods sure protection against lightning? Under what conditions may they still be struck by lightning?

Where would you seek shelter during a thunderstorm, under a tall tree or under bushes? Inside a car or outside a car? Why is it dangerous to fly a kite during an impending storm?

4. What would happen if the amber rod were removed before the spheres were separated, in Figure 4-4? Explain what would happen if the experiment were done with an electrified glass rod.

5. The leaves of an electroscope collapse even if we stand on a perfect insulator as we touch it. Why do we say that the electroscope was "grounded"?

6. If you have only a plastic comb, and you are not bald, how would you charge an electroscope negatively? How would you charge it positively? Explain what happens in each step of your experiment.

7. What is the force between a charge of 50 electrostatic units and 8 electrostatic units, in air, if the distance between them is 20 cm? What is the force if the distance is tripled? What is the force at 20 cm if the two charges are separated by water?

8. The smallest charge Millikan found on an oil drop was 4.8×10^{-10} electrostatic units. Calculate, from this number, the number of electronic charges in an electrostatic unit.

9. *The magnetism of the earth.* The north-south orientation of magnets implies that the earth is a giant magnet. What kind of pole is the pole of the earth near the geographic north pole?

The magnetism of the earth has been a subject of serious study but it is still not well understood. The south-seeking magnetic pole is not at the geographical north pole but somewhere in northwestern Canada. The north-seeking pole is *not* on the opposite place in the Antarctic. Consequently, only at a few places on the earth does the compass point true north. Moreover, the poles shift over the years. To make matters worse, the intensity of magnetism at any given place varies during the day and over the years. Though the variations seem to be related to sunspot activity, their causes are not well understood, nor is the cause of the magnetism itself understood. It certainly is not due to a steel bar within the earth, for iron loses its magnetism at high temperatures. It may be some comfort to know that other heavenly bodies, including the sun, have magnetism, similar to that of the earth (see ref. 4.10).

10. We have defined a negative charge as the kind exhibited by an electrified amber rod. Show by two independent methods that the charge on the zinc terminal of a battery is negative.

11. If a current is flowing through the wire in Figure 4-16 and produces a force of 15 dynes on a unit pole, how many amperes is the current? If the wire is made into a (nearly) complete loop of 1 cm radius, what force will it produce in the unit pole? If it is wound as a coil of 20 turns, how much force will it now produce?

12. A current of 3/4 amp flows through a lamp. How many coulombs pass through the lamp per second? How many in a minute? How many in 5 hours?

13. If you have a current of 2 amp, how many coulombs will pass through a toaster in 1 minute? How many electrostatic units of charge will pass in 1 minute? How many electrons will pass in 1 minute?

14. If you have a current of 1 amp, how many coulombs will pass through a lamp in 26 hours, 55 minutes? How many electrostatic units is this? How many electrons is this? Do you recognize this number? (See Chap. 11.)

15. What current will flow through a 660-watt iron, connected to a 110-volt line? How many electrons will flow through the iron in 30 seconds?

16. A toaster is rated as 550 watts for a 110-volt line. What current will it draw if properly connected? What is the resistance of the toaster? If the toaster is mistakenly connected to a 220-volt line, what will be the current? Is the resistance still (essentially) the same? How much energy is developed in the toaster per minute compared to the amount when properly connected? How does the heat developed compare in the two cases? What might happen to the toaster?

17. If the metals are good conductors of electricity and nonmetals are good insulators, what can you say about the "firmness" with which electrons are held, by each class of substances?

18. Since a charge in motion is a magnet, what is the implication as to the cause of magnetism in a bar magnet? Why is a piece of iron sometimes magnetized and sometimes unmagnetized?

19. *Direction of magnetic fields, electric fields, and currents.* In order to simplify description of the phenomena and keep it unambiguous, the following conventions have been adopted.

The direction of the *magnetic field* is from the north pole to the south pole. The direction of the magnetic field at any point is the direction that a tiny isolated north pole would take in that field, as a result of the forces acting on it. In what direction would a tiny south pole move in a magnetic field?

The direction of the *electric field* is from the positive charge to the negative charge. The direction of the electric field at any point is the direction a tiny positive charge would take as a result of the forces acting at that point. In what direction would a tiny negative charge move in an electric field?

The direction of the *electric current* is from positive to negative. If the current is a flow of positive charges which way do they move? From + to − or the reverse? If the current is a flow of negative charges which way do they move?

20. The so-called "right-hand rule" gives the direction of the magnetic field around a conductor. If the stretched thumb points in the direction of the current (from positive to negative), then the half-closed fingers point in the direction of the magnetic field (see Ex. 19).

If you stop the current, what happens to the magnetic field? If you reverse the current, what happens to the magnetic field?

21. Imagine a straight wire, delicately suspended from the center in the earth's magnetic field, and oriented east and west. If you send a current through the wire, connecting the east end to the positive end of the battery and the west end to the negative end, will the wire move, and if so, in what direction?

22. Imagine a loop of iron wire, with a wooden diameter pointing east-west. Now let the loop rotate on this east-west axis in the earth's magnetic field. Will a current be induced? What will happen to the current if you increase the rate of rotation? What will happen to the current if, instead of a loop, a coil of several turns is used? In what direction will the current flow on the side of the loop coming down if the wire is rotating clockwise as seen from the west?

23. *An alternate view of induction.* The electrical engineers prefer to say that it is the *voltage* that is induced rather than the *current*. The argument runs as follows: If a current flows in the secondary coil, then it must be the result of a potential difference set up between the terminals of the coil. When a magnetic field changes around a conductor, the rate of change of the magnetic field causes a certain difference in potential between the parts of the coil. This difference in potential can be calculated by the rate of change in the magnetic field or, as some prefer to express if, by the rate of cutting "lines of force." Thus if 10,000,000 lines of force are cut per second, 1 volt will be induced. The magnitude of the current depends on the "overall resistance" (or impedance) of the current. However, this is getting a bit technical for our purposes, though very useful to the engineers in designing generators.

A transformer changes alternating current from one voltage to another. If the two coils have a different number of turns, then a different number of "lines of force" will be cut by one coil than by the other. If the secondary coil has twice the number of turns it will have twice the voltage. How does the power of the two coils compare? What will be the current in the secondary, compared to the primary?

24. Why is it impossible to transform direct current?

25. *The speed of the electric pulse.* By actual measurement it is found that an absolute coulomb, which is ten times the ordinary coulomb, is 3×10^{10} electrostatic units of charge. This relation is highly interesting. If we have 1 absolute coulomb and move it with the speed of 1 cm per sec, we shall have a current of 1 absolute amp. Now if we only have 1 electrostatic unit, in order to produce a current of 1 absolute amp, we shall have to move it with a speed of 3×10^{10} cm per sec. This is the speed of light (186,000 cm per sec = 300,000 km per sec = 30,000,000,000 cm per sec). This means that the electric pulse moves with the speed of light.

To avoid the possible misconception that the electrons whiz through our wires with this dizzy speed, we must point out that this is the speed of the electric pulse, *not* of the individual electrons. The difference may be made clear by an analogy. Imagine a column of soldiers several miles long, marching at the rate of 3 miles per hour, and each soldier having his hands on the shoulders of the man ahead of him. If we now give a push to the last soldier, he in turn will push the one ahead of him, and so on. It is easy to see that the "push" may travel down the column at the rate of several hundred miles per hour, while the soldiers march with a speed of only a few miles per hour. Something analogous happens in electricity. The electric pulse moves with the speed of light, while the individual electrons may move only a few feet per hour. The analogy is a little more appropriate if you imagine many columns of soldiers, but interconnected and marching forward. In electricity there is an immense number of electrons even in a thin wire.

In talking by a transoceanic cable, there is a noticeable lag in the conversation. Assuming a distance of 6000 miles, how long does it take the "voice" to reach the other person?

5

LIGHT

1. PRELIMINARY SURVEY

According to the first book of Genesis, light was created before the sun and the stars. This apparent inconsistency has given rise to considerable controversy; yet whether by divine inspiration or remarkable insight, the author of the passage has recorded a great truth. Light is more fundamental than the sun, the obvious source of illumination on the earth.

Light—as well as the other types of radiation—is as fundamental a reality as gravitation, electricity, energy, or even matter itself. According to present theories, light has both mass and energy, and is associated with both electric and magnetic fields. Light fills all space. It is emitted by the sun and the other stars in prodigious amounts. The so-called "empty" space between the planets, the stars, and the galaxies is really a field of radiation. The light beams constitute a vast network of streamers carrying energy and messages from one part of the universe to another, thus binding it together.

We know the world largely through light. In the obvious sense, we know our surrounding and build a picture of our immediate environment from the light received directly with our eyes. But in a deeper sense, we know of the structure of matter, of molecules, atoms, and electrons, by analyzing the light they emit. On the scale of the very large, we know of the planets, the stars, and the galaxies from the extremely small amount of light received from them. We know not only of their existence and direction from the earth, but also, by decoding the wealth of information that light carries, we know their distances, motions, temperatures, chemical composition, masses, and a host of other facts concerning them. At the very foundation of Einstein's theory of relativity is the idea that the speed of light is constant for every observer and is the highest speed attainable. It is not a mere accident of speech that "enlightenment" signifies intelligence and understanding.

Light and darkness have played an important role in the mythologies and early philosophies of all peoples. Of the many such views on the nature of light, that of Plato is perhaps the most interesting, although utterly erroneous. He thought that light consists of streamers or filaments emitted by the eye, and that seeing takes place when these streamers, acting like antennas, make contact with an object. Euclid argued for the same view, asking "how else can we explain that we do not see a needle on the floor until we seek it out and our eyes have fallen upon it?" Nor can we dismiss this idea too easily. As late as 1644, the great French mathematician and philosopher, Descartes, published a book elaborating a similar theory.

However, some of Plato's contemporaries had views similar to those held today. The Pythagoreans believed that light traveled from a luminous body to the eye in the form of very fine particles, a view similar both to Newton's corpuscular theory and to the quantum theory of today. Empedocles, on the other hand, taught that light is some kind of disturbance which takes time to travel. This view is a primitive form of the wave theories of Huygens, Young, and Fresnel, which are now accepted in modified form. It is interesting that these two views, which are apparently contradictory and mutually exclusive, were destined to play the role of rival theories down through the centuries to the present time.

Until quite recently very little was known about light, and nearly all that was known—for the most part, disconnected and unrelated—was derived from ordinary experience. A summary of this scant knowledge follows as a contrast and an introduction to our general discussion on the modern concepts of light. Self-luminous bodies are directly visible, but all other objects need light from a luminous source to become visible. When light falls upon an object, the object may transmit the light, absorb it, or reflect it. The phenomenon of color, however, immediately complicates matters. Self-luminous bodies emit light of different colors. Thus the sun is white (or yellow) while some stars are blue, green, orange, or red. On being heated, a piece of iron first gives off a cherry-red color, then orange, then yellow, and finally white. Even when the same light—for example, sunlight—falls on different objects, they take on different colors. Similarly, transparent substances may appear clear (white) or colored. Different objects evidently transmit, absorb, or reflect the different colors selectively (Ex. 1-3).

By the beginning of the seventeenth century a few quantitative aspects of light were known. The Greeks knew that light travels in straight lines, and from this they had deduced the inverse square law. This law states that the intensity or brightness of light decreases as the square of the distance. The ancients also knew that when a beam of light is reflected from a mirror, the angle of incidence is equal to the angle of reflection. From these two laws all the properties of plane or curved mirrors and the images they produce could be worked out (Ex. 7).

The Greeks also knew the phenomenon of refraction as exhibited in mirages and by the fact that a stick partly immersed in water seems broken when seen from the side. They explained the latter phenomenon in terms of bending of light on passing obliquely from water to air. However, it was Snell in 1600 who gave the quantitative law of refraction; namely, that the ratio of the sine of the angle of incidence to the sine of the angle of refraction is constant for any two media (see p. 128 and Ex. 8).

Due to a lack of a comprehensive theory, however, all this knowledge was disorganized and in some respects contradictory and confusing. Various elaborations of the particle view and the wave view were used but in neither a consistent nor a thorough fashion. Either view would explain the phenomena but in *different* ways. Thus the wave theories would explain difference in color as differences in the wavelength, while the particle theories would explain it in terms of differences in the size or in the speed of the particles. The difficulty lay with the confusing nature of the phenomena themselves. It was not until new phenomena or familiar phenomena under new conditions were observed that a good start was made.

A great step forward was taken in 1666 when Newton observed that sunlight on passing through a prism broke into the colors of the rainbow. Others had done the experiment before, but he noted the significant fact that the beam of light as a whole suffers a deviation from the original path. Even more significant was his observation that different colors deviate by different amounts—red the least, violet the most, and the other colors by an intermediate amount in strict order of their position in the rainbow. On passing each of the resulting colors through a second prism he found that while each color suffered still more deviation, it did not separate further into other colors. From this Newton concluded that sunlight is a mixture of the colors of the rainbow, which

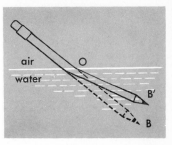

Fig. 5-1. A straight pencil appears broken when seen at an angle. On emerging from water the light from OB bends and appears to come from OB'.

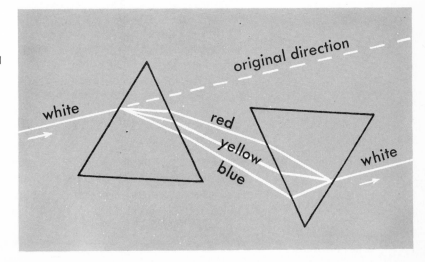

Fig. 5-2. Newton's analysis and resynthesis of white light.

are *primary,* and that the prism merely separates them because of their difference in the amount of bending (or "refrangibility") on entering and leaving the prism. He proved his conclusion by recombining the colors with another prism, thereby producing white light. Here at least we are on our way to an understanding of color, although we are far from understanding light.

The dilemma between the wave and the particle theory, however, still remained. Either theory explains the difference in bending or refrangibility of the various colors, but, of course, in terms of different ideas. According to the particle theory, the stream of particles bend their course on entering water (or glass) by being *attracted* by the particles of water. Apparently the particles of violet light are attracted more strongly than those of red light, and hence bend more. Since the attraction would speed up the particles, light should travel *faster* in water than in air, and violet light should travel faster than red light in water. The wave theory on the other hand, would explain refraction as a *slowing down* of the waves on entering water. The wave theory then goes on to say that since violet light must travel in water more slowly than the red (and both colors more slowly in water than in air), this is the reason that violet light bends more than red.

Both theories, then, explain the refraction of light, but the particle theory predicts that light should travel faster in water than in air, while the wave theory predicts exactly the opposite. If at the time of Newton the speed of light in air and in water could have been measured, the matter would have been settled in favor of one theory or the other. This, incidentally, is an example of a "crucial" experiment that decides between two rival theories. The speed of light in water, however, was not measured until 1850, when Foucault found it to be less in water than in air, as predicted by the wave theory.

Evidence of the wave nature of light came from another source in the beginning of the nineteenth century. Thomas Young observed that under certain conditions two beams of light can combine with one another to produce *darkness.* This is the phenomenon of interference, which will be discussed more fully below, and is quite analogous to the phenomenon of two waves on the surface of the water combining to produce *rest* in certain places. In fact the phenomena of interference not only demonstrate the wave nature of light but permit accurate measurement of the wavelength. Thus red light was found to have a wavelength of about 1/40,000 inch and blue light about 1/80,000 inch. During the entire span of the nineteenth century light was thought to be a wave phenomenon only.

But what kind of waves were these? Any wave implies a medium —some continuous substance in which the disturbance takes place, the disturbance itself being the vibrations of the particles of the medium. Yet light travels unhindered through a laboratory vacuum and certainly through the empty space between the planets and the stars. To satisfy this rational demand for a medium, luminiferous *ether* was invented. It had to be a fluid that fills all space, even the space between the atoms. It had to be made of extremely fine particles, far finer than the molecules and atoms (and later, electrons) of ordinary matter, and had to flow through matter quite unhindered. Ether had to be impossible to weigh or to detect by ordinary means, for no container would hold it, and the earth, traveling around the sun at 18½ miles per second, would encounter no resistance in moving through it. Yet this remarkable fluid would have to have both a rigidity and an elasticity far greater than steel in order to account for the fantastic speed of light (and electricity) through it.

So much for the medium. But how were the waves produced? In 1864 the Scotch physicist James Clerk Maxwell (1831-1879) developed a highly mathematical theory that accounted for all the then known phenomena of light. According to this theory, light consists of electromagnetic oscillations. Electric charges within the atoms of matter oscillate and send out electric and magnetic fields in all directions. A remarkable achievement of this theory is its prediction that the speed of light should be the ratio of the electromagnetic unit of charge to the electrostatic unit. On actual measurement of these two units this was found to be the case.

Fig. 5-3. Maxwell developed mathematically the theory that light consists of electromagnetic waves.

Just when all the known phenomena of light were neatly explained by Maxwell's theory, a series of new phenomena contradictory to the theory were observed. The simplest of these to visualize is the so-called photoelectric effect, which is the principle of the "electric eye." When light falls on a block of metallic sodium, electrons are ejected. On studying this phenomenon, it was found that blue light, even if extremely faint, would knock electrons from the surface of sodium.

This phenomenon may not appear puzzling at first, but after making some rough calculations its explanation in terms of waves of light appears impossible. We know the total amount of energy of the light shining on the sodium block, and we have a good estimate of the size of the electron. From these data we can calculate the amount of energy flowing around the electron. It is hopelessly small. The electron would have to wait several years in order to collect enough energy to be ejected. But electrons do come off as soon as the light is turned on. This we cannot conceive of on the basis of waves.

From this and other phenomena, the conclusion is inescapable that light cannot be a wave thinly spread over space, but must consist of concentrated packages much like bullets. This, however, is a *particle theory*. The particles of light are called *photons*. These photons do have energy, of course, but their energy depends on their *wavelength*. This is a rather strange mixture of particle and wave ideas. Nevertheless, according to this theory, the *longer* the wavelength, the *less* the energy of the photon. Thus photons of red light have about half the energy of photons of blue light, since waves of red light are twice as long as the waves of blue light.

Thus, in the mid-twentieth century we find two theories on the nature of light. The phenomena of interference prove conclusively that light has wave properties. We cannot conceive of interference in terms of particles. On the other hand, the photoelectric effect proves just as conclusively that light has particle properties. We cannot conceive of the photoelectric effect on the basis of waves. This appears and *is* contradictory. Some phenomena can be explained by the wave theory only. Other phenomena can be explained by a particle theory only. Still other phenomena can be explained by either theory. Is there a possibility of combining the two theories?

We shall return to the question at the end of the chapter. In this survey we wanted to present a general view of the entire field. In the succeeding sections we will take up in detail the problems and ideas that have been outlined here.

2. PROPERTIES OF LIGHT THAT CAN BE EXPLAINED BY EITHER THE WAVE OR THE PARTICLE THEORY

We shall first consider those properties of light that can be explained by either theory. A luminous source emits light into space and this light, whatever its nature, travels outward in all directions, carrying energy with it. In asking "What is light?" we are really hoping to conceive of some mechanical model, in terms of which we can visualize how light is produced and how it is propagated through a distance. On first thought, as well as after exhaustive analysis, we will find that there are two, and only two, ways of imagining this process. Light can be likened to bullets shot out by the source, or to waves generated by the source.

A simple analogy will add force to this argument. From a shoreline there are two, and only two, mechanical ways of transmitting energy to a boat out in the water. Bullets fired from the shore to the boat will carry the energy by virtue of the fact that they have mass and velocity and, hence, kinetic energy. Alternately, paddled water at the shore will start some waves. These waves, traveling out in all directions, will reach the boat and rock it or otherwise give it energy. There is no third mechanical way to transmit energy at a distance—that is, without actual contact. The question, then, of whether light is particles in motion or oscillating waves is basic to our understanding of it.

If light is particles in motion, then these particles should have all the properties of moving bodies. They should have mass, velocity, momentum, kinetic energy, and other mechanical properties, and they should obey all the laws of mechanics. These laws were given in Chapter 3, and after sufficient analysis we should be able to explain all the observable properties of light. If, on the other hand, light is a wave phenomenon, it should have all the properties of waves. Since we have not discussed these as yet, we will consider a few basic characteristics of waves, in order to be able to talk more clearly about them.

Concepts of
Wave Motion

On dropping a stone in a calm lake we see the familiar pattern of concentric circles, starting from the place at which the stone hit the

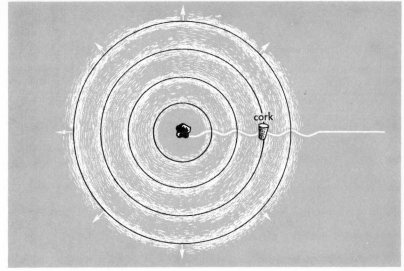

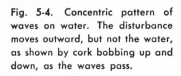

Fig. 5-4. Concentric pattern of waves on water. The disturbance moves outward, but not the water, as shown by cork bobbing up and down, as the waves pass.

water, and ever enlarging. These circles are equally spaced ridges (or crests) and troughs. It is important to note that what moves outward is the *disturbance, and not the water.* This is easily proved by placing a piece of cork in the path of the waves. If there is no wind, the cork bobs up and down as the waves pass, but is not carried forward as it would be if the water were flowing. "Bobbing up and down" means that now the cork is at the crest, then, an instant later, in the succeeding trough, then again at the crest, and so on. Quite clearly the parcel of water upon which the cork floats undergoes the same motion.

In what manner does the disturbance move forward? On hitting the surface, the stone first pushes the water down and then drags it along as the stone continues to fall, forming a roughly circular depression. While this hole is being formed the particles of water at the rim *A* are being pulled down by those neighboring particles that have already been pulled down by the stone. As a result, the particles at *A* follow the downward motion an instant later and, as a consequence, the rim enlarges. The particles now on the enlarged rim are in turn pulled down and thus the disturbance moves outward.

Meanwhile something else is happening at the place where the original "hole" was formed. While the particles of water near the center of the depression are pulling down the particles at the rim, they are themselves pulled *up,* since the attraction is mutual. This force slows the downward motion of the particles until they eventually stop. But by now this water has dropped below the level of the lake, and the attraction of the neighboring water particles (as well as the hydrostatic pressure) forces it up. The parcel of water, therefore, immediately starts speeding upward; having momentum, it does not stop on reaching the level of the lake, but continues to move upward until the attraction of the surrounding particles of water (and gravity) stop it. The water is now projecting in the form of a dome. It is then pulled down anew by these same forces and, passing the level line, forms a hole *for the second time.* The process is repeated so that this parcel of water moves up and

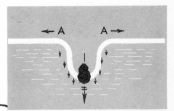

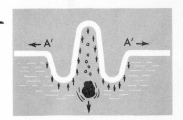

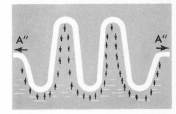

Fig. 5-5. Appearance of the disturbance at successive time intervals. The wave pattern and its outward movement is due to the forces between neighboring particles, shown by small black arrows.

down like a bouncing ball. As it executes these motions it drags the particles surrounding it, which in turn follow the identical motion, but an instant later. They in turn communicate this motion to particles further out but at later and later instants. Thus the parcel of water continues to send out waves. Due to friction, the disturbance will, of course, soon die down unless another stone is dropped just as the water in the "hole" is going down. By arranging to have a pole push down the water at the right instant and at regular intervals—that is, "in resonance"—a constant wave pattern can be established.

Continuing the analysis, we get a good idea of *wavelength*. When the original parcel of water has dropped from its crest to the level of the lake and is starting to go below it for the *second time*, the disturbance has moved a certain distance, *AB*, and the particles at *B* are starting to go below the lake level for the *first time*. Later, when the original parcel of water is starting to go below the lake level for the *third time*, the particles at *B* are starting to go down for the second time and the particles at *C* for the first time. The distance *AB* or *BC* is called the wavelength, and contains a full crest and trough. Thus the wavelength is the distance between any two successive particles of the medium moving in unison, such as two successive crests or two successive troughs. Wavelength is usually designated by the Greek letter, λ.

This picture of the wave pattern permits us to define a few more terms and to derive some simple relations. *Frequency, f,* is the number of complete vibrations per second—that is, the number of full *up and down* cycles that the source (or any other particle in the wave) makes per second. *Period, T,* is the time required for a complete cycle. Thus, one is the reciprocal of the other. If the particles make 10 complete vibrations per second, the time of each vibration is 1/10 second. Period is also the time it takes the *disturbance* to travel a full wavelength. From this relation it follows that the *velocity* of the disturbance, *v* (which is the distance divided by the time), is equal to the wavelength divided by the period.

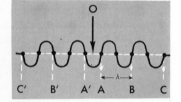

Fig. 5-6. Wavelength, λ, is the distance between two successive points such as A and B moving up and down in unison.

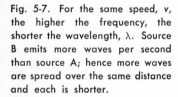

Fig. 5-7. For the same speed, v, the higher the frequency, the shorter the wavelength, λ. Source B emits more waves per second than source A; hence more waves are spread over the same distance and each is shorter.

$$v = \frac{\text{distance}}{\text{time}} = \frac{\lambda}{T}$$

A clearer idea of some of these relations is obtained by defining

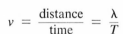

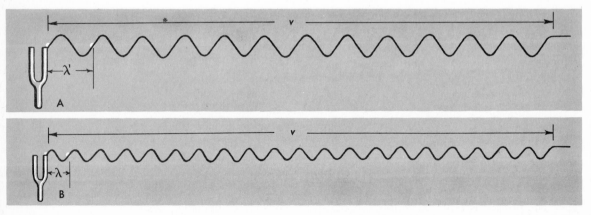

velocity as the distance the disturbance travels in 1 second. At the end of 1 second the disturbance has reached a certain point from the source. In this distance we visualize as many wavelengths spread out as the source emits per second. But this is the frequency of the source, which is the same as the frequency of the wave. The velocity therefore is equal to the wavelength, times the number of wavelengths that are contained in this distance.

$$v = \lambda \cdot f$$

From this it is also clear that if two waves have *the same speed,* then the one with the higher frequency will have the shorter wavelength.

Waves may be represented in various ways. In saying that a wave travels in a *straight line,* we mean that a wave reaches a distant object, such as a tree, following a thin wedge by the shortest possible route. If the wedge is very thin, as it would be if it reached a *point* on the tree, it can be represented by a line and is then called a *ray*. Alternately, if the wedge is thin and far enough from the source, it may be represented as a series of (almost) parallel ridges, and is called a *beam* or wave train. Any ridge or wave front is *perpendicular* to the ray. In fact a line can be used to represent the direction of motion of a wave. The line may be straight or curved, but it is always perpendicular to the wave front at every point. However, this representation is unsatisfactory because a line is also used to represent the path of a moving particle. On the other hand, a line has the advantage of showing the direction of motion of either a wave or a particle, without committing us as to which it is.

One more point should be emphasized here. In describing a wave we do speak of particles vibrating. However, these are the particles of the *medium, not of the wave*. What moves *forward* are *not* the particles of the medium or the particles of anything material; what moves forward is the *disturbance* (that is, the pulse of energy), which is immaterial. The forward movement of the disturbance is very different from the forward movement of particles such as bullets. From this analysis it is clear that a medium is needed if we are to think of a wave.

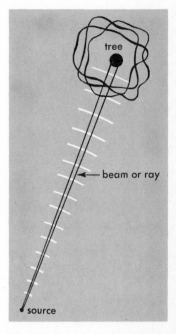

Fig. 5-8. The ray is perpendicular to the wave front. It is the shortest route of the disturbance from the source to the tree.

Properties of Light Explained

We are now in a position to consider the few properties of light that can be explained by either the particle or the wave theory.

Rectilinear Propagation. It is a simple matter to show the physical fact that light travels in straight lines. We cannot see around a corner and any opaque object in the path of light makes everything beyond invisible (but see diffraction, below, and Exs. 4, 8, and 9).

This phenomenon can be explained either by the particle theory or by the wave theory. If light consists of particles in motion, then the particles would move in straight lines according to Newton's first law of motion. If on the other hand light consists of waves in a homogeneous medium, again the rays representing the waves would move in straight lines. Thus, either view explains the rectilinear propagation of light.

We must point out, however, that the path of a particle will be straight only if the space in which it moves is free of forces, or at least of any forces except those too weak to make a perceptible difference.

Fig. 5-9 *(left).* Light bent by gravitational field of the sun. During an eclipse, star B appears in position B', nearer star C.

The theory of relativity predicts that when light travels through the strong gravitational field of the sun, it will be slightly deflected. The prediction has been confirmed by observation during solar eclipses (Fig. 5-9). These same experiments measurements of the deflection indicate that the gravitational forces of the earth are too weak to make a perceptible difference on the path of light rays near its surface. Similarly, waves move in straight lines only if the medium is homogeneous. This qualification is necessary because the speed of the waves depends on the attraction of the particles of the medium, its density, and other elastic properties. Thus, sound waves travel 1/5 mile per second in air, about 1 mile per second in water, and 6 miles per second in steel.

These considerations, incidentally, permit us to define a straight line either as the path of a material particle in space free of forces, or as the path of a wave in a homogeneous medium. (Ex. 4.)

The Inverse Square Law. Qualitatively, the observation is that a light source becomes dimmer with increasing distance from the source. Quantitatively, the brightness decreases as the *square* of the distance. The inverse square law is explained equally well by either theory. If

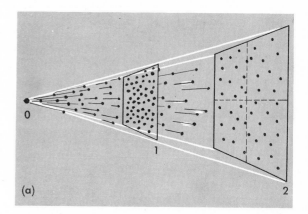

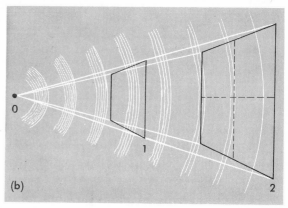

Fig. 5-10. Inverse square law explained by either particles (a) or waves (b). At twice the distance, the disturbance is spread over four times the area, in both cases.

light consists of particles, then at twice the distance the same number of particles would fall on four times the area and, hence, the number of particles per unit area would be one fourth as before. If light consists of waves, the phenomenon is again explained. At twice the distance the same energy is spread over four times the area. Hence the intensity of the disturbance is one fourth as before.

Reflection. When a beam of light falls upon a reflecting surface, the beam is turned back so that the angle of incidence is equal to the angle of reflection. By angle of incidence we mean the angle the oncoming beam makes with an imaginary line perpendicular to a surface at the point the beam meets that surface. Similarly, the angle of reflection is the angle between the reflected beam and the perpendicular. The angles are always equal, whatever the shape of the reflecting surface. This is known as the law of reflection.

If light is a particle phenomenon, the law should hold. A tennis ball, for example, bounces off a court at the same angle it meets the surface, as can be observed directly, or deduced from the laws of collision. The law of reflection should also hold if light is a wave phenomenon. This is easily observed in reflected water waves and can be proved by a simple analysis of the movement of the disturbance. Thus, the law of reflection can again be explained by either the wave or the particle theory.

Refraction. The phenomena of refraction are very common indeed. We have already mentioned mirages, most frequently seen perhaps when driving on a straight, flat road on a cold morning: part of the road and distant cars then appear as though they are in the sky. The broken appearance of a stick partly immersed in water has also been mentioned. Related to this is the common observation that ponds always appear shallower than they actually are. A very simple experiment will illustrate this phenomenon. We put a penny at the bottom of a deep cup on a table and move away from the cup until we no longer see the penny. If now the cup is filled with water, from our distant position we will see the penny and a good deal of the bottom of the cup.

This phenomenon as well as the other phenomena have been correctly explained as being due to the bending of light beams on passing obliquely from water to air or vice versa, or as passing through layers of air of different densities. In the case of the penny in the cup, the beam of light follows the path shown in Figure 5-12. Owing to the psychological fact that we "see" objects in the direction from which light comes, the penny appears in the position *A'*.

That light actually bends in passing from air to water or vice versa may be demonstrated very directly. We direct the beam of a flashlight at the surface of a glass jar. Dust particles in the path permit us to see the beam taking the path shown in Figure 5-13. If we put the flashlight in the water, the beam will follow exactly the same path in reverse direction. Thus we notice that the beam bends toward the perpendicular on entering the water from air and away from the perpendicular on entering air from water. This is evident from Figure 5-14: for if we take an inch of the beam in air, we are at a certain distance from the

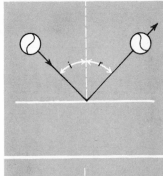
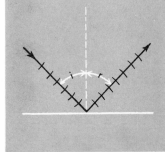

Fig. 5-11. Tennis ball and water waves reflect in the same manner. The angle of incidence, *i*, is equal to the angle of reflection, *r*, in both cases.

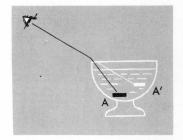

Fig. 5-12. Penny becomes visible on adding water. The penny is actually at A, but appears at A'.

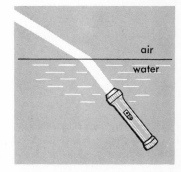

Fig. 5-13. Flashlight beam actually bends on emerging from water.

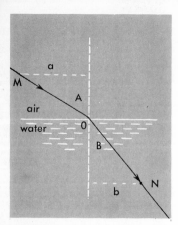

Fig. 5-14. Law of refraction. The beams OM (in air) and ON (in water) are of equal length. Point M is further from the perpendicular than point N. The ratio a/b is the index of refraction of water.

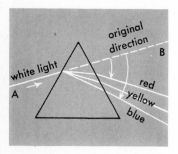

Fig. 5-15. Deviation and separation of colors by a prism. Note that the blue is deviated more than the red from the original direction of AB.

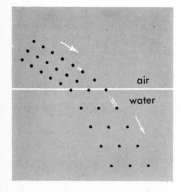

Fig. 5-16. Explanation of diffraction according to particle theory. Due to attraction, particles speed up at interface and beam bends. Note greater speed of particles in water.

perpendicular; if we also take an inch in water, we are nearer to the perpendicular.

The Dutch physicist Snell discovered that no matter at what angle the beam enters the water, the ratio of the distance from the perpendicular in air to the distance in water is constant, for the same length of the beam. This ratio is called the refractive index of water. Glass behaves exactly as water except that the bending is greater. Mathematically the index of refraction, *n*, between any two media is as follows:

$$n = \frac{\text{sine of the angle of incidence}}{\text{sine of the angle of refraction}} = \frac{\text{Sin } A}{\text{Sin } B} = \frac{a}{b}$$

Newton, who resolved white light into its component colors, discovered that different colors have different refrangibilities—that is, different refractive indices for the same substance. Understanding the formation of the spectrum then becomes a simple matter. As a beam of light containing all the colors enters the surface of the prism, the different colors are bent by different amounts and travel toward the other surface along different paths. On re-emerging into air the colors are bent further (again by different amounts) with the result that they follow separate paths. If another identical prism is now interposed in their path, with the surfaces of the two prisms respectively parallel, each color will be bent in the opposite direction in succession and the entire beam will emerge from a single point of the second prism as white light (see Fig. 5-2). This, of course, is not surprising, for the two prisms in that position may be considered as a thick plate of glass with parallel surfaces. This is in effect, a window pane, and a window pane does not produce a spectrum.

The phenomena of refraction discussed so far can be explained by either the wave or the particle theory. We have intentionally used lines for the path of light, since a line may mean either the path of particles, or the direction of the movement of the disturbance. With the particle theory of light, we must make the further assumption that the particles of water or glass attract the particles of light. Since there is more glass on the underside of the beam there is more attraction in that direction and the beam bends toward the perpendicular. This, of course, implies that the attraction speeds up the particles so that the speed of light in glass (or water) should be greater than in air. When the beam emerges on the other face of the prism, the attraction bends it *away* from the perpendicular, and at the same time slows the particles by the amount they were speeded up on entering the first surface. Another consequence of the particle theory is that blue light should have a greater speed in water than red light and, of course, both colors should have a greater speed in water than in air.

The wave theory also explains the refraction phenomena but on the opposite assumption: namely, that light travels more slowly in water than in air. A wave front on meeting water obliquely (Fig. 5-17) would have the side of the beam *AB* enter first, while the side *CD* would continue in air. By the time *CD* has proceeded to *D'*, *AB* has proceeded only to *B'*. All intermediate points such as *E* would take an intermediate path. By this time the entire wave front would be in the water and would continue in a straight line with constant speed in water, taking position $B''G''D''$, and so on. Three points are worth noting in the diagram. The wavelengths are shorter in water than in air; the index of refraction is the ratio of the wavelengths in the two media; the index of refraction is also the ratio of the velocities in the two media (Ex. 23).

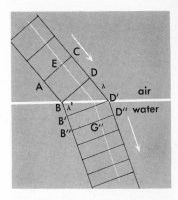

Fig. 5-17. Explanation of refraction according to wave theory. On entering water, waves slow down and beam bends. Note shortened wavelength, λ', in water.

According to the wave theory, the separation of the colors into a spectrum is explained as the difference in the speed of the various colors in water. Thus red light is bent less because it moves faster in water than blue light. In other words, the red light is slowed down by a lesser amount than the blue. If the theory is correct, then the wavelength of red light in air should be longer than that of blue, and yellow should be intermediate.

If in the seventeenth century it had been possible to measure the speed of light in air and in water, or the speed of the various colors in water, the matter could have been decided in favor of one theory or the other. Similarly, if the wavelengths of the various colors could have been measured and compared, the decision could have been made. However, none of these measurements could be made until the beginning of last century. The speed of light in water was measured for the first time in 1850. In fact, the speed of light in air or vacuum was not measured in laboratory experiments on the earth until about that time (although measured from astronomical observations by Roemer in 1676, as discussed below).

The Measurement of the Speed of Light

Whether light travels instantaneously or with finite speed was not known until almost the end of the seventeenth century. We have seen that Empedocles taught that light takes time to travel, and this was believed by most of the ancient world. Aristotle accepted this on the general principle that "moving" means going from one place to another and this necessarily takes time. Instantaneous speed, Aristotle argued, implies that something must be in two places at the same time, and this is impossible. Yet the modern scientists were divided on the subject, with the majority in favor of the instantaneous speed.

The matter remained unsettled because all early attempts to measure the speed of light had met with failure. Galileo tried to measure the time a light beam takes to travel to a distant mirror and back, but the time interval was too short. Members of the Florentine Academy tried the experiment with longer distances using a similar method, which they had found successful with sound (Ex. 24). They had two groups of observers with covered lanterns on two distant mountain tops. The first group would uncover the lantern and the second group would uncover theirs the instant they saw the light of the first lantern. The first group then attempted to measure the time between the uncovering of their lantern and *seeing* the light of the other lantern. The time was extremely short and they soon realized that they were only measuring the time it took them to uncover their lanterns.

These results were generally interpreted as meaning that light travels instantaneously. Descartes added the argument that we see the eclipse of the sun at the moment the moon is between us and the sun,

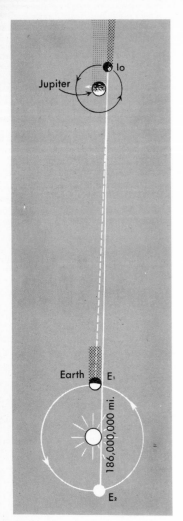

Fig. 5-18. Roemer's measurement of the speed of light. Light takes 16 minutes (1000 sec) to travel across the diameter of the earth's orbit, which is about 186,000,000 miles.

as calculated from celestial mechanics. Huygens countered that this only means that light travels very fast.

Using larger astronomical distances, the Danish astronomer Olaus Roemer (1644-1710) in 1676 proved that light takes time to travel and obtained a good estimate of its speed. While studying the satellites of Jupiter he was puzzled to find that they were slightly irregular in their periods, which is contrary to Newton's law of gravitation. The innermost satellite, Io, has a period of about $42\frac{1}{2}$ hours, and is eclipsed by Jupiter at each revolution. It disappears almost instantly behind the shadow of the planet, so that its period can be measured with high precision. Roemer noticed that when the earth was nearest Jupiter, the period of Io was precisely constant for several days. After a few weeks, however, Io began to lag behind, and the lag increased steadily so that at the end of about 6 months the eclipse was as much as 16 minutes behind the predicted times. For the rest of the year the period between eclipses became shorter and shorter, until about 6 months later, when the earth was again nearest Jupiter, the eclipses were again on time.

Roemer correctly interpreted this phenomenon. When the earth was opposite Jupiter, it was the light that was late and not the satellite. The eclipses still occurred at the predicted time, but the light carrying the message did not reach Roemer until it had traveled the extra distance across the diameter of the earth's orbit. From the then accepted value of the distance of the earth to the sun, he calculated the speed of light as 192,000 miles per second (Ex. 25).

It took several hundred years to develop laboratory methods to measure this fantastic speed. Armand Fizeau (1819-1896), improving the original idea of Galileo, had a beam of light pass between the teeth of a rotating circular saw. On reflection from a distant mirror and if the saw was rotating fast enough and at the right speed, the beam would return through the next opening. We shall describe a still further improvement of this method, perfected by Michelson.

Albert Michelson (1852-1931) made a very exact octagon-shaped mirror and mounted it on an axle so that it could be rotated rapidly by blowing air on it. He then devised the following experiment. A beam of light from L is reflected by side a, which is so adjusted as to send the beam to a distant mirror M. On reflection from M the beam returns to side c and on further reflection is observed at O. If the octagon mirror is now rotated slowly (say a few times per minute), the beam can still be seen at O, though somewhat intermittently. This is so because every time any face is in the exact position of a, the beam is reflected onto the distant mirror and returns to the side at c before the octagon mirror has time to turn by any detectable amount. The rest of the beam is, of course, reflected at other angles at a and is lost.

If the mirror is rotated more rapidly, however, the beam (which is always sent to the mirror M from a face in the exact position of a) on its return would find face c at a slightly different angle. Hence the beam would be reflected to some position O'. As the speed of rotation is increased, the beam deviates more and more from O and ultimately becomes unobservable. But if the mirror is now rotated still faster, a speed will be reached at which face b will occupy the exact position

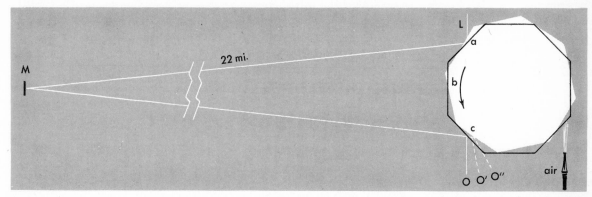

formerly occupied by face *c,* by the time the beam returns. At this speed the beam will again be observed and the pulses, being very rapid, will appear as steady light. Knowing the time the octagon mirror takes to make one eighth of a rotation, and the distance to mirror *M* and back, Michelson obtained a very accurate value of the speed of light. He received the Nobel Prize for this experiment.

Michelson also measured the speed of light in water and other common substances and found them as predicted by the wave theory. Thus, in water, the speed of red light is about 150,000 miles per second while that of blue light is about 120,000 miles per second—both less than in air.

The speed of light in vacuum is one of the most important constants in nature. It enters the calculation in measuring the sizes and distances within atoms, the energy of atoms, and the distances and motions of atoms. In astronomy, the distance light travels in a year, called the *light year,* is one of the basic yardsticks in measuring distances of stars. In Einstein's theory of relativity, the speed of light is the highest speed possible in nature (Ex. 41). The most recent value is 299,876 kilometers per second or 186,424 miles per second.

Fig. 5-19. Michelson's measurement of the speed of light. The beam becomes again visible at O if the octagon mirror rotates a little over 500 times per second; that is, light travels 44 miles in a little less than 1/4000 second.

3. THE EVIDENCE FOR THE WAVE NATURE OF LIGHT

The observation that light travels more slowly in water than in air constitutes strong evidence for the wave theory. The bending of a beam of light toward the perpendicular is exactly what is predicted for waves slowing down on entering the water. If light were a swarm of particles, they should be speeded up by attraction. The evidence, however, is not decisive. It is possible to construct a particle theory of light that would explain the bending as due to attraction before entering the surface of the water, and still explain the subsequent slowing down as due to the resistance of the water after the beam has entered the surface. There are, however, phenomena that are impossible to conceive of in any other way than by a wave theory. These are the phenomena of interference and diffraction.

Although the phenomena of interference and diffraction are very common and have been observed for a long time, they were not interpreted as wave phenomena until the beginning of last century. Thus, the color of soap bubbles or oil films on the pavement are due to interference. The colors of peacocks or of the wings of certain butterflies are due to diffraction and interference. The "rainbow" around the moon on a wintry night or the colors seen on looking at a light through an open umbrella or a thin handkerchief have the same causes. Moreover, shadows of very sharp edges are not sharp, even when the source of light is very small, like a point. The reader may examine the shadow of a razor blade, or a thin needle. Better still, he may look at a light with one eye, holding a needle or a razor blade about 5 inches from the eye. Instead of sharp edges he will see a series of dark and bright bands. A still simpler experiment is to bring the index finger against the thumb, until they just touch. As one looks with one eye through the space between them against a light, he will see a series of black and white bands. We shall explain some of these phenomena after the principles are established.

Interference

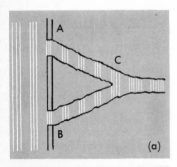

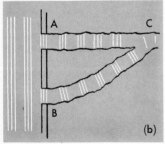

Fig. 5-20. Reinforcement and interference of water waves. In (a) the canals are of equal length. In (b) BC is longer than AC by a half wavelength.

Let us first investigate the phenomenon of interference and see how it is characteristic of waves. Imagine a series of waves on a lake meeting a barrier through which two canals lead to calm water beyond. The waves will continue in the canals. If the canals are bent so that they meet at a point *C,* the waves on going through the canal will merge at *C* and beyond. If the distances *AC* and *BC* are equal, the merging will result in waves double the height, because each parcel of water will receive at precisely the same instant twice the energy from a similar parcel in the branches of the canal. The waves are said to *reinforce* one another. On the other hand, if the canals are unequal, and particularly if the canal *BC* is longer than canal *AC* by half a wavelength, then the waves will destroy one another at the juncture *C.* The crest from *AC* will meet a trough from *BC,* so that the parcel of water at *C* will receive an impulse from *AC* to go up at the same instant it receives a pulse from *BC* to go down. The result is that the parcel of water will do neither, and the water beyond *C* will remain calm. This is called destructive interference or simply *interference.* It is characteristic of waves. It is difficult to see how particles (or boats or missiles) carrying energy through the canals can "interfere" with one another in this way. (Again we must not confuse bulletlike particles carrying energy and the particles of the medium.)

If light has wave properties it should show interference phenomena. This means that under certain conditions *light added to light* should produce *darkness.* Strange as it may sound, this is so, and the phenomena are not difficult to observe. We take a plate of glass and silver

Fig. 5-21 (Right). Glass wedge, showing alternate bright and dark ridges. Angle of wedge and distance, *d*, between ridges are highly exaggerated. D is about 10 inches long; *t* is the thickness of the cellophane.

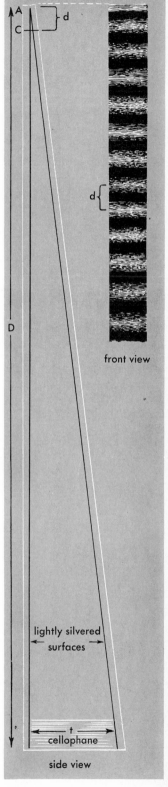

it thinly so that it will partly reflect and partly transmit light. If we shine light on it, preferably of one color, say yellow from a sodium fog light, we will observe a uniform yellow reflection.

We now take another plate of glass similar to the first and make a very thin wedge of the two by putting a thin piece of Scotch tape between them at one end. On shining light on this combination we would expect brighter reflection than from a single plate since we have two reflecting surfaces. Instead, we see a series of alternating dark and yellow bands. Along the yellow bands the brightness is roughly twice as bright as before. Along the dark bands, which were yellow before, there is now no light, of course. Thus, in certain positions, light from the upper surface plus light from the lower surface produces a brighter color; at certain other positions, light from the upper surface added to light from the lower surface produces darkness (Fig. 5-21).

The phenomenon is easy to explain on the basis of waves. At the very edge *A* (Fig. 5-22), the surfaces touch so that reflection is brighter than before. But at some distance *d*/2, where the first dark band appears, the distance between the plates is equal to a quarter of a wavelength. When a crest meets the upper surface, a part of the crest is reflected. The other part continues until it meets the lower surface and is reflected there. If the distance between the two surfaces is precisely 1/4 wavelength, the part of the crest reflected from the lower surface will return to *B* just as the following trough is coming from the original source. Crest and trough will then interfere with one another and the result will be darkness. At point *C* further down on the wedge, the distance between the plates is 1/2 wavelength. The transmitted crest makes the journey and back just in time to meet the next oncoming crest and

Fig. 5-22. Explanation of alternate dark and light ridges. The surfaces are 1/4 wavelength apart at B, resulting in interference; 1/2 wavelength apart at C, resulting in reinforcement. C is at the distance d is from the edge in Fig. 5-21.

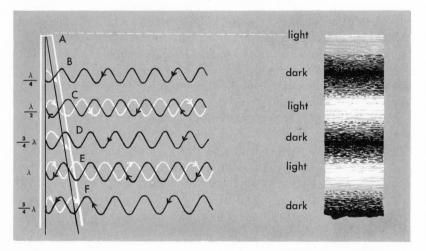

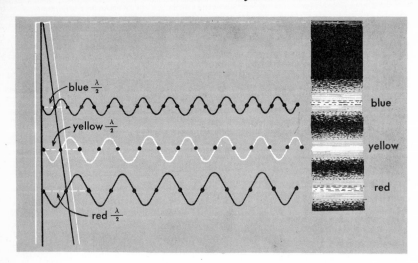

Fig. 5-23. The longer red wavelengths reinforce further from the edge than the shorter blue wavelengths. The yellow and the intermediate colors reinforce at intermediate points, resulting in the spectrum.

so they will reinforce one another, thus increasing the brightness. At D the distance is 3/4 wavelength, making the double journey for the transmitted ray $1\frac{1}{2}$ wavelengths, so that again the two beams are out of phase and darkness results. At E the distance is 1 wavelength and the reflected beam will be 2 wavelengths behind. Thus we get alternate dark and bright ridges.

This phenomenon not only demands that light be a wave phenomenon but provides a method for the measurement of the wavelength. The distance between the plates where the first band appears ($\lambda/2$) bears to the distance from the edge (CA) the same ratio as the thickness of the scotch tape (t) to the length of the plate (D); that is, in Fig. 5-21,

$$\frac{\lambda/2}{CA} = \frac{t}{D}$$

The first quantity is half of the wavelength; since the other distances can be measured, the wavelength of yellow light can be calculated. It is about 0.00006 cm, or about 60,000 wavelengths to an inch.

The same phenomenon is observed when we shine red light on the glass wedge, except that the bands are further apart. This can only mean that the red light has a longer wavelength than the yellow, for it is necessary to go further down on the wedge to be half a red wavelength apart from the two surfaces. On the other hand, the bright bands of blue light are closer together than the yellow, indicating a shorter wavelength. On actual measurement of the distance between the bands we find the wavelength of red light about 40,000 to the inch and blue about 80,000 to an inch (Ex. 28).

On shining white light on the glass wedge we obtain the spectrum characteristic of the rainbow. Each color occupies a position in accordance with its wavelength. Red is the furthest from the edge and hence has the longest wavelength; yellow is intermediate; and violet is nearest the edge. This, incidentally, is the reverse order of the rainbow or of the spectrum produced by a prism.

Interference phenomena are very common. Soap bubbles or oil films, for example, show various colors. Their thicknesses are about the same as the wavelengths of light, but they vary in thickness and act like wedges reflecting from both their inside and outside surfaces. At the places at which the thickness is just right they reinforce to give red light. At other places they give yellow, blue, or other colors.

Diffraction

Closely related to interference is the phenomenon of diffraction, which is also characteristic of waves. Diffraction is not to be confused with refraction, which is the bending of waves or the passing of waves obliquely from one medium to another (see p. 127). Diffraction is the bending of waves around corners, or on the passing of waves through small openings—small, that is, compared to their wavelength.

The phenomenon is easy to observe with water waves. Figure 5-24 illustrates water waves on a lake coming against (toward) a barrier that has an opening in the middle. The passage of the original wave from the left causes the water in the opening to bob up and down with the passage of the crest and the trough, respectively. But this causes another phenomenon to arise. The bobbing up and down of the water due to the passage of the wave is no different from the situation in which the parcel of the water at the opening bobs up and down due to the dropping of stones or paddling. Therefore here the parcel of water in the opening acts as an *original source,* producing concentric waves on the other side of the barrier. "Bending" may not be a well-chosen word, but it is clear that the waves on the *right* side of the barrier move generally in directions different from the direction of the original waves. Diffraction, therefore, is the bending of waves in passing through small openings. A slight extension of the analysis also explains that there is some bending of the waves at the edges, since the parcel of water there also acts as a source of waves.

If the opening in the barrier is enlarged, the waves will tend to become stronger in the original direction. This is because the vibrating water in the opening of the barrier becomes more nearly like a part of the original wave. If the barrier is enlarged to several times the wavelength, each edge of the opening will then be no different from any other edge and only a slight curving at the end of the wave will result.

It might be a surprise to the reader that light shows diffraction; that is, it *bends around corners,* and spreads out, in passing through small openings. However, since the wavelengths of light are exceedingly short, we need very small openings to observe the bending. We shall describe an experiment first performed by the Jesuit Francesco Grimaldi in 1650 and repeated by Thomas Young around 1800. It was this experiment that Fresnel used to convince the scientific world of the wave nature of light.

We make a tiny pinhole on a card and shine light through it. For best results we use light of one color, say yellow, and from a source of small area. On the path of the light from the pinhole and at right angles to it, we place a second card to act as a screen. This second card is placed several inches from the first, and is well shielded from indirect light. We are surprised to see on the screen a large disk of light instead

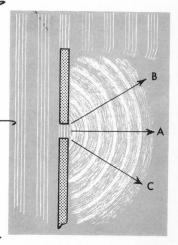

Figure 5-24. Diffraction of water waves through a small opening of a barrier. In general, the waves on right (B or C) move in directions different from that of the original waves on the left.

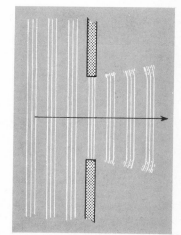

Fig. 5-25. If opening is large relative to wavelength, no "bending" occurs except at the edges.

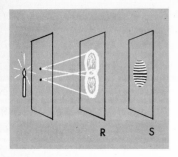

Fig. 5-26. Diffraction of light through pinholes. When *either* hole is open the pattern on the screen is a disk opposite the hole, as in R. When both holes are open the pattern is a disk with ridges, as in S.

of a single spot. The disk is brightest at the center and dimmer toward the edges, but it has an overall area of 1/4 inch or more, depending on the size of the pinhole. Light, therefore, on passing through a small opening diffracts or spreads out like a wave.

If we make another hole below the first one and then cover the first hole, we get, of course, a similar disk a little further down. If light is now allowed to go through *both* holes, an unexpected result is observed. The brightest spot is now a *band* and is at neither of the former positions, but halfway between them. There is also a series of bright ridges of less intensity on either side of the central bright band, separated by completely dark spaces between them.

Augustin Fresnel (1788-1827) explained the phenomenon as follows: The wave fronts from the light source meet the two holes at the same time and start simultaneous diffraction waves at both holes (Fig. 5-27). Now if point *M* is equidistant from both *A* and *B,* a crest from *A* will meet a crest from *B,* and also a trough from *A* will meet a trough from *B.* These two waves will then reinforce one another at all phases resulting in a bright spot. Since all points above *M* are further from *B* than from *A,* there must be a point *P* that is further from *B* than from *A* by a *half a wavelength.* At this point a crest from *A* will meet a trough from *B,* and a trough from *A* will meet a crest from *B.* These will interfere, resulting in darkness. At point *Q,* which is a whole wavelength further from *B* than from *A,* crest again will meet crest and we shall have another bright spot. Continuing this reasoning we can explain the other bright and dark spots above as well as below *M.*

With red light (instead of yellow) the same pattern is obtained except that the spots are further apart, just as in the case of the wedge. We shall not repeat the explanation here except to point out that this phenomenon provides another method of measuring wavelengths of light. We can measure the distance from the screen, the distance of the first bright spot above the brightest spot, and the distance between the two holes. From this we can calculate how much further *Q* is from *B* than

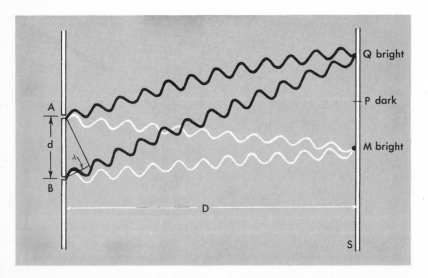

Fig. 5-27. Fresnel's explanation of bright and dark ridges. Point Q is one wavelength further from B than from A.

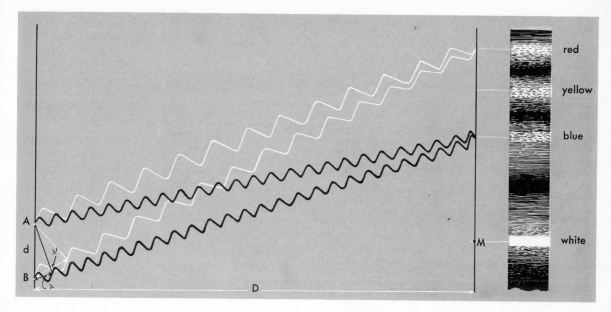

Fig. 5-28. Red reinforces at a point further from the central white image, M, than the blue.

from *A,* and this difference is the wavelength. Thus, it is clear from Figure 5-27 that

$$\frac{\lambda}{AB} = \frac{d}{D}$$

and by measuring *d, MQ,* and *D,* we can calculate λ (the wavelength).

This method lends itself to very high precision. The "holes" can be brought closer together, and this will increase the distance *MQ.* More "holes" can be added in order to get more light. This is achieved by making scratches, rather than holes, on glass—as many as 30,000 per inch giving a distance *d,* 1/30,000 inch. The spread produced by such a diffraction grating is enormous. It spreads each of the primary colors of the rainbow into bands of several feet or more.

Diffraction gratings may also be produced by ruling a large number of equally spaced parallel lines on a metal surface. These gratings produce spectra in exactly the same way as the glass grating except that they reflect the light from the ridges and from the grooves. A phonograph record is such a grating, although rather coarse. Holding an LP record somewhat edgewise so as to reflect the light from a lamp will form a spectrum. Peacock feathers and wings of certain insects have ribbed structures and act as gratings, producing colors.

Thus the phenomena of interference and diffraction demand a wave theory for their explanation. We cannot explain them in any other way. The theory in turn explains all the phenomena considered so far, and gives good answers to some fundamental questions. To the question, "What is light?" the theory answers that it is some kind of vibration of extremely short wavelength ranging from 3.8×10^{-5} cm for violet, to 7.6×10^{-5} cm for the longest visible red. To the question, "What is color?" the theory answers that a certain range in these wavelengths produces the sensation of red, another range produces the sensation of orange, and so on for the other colors. To the question, "Why do some stars appear red while others appear blue?" the theory answers that the light of the former is richer in red than is white light, while the light from the latter is richer in blue than is white light. To the question, "Why does a rose appear red?" the theory answers that the rose reflects a good deal of light in the wavelength range of the red, but absorbs some or all of the other wavelengths. These answers can be checked directly by analyzing the light with a diffraction grating or a prism.

No sooner, however, have we answered some of these questions than new and deeper ones arise. Why should a certain range of wavelengths produce the sensation of red while other wavelengths of presumably the same kind of disturbance produce the sensation of blue? Are there any wavelengths that produce no visual sensation at all and hence are invisible? What kind of waves are they? Since the velocity of light waves is so high and their wavelengths are so short, their frequency must be exceedingly high. What kind of medium is it that vibrates so rapidly? What kind of source can vibrate rapidly enough to produce these waves?

We shall attempt to answer some of these questions in the following sections.

4. THE ELECTROMAGNETIC THEORY OF LIGHT

Color and Wavelength

The wave theory provides a definite and objective interpretation of color. Wavelengths of a certain range produce on the eye the sensation of red, while those of another range produce the sensation of blue. This, of course, does not explain what the sensation is nor how a mere difference in the wavelength results in such a marked subjective difference in the sensation. It does, however, permit us to speak objectively of colors and to study them with physical methods. Once put on this basis, color is capable of sharper definition and extension.

On examining the various bands of the so-called primary colors— say the red band—and isolating different portions of this band, we get a red sensation from each portion, although the sensation shades gradually and imperceptibly into the orange as the wavelengths become shorter and shorter. Thus there is a whole family of red colors. To the eye they all appear practically the same but to the prism or the grating they are different "colors," that is, different wavelengths. Carrying the idea one step further, we may speak of each wavelength as a different "color."

We analyze light and study the specific colors or wavelengths it contains by means of a spectroscope. The essential part of the instru-

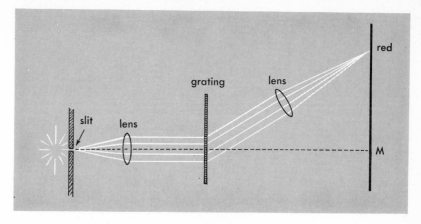

Fig. 5-29. A diffraction grating spectroscope. Each wavelength is focused at one position producing a line which is the image of the slit in that color.

ment is a prism or a grating. However, in order to avoid overlapping of the neighboring colors the light to be analyzed is passed through a narrow slit. The narrower the slit, the better the resolution of the neighboring wavelengths. The slit, of course, should not be too narrow; for then it would admit very little light. A lens is placed between the slit and the grating to make the rays parallel, so that they fall at the same angle on the grating. Finally another lens is placed after the rays have been diffracted, in order to focus all the rays of each color on the same position on the screen. Each color, therefore, is focused at a definite position of the screen according to its wavelength, forming an image of the source, which in this case is the slit. This gives the so-called "lines" of the spectrum—the lines being the images of the narrow slit in different colors or wavelengths.

Passing the light from white-hot lime (the "limelight" of the theater) through the spectroscope will give all the colors of the rainbow and, within each color, a continuous range of all the wavelengths. No matter how narrow the slit, or how much the colors are spread by means of gratings with more lines per inch, all the wavelengths will be present from the shortest violet to the longest red. A similar spectrum is obtained from almost any white-hot solid or liquid, or even from a gas at very high densities, as it would be under high pressures (see frontispiece).

A different result is obtained by analyzing the light from the sodium vapor of a fog lamp. Instead of a yellow band, which we might have expected, a single yellow line, with a wavelength of about 0.000059 cm, appears if the grating is coarse. Using a finer grating, the line breaks up into two lines, one at 0.00005890 cm and the other at 0.00005896 cm. Thus sodium light not only is devoid of all colors other than yellow, but it does not even have much of the yellow. Except for these two wavelengths, all other positions of the spectrum are dark.

The situation is not unique with sodium. On examining the light from a photographer's mercury vapor lamp, we find two strong yellow lines close together (but in different positions from those of sodium), a very intense green line and several blue and violet lines. We get a similar but more complicated pattern from neon in a neon sign. In fact every element when in the vapor state, if sufficiently hot and under the proper conditions, emits its own characteristic pattern of wavelengths.

The frontispiece shows the characteristic spectra of some common elements. The spectral pattern is even more characteristic of each element than are the fingerprints of persons. It is therefore used to identify an element. The spectroscope is widely used in chemical analysis for this purpose. Light from the stars, for instance, can be analyzed so that the elements present in the outer part of a star can be identified as easily as they would be if the star were in the laboratory. We shall return to this interesting subject in Chapter 14.

Invisible Colors

The term "invisible light" sounds like a contradiction and in the obvious sense it is. However, if we spread sunlight or limelight into a spectrum, we find energy in the dark region beyond the red. In this region wavelengths longer than red would reinforce one another. Even though this region is dark, it is warm to the hand and a sensitive thermometer registers a rise in temperature. Using a sensitive thermometer to explore the entire region, we find that energy extends to wavelengths well beyond the visible range.

We identify this *infrared* (below the red) region with radiant heat. A hot pressing iron, which is not hot enough to glow, radiates heat that is invisible, even though easily felt. When sent through a grating, the heat radiated by the hot iron spreads out according to wavelengths. Thus, radiant heat is really light, or of the same nature as light except for the important difference that the wavelengths are longer.

A similar situation exists beyond the violet end of the spectrum, in the so-called *ultraviolet* region. In this region wavelengths shorter than violet would reinforce. On examining the spectrum from sunlight we also find energy in this region. If we put our hand there, we notice warmth and rather quick tanning from the invisible ultraviolet radiation; and by photographing the spectrum, we find darkening of the photographic plate, well beyond the visible violet. Using light from mercury vapor, we can identify additional characteristic lines of mercury in the ultraviolet region.

Thus visible light seems to be only a part of a larger phenomenon— that of radiation in general. The radiation seems to extend indefinitely into the shorter and the longer wavelengths. Whatever theory would explain light should also explain these other types of radiation.

Maxwell's Electromagnetic Theory

As a matter of historical fact an understanding of the nature of light resulted from the recognition that light is only a part of the more inclusive phenomenon of radiation. The explanation came from an apparently unexpected source, and was given by the Scotch physicist James Clerk Maxwell. Although his theory is highly mathematical and very complicated, its basic ideas can be presented in relatively simple terms that impart a fair pictorial understanding of them.

Maxwell was investigating mathematically how an electric charge affects another electric charge at a distance. Consider a positively charged pith ball at *A* and another one at *B* (Fig. 5-30). According to the behavior of electric charges, there is a repulsion between them even if they are separated by a vacuum. It is best for our purpose to think of the repulsion on *B* as being due to the force of the electric field of *A*.

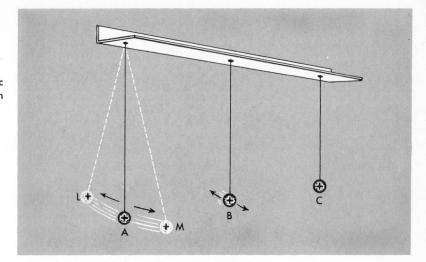

Fig. 5-30. The oscillating electric charge, A, causes oscillations in charge B, at a distance.

The strength and direction of these forces depend on the size of the charge on *A* and the distance and direction from *B*. As long as *A* remains stationary, the forces around *B* will be constant and *B* will take a position of equilibrium, remaining suspended and stationary.

Let us now swing charge *A* in the direction shown in Figure 5-30. From the laws of electricity we can predict that charge *B* will be affected, and indeed follow the swing of charge *A*. As *A* is moving in the direction of *L,* both the direction and the amount of repulsion are changing; as *A* returns in the direction of *M,* the repulsion changes in the opposite direction. In other words, the swinging of charge *A* alters the strength and the direction of the field at *B* and causes the charge *B* to swing also.

The changes in the electric field, however, are only one aspect of this effect. Equally important are the changes in the magnetic field around charge *B*. As the charged body *A* moves in the direction of *L,* it constitutes a current; for as we have learned, any moving charge is a current and generates a magnetic field at right angles to its motion. Therefore as the charge *A* swings back and forth, it produces a magnetic field which changes around *B* both in direction and in strength. This changing magnetic field then affects the charge at *B* and causes it also to swing. The swinging of the charge *A* results in changing electric and magnetic fields in the vicinity of *B* and thus causes the charge *B* to follow the swinging of *A*.

On a little reflection we see that the electric and magnetic fields change in the region surrounding *B,* whether *B* is there or not. This is true of all points of space surrounding *A;* or, in the language of Maxwell, an oscillating (or accelerating) electric charge causes changing or pulsating electric and magnetic fields in all points of space surrounding the charge.

Maxwell then investigated the speed of the disturbance. Intuitively we feel that if we start swinging charge *A* and there is a third charge *C* beyond *B,* then C should be affected *after* B. In other words, the disturbance of the electric and magnetic fields takes time to travel outward from the oscillating charge. Maxwell argued that if a distant charge is to be affected by both the electric and the magnetic fields *at the same time,* then there must be a definite value to the speed. Using the exact quantitative relations touched upon in Chapter 4 (Ex. 25), he came to the conclusion that the speed must be numerically equal to the ratio of the electromagnetic unit of electric charge (the absolute coulomb) to the electrostatic unit of charge. By actual measurement this ratio is found to be 3×10^{10}. But this is the speed of light in vacuum, expressed in centimeters per second. Therefore oscillating electric charges produce electromagnetic disturbances which move outward in all directions with the speed of light (Ex. 33).

This interesting result led Maxwell to propose the theory that visible light as well as the infrared and ultraviolet radiations are in reality electromagnetic disturbances produced by charges oscillating in the emitting source. They all travel with the same speed in vacuum. These radiations differ from one another only in having longer or shorter wavelengths. The differences in wavelength must be due to differences in the frequency of oscillation of the electric charges that produce them. Since we can measure radiation wavelengths with gratings and since we know their speed, we can calculate their frequencies. They are exceedingly high. Thus, for red light the frequency is $(3 \times 10^{10})/(7 \times 10^{-5})$, or about 4.2×10^{14} oscillations per second. For blue light, the frequency is about twice that value.

It is not easy to give a direct proof of this theory, for it is mechanically impossible to swing a charged pith ball so rapidly as to produce visible light or even infrared radiation. But we can build up the proof gradually and extend the electromagnetic spectrum in the process. In principle we can produce electromagnetic radiations of any wavelength merely by having the charge oscillate with the desired frequency. Thus if the charge oscillates once per second, the wavelength must be 186,000 miles long; if 10,000 times per second, the wavelength will be 1.86 miles long. The limitations would be our inability to find ways of oscillating the charge rapidly enough.

The Electromagnetic Spectrum　　　　Later discoveries confirmed the expectation that it is possible to produce radiations of any wavelength. Since the theory was first proposed, radio waves were discovered, as well as radar, in the region of waves longer than infrared. Likewise, x-rays, gamma rays, and cosmic rays were discovered in the region of waves shorter than ultraviolet. The complete range of these waves is called the electromagnetic spectrum (Fig. 5-32). A preliminary acquaintance with the various radiations will permit the reader to follow the discussion more easily as we proceed to show how Maxwell's theory explains all of them as well as light, and in fact how the theory led to the discovery of some of them.

One of the great triumphs of the theory was to predict the existence of long electromagnetic waves, now called radio waves. Consider an antenna with a rotating device in the middle which alternately charges the upper and lower halves of the antenna positively and negatively. According to Maxwell's theory, in this device all the conditions for electromagnetic radiation are present. As the rotor turns, it essentially

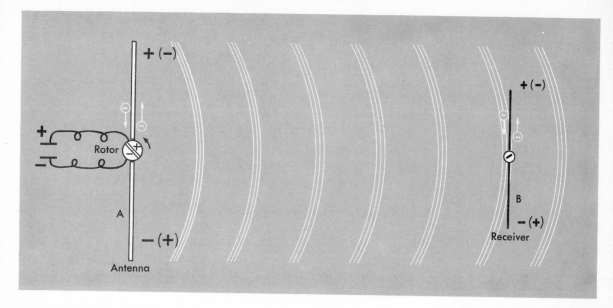

Fig. 5-31. The charges surging up and down the broadcasting antenna, A, send out waves which cause similar oscillations in receiver B.

sends electric charges up and down the antenna and this sends out electromagnetic disturbances in all directions. If there is another wire antenna at some distance from the transmitter, the electric charges in the wire will move up and down in response to the changes in the electric and magnetic fields surrounding them. A very sensitive galvanometer in the middle of the receiving wire will register a pulsating current.

Only a few years after Maxwell predicted the existence of these waves, the German physicist Heinrich Hertz (1857-1894) produced and detected them. These were the first radio waves produced. The sending antenna was later elaborated into the broadcasting transmitter and the receiver was elaborated into the radio set. The speed of the waves was measured and found to be that of light. Oscillating charges, therefore, can produce electromagnetic waves, as Maxwell predicted.

Of considerable interest is the manner in which the frequency of oscillation is controlled, for that determines the wavelength. The frequency of commercial broadcasts ranges from 550,000 cycles (550 kilocycles) to 1,500,000 cycles per second. No mechanical device can rotate that rapidly. The problem was solved by realizing that small crystals vibrate naturally at these high frequencies, much as a bell vibrates at its own frequency when struck. The frequency of vibration of a crystal depends on the elastic properties of its material and upon its size and shape, much as the frequency of a bell or a piano wire depends upon its thickness, length, and tension, as well as on the density of the material from which it is constructed. Accordingly, small crystals of quartz or similar material are ground to the right size and shape, and as these vibrate they control the frequency with which the electric charge is sent up and down the antenna. Each radio station therefore has its own crystal and emits its own wavelength or "color" (Ex. 34 and 35).

By using smaller crystals, the frequency is increased still higher

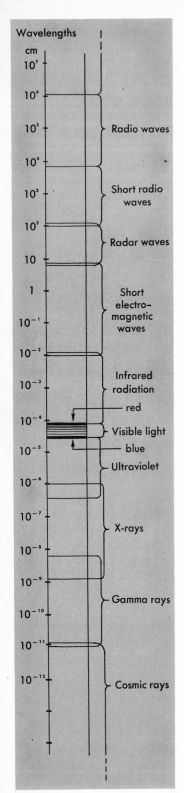

Wavelengths
cm

Radio waves

Short radio waves

Radar waves

Short electro-magnetic waves

Infrared radiation

— red

Visible light

— blue

Ultraviolet

X-rays

Gamma rays

Cosmic rays

Fig. 5-32. The electromagnetic spectrum.

until it enters the region of short-wave broadcast. With still smaller crystals, radar waves are produced which range in length from a few centimeters down to about 0.02 cm. Waves at this range begin to behave as heat rays. Beyond this point, however, crystals become too small to manipulate. It is not possible to produce still shorter waves with crystals and thus prove directly the electromagnetic nature of infrared waves and visible light.

It is possible, however, to go further by reasoning. We can calculate the size of the crystals that would emit heat waves and find that they must be the size of molecules. This leads to the idea that perhaps the heat waves are produced by vibrating atoms and molecules carrying electric charges. To obtain visible light and ultraviolet, we need particles still smaller than molecules and atoms. For further discussion of this point we must wait until after the study of molecules, atoms, and electrons within the atom. However, we can definitely say at this point that according to this theory, infrared, visible light, and ultraviolet are emitted by oscillating electric charges within the molecules and atoms of matter.

It is also possible at this point to amplify somewhat on how the theory explains the fact that each element emits its own characteristic wavelengths. Since the characteristic spectral pattern is unique for each element, the oscillating charges which emit the light must be located within the atoms of the specific element. This implies that in the atoms of each element there are certain natural frequencies of oscillation of the charges, and these frequencies are different for different elements. This situation is analogous to the fact that each bell or other vibrating source emits its own characteristic sound. Conversely, we can gain a great deal of information about the structure of the atoms that emit the light by analyzing the frequencies of the light. We shall return to this imporant topic in the study of the structure of the atom (Chap. 11).

The theory further permits us to understand radiations beyond ultraviolet light. After their discovery in 1897, x-rays were found to have wavelengths even shorter than those of ultraviolet light. The wavelengths of x-rays were measured by diffraction gratings. These gratings were not made by ruling lines on a metallic surface, for that would require many millions of lines per inch. Instead "natural gratings" were used. The happy discovery was made that atoms in a crystal are arranged in regular rows, as shown in Figure 5-33 for a crystal of rock salt or sodium chloride. These rows are just far enough apart to act as gratings for the extremely short waves of x-rays.

The method of production of x-rays provides a further and independent proof that all these radiations are produced by accelerating charges. Wilhelm Roentgen (1845-1923) discovered x-rays by sending through the empty space of a vacuum tube a beam of electric charges (electrons) at very high speed, using very high voltages. When these charges hit a target of a metallic block, they send out x-rays as shown in Figure 5-34. In terms of Maxwell's theory, it is easy to see what happens here. On hitting the target, the high-speed charges are either stopped or deflected very suddenly; that is, they suffer a tremendous *acceleration*. But acceleration of charges implies radiation, and high acceleration implies radiation of extremely short wavelengths. This can be checked, in part, because the higher the speeds of the charges—that is, the greater the rate of stopping of these charges—the shorter the wavelength of the x-rays produced. It is possible to calculate the maximum wavelength of the x-rays expected. Experimentally, they are found as calculated from Maxwell's theory.

Beyond the x-ray region of the spectrum lies the region of gamma rays, which are of still shorter wavelength. Gamma rays were discovered in the study of the breaking up of nuclei of atoms, in the process called radioactivity. Some of the gamma rays can now be produced by stopping extremely fast charges suddenly, thus demonstrating that they are very short x-rays. Gamma rays are now produced in dangerously high amounts during atom-smashing experiments, or during explosions of atomic and hydrogen bombs. Their production indicates that within the atoms there are extremely strong electric fields in which electric charges are accelerated at inconceivably high rates.

Beyond the gamma-ray region, one more region is sometimes recognized—namely, the cosmic-ray region. These mysterious rays bombard the earth from all directions and undoubtedly come from the outer cosmos of the sun and the stars. Their nature is complex and not too well understood as yet, but some (though certainly not all) of the rays are actually gamma rays of still shorter wavelength. There seems to be neither a lower limit to their wavelength nor an upper limit to their energies.

All these electromagnetic radiations are fundamentally alike in that they are produced by oscillating electric charges. All have the same speed in vacuum. They do, however, differ greatly in frequency or wavelength, ranging from the electric waves miles in length to gamma rays measuring less than 0.000,000,000,1 cm in length.

The tremendous range in frequency or wavelength between these radiations makes them different in many other respects. An obvious and important difference is in their energies. The higher the frequency of oscillation, the greater the amount of energy sent out per second, or received per second at any one point. This also implies that the very long waves contain very little power and become very weak in short distances, while short waves are still strong at greater distances. Thus, oscillating pith balls do not perceptibly affect charges a few inches away. Radio waves on the other hand are detectable several hundred miles away, while short radio waves are still detectable after traveling stupendous interstellar distances (see Chap. 14, p. 515).

The great range in wavelength also implies differences in methods of detection and other related properties. Thus radio waves are detected by ordinary sets, short waves by differently designed sets, and radar by special equipment. Heat rays ignore the radio set but affect the molecules of ordinary matter, and light waves affect the optic nerve. This, incidentally, explains why only radiation within a certain range is visible while outside this range it is invisible. The eye, or rather the molecules of the visual purple in the retina, respond only to certain wavelengths much as a radio set has a limit of frequency response. On the other hand, ultraviolet, while invisible, causes skin burns as it is absorbed by

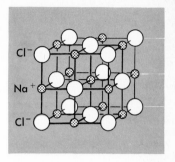

Fig. 5-33. Crystal of rock salt, NaCl. The rows of atoms (Na⁺ and Cl⁻ ions) are of the order of an x-ray wavelength apart. They act as natural gratings for x-rays.

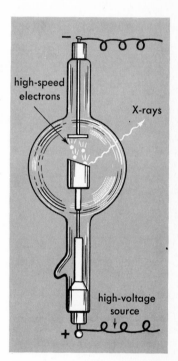

Fig. 5-34. X-rays are generated by the very sudden stopping of moving charges (electrons).

the molecules of certain substances under the skin. Radiations from the near infrared region, through the visible and down to the x-ray region, affect the photographic plate. The grains of silver chloride or bromide act like receiving sets and absorb the radiation, becoming black metallic silver in the process. This is an example of a chemical reaction produced by light. We shall return to this topic later.

One interesting property of the radiations is their penetrability. Radio waves go through the air but not through metals. Infrared radiation goes through a dry atmosphere but not through water vapor. Visible light goes through glass, but ultraviolet does not. On the other hand, x-rays go through any kind of matter, but with some absorbtion. Any given material—depending on its structure—absorbs, reflects, or transmits a given radiation selectively. The material acts in a sense like a receiving set, which can absorb or reflect certain wavelengths depending on its structure and how it is "tuned."

Thus, what started as a relatively simple inquiry into the nature of light and color resulted, in terms of Maxwell's theory, in the discovery of a whole world of radiations of diverse types and wavelengths. Radiation is transversing interstellar space in all directions and is produced by electric charges within the atoms in the stars or in interstellar space. The earth is bathed in a flood of radiation—not only sunlight, but also heat rays, ultraviolet, and possibly all the other types of radiation. Only recently radio waves from the sun and the stars have been detected (Chap. 14). Moreover, many of these radiations are produced from natural causes on the earth or under controlled conditions in the laboratory. Maxwell's theory provides a very good picture of the nature of these radiations and permits us to understand the phenomena associated with them. Further, with the aid of the theory we can explore hitherto unknown aspects of nature and delve into the intimate structure of matter and, through it, into the structure of the stars and the stellar universe.

5. THE PARTICLE THEORY OF LIGHT

If the preceding section had been written at the beginning of this century, it would have ended with some sweeping statement to the effect that, beyond the slightest doubt, light is a wave phenomenon. All the phenomena of light led inevitably to the wave theory. Wavelengths were measured with high precision, not only for light but for all the electromagnetic radiations. All these radiations exhibit diffraction and interference and thus have properties which *cannot be conceived* of in any other way than as waves. Moreover, all the vast number of phenomena could and still can be interpreted as waves by Maxwell's theory. There is no question that light has wave properties.

There was *one* phenomenon, however, observed in 1883, that the theory was not capable of explaining. This was the now famous photoelectric effect. Most physicists considered the phenomenon an interesting oddity, an intriguing and stubborn puzzle. Yet the comfortable feeling prevailed that some one would explain it someday in terms of the wave theory.

With the turn of the century, however, new phenomena were discovered by more powerful tools of research which delved into the interior of the atom. When these phenomena were subjected to mathematical analysis, they led just as inevitably to the conclusion that light has particle properties. Let us strip this reasoning of its formidable mathematical complexity and see what it means in simple pictorial terms.

The photoelectric effect is rather easy to observe and describe. It is the principle of the "electric eye"—that interesting device which opens doors, turns on the faucet, or counts cars passing a given point. In this device a beam of light acts as a switch that turns the current on or off.

In an evacuated glass vessel is a block of sodium and the lower part of which is connected to the negative end of a battery (Fig. 5-35). Above the sodium block is a sealed copper plate which is connected to the positive end of the battery. No current flows, of course, because there is a gap in the circuit and hence the galvanometer shows no deflection. When light shines on the sodium block, a current instantly flows through the galvanometer. Apparently, the gap becomes a conductor, and the negative charges from the sodium plate flow through the gap, thus completing the circuit. This current can be used to operate a counter, a motor, or an electromagnet, and thus to open or close a door, or do anything else we desire.

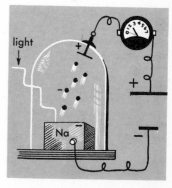

Fig. 5-35. The photoelectric effect. Light ejects electrons from the surface of metallic sodium, Na.

Let us now inquire further into what happens in the gap and on the surface of the sodium block. The light shining on the block knocks off some of the negative charges from the sodium surface; these charges are then repelled by the negative sodium surface and are attracted by the positive copper plate. It is now known that these negative charges are electrons, and ways have been discovered of measuring their size, mass, and speed (see Chap. 11). Therefore, light is capable of knocking electrons from a metal surface. At first sight, this appears easy to understand. Light waves have energy and can knock off the electrons, much as water waves rock a boat or any other object floating on the surface.

The phenomenon becomes interesting and puzzling when we try to visualize in detail how the light waves knock off the electrons, and to calculate the energy the waves give to the electrons. Knowing that the wavelength of violet light is about 4000 Angstrom units (0.00004 cm), we can calculate the energy per wave. The size of the electron is also known. It must be much smaller than the atom which itself is only 1 or 2 Angstroms in diameter. These facts considered together are difficult to understand. An electron must wait several months before it can gather enough energy to be ejected and to gain the speed it attains (which can be measured as it is moving up the gap). But this apparently contradicts the fact that the current appears at the instant the light is turned on, which means that electrons get the energy instantaneously or almost instantaneously.

There is, then, something wrong with this explanation for it contradicts the phenomena. Since there is nothing wrong with either the logic or the measurements discussed above, there must be something wrong with the idea that light consists of waves with its energy thinly spread out. This experiment forces the conclusion that the energy of light is *concentrated in packages.* When this package meets an electron, the electron absorbs the energy of the package in a single collision and is knocked off. Thus we are led to the idea that light consists of a stream of tiny bullets, called *photons,* each having a definite amount of energy.

The idea is further strengthened by additional experiments. If we shine violet light on sodium, a certain number of electrons come off with a certain speed. If we now increase the brightness of the violet light, more electrons come off; however, their speed is no greater than before. Regardless of the brightness, as long as the light remains violet the speed of the photoelectrons does not increase. This must mean that each package of violet light has so much energy, which it gives to the electron it happens to meet. Brighter light merely means more packages of light (more photons), and hence more electrons knocked off, but the amount of energy per package is still the same as before.

An analogy might help illustrate the idea. Suppose a storm rocks a certain number of boats in a harbor. What would we say if the storm increased in violence and we observed no increase in the amount of rocking but only an increase in the *number* of boats rocked. We would not be able to understand it, of course. But we could understand it if the "storm" was not really a storm on the surface of the water, but consisted of a spray of small torpedoes. The greater the "storm"— that is, the greater the number of torpedoes—the greater the number of boats rocked. Yet each boat would not be rocked more violently than before. This is analogous to what happens with photoelectrons. It is this reasoning that leads to the conclusion that light consists of particles.

We can, however, increase the speed of the photoelectrons by shining ultraviolet light rather than violet. We now find a still more interesting relation. The shorter the wavelength of the light used, the greater the speed of the ejected photoelectrons. We can calculate the energy required to remove the electrons from the sodium surface, and we can measure the energy they still have after being ejected. The latter is obtained by measuring the speed of the electrons in the gap. Comparing the total energy received by the electron with the wavelength of the light shining on it, we find them to be inversely related. The shorter the wavelength, the greater the energy received by the photoelectrons. This must mean the shorter the wavelength of light or the greater its frequency, the greater the amount of energy per photon package.

We can now summarize the argument and present the *photon* theory of light. Light and the other electromagnetic radiations consist of photons or packages of electromagnetic energy. The energy of each photon is proportional to the frequency or inversely proportional to the wavelength. Mathematically,

$$E = h \cdot f$$

and since

$$f = \frac{c}{\lambda}$$

$$E = \frac{h \cdot c}{\lambda}$$

where h is a constant, and c is the velocity of light. Thus the electromagnetic radiations range enormously in the amount of energy their photons contain. Photons of blue light have about twice the energy of photons of red light, since blue light has about twice the frequency of red light. Photons of x-rays and gamma rays have tremendous energies. This explains why these photons can penetrate concrete walls, or go through the human flesh tearing up the cells in the process. On the other hand the photons of heat rays have very little energy and those of radio waves much less.

The dependence of the energy of the photon on the wavelength is confirmed in still another way. On shining red light on sodium no photoelectrons are ejected, no matter how intense the red light. Apparently the photons of red light do not have enough energy, individually, to knock off an electron from the surface of metallic sodium. Blue light on the other hand, even if weak, readily ejects the electrons, giving them considerable speed; ultraviolet light not only ejects them, but gives them a higher speed than blue light.

The photon theory explains not only the photoelectric phenomenon, but many other phenomena as well. In fact the theory was proposed in 1900 by Max Planck (1858-1947) to explain how the energy emitted by a hot source is distributed among the various wavelengths. We shall not discuss that phenomenon, except to mention that Planck could explain the observed distribution only if he assumed that light comes in packages or *quanta*. Soon afterwards, Niels Bohr (1885———) used the theory to explain how the light is emitted by the atoms of the various elements and how the analysis of the light yields information about the structure of the atom. We shall take up this important subject in the study of atomic structure. But we can state at this point that, as in the case of the photoelectric effect, we cannot explain these phenomena without postulating that light consists of *packages* of photons.

Thus we are in the embarrassing position of having two contradictory theories of light—one based on waves, the other on particles. However, these theories complement one another. There is a group of phenomena, such as interference and diffraction, that can be explained only by the wave theory. There is another group of phenomena, such as the photoelectric effect, that can be explained only by the particle theory. In addition, there is a group of phenomena that can be explained by either theory. Moreover, all the known phenomena of light can be explained by either one theory or the other. In general, for radiations of very high energies, the particle properties are more pronounced; while for radiations of low energies (long wavelengths), the wave properties are more prominent. However, one and the same radiation, say yellow light, has *both* wave and particle properties.

It is not that we cannot explain the phenomena, but rather that we need two theories to do so, and these theories are contradictory. We cannot visualize how one and the same thing can be both a wave and a particle at the same time.

One answer to the problem is to construct a mathematical theory that combines the two aspects and to use it to explain any phenomenon. This has been done in a theory called *wave mechanics*. Physicists are using it continually and freely and always get the right results. In fact most of them get used to the idea of the dual nature of light and are not in the least unhappy about it. They regard it as a fundamental fact of nature, to be accepted even if not visualized.

We might admit, of course, that we have failed to develop a consistent theory of light. This, however, does not dispose of the difficulty. Analyzing the situation more deeply we realize that such a failure is essentially our inability to construct a *mechanical* picture of light. Perhaps light is a phenomenon that is not mechanical and cannot be understood in mechanical terms. Perhaps our idea of "explanation" needs revising. "Explanation," as we know it, is derived from everyday experience—from observations of moving baseballs or water waves. Do we have a right to expect electromagnetic radiations to behave as they do? Here, and in other phenomena within the atom, we are dealing with a realm of reality far removed from the world of ordinary experience. We might mention in this connection that electrons, which until recently have been considered as typical particles, show wave properties. In fact, the operation of the electron microscope depends upon the "wave" properties of the electrons. The phenomena from this realm of reality relentlessly point to the conclusion that we must revise our concepts of ordinary experience if we are to understand the world of atoms and electrons. We shall pursue this problem a little further in a later section, but now may regain some comfort if we restate that all the phenomena of light can be understood by using appropriately the two theories.

NOTES AND EXERCISES

1. The process of seeing involves a source of light, the light itself and the eye. Self-luminous bodies are seen as the light passes directly from the source to the eye. The colors the source emits are the same colors contained in the light and received by the eye. What conditions are necessary before a person can see blue color by looking directly at a source? What happens when a color-blind person, blind to blue, looks at a source of light emitting pure blue light?

2. Objects that do not emit light are visible by reflection. Colored objects absorb some colors and reflect others. What is white light? What is a white object? What is a red object? What is a black object?

3. Certain objects appear colored when white light passes through them. What happens when a piece of glass appears red on looking through it? What colors does it absorb and what colors does it transmit? What is an opaque object? What is a "colorless" object? If you look at a blue source through red glass, what will you see? Explain.

4. We glibly say that light travels in straight lines. How would you prove that? It will not do to apply a ruler to the path, because we decide that the straight edge is straight by sighting it—that is, by using light. This merely proves that light travels *the way light travels*. Can you do it in some other way? (See also Ref. 5.8.)

5. An electric light throws 5 candles per sq in. when it is 2 ft from the surface of a table. What is the brightness on the surface of the table if the light is removed to 8 ft?

6. The nearest star is roughly 300,000 times further than the sun. How bright would the sun appear compared to its present apparent brightness, if it were at the distance of the nearest star?

7. *Mirrors.* It is an everyday fact that in plane mirrors, objects appear identical to the real objects and just as far back of the mirror as the objects are in front (Fig. 5-36). This follows from the fact that light travels in straight lines and that the angle of incidence is equal to the angle of reflection. Thus the ray from the head of the arrow A is reflected at M_1 and follows the path AME. The eye sees the point at A' owing to the psychological fact that we "see" objects in the direction from which light comes. Similarly, for the tail C, the image appears at C'. For all intermediate points of the object, there corresponds a point on the image. It follows from the geometry of these lines that any point A of the arrow will be as far in front of the mirror as the corresponding point A' of the image appears behind the mirror.

In curved mirrors the same laws apply, but owing to the fact that the reflecting surface is curved, the effects are different (Fig. 5-37). Thus for concave mirrors, rays from a point of the object meet the surface at different angles. However, at every point, the angle of incidence is equal to the angle of reflection. Therefore, on reflection the rays are not parallel but meet at a point. This gives an inverted image, which is real; that is, the light rays actually focus and produce an image there.

By tracing parallel rays from the sun (or a star) can you show why they come into focus on reflection from a curved mirror?

For a convex mirror, the rays originating from a given point of the source meet the surface again at different angles but are diverging on reflection (Fig. 5-38). They do not meet at a point. However, they *appear* to come from a point behind the mirror, and hence a virtual image is observed by the eye. Is the image formed by a convex mirror smaller or larger than the object?

8. For a fish or a swimmer under water, all the world above the surface of the water appears contained in a cone of 67 degrees (Fig. 5-39). Objects on the horizon appear along the line OA or OB. Similarly, the light entering the eye is refracted by the lens of the eye, so that we can see "with the corner of our eye" objects directly to our right or left, even though we are looking straight forward. They are of course distorted. In looking straight ahead, how much of the total space can we see?

9. At sunset the sun is still visible even though it is below the horizon. Can you explain?

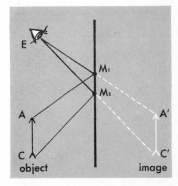

Fig. 5-36. Virtual image produced by plane mirror.

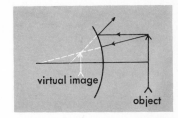

Fig. 5-37. Real image produced by a concave mirror.

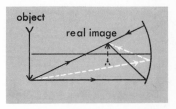

Fig. 5-38. Virtual image produced by a convex mirror.

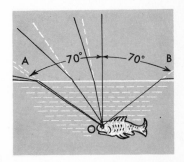

Fig. 5-39. The world of a fish, above the surface, is contained in a cone less than 70 degrees.

10. If light consists of particles and refraction is due to attraction of the water particles for the particles of light, explain why this should imply a speeding up of the light particles in water. Why should the light particles slow down on emerging from water into the air? Which particles should bend more, those of blue light or those of red?

11. If light consists of waves, why should their direction bend on entering the water from the air? If the speed is greater in water than in air, which way should they bend? If the speed is less in water than in air, which way should they bend? If blue light waves bend more than red, which of these moves faster in water?

12. How many wavelengths of red light are there in a yard? What is the wavelength of blue light? How does it compare with that of red light?

13. (a) An oarsman in a stationary boat produces some ripples by striking the water with his oar. You are in a rowboat, also standing still and some distance away, observing the ripples passing by. What is meant by the wavelength of the ripples and how can you measure it? What is meant by the frequency of the ripples and in what *two* ways can you measure it? In what *two* ways can you determine the speed of the waves? If the oarsman keeps up the waves by striking at regular intervals, does he have to strike once in a period? Explain.

(b) The height of the waves is called the *amplitude* and is a measure of the energy the waves contain. It is clear that the amplitude depends on how hard the oarsman strikes and how frequently. It also depends on the distance from the source. Can you explain why the amplitude should drop as you go further out from the source, even if there were no friction? What will be the height of the waves at three times the distance from the source?

14. In sound, amplitude corresponds to loudness; in light, it corresponds to brightness. However, in general both sound and light are sent out in three dimensions. How loud would a sound appear at twice the distance from the source? How bright would a light appear at three times the distance from the source?

15. The inverse square law must not lead us to the misconception that light (or sound) always weakens as the square of the distance. The law holds only if light is emitted in all directions from the source, which is a point, or may be considered as a point. This is obvious if we analyze the argument for the derivation. By using various shapes of reflecting surfaces, we can send light in other than all directions, and we get different relationships. For example, automobile headlights send out an essentially parallel beam. If the beam were exactly parallel (an impossible thing to do since a physical source has to be larger than a point) and there were no absorption and scattering in the path, the beam would be just as strong a million miles away. How do you suppose a reflection from the moon was obtained (1951) using a beam of radar?

16. Why is it that the law of reflection does not help us decide whether light is like bullets or like waves?

17. Can you explain why a stick appears broken if half immersed in water? Trace the path of light beams from the various parts of the stick through the water and the air to the eye.

18. In a mirage, what appears as a lake is really the sky. Consider the various layers of air as so many plates of glass of different refractive index and trace the path of rays from the sky to the air near the ground and to the eye.

19. Explain that if light were composed of particles and water attracted them, the particles would be accelerated and also bent in their course.

20. If light is waves, and water slows them down, what is the ratio of the wavelength in air to that in water? How does the ratio of the wavelength compare with the ratio of the speeds in the two media? How does this ratio compare to the index of refraction?

21. Can you explain how a diamond produces brilliant colors? The index of refraction of diamond is 2.4173, one of the highest for transparent substances.

22. The speed of yellow light in air is 186,000 miles per sec. What is the speed of yellow light in water ($n = 1.33$)? What is the speed of yellow light in diamond?

23. The index of refraction of red light in water is 1.45, that of violet, 1.22. Calculate the speed of red and violet light in water.

24. Members of the Florentine Academy accurately measured the speed of sound in air as follows: Two groups of experimenters were stationed at two distant mountain tops. The first group would fire a gun, and the other group would fire a second gun the instant they heard the first shot. The first group recorded the time between the firing of the first gun and the *hearing* of the second shot. Knowing the double distance between the mountaintops, the speed of sound was obtained as 1100 ft per sec at the prevailing temperatures. How far away did lightning strike if the thunder is heard 3 sec after the flash?

25. The time lag in the eclipse of Io, the satellite of Jupiter, can be used to measure the distance of the sun from the earth. We know, from laboratory measurements, the speed of light to be 186,000 miles per sec. The eclipse of Io is observed about 1000 sec later, when the earth is opposite the sun from Jupiter, than it would if the earth were between the sun and Jupiter. Calculate the diameter of the orbit of the earth and the distance from the earth to the sun.

26. We know that all colors travel in vacuum with exactly the same speed from the following astronomical observations. In an eclipse of the sun, the moon cuts off all colors at the same time and after totality, it readmits them at the same time. If, for example, the blue traveled faster than the red, then the sun would appear blue at first and not white until all the colors had reached us. The effect would be greater for Io, which is roughly 500,000,000 miles from the earth. We observe stars that eclipse one another many light years away. If one color traveled even 1 millionth of 1 percent faster than the others, it would reach us hours or even days before the other colors. Yet in all these eclipses all the colors come to us at the same time. Assume that an eclipsing star is 186 light years away, and that red light is 1 percent slower than blue, calculate by how much the red would lag behind the blue.

27. Calculate the wavelength of yellow light from the following experiment. The glass wedge is 30 cm long. The cellophane comes from a roll, 2 cm of which contains 600 turns. Calculate the thickness of the cellophane. By actual count, we find 80 bands in 2 cm of the glass wedge. Calculate the distance between the bands which is the distance D in Figure 5-21. Now calculate the wavelength of yellow light.

28. Knowing the wavelength of red light (about 7×10^{-5} cm), estimate the thickness of a soap bubble at the part at which it has a red color.

29. The spectrum formed by a prism is the reverse of the spectrum formed by a grating. Why is the red deviated less than the blue in the prism spectrum? Why is the red deviated more than the blue in the grating spectrum?

30. Both sound and light are wave phenomena, though of a different type. Why can we hear a person talking around corners but cannot see him? What is the essential difference in the two waves for this problem? Could we "see" him around a corner if he emitted radio waves? Explain.

31. For display or advertising purposes black light is used. What is this particular "black" light and how does it work?

32. Can a photograph be taken in a room which is completely dark, so far as the eye can see? Explain.

33. How does Maxwell's theory explain the propagation of light through empty space? Should the speed of light be less or more in a material medium than in empty space?

34. A radio station broadcasts at 750 kc. What is the wavelength of the station? What is the wavelength of a short-wave transmitter broadcasting at 7.5 meg? How does the wavelength of this transmitter compare with the above mentioned radio station?

35. Why do we need radar waves to detect airplanes rather than ordinary short waves?

36. If the wavelength of certain x-rays is about 1/1000 of the wavelength of blue light, and they are diffracted by a crystal of salt, what can you say about the distance between sodium and chlorine atoms in the crystal.

37. If a beam of gamma rays has a wavelength of 0.000,000,000,1 cm, what is the frequency?

38. The first World's Fair was held in Chicago in 1893. In 1933 the light from the star Arcturus was focused on an "electric eye" by the telescope at Yerkes observatory and opened officially the second World's Fair in Chicago. Why do you suppose Arcturus was selected?

39. Which has a greater frequency, a photon of red light or a photon of blue light? A photon of x-rays or a photon of γ rays? Which would be more destructive to living cells?

40. Compare the wave and particle properties of the various radiations. What properties are more pronounced in radio waves? What properties are more pronounced in x-rays?

41. According to Einstein's theory of relativity, the mass of an object in motion increases according to the equation

$$M_v = \frac{M_0}{\sqrt{1 - \dfrac{v^2}{c^2}}}$$

where M_v is the mass at the velocity v, M_0 is the mass at rest, and c is the velocity of light. What will be the mass of a body if it moves with the speed of light (that is, if $v = c$)? What force is necessary to be accelerated to the speed of light? Is it possible to accelerate it beyond the speed of light?

6

MATTER AND ITS ULTIMATE STRUCTURE

1. CORPUSCULARITY AND STRUCTURE OF MATTER

To the average person the material things that make up the world appear as distinct objects and as compact units. A piece of steel, a glass of water, or even a sample of air, appear as perfectly smooth, as perfectly continuous. But to a scientist, this appearance is deceptive. He imagines these objects as made up of an immense number of very small particles, separated from each other by empty spaces, and constantly moving or quivering. To him, not only the thin air, and the fluid ocean, but even the "solid" chairs upon which we are confidently sitting are assemblages of moving particles. The steel cable that holds up an elevator at the tenth floor is not perfectly solid. It is more like a rope of sand, or like rows of angry bees, each distinct from the other, moving back and forth in all directions in the spaces between them, and colliding with one another. True, there are attractive forces between them but these forces are not material. This is an admittedly strange idea.

The man on the street has heard, of course, of molecules, and accepts the idea without thinking much about it. He glibly says that all matter is made up of molecules. He even goes on to say that molecules consist of smaller particles, the atoms, and that the atoms are made of still smaller particles, the protons, the neutrons, and the electrons. In short he accepts the idea that matter is granular in character and that it has structure. However, he accepts these ideas on faith, on the authority of the scientists. In this and subsequent chapters we propose to recite the story from the beginning, to examine the evidence, and to show how the scientists came to these ideas. We begin by analyzing the concept "matter."

Matter is by far the most obvious and tangible reality in the world. It is also the most fundamental. The world contains innumerable objects such as chairs, stones, rivers, icebergs, trees, animals, mountains, and stars. All these objects contain matter, or rather are made of matter. In fact these objects are considered "real" *because* they are made of matter. Care must be taken, however, not to confuse *reality* with *materiality*. We have seen that gravity, energy, electricity, magnetism, and light are also real, though not material in the ordinary sense of the word (void, mind, etc., are also real. See Ex. 1).

Yet in a sense, matter is more fundamental than these other realities. Gravity is exhibited by matter; it is a property of matter. Energy, in the ordinary sense, is either the kinetic energy possessed by moving bodies or the potential energy possessed by bodies in a field of force, such as lifted weights. Electric charges are inseparably connected with matter, and electric or magnetic fields depend upon charges for their existence or generation. Light is emitted by material objects such as lamps or stars, or at least by the electric charges in these bodies. In all these phenomena it is necessary to have matter somewhere. Matter is the underlying substratum, the underlying reality, ultimately responsible for these phenomena. In a sense all these phenomena are properties or manifestations of matter.

Forms of Matter

A clearer idea of the meaning of *matter* may be obtained from a familiar example. A carpenter having lumber at his disposal may make a chair, a table, or a shelf. These objects are different in having different shapes. What is common to these objects is the *wood,* the matter of these objects. If the carpenter cuts down a table and makes it into a chair, the shape alters and he gets a different object. But the wood, the matter, remains the same. It persists, as the underlying substratum. Further, a metalsmith may make a chair or a table from aluminum or iron. The wood, the aluminum, and the iron are the matter of these objects, respectively.

These examples, and a little reflection, bring out the significant point that matter exists (and comes to our attention) in an immense variety of forms. Wood is one form, iron is another, sugar is a third kind, and so on. Each of these forms is a distinct *kind of material.* Clearly, then, the forms of matter should not be confused with the shape of objects.

At this point we might ask why all these diverse forms of existence are considered *matter*. For the implication is that all the objects are made of the same fundamental "stuff." There are several good reasons for considering the various forms as matter. All objects, regardless of what they are made, have certain properties in common. They all occupy space, or as the philosophers prefer it, they have extension. All material objects have the fundamental property of inertia or resistance to acceleration, as we have seen earlier. All material objects have the equally fundamental property of attracting one another by the force called "gravity." The latter means that all objects on the earth have weight. Also, while the various forms of matter undergo many changes, as we shall presently see, the total amount of matter—as measured either by the weight or by the inertia—is constant. Further, the very fact that such a wide variety of distinct forms exist and that these forms are constantly transformed into one another confirms the view that matter is fundamenally a single entity, even though it exists in a variety of forms.

We recognize the various forms of matter by their properties and we distinguish them from one another by the differences in their properties. By *properties* of materials we simply mean the way they affect our senses or our instruments, and also by the way they behave under certain conditions or toward other materials. Thus, we recognize charcoal by its black color and its ability to burn in air; sugar by its white color, its sweetness, and its solubility in water. We distinguish aluminum from iron by its lightness, its low strength to bending forces, and its resistance to rusting. For these reasons these properties are called *characteristic properties.*

Properties are usually classified as *physical, chemical,* and *physiological.* Among the physical properties are color, density, solubility in water or in other media, melting point, boiling point, hardness, electrical conductivity, and many others. Chemical properties are such behavior as ability to burn in air, to char on heating, and in general to react (or *fail* to react) with other substances. Physiological properties are such properties as odor, taste, ability to act as a medicinal or a poison. The exact classification is not too important, at present, except to bring out the significant point that many and diverse properties may be used to identify a kind of matter and to distinguish it from all other kinds. Many of the properties can be measured with high precision. Each kind of material has but one set of properties. It differs from all other kinds in at least one property.

We shall single out *density* as an example of a property and define it more precisely. Density is a measure of "lightness" or "heaviness" of materials. It is a measure of the compactness of matter. More precisely, density is the amount of matter per unit volume, that is,

$$\text{density} = \frac{\text{mass}}{\text{volume}}$$

or in symbols

$$D = \frac{m}{V}$$

Density can be measured with high precision. Thus the density of the "light" aluminum is 2.702 grams per cubic centimeter, and that of the "heavy" lead is 11.3437 grams per cubic centimeter. The densities of water, ice, iron, mercury, and gold are 1.000, 0.9168, 7.12, 13.5951, and 19.3 grams per cubic centimeter, respectively. Liquids and solids range in density from a fraction of a gram per *cubic centimeter* for such substances as cork to 22.48 grams per *cubic centimeter* for osmium, the densest substance known. Gases, on the other hand, are about 1000 times lighter under ordinary conditions—their densities being of the order of a few grams per 1000 *cubic centimeters*. Each substance has its own precise density. The same thing is true of the other properties.

Important in this connection is the concept of "pure substance" and its distinction from a *mixture* of substances. Ordinary inspection reveals that a piece of granite, a block of concrete, or a cake is not uniform throughout, but consists of several kinds of matter. We see visibly that granite consists of black particles of mica, reddish particles of feldspar, and white particles of quartz. The color of granite, therefore, is not definite but depends on the proportions of the black, reddish, and white particles. Thus we find red granites and blue granites. Further, the density and all the other properties of granite depend on the proportions of these particles.

On the other hand, all quartz particles appear exactly alike, and always show the same color, density, hardness, and all the other properties. Similarly, in a sample of cane sugar, all the grains show the same properties. The fact that a sample of sugar may be dirty or colored does not invalidate the idea of pure substance but rather adds clarity to it. For the sugar can be purified and the dirt and the color removed, resulting in pure cane sugar with a definite set of properties. Every grain of every sample of purified sugar has the same density, solubility, and all the other properties as every other grain. Similarly, every speck of pure quartz has the same set of properties as any other speck. By careful purification and extensive study over half a million pure substances have been identified as distinct forms of matter. Each substance has its own set of properties, different from that of all other substances.

The existence of mixtures can be disposed of rather easily. A mixture is simply an aggregate of pure substances. The constituent substances retain their characteristic properties and confer their properties upon the resulting material. Thus a mixture of sand and sugar tastes sweet, its sweetness being in proportion to the percentage of sugar. Furthermore, a mixture of sand or sugar still has two sets of properties, even if ground fine enough to appear perfectly uniform under a microscope. If this aggregate is put in water, a part of it, the sugar, will dissolve and a part of it, the sand, will settle to the bottom. Thus, this analysis shows that every material object is either a pure substance or is a mixture of two or more pure substances.

Physical and Chemical Changes

Next to their immense diversity, the most important fact about materials is that they are constantly changing. We may note, but dismiss as rather trivial, such superficial changes as tearing a piece of paper, crushing a rock, or mixing the materials for a cake. For in these changes the characteristic properties remain the same as before. Also rather superficial are such changes as heating a substance or putting pressure on a gas. It is true that these changes alter the precise properties somewhat. Obviously, a gas has a greater density under high pressure than at low pressure. A copper wire has greater electrical resistance when hot than when cold. But these changes are gradual and do not alter the substance. To be perfectly clear, we say that the properties of a given substance are definite only at specified external conditions. When the properties alter due to changes in the external conditions, we still call it *the same substance* (Ex. 2).

Somewhat more drastic are changes such as melting, boiling, and dissolving of one substance into another, and the opposite changes of freezing, condensing, or coming out of solution. In these processes some properties change markedly. Solid ice, on melting, becomes water which is mobile and liquid; and water, on boiling, becomes steam, which is an invisible gas. However, we do not consider these changes as changes in substance. Though we call them ice, water, and steam, respectively, we still consider them as solid, liquid, and gaseous forms of the same substance. In this we are justified for several reasons. It is the rule that all solid substances melt on heating and all liquids boil. (The exceptions are those substances that decompose on heating, before melting, or boiling.) Further, these processes are reversed on cooling, so that at any temperature and set of conditions the same properties reappear, and are definite. Moreover, many of the properties, particularly the chemical properties, remain the same or essentially the same, in all these changes. For similar reasons, dissolving sugar in water is not considered a change in substance, for the sugar still tastes sweet in solution, and is recovered unchanged on evaporation of the water. All these changes are called *physical changes*.

Far more drastic and thoroughgoing are the transformations called *chemical changes*. In these, substances are transformed into other substances. Thus after a piece of wood burns, nothing characteristic of the wood remains. The ashes and the gases produced are substances that in no way resemble wood. When sugar is charred, it changes into charcoal and water. The sugar *disappears* as a substance. Its sweetness, its color, its solubility, and all its other properties are no longer there. In place of the sugar two other substances appear—the black charcoal and the liquid water. These substances are different from sugar and from each other in all their properties. They are different substances. Even more remarkable are the changes going on in life processes. The egg changes into the tissues of a chick, and the milk becomes the tissue of the eye or the muscle of a baby.

Thus the significant fact is that matter exists in a multitude of forms and that these forms are constantly being transformed into one another. Early in the history of thought, consideration of these facts led to the idea that *matter must consist of particles*. The problem of the nature of matter was first raised by that remarkable group of thinkers, the philosophers of the sixth and fifth centuries, B.C. in ancient Greece. To them the immense multiplicity of forms and their constant inter-transformations had a bearing on the structure of matter. For if matter

Atomicity of Matter

is fundamentally one, if it is the ultimate *"stuff,"* how can this multiplicity and these changes be accounted for? What is the nature of matter and what is its structure? Is matter continuous like a geometric solid, infinitely divisible; or is it discontinuous, like a crate of oranges, each discrete and separate from the others, and of definite size?

Let us take a specific instance, and restate the question. Is a piece of copper wire like a mathematical line or is it like a string of beads? If it is like a mathematical line, then (in principle) it can be divided into shorter and shorter pieces, with the process never ending. If, on the other hand, it is like a string of beads it can be cut into shorter and shorter strings *only* to the point of the last bead. For *we cannot think of* a "string of beads" of less than one bead. The question then is, which of these is the structure of the copper wire?

We are indebted to Democritus (485-425 B.C.), more than to any other person, for the answers to these questions. By analyzing the phenomena philosophically he came to the conclusion that matter must be corpuscular in character. He said that the multiplicity and the changes in matter are understandable only on the assumption that all materials are made of very small particles of definite size. He called these particles "atoms," meaning that they "cannot be cut." His meaning of the word must not be confused with the same word as used today with special meaning for one kind of particle—the *atoms* of the elements. His meaning, in a sense, would refer to any kind of ultimate particles (Ex. 11).

According to Democritus, the "atoms" of all materials are alike in substance; that is, they are made of the same "stuff," having the same density, consistency, hardness, and all other properties. But they do differ in size, shape, motions, and positions or arrangement among themselves. In a simple substance the atoms are alike in all respects, and for that reason a sample exhibits the same properties throughout. In a different substance the atoms are of different size or of different shape, or have different motions or different arrangements and therefore will exhibit different properties from the first substance. According to the Democritan view, a change of one substance into another is really not a change in substance, but a change in the arrangement or in the motions of the atoms. The atoms themselves are actually the same. Thus all material change is in a sense superficial; it is only apparent. According to his idea, all the changes can be understood in terms of *loco*motion, which is change of position of particles (see Chap. 3).

Democritus gave a powerful but difficult philosophic argument for the existence of atoms. (The interested reader is referred to Ex. 8.) His followers gave additional arguments, one of the simplest to understand—using density—being given by Epicurus. He reasoned that if lead and wood are both matter—that is, if both are made of the same "stuff," with the same density—why then is wood lighter than lead? This can only mean that there are empty spaces in the wood, and these spaces separate the pieces of matter from each other. In other words, matter is *divided* in the wood. But lead itself must contain empty spaces since it is lighter than gold. The argument can be extended to all the substances (except the one which is densest) and supports the view

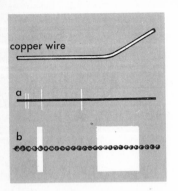

Fig. 6-1. Continuity versus discontinuity. Is a copper wire infinitely divisible like a mathematical line (a), or is it corpuscular like a string of beads (b)?

copper wire

a

b

Fig. 6-2. Democritus. The world consists of atoms and void. *(The Bettmann Archive.)*

that all matter consists of pieces. In a modern setting, the fact that water expands 1750 times on changing into steam argues that, in steam at least, matter is divided, and the pieces of matter are separated from one another by large spaces.

There were many similar arguments, some strong, others weak, but all supporting the basic idea that matter consists of particles. A whole school of philosophy was founded on this idea and many of the thinkers of antiquity accepted it. Of particular interest is the Roman poet Lucretius who wrote a long poem, entitled "On the Nature of Things," in which he expounded the theory in great detail (Ref. 6.4). Throughout the centuries up to modern times thinkers accepted the atoms and used them in their thinking. From the beginning of the nineteenth century onward, however, the idea received powerful experimental support and development. Many more arguments were added, based on extensive experiments, delicate measurements, and the powerful mathematical reasoning of modern science. The basic idea, however, comes from Democritus: that matter and the nature of the world is to be understood in terms of arrangements and rearrangements of finite particles of matter—*the idea that matter has structure.*

Today we recognize several kinds of submicroscopic particles of different sizes and orders of complexity. The "atoms" of Democritus are now differentiated into molecules, atoms, ions, nuclei, protons, neutrons, electrons, mesons, and even particles of light and energy. Each of these kinds of particles represents a stage in the organization of matter. The smaller particles group themselves into larger packages, which are in turn the units or "atoms" of the next stage. Thus neutrons, protons, and mesons group themselves into nuclei and these, together with electrons, form the larger units—the atoms of the elements. The atoms in turn combine to form the molecules of substances. The molecules then combine to form crystals of solids or droplets of liquids and these, in turn, form the objects of ordinary experience.

The idea of structure and units of organization can be extended into the visible world and the very large. In the material structure of the biological world, molecules combine to form giant supermolecules of proteins and viruses. A complex of molecules forms a living cell, which is a living *unit;* cells form tissues and tissues form an individual, such as a man or a bird. These units then form groups—families, towns, nations, the whole human race, the whole biological world. Returning to the inorganic world, groups of molecules form crystals of minerals. These, in turn, form rocks and rocks form mountains and continents. This group of units forms a single planet, the earth. Then groups of planets form solar systems, and these form systems of stars. The systems of stars form galaxies, the galaxies form supergalaxies, and the entirety forms the universe. From the smallest to the largest the Democritan idea of structure and units of structure pervade. We are all Democritans in our thinking.

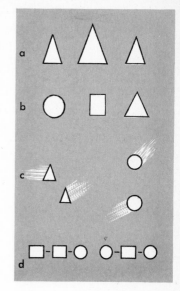

Fig. 6-3. Atoms according to Democritus. The atoms are made of the same ultimate material but differ in (a) size, (b) shape, (c) motion, or (d) arrangement.

2. THE MICROWORLD OF THE SCIENTIST— A FAIRY TALE?

Before continuing the argument and presenting the evidence for the existence of the several kinds of submicroscopic particles and the relationships between them, we shall sketch the completed picture as the scientists have developed it up to the present time. This will be a fairy tale, in the sense that little or no evidence will be presented at this time. However, it may help the reader to visualize the complex structure of the invisible microworld and to understand more clearly how the evidence, when it is presented, supports this conception.

We may start with the visible world and approach (but not reach) the microworld by magnifying the objects of ordinary experience. On examining a piece of cake under a microscope we see crystals of sugar, grains of starch and chocolate, and droplets of water and cream. The larger crystals are distinct, but the smaller are fuzzy and there must be some crystals too small to be visible. As we increase the power of the microscope the smaller crystals become larger and more distinct and others become visible. However, we cannot continue the magnification indefinitely. Beyond a certain magnification the crystals appear larger, but not more distinct. There is nothing wrong with the microscope. The trouble is with light itself. The light waves are too long to be reflected sharply by crystals much smaller than their wavelength, just as water waves are not reflected by small obstacles such as slender trees or sticks. The light microscope does not reveal as distinct an object smaller than about 0.000,01 of an inch. Thus particles smaller than this are not visible to physical eyes (Ex. 12).

The Molecular Level

In order to reach the microworld we must continue with the imagination. If magnification 1000 times greater than that of the finest modern light microscope were possible, we would "see" the individual molecules of sugar in the crystal, and a tenfold further magnification would permit comfortable observation. For we know from indirect evidence to be given later that ordinary molecules are a few Angstroms (10^{-8} cm) across, so that at this magnification they would appear the size of small marbles. However, "see" is not an appropriate word, since "seeing" involves light, its reflection from the object and its reception by the eye. Light is too gross and has too much energy to be reflected by an individual molecule without disturbing it (Ex. 12 and 13). We would have to imagine that we see the molecules with some kind of very fine "light" that, while not disturbing the molecules or the smaller particles, affects the eye like visible light. It is in this sense that the word "see" or "observe" is used in the subsequent discussion. For by using the imagination, we can "see" things of any size, draw pictures of them, and even make models.

At this magnification we would "see" the tiny crystals of sugar

Fig. 6-4. Reaching the microworld through successive magnifications. (A) A particle barely visible with the naked eye. (B) Smallest particle visible through a microscope, magnified 1000 times. (C) Water molecules. (D) A water molecule magnified about 10^8 times. (E) The oxygen nucleus magnified 10^{12} times. (F) The oxygen nucleus magnified about 10^{13} times.

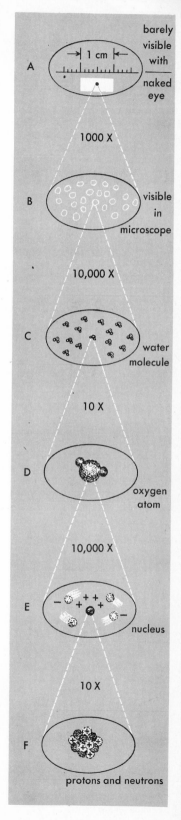

made up of little blobs, arranged in regular order in the form of a cube. The droplet of water would appear granular like a large pile of tiny glass marbles, moving in all directions. If there is any sugar dissolved in the water, the sugar molecules would appear as somewhat larger particles moving among the water molecules. Even in the air surrounding the drop, we would see molecules of oxygen and nitrogen moving in all directions like flying bullets and colliding with each other.

Magnification alone, however, would not permit us to see any of the things just described. The molecules move and vibrate with speeds of hundreds or thousands of feet per second, at ordinary temperatures. The sugar molecules in the crystal would vibrate so rapidly they would appear as blurs, much like a rotating propeller of an airplane. They need to be slowed down or stopped altogether if we are to see and examine them. If this were possible without altering anything else, we would see them as individual units of a definite size and shape. It is true that molecules are slowed down by cooling, but then water becomes ice and even air becomes liquid. We will, therefore, have to visualize the molecules in slow motion or follow their very rapid motion mentally. All molecules of sugar will appear alike; and on examination we will find that while the molecules within each pure substance are the same, they differ from those of all other substances. In a mixture, of course, we would see the various kinds of molecules still distinct, but mingled together.

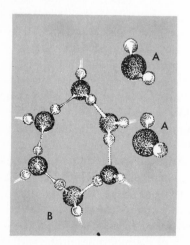

Fig. 6-5. In water, molecules separate in liquid water (A), but joined with other molecules in an ice crystal (B).

With this imaginary microscope we could follow changes such as melting or boiling. In a crystal of very cold ice, for example, the individual molecules are arranged in a hexagonal pattern, as shown in Figure 6-6. The individual molecules move rapidly back and forth about an equilibrium position, as though held to each other by invisible springs. These are the attractive forces between the molecules. Heating

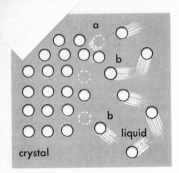

Fig. 6-6. Melting and freezing. Molecule (a) is about to leave the crystal, resulting in melting. The molecules (b) are about to take the positions indicated by the dotted circles, resulting in growth of crystal.

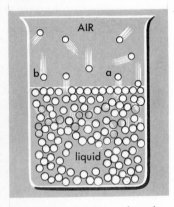

Fig. 6-7. Evaporation and condensation. Molecule (a) has just escaped from the liquid, molecule (b) is about to return.

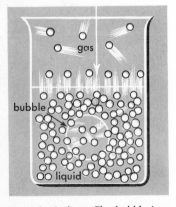

Fig. 6-8. Boiling. The bubble is a gas, with molecules escaping into it and out of it. The pressure inside the bubble is equal to the pressure of the atmosphere, shown by white arrow.

the ice increases the vibration of the molecules. The higher the temperature rises, the faster the molecules vibrate. At some point, the molecules vibrate so violently that they break loose from the orderly arrangement in the crystal and move haphazardly, gliding over each other. The solid ice has melted and has become liquid water, and the temperature at which this happened is 0° C or 32° F.

The process of freezing is exactly the opposite of melting. In a liquid the molecules move haphazardly, constantly colliding with each other. As the molecules collide, some are speeded up, others are slowed down. A few may even stop altogether, but only for a moment, for other molecules hit them, starting their motion again. Cooling the liquid causes a general slowing down of the molecules, although some still move faster than the others. At some temperature (the freezing point, which is the same as the melting point) the attractive forces are strong enough to hold the slower molecules and cause them to vibrate about fixed positions. Like well-trained soldiers, the molecules take regular positions and form the pattern of a crystal. The more heat withdrawn from the liquid, the more molecules deposit and the larger the crystal grows.

Similarly we can follow the process of evaporation and boiling. If we observe water near the surface, we see a new phenomenon. A few of the molecules in the liquid move so fast that they overcome the attraction of their neighbors and fly into the space above. If there is air above, the molecules of water mingle and collide with the molecules of air. All the molecules are now relatively far apart from each other and constitute a gas, water vapor. Even when there is no air above the liquid, the fast-moving molecules still escape and are soon joined by other molecules, constituting a gas of water vapor.

As the temperature is raised, there is a general increase in the motion of the molecules and, of course, a greater number of molecules now move fast enough to escape. Hence the rate of evaporation increases. At some point the molecules escape so rapidly that the water vapor molecules literally push up the molecules above them, be they water molecules or air molecules. At this point the liquid boils, and bubbles of steam rise even from within the liquid. In fact we can observe a bubble enlarge as it rises. Molecules escape into the interior of the steam bubble, increasing the amount of gas in it and hence its volume.

At the surface of the liquid, even before boiling we can observe the opposite process of condensation. Some of the vapor molecules that have escaped fly back into the liquid and are trapped there by the attractive forces. In fact these attractive forces show themselves in another way. If a relatively slow molecule in its wanderings comes near the surface, the combined attraction of the molecules at the surface pull the molecule into the liquid. As expected, the lower the temperature and the slower the molecules in the vapor state, the greater the rate of condensation.

The process of dissolving of a solid and the opposite process of crystallization from solution are very similar to melting and freezing, except that two substances are involved. If we observe a small crystal of sugar dropped into water, we see the sugar molecules leave the crystal and mingle with the molecules of water. Obviously there must be attraction between the sugar molecules and the water molecules, and this attraction must be greater than the attraction of the sugar molecules for each other in the crystal. The crystal *disappears,* its molecules having dispersed in the liquid. As more crystals are added, they dissolve too, but the process does not continue indefinitely. Sooner or later a point is reached at which an added crystal does not dissolve. The solution is *saturated*—that is, the water holds as much sugar as it can—at this temperature.

Observing closely what happens at the crystal in a saturated solution, we see sugar molecules constantly leaving from some parts of the crystal, but just as many other molecules depositing somewhere else on the crystal. Just as many leave as deposit per unit time. This is to be expected, since sugar molecules in the crystal have attraction for each other and for the sugar molecules in the solution. Even before the last crystal was added some molecules must have been depositing on the crystals that *did* dissolve, although more of them were leaving; at saturation, therefore, just as many leave as return per second. This is an instance of *dynamic equilibrium.* If some of the water evaporates, the remaining water cannot hold all the sugar molecules, so that more molecules deposit than leave the crystal, and the crystal grows. This is crystallization.

The Atomic Level

So far we have treated molecules as units, as they would appear at a magnification of about 100 million times. However, even at this magnification, the molecules would not appear as perfectly smooth blobs, but would show some structure. For ease of observing them, let us magnify them a few more times, say tenfold. We can now see clearly that the molecules are made of smaller particles. These are the atoms of the elements. We can count them and find out how many there are in each molecule. Thus we would find 3 atoms in a water molecule, 7 atoms in an alcohol molecule, and 45 atoms in a sugar molecule. We would find only 2 atoms in an oxygen molecule and also 2 atoms in each molecule of hydrogen, nitrogen, chlorine, or hydrogen chloride. In a few instances, as in neon or mercury, we would find only 1 atom per molecule. Thus, some of the smaller molecules are not much larger than the atoms. Of course, in the case of neon or mercury the molecules and the atoms are identical. In general, however, the molecules are large and complex, and some of them can be very complex indeed, consisting of thousands of atoms.

We would find different kinds of atoms making up the molecules. Some atoms are a little larger than the others, but they do not vary much in size. However, some would appear more transparent than others and are probably denser. If we could weigh the atoms, then we would certainly find decided differences. The heaviest atom weighs more than 250 times the lightest. The heaviest found in nature is the uranium atom, which weighs 238 times the hydrogen atom, which is the lightest.

If we can learn to identify the atoms (chiefly by their weight) we

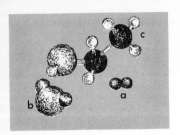

Fig. 6-9. Models of molecules of (a) hydrogen, (b) water, (c) alcohol.

can count how many atoms of each kind there are in a molecule. Thus in a molecule of water there are 2 hydrogen atoms and 1 oxygen atom; in an alcohol molecule, 2 carbon atoms, 6 hydrogen atoms, and 1 oxygen atom; in a sugar molecule, 12 carbon atoms, 22 hydrogen atoms, and 11 oxygen atoms; in an oxygen molecule, 2 oxygen atoms only; in a hydrogen chloride molecule, 1 hydrogen atom and 1 chlorine atom. The chemist symbolizes this information by writing: H_2O, C_2H_6O, $C_{12}H_{22}O_{11}$, O_2 and HCl, respectively.

We would discover one more thing. The atoms have a definite arrangement in the molecules. Thus, in the water molecule each of the hydrogen atoms is joined to the oxygen atom. In an alcohol molecule, 1 carbon atom is joined to 3 hydrogen atoms and another carbon atom. This second carbon atom is joined to 2 hydrogen atoms and 1 oxygen atom. The oxygen atom is in turn further joined to 1 hydrogen atom. This arrangement can be drawn on paper or it can be shown in three dimensions (Fig. 6-9).

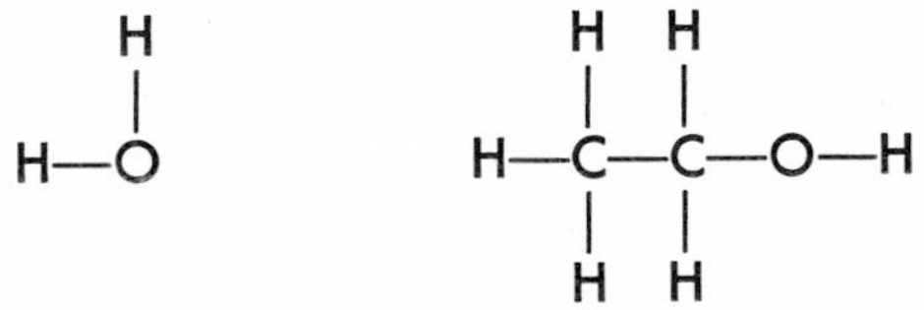

$$
\begin{array}{c}
H \\
| \\
H\!-\!O
\end{array}
\qquad\qquad
\begin{array}{c}
H\quad H \\
|\qquad| \\
H\!-\!C\!-\!C\!-\!O\!-\!H \\
|\qquad| \\
H\quad H
\end{array}
$$

Fig. 6-10. Structural formulas of water and alcohol.

At this magnification we could see clearly that the molecules of a given pure substance are not only alike in size, shape, and weight, but also in composition. Each molecule has the same kind of atoms, the same number of each kind, and in each the arrangement of the atoms is the same. The molecules of some other pure substance have different kinds of atoms, or a different number of them, or a different arrangement. No pure substance has the same kind of molecules in all these respects as any other pure substance. Throughout all the changes of melting, boiling, and dissolving, the molecules remain intact. These changes, it will be remembered, are called physical changes.

In the more drastic changes, called "chemical," the molecules themselves alter in structure. The molecules break into fragments and these fragments recombine to form new molecules. In some cases these fragments are groups of atoms, in other cases the fragments are individual atoms. Moreover, the fragments themselves are stable structures and remain as units; they are then merely the molecules of another substance. In other instances, molecules of two substances simply combine to form molecules of more complex substances. If we were to observe the chemical changes at the magnification of 100 million times, we would see the molecules breaking up and recombining with only the atoms remaining intact. This, at any rate, is our present understanding and explanation of the world of chemical change.

Since the atoms are the units making up the molecules, it might be of interest to see how many kinds there are. In the molecules of diverse substances the same kind of atoms appear again and again, as identified by their size and weight (chiefly by the latter). An inventory will show that there are about 100 kinds of atoms. They range in weight from the hydrogen atom, which is the lightest, to the oxygen atom, which is about sixteen times as heavy; the silver atom, 108 times as heavy; and to the uranium atom, 238 times as heavy. (More recently a few heavier atoms have been produced in atom-building experiments.) The atoms of any given element have the same, or roughly the same, weight. The fact that they differ somewhat is a detail that need not concern us at present (see isotopes, p. 169).

The fact that the number of *kinds* of atoms is so small has tremendous implications, both philosophic and practical. It means that the same kinds of atoms combine and recombine to form the molecules of all the substances known and indeed of all the substances possible. It means that the whole material universe can be broken down or separated into about 100 different substances, the *elements*. All the possibilities of material existence are contained in these relatively few kinds of atoms. In the practical world, the world of manufacture, it means that any kind of material can be made from other materials containing the same atoms if researchers but find the conditions under which the molecules of the original material break up and the fragments recombine to form the molecules of the desired substances. Thus, it is now possible to make from coal, water, air, and salt, any number of substances, such as synthetic rubber, nylon, gasoline, alcohol, medicinals, and countless others.

The Electronic Level

In the complex chemical changes, whether in the kitchen, in industrial plants, or in living things, atoms constantly combine and recombine. But they themselves remain intact—they behave as units. Are the atoms the ultimate units of matter or do they consist of still smaller particles? Do the atoms have any structure?

If we look at an atom just visible under our imaginary microscope, and magnify it further tenfold, a hundredfold, or even a thousandfold, we will not see any structure. It will be blurred and consist mostly of empty space. Yet there must be forces and some matter throughout the volume, because another atom could not occupy the same space. At five additional magnifications, however, some structure will appear, and at ten magnifications the structure becomes fairly clear.

Thus, if we enlarge a barely visible atom about another 10,000-fold (that is, a total magnification of 1 million—millionfold its natural size), we will find that it has the general structure of a peach. At the center is the dense core, and filling the rest of the space are the very light electrons. It differs from a peach, however, in several particulars. The core, called the nucleus, is very small compared to the rest of the atom. The diameter of the nucleus is only about 1/10,000 the diameter of the atom, so that at the new magnification it is barely visible as a tiny dot. Yet this small nucleus contains nearly all the mass of the atom. Hence it must be exceedingly dense. If there were means of detecting charges we would find the nucleus positively charged—that is, having the same kind of charge as an electrified glass rod.

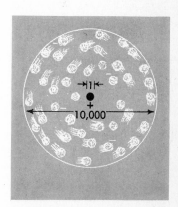

Fig. 6-11. Basic pattern of the atom, showing relative size of atom and nucleus (not to scale). The diameter of the nucleus (black circle) is about 1/10,000 that of the entire atom. The vast space around the nucleus is fairly empty, occupied only by light electrons (white circle).

In the relatively large spaces around the tiny but heavy nucleus are the negatively charged electrons. These are very small particles, perhaps smaller than the nuclei in size. But they are exceedingly light, literally thousands of times lighter than nuclei, and contribute very little mass to the atom. They are held in the atom by the attraction of the positive nucleus. We imagine them as moving; for if these electrons stood still, they would fall into the nucleus. At one time the theory was that the negative electrons whirled around the nucleus of the atom much as planets revolve around the sun. And although it is now known that the situation is not so simple, for most purposes this simplified picture is still used in thinking and talking about the inside of the atom.

Let us get a picture of the atom nearer the right proportions. We magnify a nucleus until it appears the size of a baseball. On the same scale the atom appears as a huge soap bubble more than two city blocks in diameter. In the vast space between the baseball and the surface of the soap bubble, the electrons—each about the size of a ping-pong ball —revolve about the baseball in orbits or perhaps in "waves." The rest of the space is empty, or rather it is a region of electric and magnetic fields. There is no sharp surface to the bubble, of course, but it represents the outskirts of the atom, where the electric and magnetic fields rapidly fade away. Within this boundary—inside the atom—the fields are very strong. Another atom, pressing in so that its fields encroached in this region, would experience strong repulsive forces.

A surprising simplicity will be found if we count the number of electrons in neutral atoms. In the lightest atom, the hydrogen atom, there is one electron. In the next lightest, the helium atom, two. In the third lightest, three. This regularity continues (with minor complications to be explained later) through the entire list of the 102 elements now known. That is, if we arrange the elements in the order of the increasing weight of their atoms, we find that the atom of each element has one more electron than the preceding one. Starting from the hydrogen atom, which has one electron, we find every whole number of electrons represented up to the nobelium atom, which has 102 electrons. Thus we have discovered all the elements that exist up to nobelium. This *serial number* of the element from the lightest to the heaviest is called the "atomic number," and represents the number of electrons in each neutral atom.

Although it is not definitely known how the electrons move around the nucleus of the atom, it is assumed that they are arranged in some pattern from the fact that some electrons are easier to remove than others. It appears reasonable that those easily removed must be in the outer part of the atom while those more difficult to remove are probably deeper in the atom. In a complex atom a few electrons are rather easily removed. Significantly, roughly the same amount of energy will remove any one of these electrons. Hence these electrons are held in the atom about equally firmly. The next group of electrons are more difficult to remove, but again each requires about the same amount of energy for removal. The third group are still more difficult to remove, but each still requiring about the same amount of energy. So we imagine the electrons arranged in concentric shells at various distances from the

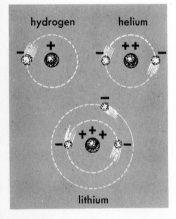

Fig. 6-12. The three lightest atoms —hydrogen, helium, and lithium.

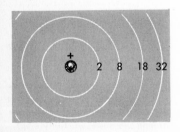

Fig. 6-13. Maximum number of electrons in the first four shells.

central nucleus. In the innermost shell there are at most 2 electrons; in the second shell, 8 electrons; in the third shell, 18. In the heaviest atoms, having more than 86 electrons, there are 7 shells altogether.

If we were to observe atoms reacting, we would find that in many instances some of the outer electrons leave one atom and attach themselves to other atoms. These changes result in electric attractions, which are the forces that bind atoms together in molecules. In this way the chemical reactions are explained.

Let us now examine the tiny nucleus. At the 10,000-fold further magnification of a barely visible atom, the nucleus would not show much structure. But at a 10-fold further magnification we would find that the nucleus itself consists of smaller particles. Two kinds of particles are found in the nucleus: the *protons* and the *neutrons,* both of about the same weight. Although they are comparable to the electrons in size, they are nearly 2000 times heavier than the electrons. In fact each has about the same weight as the whole hydrogen atom. The proton has a positive electric charge, the amount of charge being equal to that of the electron but opposite in sign. In fact, the proton *is the nucleus* of the hydrogen atom. The neutron is a trifle heavier but it has no charge, as the name indicates. Since these two particles make up the nuclei, they are known collectively as *nucleons.*

The nuclei contain nearly all the mass of the atom. Hence the nuclei of the different elements have different weights, since the atoms themselves differ in weight. The nuclei also vary in size. They are like small liquid drops whose size and weight depend on the number of particles they contain. The weight of the nucleus is the sum of the weights of the protons and the neutrons it contains. Therefore, the weight of the nucleus (relative to the hydrogen atom) is readily obtained by simply counting the total number of nucleons in it.

Of great interest is the fact that the nuclei of a given element contain the same number of protons. Thus the nuclei of all the oxygen atoms contain 8 protons; the nuclei of all the chlorine atoms contain 17 protons. We notice further that in oxygen—the eighth element—the number of planetary electrons is also 8. Similarly the chlorine atom, which is the seventeenth element on the list and has 17 planetary electrons, has also 17 protons. We would expect the number of protons to be the same as the number of planetary electrons. Since the atom as a whole is neutral, the number of protons in the nucleus must balance the number of planetary electrons. Thus the number of protons in the nucleus is the same as the atomic number.

However, the number of neutrons in the nucleus is not so definite or so simple. In a given element, the number of neutrons may vary somewhat. Thus in ordinary chlorine there are two kinds of chlorine atoms, one containing 18 neutrons and the other 20 neutrons. Since both contain 17 protons, the first atom must weigh 35 times as much as the hydrogen atom, and the second 37 times as much. These two kinds of chlorine atoms are called isotopes. They are atoms of the same element, having in their nuclei the same number of protons but different number of neutrons, and hence having different weights.

The Nuclear Level

Fig. 6-14. The fluorine nucleus. Contains 9 protons (white spheres).

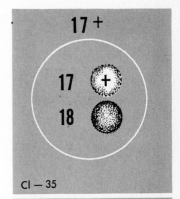

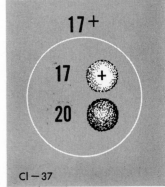

Fig. 6-15. Two kinds of chlorine atoms. The nucleus of the lighter Cl³⁵ contains 18 protons and 18 neutrons; that of the heavier Cl³⁷ contains 17 protons and 20 neutrons.

Many elements found in nature consist of two or more stable isotopes. Some elements have several isotopes, tin, for example, having no fewer than twelve. However, for a given number of protons, the number of neutrons does not range too widely. In the lighter elements there are usually about as many neutrons as protons. In the heavier elements the ratio increases gradually to about 1½ to 1. Thus in the most common uranium atom we find 146 neutrons and 92 protons.

This ratio represents the combinations of neutrons and protons which are stable. For there are both attractive and repulsive forces between the particles, and the attractive forces must be greater than the repulsive forces for the nucleus to be stable. If there are too many or too few neutrons for a given number of protons, the nucleus is unstable and breaks up into other nuclei. This explains atom smashing, atom building, and radioactive disintegrations.

Does the nucleus itself have a more elaborate structure? What forces hold it together? Are there any other particles in the nucleus besides the neutrons and the protons? Current research is tackling these questions. For example, several kinds of light particles have been observed coming out of the nucleus. Electrons, positrons, several kinds of heavy electrons (mesons), neutrinos and photons of radiant energy come out during atom smashing. A great deal is known, but what it all means is not yet clear. This is the frontier of knowledge. We cannot go any deeper here into the structure of matter until the scientists find out more about it.

This, then, is a simplified sketch of the structure of matter as scientists imagine it. At some places we have oversimplified it. At other places we may not have simplified it enough. The reader should avoid

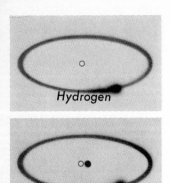

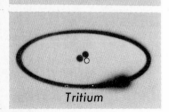

Hydrogen

Deuterium

Tritium

Fig. 6-16. Three isotopes of hydrogen.

Fig. 6-17. Electron microscope picture of virus molecules. The small dots are believed to be actual individual molecules, and the picture shows how these molecules are arranged in orderly rows to form a crystal. (From Ralph W. G. Wyckoff, *World of the Electron Microscope*, Yale University Press, 1958. Courtesy Dr. Ralph W. G. Wyckoff.)

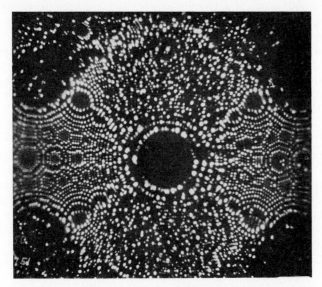

Fig. 6-18. Tungsten atoms on a photograph of image produced by electron emission microscope. Magnification 10^7
times. (E. W. Müller, Pennsylvania State University.)

details at this point and try to get the general pattern. Figure 6-4 may
help to illustrate the structure as a whole.

In describing the microworld in some places we have been more
concrete than we had a right to be. When we speak of a world which
will be forever invisible, we must represent it in pictures from everyday
experience. We shall probably never know if the diagrams represent
in all respects accurate "photographic" representations. In fact we have
reasons to doubt that the representations are exactly faithful. We do
not even know whether space, time, material particle, or wave have the
same meaning in this microworld as in ordinary experience.

The skeptical reader will no doubt remark at this point, "This is a
nice fairy tale—but what is the evidence for all this?" But is it a fairy
tale? There is evidence for every statement we have made—for every part
of the picture. To be sure, the evidence is indirect and has been pieced
together from many experiments and observations. All the countless
experiments and carefully made measurements lead to this picture.
Only by this picture can we understand, predict, and control the phenomena. It is not possible to give the evidence "in a nutshell" for so
complex a picture. However, we can take any part of the picture and
give the evidence for any such specific questions as "How do we know
how fast the molecules move? How many atoms are in a molecule?
How many electrons are in an atom?"

NOTES AND EXERCISES

1. *Reality of Void.* One of the problems of ancient and medieval
philosophy was whether a vacuum is possible. Aristotle argued that a

vacuum cannot exist. If a vacuum existed, then a moving body, finding no resistance, should move through it with infinite speed. This means that it would be in two places at the same time, and that is inconceivable. Galileo countered that a moving body meeting no resistance in a vacuum would move with constant but *finite* speed—it would merely *not be slowed down*. For Newton, there are two fundamental realities in the word—matter and void. Void is just as real as matter. His entire mechanics is built on this basis. Do not confuse reality with materiality. Would you call forces, momentum, magnetic fields, real? Would you call mind, life, love, democracy real? Are they "material"?

2. From the point of view of definition, a substance is the sum total of a set of properties. "Artificial" silk is not silk. Can you think of any properties that distinguish between them? The fact that one is "synthetic" and the other is "natural" in that it comes from silk worms is not relevant. Cane sugar and beet sugar come from different sources, yet if pure, they have identical properties. Would you pay more for cane sugar than for beet sugar, if both were equally pure?

3. Calculate the density of a block of iron, if its dimensions are 2 cm × 3 cm × 4 cm and its weight is 250 grams.

4. The density of gold is 19.3 grams per cc. How many grams does 1 cc weigh? How many grams does 50 cc weigh? If you have a piece of gold weighing 195 grams, what volume would it occupy?

5. The density of ice is 0.9 grams per cc. If you have 1 gram of ice, what volume would it occupy? Can you tell why ice floats on water? Would iron float on mercury? (See p. 562.)

6. The density of air is 1.29 grams per liter at 0° C and 760 mm of mercury. How much does a gallon of air (approximately 4 liters) weigh under these conditions?

7. Which of the following are characteristic properties of a piece of iron? Its density; its weight; its melting point; its temperature; its color; its ability to be magnetized; its resistance to acceleration; its tendency to rust; its insolubility in oil.

8. We can hardly do justice to the philosophic argument of Democritus without going far afield into the meaning of his terms. Nevertheless, a sketch may be attempted, giving the *sense* of the argument.

Matter is a fundamental reality in the world. Its existence is undeniable. It makes up everything that fills the world. Moreover, matter is the principle of permanence. It is the matter of the tree that persists in a certain form and is known and recognized as a tree. All changes are superficial. This led a school of philosophy to hold as their basic motto that "Nothing is new under the sun."

On the other hand, change is an equally undeniable fact in the world. The tree grows, ages, withers, and dies. You never step into the same river twice. Nothing remains the same. This led another school of philosophy to the motto "Everything flows."

Now, these two views are contradictory. Parmenides sharpened the conflict, by posing his famous problem:

(a) Being is fundamentally one. To *be* means to *exist*—for all time.

(b) *Being is.* Nonbeing *is not.* What is, exists. What is not, does not exist.

(c) Change means either going from *what is* to *what is* or from *what is* to *what is not.*

(d) But Being cannot change from what is into what is not; for Being cannot become Nonbeing.

(e) Further, Being cannot change from what *is* into what *is;* that is no change. Whatever *is, is.*

(f) Therefore, change is impossible. Impossible to conceive and therefore impossible of existence. ("The inconceivable cannot exist.")

Democritus considered the problem and said there is only one way out of the contradiction. Matter must be made of *atoms.* The atoms are *eternal* and thus the principle of permanence remains. But the atoms can, and do, rearrange themselves, producing apparent change (real change as far as our senses are concerned). Thus only *by the existence of atoms* can we understand that *permanence* (matter) and *change* can exist in the same world. For those interested in the full argument, consult any good book on philosophy. A very adequate version of the argument is found in Ref. 6.5.

9. The contrast between continuity and discontinuity has been expressed in several pairs of opposites, in various connections. For example: continuity versus corpuscularity (or granularity, or discreteness, or "package-like"); continuity or wholeness versus individuality of parts; perfect homogeneity versus heterogeneity; arithmetic of natural numbers versus geometry of lines; infinitesimal (parts) versus finite (parts); waves versus particles; field physics versus particle physics.

Give several examples of things which, to the limit of ordinary observation, are continuous; give several examples of things that are discrete.

10. Can a perfectly continuous body have structure? Must a discontinuous body have structure?

11. Today we say that a molecule of water consists of two hydrogen atoms and one oxygen atom. An atom of oxygen, in turn, consists of protons, neutrons, and electrons. Which of these would Democritus call atoms? In what sense would he call each of these atoms?

12. The size of the particle still clearly visible under the highest magnification of the microscope depends on the wavelength of light. Therefore, the shorter the wavelength, the smaller the particle that can be seen. Microscopes have been developed, using ultraviolet light, and even x-rays. With these instruments it is possible to see particles with a diameter of about 10 Angstrom units. If the particle has roughly 100 atoms, and the diameter of the atom is about 1 to 2 Angstroms, how many atoms are there in the particle? How much detail could one obtain for such a particle? (Ref. 5.)

13. *Electron Microscope.* A wholly new type of instrument was developed, using the wave properties of electrons (see Chap. 12). The "wavelength" of a beam of electrons is about 0.01 Angstrom. Such a beam is not focused by mirrors or lenses, but by magnetic fields. The effective resolution of the electron microscope is about 10 Angstroms. With this instrument, giant molecules of proteins and viruses can be seen in detail. If a virus molecule is 20×60 Angstroms, how many atoms does it contain? (Ref. 5.)

14. To follow the magnification discussed in Section 2 (p. 162), consider a model in which the proton (or neutron) is about 1 in. in diameter. On this model, how large is a nucleus of an oxygen atom having 16 nucleons? How large is the whole oxygen atom? How large is a water molecule? How large on this scale is the wavelength of yellow light (0.000059 cm)? How large is a cube of ice 1 cm in edge?

7

THE WORLD OF MOLECULES

I. EVIDENCE FOR MOLECULES

The kinetic molecular theory is a comprehensive, logical structure that explains in great detail and with remarkable accuracy the properties and behavior of gases, liquids, solids, and solutions, as well as the processes of melting and freezing, boiling and condensing, dissolving and crystallizing. In terms of the basic idea that gases consist of molecules in motion and a few additional simple concepts, the theory correlates a wealth of information and illumines a wide range of phenomena. We shall elaborate the theory in considerable detail and in the process provide the experimental evidence for it. We shall proceed in two ways. By describing the phenomena, we can show how the phenomena lead to the theory. Conversely, we can use the theory to understand and to explain the phenomena. Both of these approaches constitute evidence for the theory, and both are characteristic of the method of science.

Let us begin with the phenomena. We have already mentioned the well-known fact that matter exists in the solid, liquid, and gaseous states. A solid is characterized by having a definite shape and a definite volume. A liquid has a definite volume—a definite number of fluid ounces—but has no definite shape. It takes the shape of the container. A gas has neither definite shape nor definite volume. It expands indefinitely, filling all space available to it and taking the shape of the container. Only when the quantity of gas is very large, such as the earth's atmosphere, or a star, do the gravitational forces limit the size or determine the shape of the mass of gas (Ex. 1).

Qualitative Properties of Gases   Although gases are less tangible than liquids and solids, they exhibit properties that are simpler to understand and serve as a starting point for the development of the theory. We shall begin with some of the more easily observed properties of gases, and show how they point to the existence of molecules.

Mass of Gases. It may seem unnecessary to demonstrate that gases have weight. Yet not until the sixteenth century was it realized that air, the most common of the gases, has weight. The first evidence was indirect. In 1643 Evangelista Torricelli (1608-1674), a student and associate of Galileo, discovered atmospheric pressure during his famous experiments with mercury. He sealed a long glass tube at one end and filled it with mercury. Putting his thumb at the other end, he inverted the tube into a cup of mercury, and removed his thumb. The mercury in the tube dropped a short distance but remained about 30 inches higher than the outside surface. He repeated the experiment with other tubes of various diameters, always with the same result. No matter how long the tube was, provided it was longer than 30 inches, the mercury descended until the column was about 30 inches, or 76 centimeters, above the outside surface.

The intriguing question arose: what held the mercury up at 30 inches? Torricelli discussed the phenomena with Galileo and they found the currently accepted theories inadequate. For centuries the Aristotelians had explained the phenomena of suction by the principle that "nature abhors a vacuum." We are all familiar with the phenomenon of drawing on a straw and having the water come up. The Aristotelians would explain it by saying that as we draw, we attempt to create a vacuum. Since nature "abhors a vacuum," the water rises to fill it. Similarly this principle could explain that mercury is held up in the tube, for at the top of the tube there is a vacuum. But why only 30 inches? Galileo wistfully remarked that apparently the abhorence of nature for a vacuum did not exceed 30 inches!

Galileo suggested an alternate explanation. Instead of a "pull" of the vacuum from the inside, it was a *push* of the air from the outside. He concluded that the cause must be the air pressing on the outside surface of the mercury. The pressure must be due to the *weight* of the air, which envelopes the earth and presses down as a fluid. Torricelli checked this conclusion by performing the experiment on a mountain. If Galileo's explanation was correct, Torricelli reasoned, then the mercury column should drop on going up a mountain, since the amount of air above the outside surface decreases. As expected, the height of the mercury column was lower at higher elevations.

Torricelli's apparatus is now known as the "barometer" (*baros* = weight; *metron* = measure) and is used to measure the pressure of the atmosphere. Pressure is defined as force per unit area; that is,

$$\text{pressure} = \frac{\text{force}}{\text{area}}$$

or in symbols,

$$p = \frac{f}{A}$$

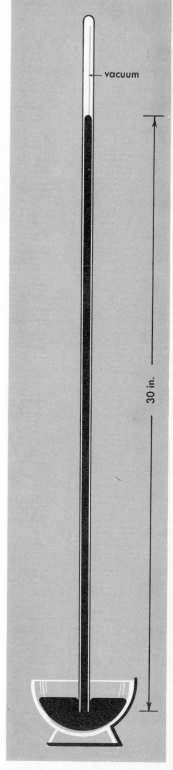

Fig. 7-1. Torricelli barometer.

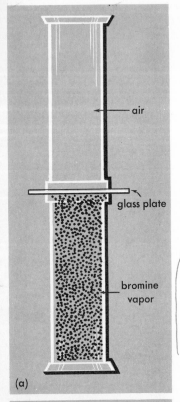

air

glass plate

bromine
vapor

(a)

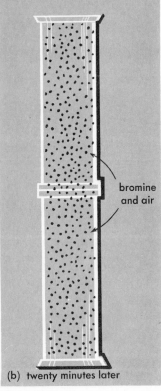

bromine
and air

(b) twenty minutes later

and may be expressed in any convenient units of force and area, such as pounds per square inch, grams per square centimeter, or dynes per square centimeter (Ex. 2, 3, 4, 5).

The pressure of the atmosphere can be calculated from Torricelli's experiment. If the column of mercury stands 76 cm high and is contained in a tube 1 sq cm in cross-section, the volume will be 76 cc of mercury. Since each cubic centimeter of mercury weighs 13.6 grams (the density of mercury), the total weight of the column is 76 × 13.6 or 1003 grams. The pressure, therefore, is 1003 grams per sq cm. If we use a larger tube, say twice the cross-section, we have twice the weight of mercury—that is, twice the total force—but on an area of 2 sq cm. The pressure, or force per square centimeter, is the same as before. Since the mercury column is balanced by the atmosphere, the pressure of the atmosphere is 1003 grams per sq cm, which corresponds to 14.7 lb per sq in.

At any given place on the earth, the pressure of the atmosphere depends on the elevation. Moreover, for a given place, the pressure varies somewhat during the day, and from day to day. The variation is due to movements of the air resulting in greater or less amounts of air above a given place. These variations, as the reader is probably already aware, are related to weather conditions. At sea level, the height of the column averages about 76 cm. Accordingly, the *standard* atmospheric pressure is defined as exactly 76.00 cm, equivalent to 1003 grams per sq cm (Ex. 5, 6).

The weight of air by direct measurement was first obtained in the latter half of the seventeenth century. Since that time, with the development of chemistry, other "airs" or gases have been recognized and weighed with more and more accurate balances. Nowadays gases can be weighed with high accuracy, using the analytical balance of the chemist. An evacuated flask is weighed, filled with the gas and weighed again. The difference in the two weights is the weight of the gas. Thus, at atmospheric pressure and 0° C, a liter of air weighs 1.29 grams; a liter of oxygen, 1.43 grams; a liter of hydrogen, 0.09 grams. (A liter is almost exactly 1000 cc, and is slightly larger than a quart, which is 950 cc.)

Densities of Gases. The examples just given illustrate the general fact that gases have low densities. Under ordinary pressures and temperatures, the densities of gases are a few grams per thousand cubic centimeters, as compared to liquids and solids, which range in density from a fraction of a gram to about 22 grams per cc. The *matter* of the gas must be thinly dispersed. This fact is significant and suggests the clue that if gases consist of molecules, they must be far apart from one another in gases.

Compressibility of Gases. Another property of gases is their high compressibility. A given quantity of gas can easily be squeezed into a smaller volume. Under sufficient compression, the volume of a given

Fig. 7-2. Diffusion of bromine and air. The dense bromine vapor moves spontaneously into upper cylinder after removal of glass plate.

sample of gas can be decreased hundreds, or even thousands, of times. This property gives further support to the idea that the molecules of a gas are separated by large spaces. The suggestion is strong that in compressing a gas we really do not "compress matter" but merely crowd the molecules closer together.

Diffusion of Gases. Diffusion is another interesting phenomenon exhibited by gases. Gases diffuse or "mix" with one another, without the necessity of stirring and in the absence of circulating currents. The phenomenon may be shown with two cylinders, one inverted over the other and separated by a glass plate (Fig. 7-2). The lower cylinder contains bromine vapor, which has a deep brown color and is about 5½ times denser than air. The upper cylinder contains ordinary air. Removal of the glass plate that separates the two gases—with as little stirring as possible—will show, within a few minutes, the brown vapor moving slowly upward into the space formerly occupied by air. At the same time some of the lighter air will have moved downward, for the brown color in the lower cylinder has decreased in intensity. In about 20 minutes, the two gases have mixed completely, as shown by the uniform color throughout the two cylinders.

The significance of this experiment becomes clear upon further consideration. The brown (bromine) gas, although more than five times denser than air, has moved upward against the force of gravity. Ordinarily, we would expect the denser fluid to remain below. Certainly when water and gasoline are placed in a vessel, the denser water settles to the bottom and the gasoline floats on top. And the further addition of mercury into the vessel will create three layers, with the mercury below the water. Even if the mixture is shaken violently, after standing for a few seconds, the fluids will separate according to their densities.

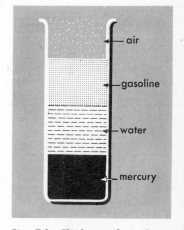

Fig. 7-3. Fluids stratify in layers according to density.

The behavior of bromine and air (and all gases) is therefore different. Without the addition of any energy from the outside, the bromine moves upward against the force of gravity. This strongly suggests that there is motion *inherent* in the gas. Although the bromine gas as a whole has no motion, its particles must be constantly moving. Accordingly, we can explain diffusion, not as a process in which one gas moves bodily into the other gas, but as a process in which the individual particles of one gas move into the spaces between the molecules of the other.

These ideas can be checked with further experiments. For instance, if the molecules move, they must collide with each other frequently. This must be the reason that bromine diffuses rather slowly into the air. For we would expect the bromine molecules to collide with the air molecules, and thus to encounter hindrance in their upward motion. Continuing the reasoning, we would expect the diffusion to be faster if both gases were thinned out by pumping some of them out. For then there would be fewer molecules in the same volume, and they should collide less frequently. On performing the experiment with both gases at lower pressure, we find that the gases diffuse faster into one another.

Another variation of the experiment points to the same conclusions, and gives additional insight into the structure of the gas. With the glass plate in place separating the two cylinders, we evacuate the upper cylinder only. A wide rubber band around the separation will prevent the outside air from rushing in. On moving the glass plate to the side, we see the bromine vapor rushing into the upper cylinder, filling both cylinders almost instantly. This is exactly as expected, for there are no molecules in the upper cylinder to hinder the upward advance of the bromine molecules. With these ideas we can also understand how a gas expands indefinitely. The molecules, having inherent motion, simply move into all the space available to them. Moreover, since the expansion is almost instantaneous, the molecules must move with very high speeds.

Pressure of Gases. These ideas are further reinforced by consideration of a related property of gases: namely, that they exert pressure. The pressure of gases must not be confused with atmospheric pressure. Atmospheric pressure is fluid (or hydrostatic) pressure due to the weight of the atmosphere acting as a fluid. Even if the envelope of air surrounding the earth were to liquefy, we would still have (on a smooth earth) the same atmospheric pressure, 14.7 lb per sq in. at sea level. The pressure of a gas, be it air or any other gas, is something different. It is an *expansive* force pushing outward in all directions, and it is *inherent* in the gas.

The following experiment illustrates gas pressure most simply. If we put a small quantity of a gas in a lax rubber balloon and place it in a vacuum, we see the balloon filling out and expanding indefinitely. With very thin and weak rubber, the balloon can be made very large with only a very small quantity of gas. Thus the pressure is inherent in the gas, and can be thought of as a force exerted by the moving molecules hitting the sides of the container.

We do not ordinarily realize how large this force of expansion is. An empty gallon can with a stopper on it will reveal the magnitude. The can is not empty, of course, but contains about 5 grams of air. On the outside the atmosphere is pressing on the can with a force of 14.7 lb for every square inch of its surface. For a gallon can 4 × 6 × 8 in. (with a total area of about 200 square inches), the total force must be nearly 1½ tons. Yet the few grams of air inside exert enough pressure to permit the can to retain its volume. The fact that the air on the outside is also a gas is irrelevant. If we were to submerge the 1-gal can in 33 ft of water and remove the atmosphere above the water, the can would still retain its volume. (At a depth of 33 ft of water or 30 in. of mercury, the fluid pressure is about 15 lb per sq in.—that is, equal to one atmosphere. See Ex. 4 and 5.)

The magnitude of the pressure of the gas is strikingly demonstrated by evacuating the can. On removing the air from the can with a pump, the can collapses, becoming twisted and crushed. Thus the air in the can, although only a few grams, is capable of exerting a force of 1 ton or more—well out of proportion to its weight. Similarly, a few pounds of steam can exert enough pressure to explode a steel boiler. When dynamite explodes, it produces gases in a very small volume. It is the pressure of these gases that tears down a building or splits a rock. The

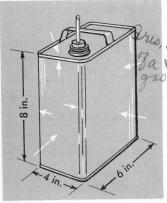

Fig. 7-4. Total force of the atmosphere on a can 4 × 6 × 8 inches is about 3000 pounds.

Fig. 7-5. Can is crushed by atmospheric pressure on evacuation of a few grams of air, by connecting V to pump.

[handwritten margin notes:] not confused — atmos. press. is fluid — pres. 7 a gas

pressure of gases is due to the incessant bombardment of an immense number of molecules moving at high speeds.

The kinetic molecular theory receives further support from certain regularities in the behavior of gases, known as the "gas laws." The relations between the volume, the pressure, and the temperature of a gas are mathematically simple. These relations are exhibited by all gases with a fairly high degree of accuracy and within very wide limits.

The Gas Laws

Boyle's Law. The relation between volume and pressure of a gas is known as *Boyle's law*. We all know this law, qualitatively, from general experience. Anyone would predict that putting pressure on a gas will decrease its volume and, conversely, reducing the pressure will increase its volume. However, it was Robert Boyle (1627-1691) who discovered the quantitative relationship. On extensive experimentation he observed that, at constant temperature, doubling the pressure on a sample of gas decreases the volume to one half of the original; tripling the pressure reduces the volume to one third; reducing the pressure to one tenth results in the gas expanding to tenfold in volume. In other words, at constant temperature the volume is inversely proportional to the pressure. Mathematically, at constant temperature,

$$V = \frac{\text{constant}}{p}$$

or

$$pV = \text{constant}$$

where p is the pressure and V is the volume. Thus, a gallon of gas at 1 atmosphere will occupy only 1 qt if the pressure is increased to 4 atmospheres (Ex. 7 and 8).

The implications of Boyle's law become evident by considering the pressure *of* the gas rather than the pressure *on* the gas. By Newton's third law, of course, they are equal. A gallon of a gas at room temperature exerts a certain pressure due to the impact of the molecules per square centimeter of the surface of the container. If the gas is now crowded into one fourth of its former volume, there will be four times as many molecules per unit volume. Other things being equal, and specifically if the temperature remains the same, four times as many molecules will strike the wall per second. The pressure, therefore, should increase fourfold. Thus Boyle's law is a further confirmation of the correctness of the theory.

Charles' Law. The relation between volume and temperature in a gas is known as *Charles' law* (Jacques Charles, 1746-1823). Again, we know this law qualitatively, from general experience. We all know that a gas expands when heated, thus increasing in volume; when cooled, it contracts, thus decreasing in volume. However, the quantitative relation is not very simple. The volume does not increase in proportion to the centigrade temperature (or to the Fahrenheit temperature for that matter).

To illustrate this point let us take a specific problem. Suppose we start with 200 cc of a gas at 30° C and raise the temperature to 60° C, keeping the pressure constant. What will the new volume be? One possible guess might be that it will double to 400 cc, but that is the wrong answer. The reader will recall that 0° C is arbitrarily defined as the temperature at which water freezes, and 100° is that at which it boils (under standard pressure). The zero point of the scale is in no basic sense a "zero," and the size of the degree is equally arbitrary. They depend on the properties of water. Had we chosen some other substance, such as benzene or alcohol, we would have had different zero points and different scales. Thus 60° C is not "twice as hot" as 30° C, in any fundamental sense. The reader is advised to review at this time the discussion on temperature and temperature scales in Chapter 3. He should thus be able to see that if the volume of a gas *did* double, it would be sheer coincidence.

What then is the new volume of the gas in the problem stated above? The answer cannot be obtained from what has already been discussed. It must be obtained from further experiments. In the example given above, the volume measures 220 cc. If the same gas is heated to 120° C, the volume becomes 259 cc. If we start with 220 cc at 20° C and heat it to 40° C, the volume increases to 213.5 cc. Although these numbers may not seem logical, a good mathematician will have no difficulty in finding a simple relation between them. We can, however, achieve simplicity by carrying out the experiments in a more systematic fashion.

Starting with a given volume of a gas at 0° C and keeping the pressure constant, we change the temperature and measure the resulting volume. If we raise the temperature to 1° C, the volume of a gas (any gas) will increase by 1/273 of the volume it had at zero. Raising the temperature to 10° C increases the volume by 10/273 of the volume at zero. This regularity continues for any rise in temperature and is also observed in cooling. Thus cooling the gas to −1° C *decreases* the volume by 1/273; cooling it −100° C the volume decreases by 100/273 of the volume. Thus if the regularity continued, and the gas remained a gas, then on cooling to −273° C the volume would decrease by 273/273. In other words, the gas would have no volume at all. As a matter of experimental fact, however, all known gases liquefy before this temperature is attained, so that the law ceases to apply before −273° C is reached.

The regularity becomes clearer by starting with a definite volume of gas, conveniently chosen so as to simplify the arithmetic. If we start with 546 cc at 0° C, and raise the temperature to 1° C, the volume will increase by 1/273 of 546 or by 2 cc. Therefore, at 1° C the volume will be 548 cc. Heating from 0° C to 10° C, the volume will increase by 20 cc, resulting in a volume of 566 cc. Likewise for every degree cooling below 0° C, there will be a decrease of 2 cc in volume. For several other temperatures the volume which the sample of gas will occupy is shown in column 2 in Table 7:1.

The Absolute Temperature Scale. The relation of volume and tem-

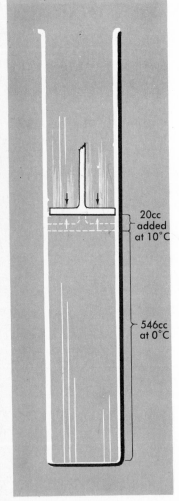

20cc added at 10°C

546cc at 0°C

Fig. 7-6. Apparatus for deriving absolute temperature scale. A 10-degree rise increases the volume by 20 cc, making the volume 566 cc. At −273°C the volume would decrease to zero, if the substance remained a gas.

perature now becomes simple *if we define* a new temperature scale by adding 273 degrees to the centigrade temperature. This scale, called the "absolute" temperature scale, is symbolized as ° A. Thus 10° C becomes 10° + 273° or 283° A; 0° C becomes 273° A; −23° C becomes 250° A; and −273° C becomes the new *zero*. The corresponding temperatures on the absolute scale are given in column 3 of Table 7-1. Comparing the volume in column 2 and the temperature in column 3, we notice that the volume is proportional to the temperature on the new scale. Thus at 50° A, the volume of our sample is 100 cc; at the temperature 200° A, the volume is 400. Thus at four times the absolute temperature, the volume becomes four times as great.

TABLE 7-1

Temperature in degrees centigrade	Volume in cc	Temperature in the new scale °A = °C + 273°
273	1092	546
100	746	373
10	566	283
1	548	274
starting 0	546	273
−1	544	272
−23	500	250
−123	400	200
−173	200	100
−223	100	50
−273	0	0

We are now in a position to state Charles' law. *At constant pressure, the volume of a gas is proportional to the absolute temperature.*

$$V \propto T$$

or $$V = kT$$

where V is the volume, T is the temperature in degrees absolute, and k is a constant which depends on the quantity of the gas and the units chosen for the volume.

Thus one of the advantages of the absolute temperature scale is that it permits expression of the volume-temperature relation in a simple mathematical form. The designation "absolute," however, has a deeper significance, as we will presently see.

Pressure-Temperature Relationship. The law relating pressure and temperature at constant volume can be derived mathematically from the laws of Boyle and Charles. However, we obtain a better insight into the structure of the gas by deriving it afresh from experiments.

In a rigid vessel, such as a glass milk bottle that is tightly covered,

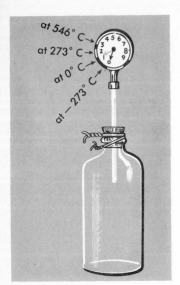

Fig. 7-7. Relation between pressure and temperature of a confined gas. At 273°C the pressure is twice that at 0°C.

the volume of the contained gas will remain constant. A gauge through the stopper will measure the pressure of the gas inside. If we now raise the temperature, we notice an increase in the pressure and if we lower the temperature, a decrease in pressure. Starting at 0° C and measuring the pressure, we find that for every degree rise in temperature the pressure of the confined gas increases by 1/273 of the pressure it had at 0° C. Similarly, for every degree of cooling the pressure drops by 1/273 of the pressure at 0° C. In other words, *the pressure of a confined gas (at constant volume) is proportional to the absolute temperature.* In symbols,

$$p = kT$$

The implications of the pressure-temperature relation (at constant volume) become immediately clear. Since we have already explained pressure as due to the impacts of molecules, then the increase of pressure on heating means that more force is exerted on a given surface. Since the number of molecules in the same volume is the same as before, the increase in force must mean either that the molecules hit the wall of the container more often or that they hit harder, or both. In any case the molecules must move faster at higher temperatures. For if the molecules move faster, they must collide more often with each other and with the surface of the container. Moreover, if they move faster, they will have a greater momentum, *mu* (*m* = mass *u* = velocity), and will exert more force per impact. Conversely, the molecules must move more slowly at lower temperatures.

At absolute zero, if the gas remained a gas, it would exert no pressure. This means there would be no impacts, which implies that there would be no motion of the molecules. Thus we are led to the significant idea that the absolute temperature is a measure of the speed of the molecules. The higher the temperature, the higher the speed.

We obtain an exact relation between the absolute temperature and the speed of the molecules on further analysis. Qualitatively, the faster the molecules move, the more often they collide with each other and with the wall of its container. Moreover, the faster the molecules, the more momentum they possess, and hence the harder they hit each time they collide. It is, therefore, not difficult to see that with *double* the speed, the molecules get around the same space in half the time, which means that they hit the surface *twice* as often. Moreover, with twice the speed, the molecules have twice the momentum, *mu,* and hence exert twice the force per impact. Therefore doubling the speed of the molecules produces a pressure *four* times as great as before. Tripling the speed results in three times as many collisions per second with the surface, and three times the force per collision, or nine times the total force. More generally, the pressure is proportional to the *square* of the speed.

The reader will recall from the section on mechanics (p. 73) that the kinetic energy of a moving body is proportional to the square of the speed. The logical conclusion, therefore, is that the pressure is proportional to the kinetic energy of the molecules, and more significantly, that the *absolute temperature* is proportional to the kinetic energy of the molecules. Mathematically,

$$T \propto KE$$

or

$$T = k \ KE$$

or

$$T = k \cdot \tfrac{1}{2}mu^2$$

where T is the absolute temperature, m is the mass of a single molecule, and u is the speed of the molecule.

The Ideal Gas Law. The adoption of the absolute temperature scale permits us to express the volume-temperature relation and the pressure-temperature relation in simple mathematical form. The three gas laws can be combined into one single formula. We can combine them using algebra, or by reconsidering the results of the experiments. Thus, the volume of a sample of gas is directly proportional to the absolute temperature, and inversely proportional to the pressure. Expressed mathematically,

$$V \propto \frac{T}{p}$$

or

$$V = k \frac{T}{p}$$

and hence

$$pV = kT$$

or

$$p = \frac{kT}{V}$$

where V is the volume, p is the pressure, T is the absolute temperature, and k is a constant number depending on the amount (weight) of gas in the sample and the units chosen for the pressure and the volume.

The expression, in any of the various forms, is known as the *ideal gas law*. It applies to all gases. The adjective "ideal," however, is used as a reminder of the fact that in actuality gases do not obey the law exactly. When accurate measurements are made, it is found that all real (that is, all actual) gases deviate from this law by small amounts. The deviations depend on the gas and on the temperature and pressure. In general, at low pressures and high temperatures, the discrepancies become small and negligible for any gas. Despite the small deviations, the ideal gas law summarizes in a single formula the behavior of all real gases, and hence it is a big step in organizing our knowledge of nature. Moreover, the molecular theory is developed by first neglecting the small irregularities.

2. THE KINETIC MOLECULAR THEORY OF GASES

We could continue to analyze other implications of the gas laws and the other properties of gases. We could also describe additional phenomena, derive clues, and accumulate more and more evidence for these clues. However, there are two disadvantages in continuing by this method. In the first place, as the critical reader has no doubt observed, the clues from any one experiment are not too convincing. The argument becomes strong only when it is realized that many different experiments lead to the same clues. As in a case at court, any one piece of evidence may not be too impressive, and can be explained away. But the concurrence of evidence cannot be so easily dismissed. Similarly, in the case of a theory, it is the weight of the evidence from diverse sources that makes it significant and convincing.

The second disadvantage of continuing in this manner is that the argument becomes long and unwieldy. The very wealth of the evidence becomes a burden. It is very difficult to keep all the relevant factors in mind, even for a trained scientist. It is even more difficult to explain it to others. Consequently the scientist often reverses the process of reasoning. He first summarizes the clues into a coherent system. He *induces* a theory from the phenomena. He then argues *deductively* from the clues taken together, to see if the phenomena can be explained logically and without contradictions. In the *deductive* process, the theory *begins* with clear statements of the clues.

Assumptions   For an *ideal* gas, the kinetic molecular theory begins with the following *assumptions:*

> **Assumption 1.** *Gases consist of discrete particles of matter called molecules. (Latin: molecule = little particle of matter.)*
>
> **Assumption 2.** *The molecules are in constant motion.*
>
> **Assumption 3.** *The molecules are far apart from one another, relative to their size.*
>
> **Assumption 4.** *As the molecules collide with each other and with the walls of the container, they rebound elastically; that is, they collide without loss of kinetic energy.*
>
> **Assumption 5.** *The speed of the molecules depends on the temperature. More precisely, the absolute temperature of the gas is a direct measure of the average kinetic energy of the molecules.*

We have called these statements "assumptions." To be sure, they are the clues suggested by the experiments (*induced* from experiments), as the previous argument has shown. They are reasonable inferences, but they are not "proved" beyond all doubt. To be on the safe side, we call them assumptions, and treat them as "if" statements. We then proceed to see what conclusions follow logically from them.

The term "theory" is applied to the whole logical structure—the set of assumptions and all the conclusions that can be drawn from them. All the statements in the theory are consistent with the assumptions and with each other. If the assumptions are valid, then the theory should be able to explain the phenomena. As discussed in Chapter 1, this is one of the important functions of a theory.

On drawing conclusions from this set of assumptions, we are gratified to find a simple, logical, and consistent explanation of the phenomena. For example, the fact that gases are easily compressible is explained as follows: *If* the gas consists of discrete particles (assumption 1) and the particles are separated from one another by large spaces (assumption 3), then it should be easy to compress a gas by merely crowding the molecules closer together. Similarly, the fact that bromine gas diffuses upward into air against the force of gravity is explained as follows: *If* gases consist of molecules (assumption 1) and the molecules are separated by large spaces (assumption 3) and *if further* the molecules are in constant motion (assumption 2), then the bromine molecules should move into the spaces between the molecules of air, and *vice versa*.

In a similar way, the other phenomena thus far described can be logically explained. We shall not do so here, for that would only be repeating the same arguments in reverse. However, the reader is advised to carry out this reasoning, and explain the remaining phenomena as indicated in Exercises 13 and 14. It will serve as a review of the material presented so far and provide some practice in the deductive method of science.

An important point, however, must not be missed. By using the set of only five assumptions, and drawing conclusions from them, we can explain all (or nearly all) the phenomena presented so far. Thus one of the values of the theory is to correlate and make understandable a wide range of phenomena, many of which appear unrelated at first sight (see Chap. 1, p. 9).

A second important value of the theory is that it can explain many of the other properties of gases that have not yet been considered. To illustrate this point we shall take two rather simple examples. In the experiment of diffusion of bromine and air, suppose we want to know if the diffusion will be faster at *higher* temperatures. Since according to the theory the molecules move faster at higher temperatures, we predict that mixing should be more rapid. An experiment proves this to be so. In fact, from the assumption that the absolute temperature is proportional to the kinetic energy of the molecules, we can calculate the expected rate of diffusion at any temperature. Here, again, experiments confirm that the observations agree numerically with the predictions.

Deductions—Explanations

We may use the theory to answer another question commonly raised. Why is it that gases do not settle on standing? If a gas in a container consisted of little billiard balls, all experience shows that billiard balls sooner or later would lose their kinetic energy and lie motionless on the bottom of the vessel. The theory answers this question directly. Unlike the collisions of billiard balls, the collisions between molecules are elastic (assumption 4). Consequently the molecules do not lose kinetic energy but are eternally in motion (see below).

Interpretation of Temperature and Heat

Temperature. Assumption 5, suggested in part from a consideration of the dependence of pressure on temperature, states that the absolute temperature is proportional to the average kinetic energy of the molecules.

The idea "average" may require further elaboration. Since the molecules collide with each other millions of times per second, the speed of a given molecule at any given instant is not too significant. At some instant, a given molecule may be moving very fast or very slowly. At some instant a molecule may even stop altogether, as it would if it happened to collide with a molecule of the same but opposite speed. At the very next instant, however, it would be set in motion, and in successive collisions it might attain very high speeds.

If we assume that the molecules behave like perfectly elastic billiard balls, then from the laws of Newton's mechanics we see at once that as the molecules collide and exchange kinetic energy whatever energy one molecule loses, the other gains. This is another way of saying that the average kinetic energy remains the same. The term "average" may have either of two meanings. A given molecule, over a long period of time (a few seconds or less), will have a definite kinetic energy, *on the average*. Alternately, at any given instant the average kinetic energy of all the molecules will have a definite value. Thus, as the result of collisions some molecules may be speeded up and others slowed down, but the average speed can neither increase nor decrease. It can be shown further, though we shall not attempt it, that after a large number of collisions, most of the molecules will have near the average kinetic energy, with fewer and fewer molecules having much higher or much lower kinetic energies than the average (Ex. 15, Maxwell's distribution).

It is the *average* kinetic energy that is a measure of the absolute temperature. For as we add heat from the outside of a vessel and raise the temperature of the gas inside, the added heat soon distributes so that the average kinetic energy of the molecules increases. We find, further, that for a (nearly) ideal gas such as helium, the amount of heat added increases the temperature in proportion to the amount of heat added. In technical language this means that the specific heat of an ideal gas is constant. We conclude, therefore, that the absolute temperature is proportional to the *average* kinetic energy of the molecules.

Quantity of Heat. While temperature represents the average kinetic energy—that is, the amount of kinetic energy *per* molecule—the total heat contained in a sample of gas must be the *total* kinetic energy of all the molecules. Mathematically,

$$\text{temperature} \propto \text{average KE}$$
$$\propto \tfrac{1}{2}mu^2$$

and

$$\text{quantity of heat} = N \times \text{average KE}$$
$$= N \cdot \tfrac{1}{2}mu^2$$

where N is the number of molecules in the sample, m the mass of the individual molecules, and u^2 is the average of the square of the speeds.

Temperature as the Sole Measure of Molecular Kinetic Energy. A further consequence of the theory is that at any given temperature, the average kinetic energy of the molecules of any two gases is the same, regardless of the masses of the molecules. As will be explained in Section 5, the molecules of different gases differ in weight. Thus oxygen molecules are about sixteen times heavier than hydrogen molecules. In a mixture of oxygen and hydrogen, according to the theory, the average kinetic energy of either the hydrogen or the oxygen molecules is the same. This conclusion follows directly from the laws of mechanics as applied to elastic collisions. As the molecules collide, the lighter molecules rebound with higher speeds, on the average, because they have smaller masses, but undergo the same momentum change as the heavier molecules (Newton's third law). Thus, in a mixture, the lighter molecules move faster and the heavier slower, but their average kinetic energy is the same in both cases.

Even if the gases are separate, the average kinetic energy of the lighter hydrogen molecules is the same as that of the heavier oxygen molecules, provided the temperatures are the same. This conclusion follows from the fact that on mixing hydrogen gas and oxygen gas at the same temperature, in any proportion, the temperature does not change. This would not happen unless the average kinetic energy was the same in the separate gases before mixing, and the same in the resulting mixture (Ex. 16).

The conception of heat as molecular energy explains another question that is often asked. What right do we have to assume that the collisions between molecules are elastic—that is, that there is *no friction* in the collisions between molecules? To answer the question, let us suppose for a moment that *there is* friction. Then the molecules, on losing kinetic energy in the collision, would produce heat. But what is heat? Heat is molecular energy. Therefore, in the collisions between molecules their kinetic energy cannot change into heat, *because it is already heat.*

To avoid a possible misconception at this point, we must remind the reader that this interpretation of heat holds only for an *ideal gas*. That temperature is proportional to the absolute temperature holds also for real gases, and for liquids and solids as well. However, that heat is the total kinetic energy of the molecules is only a part of the story for real gases, liquids, and solids, as we shall show in section 5. Heat is molecular energy in all cases, but in some cases it may be potential molecular energy as well as kinetic.

In fact most of the interpretations made so far are strictly applicable to ideal gases. It is, nevertheless, remarkable that only five assumptions, strongly suggested by the experiments, can be woven into a logical structure—*the kinetic molecular theory*—that can explain, qualitatively at least, such a wide variety of phenomena. It is this fact that is the strongest argument for the theory, far stronger than any one experiment, however cogent or psychologically satisfying. Herein also lies the value of the theory. The theory permits us to integrate and correlate many phenomena already known and points the way to the discovery of new phenomena.

With a few added assumptions, suggested by additional experiments, this theory can be refined to explain all the phenomena of gases, and can be extended to explain the phenomena of liquids, solids, and solutions. To this task we shall turn in the next section.

3. EXTENSION OF THE KINETIC MOLECULAR THEORY (TO REAL GASES, LIQUIDS, SOLIDS, AND SOLUTIONS)

In the preceding section we have shown how five simple assumptions, suggested by experiments, can be woven into a logical structure—the kinetic molecular theory—which can then be used to explain a very large number of phenomena. However, this simple theory, which was developed for ideal gases, has two kinds of limitations. In many cases it explains the phenomena of real gases only qualitatively or only approximately. For example, the theory does explain why increasing the pressure on a gas decreases the volume and, indeed, predicts that doubling the pressure reduces the volume to one half of the original. But it does not explain why, in the case of real gases, the volume is not *exactly* one half when the pressure is *exactly* doubled. Nor does it explain why the different gases deviate from the ideal gas laws by different amounts. For some gases, and for all gases under certain conditions, the disagreement between theory and experiment can be quite large.

The second limitation of the simple theory is that it fails altogether to explain some phenomena. One of the most obvious but significant observations is the fact that all gases condense into liquids, if sufficiently cooled. According to the simple theory, gases should remain in the gaseous state and exert their characteristic pressure until their molecules have stopped moving, at or very near absolute zero. Yet all gases condense on cooling, long before absolute zero is reached. Thus iron vapor condenses at 3000° C, steam at 100° C, and nitrogen at

−210°. Even helium, the most "ideal" gas, condenses at −269° C, which is 4° above absolute zero. Furthermore, the simple theory does not explain even qualitatively most of the properties of liquids and solids.

Of course, if we are satisfied with only qualitative or approximate explanations of only some of the phenomena, we may use the theory as it is. It is sufficient for that. Preferably, however, the theory should explain as many phenomena as possible, and as accurately as possible. It should approach the "truth." If the theory is basically sound, we should be able to refine it and develop it further. Therefore, we proceed to modify it by altering some of the assumptions and adding a few other assumptions. On doing this we find that the kinetic molecular theory, without becoming much more complicated, can explain nearly all the phenomena of gases, liquids, and solids with almost absolute precision.

In order to explain the deviations of the real gases from the ideal **Real Gases** gas law and the phenomena of condensation, we need three additional assumptions, all of which are suggested by experiments.

Assumption 6. *There are attractive forces between molecules.*

Assumption 7. *The molecules have a finite volume.*

Assumption 8. *In liquids (and solids), the molecules entangled in each other's fields of forces are practically touching one another.*

Let us now consider each of these assumptions, the phenomena which suggest them and how the assumptions help interpret the phenomena.

Attractive Forces. The very fact that gases liquefy leads directly to the assumption that there are attractive forces between the molecules. Since we have evidence that molecules move at very high speeds even at ordinary temperatures, the logical conclusion is that in a liquid there must be strong attractive forces between the molecules to keep them from flying away from one another. Furthermore, since different gases liquefy at different temperatures, the attractive forces must be greater for some gases than for others. Thus, the attractive forces between the steam molecules must be strong enough to cause steam to condense even at 100° C (373° A); while in helium the attractive forces must be rather weak, since this gas does not condense until it is cooled to 4 degrees above absolute zero.

These attractive forces are far stronger than gravitational forces. In both gases and in liquids we know the masses of the molecules and the average distances between them. On calculating the amount of gravitational attraction, using Newton's law, we find it much too weak to account for the liquefaction even of helium. As the reader will see later, these forces are of electrical and magnetic origin.

Whatever the nature of the forces involved, they are stronger at close range and become weaker at greater distances. This explains why condensation of a gas into a liquid is favored by high pressures. For at high pressures, the molecules of a gas are forced closer together, so that the attractive forces can become sufficiently effective to liquefy the gas.

Finite Volume of Molecules. The assumption that the molecules have finite volume is not really new. It was implied in the simpler theory (assumption 3), where the statement was made that the molecules are far from one another *relative to their sizes.* In gases at low pressures, the volumes of the molecules themselves may be neglected, as compared to the total space occupied by the gas. In explaining the gas laws by the simple theory, we drew conclusions neglecting (that is, considering as zero) the volume of the molecules. However, for gases at high densities the molecules are close together, and the volume they occupy is a considerable fraction of the total space occupied by the gas. Consequently, their actual volume can no longer be neglected.

Molecules in Liquids. If the volume of the molecules cannot be disregarded in dense gases, it certainly cannot be disregarded in liquids. Liquids are thousands of times denser than the gases from which they are formed, and hence the molecules must be very close to one another. Therefore, there must be very little free space between the molecules of the liquid. This idea is reinforced from the observation that unlike gases, liquids are practically incompressible. The reader will recognize the consistency of this argument. Just as we say that gases are nearly all empty space *because* gases are easily compressible, so do we say that molecules in liquids practically touch, *because* liquids require enormous forces to be compressed even slightly. Carrying the reasoning one step further, we can obtain a fair estimate of the total volume of the molecules in a sample of gas by merely measuring the volume occupied by the material when it is a liquid. Thus, since 1750 cc of steam on condensation forms 1 cc of water, the volume occupied of the molecules in steam is 1/1750 of the total volume.

Using the extended theory, the behavior of the real gases can now be understood and explained with high precision. According to the theory, the deviation of the real gases from ideal behavior is due to two causes—attractive forces between the molecules, and volume occupied by the molecules. For any given gas we can estimate the strength of the forces from the temperature at which it boils; and the volume of the molecules, from the volume of the liquid formed on condensing. In some situations the deviations are rather large.

Real gases, at high pressures, deviate markedly from Boyle's law. Starting with 1000 cc of a gas at 10 atmospheres of pressure, and doubling the pressure to exactly 20 atmospheres (keeping the temperature constant), we find the volume not exactly 500 cc, but somewhat larger. The exact volume will depend on the gas and on the temperature, but a representative value may be around 505 cc.

The theory can explain this type of deviation in terms of the volume of the molecules. In a sample of gas of 1000 cc, the fraction of the volume occupied by the molecules is of the order of 10 cc. The free space, therefore, is only about 990 cc. Doubling the pressure reduces to one half, not the total space occupied by the gas, but only the free space. The free space, therefore, has become one half of 990 cc or

495 cc. Since the molecules themselves are not compressed but continue to occupy 10 cc, the total volume of the gas will be 495 cc + 10 cc, or 505 cc. In another gas the volume of the molecules may be 20 cc. In this case, the volume at 20 atmospheres will be one half of 980 + 20 or 510 cc.

From this explanation it is clear that for any gas the lower the pressure, the smaller the deviation. At lower pressures, there are fewer molecules in a given volume, and hence the volume occupied by the molecules becomes a *smaller fraction* of the total volume. At very low pressures the volume occupied by the molecules may be negligible so that ignoring it may make little or no detectable difference. Thus we can also explain why Boyle's law holds best for gases at low pressures and poorest for those at high pressures.

Deviations are also observed in the pressure of gases when they are cooled. If a gas in a rigid vessel (constant volume) exerts a pressure of 4 atmospheres at some high temperature, say 600° A (327° C), and it is cooled to 300° A (27° C), the pressure will not be exactly 2 atmospheres, but less, again depending on the gas. For gases such as nitrogen or oxygen, it may be about 1.9 atmospheres. For chlorine or sulfur dioxide it may be as low as 1.5 atmospheres.

The kinetic molecular theory explains this deviation as due to the attractive forces between the molecules. At high temperatures, 600° A in the example above, the kinetic energy is high, so that the attractive forces cannot appreciably effect the motion of the molecules. Therefore the molecules hit the wall of the vessel almost as hard as they would in the total absence of attractive forces. However, when the gas is cooled to 300° A, the attractive forces become more effective for two reasons. Since the kinetic energy has been decreased, the same forces show a more marked reduction in the force with which they hit. Taking ten dollars from a rich man will not affect his bank account appreciably, but taking the ten dollars from a poor man will. Further, since the molecules have slowed down, they spend more of their time in the neighborhood of the other molecules where the forces are strong. Thus, in cooling the gas from 600° A to 300° A the average kinetic energy has been decreased by *exactly* one half, but the force with which the molecules hit the container wall has been decreased by more than one half. By how much more depends on the gas. For helium, the difference is very small; for carbon dioxide, it is quite appreciable. For any gas, the deviations become smaller at higher temperatures, and the behavior becomes more nearly ideal when the gas is far above its condensation temperature.

Thus, the behavior of real gases and their deviations from ideality can be explained on the assumption of attractive forces and finite volume of molecules. For gases at high temperatures and low pressures, and especially for gases with inherently weak attractive forces, the deviations are small and may be barely detectable. Conversely, at high pressures and low temperatures the deviations become large. For any given gas an estimate of the inherent magnitude of the attractive forces is available from the temperature at which the gas condenses. Similarly, we can estimate the volume of the molecules from the volume of the liquid formed when the gas condenses. There are also several other and independent ways for estimating these quantities. On making the appropriate corrections to the ideal gas law, the behavior of real gases is predictable by the theory to a very high degree of accuracy.

The same assumptions permit us to explain the phenomena of condensation of gases into liquids. From observations we know that any gas will condense if the temperature is lowered sufficiently; also that increase in pressure facilitates condensation. According to the theory, as the temperature of a gas is lowered, the average kinetic energy of the molecules decreases, so that the attractive forces between molecules become more effective. Sooner or later a temperature will be reached at which the average kinetic energy of the molecules will no longer be sufficient to overcome the attractive forces. The molecules then become entangled in each other's fields of force, and form aggregates or bunches which, if large enough, will appear as droplets of the liquid. Increasing the pressure forces the molecules closer together, so that the attractive forces become effective at temperatures higher than they otherwise would. Thus, any gas will condense if the temperature is lowered sufficiently, and increase in pressure facilitates condensation.

Liquids

The kinetic molecular theory has already given us a picture of a liquid. The molecules are still moving as discrete particles with kinetic energy corresponding to the temperature. Their motion, however, is constrained. At all times the molecules are in the strong fields of force of the other molecules. They collide with the other molecules even more frequently in liquids than in gases. Since there is not much empty space between them, the molecules move in a series of "pushes" much as a person moves through a thick crowd. They make headway very slowly.

The theory explains simply and directly nearly all the properties of liquids. Thus, for example, liquids have much higher densities than gases because there is little free space between the molecules. Liquids are practically incompressible for the same reasons. The strong mutual forces have pulled the molecules until they practically touch. Further compression would imply that the molecules themselves are compressed and distorted. Liquids flow because molecules glide over one another. Liquids have a definite volume, because the molecules have crowded themselves as close as possible, to the full strength of their mutual forces. Liquids expand only slightly on heating, because the higher agitation causes harder and more frequent collisions, resulting in a slight spreading out. Liquids diffuse into one another, but much more slowly than gases because the molecules encounter many collisions and there is very little free space between them (Ex. 21).

Surface tension is an interesting property of liquids, requiring a little more explanation. The reader has probably observed insects walking on the surface of water, apparently defying the laws of gravity. Similarly, a steel needle will float if carefully placed on the surface of water. However, if the needle breaks through the surface, it promptly sinks, and insects will sink and drown if pushed into the liquid. Apparently, the surface of the liquid acts as a skin.

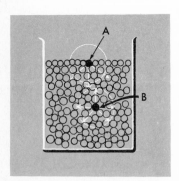

Fig. 7-8. Surface tension. Molecule A, at the surface, is attracted only toward the liquid; molecule B, in the liquid, is attracted from all directions.

The theory explains this phenomenon as follows: Within the body of the liquid the molecules are attracted by the neighboring molecules from all directions. However, the molecules at the surface are attracted only on one side—namely, from the molecules within the liquid. This produces an extra compression in the first few layers and the surface acts as a skin. Thus, unlike a crowd of people, liquids have sharp surfaces. The forces at the surface are called "surface tension." They explain, for example, why small drops of liquid always tend to assume a spherical form.

One of the important properties of liquids is the fact that they boil, becoming gases. Boiling can be understood in a general way by merely considering it as the reverse of condensation. On heating a liquid and increasing the kinetic energy of the molecules, a temperature is reached, sooner or later, at which the kinetic energy is sufficient to overcome the attractive forces. Above this point the liquid becomes a gas; below this point it remains a liquid.

However, the phenomena of boiling and evaporation require further elaboration. Liquids evaporate even below their boiling points. Water left in an open dish will evaporate and become a gas, even at room temperature, which is about 20° C. To understand this phenomenon the reader should remember that temperature is a measure of the *average* kinetic energy of the molecules. This term "average" implies that about half of the molecules are slower than the average, while about half are faster than the average. At any given instant, a small fraction of the molecules will be considerably faster than the average. Now if these very fast molecules happen to be at or near the surface, and are moving in the right direction, they will be able to overcome the strong attractive forces of the surface and fly into the space above the liquid, thus becoming molecules of a gas. Thus, while at 20° C, the average water molecule does not have sufficient speed to overcome the attractive forces and, as a consequence, water is a liquid, nevertheless a small fraction of the molecules will continue to leave the surface and in time all the water will evaporate.

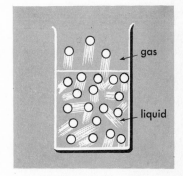

Fig. 7-9. Evaporation. Fast molecules escape through the surface of the liquid.

This explanation is further confirmed by the fact that on a warm day water evaporates faster. At the higher temperature not only the average speed is higher, but, more important, a greater fraction of the molecules move fast enough to escape at any given instant. Hence, evaporation is faster.

A related phenomenon is the dependence of evaporation on humidity. Evaporation is faster on a dry day than on a humid day, even though the temperature is the same on both days. The theory explains this by considering both evaporation and condensation at the surface of the liquid. When a moist cloth is in a dry atmosphere, the molecules leave the surface of the liquid in proportion to the number of molecules that are fast enough to escape at that temperature. They mingle with the air molecules, and gradually diffuse out. (If there are any air currents, they are carried away even faster.) However, on a humid day there are water vapor molecules mixed with the air molecules moving in all directions. Some of the molecules of water vapor will fly into the liquid. Others, finding themselves near the surface, will be pulled into

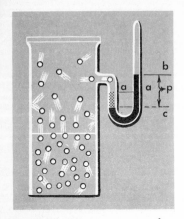

Fig. 7-10. Vapor pressure of a liquid, *p*, is measured by height, *bc*.

the liquid by the attractive forces of the molecules in the liquid. Thus some condensation takes place so long as there is some moisture in the air. The net evaporation is the difference between these two processes. The more humid the atmosphere, the less rapid the net evaporation.

This counteracting effect of evaporation and condensation is understood more clearly in the absence of the air. We place some water in an evacuated vessel, and attach a pressure gauge. At first the gauge shows no pressure, of course, since there is a vacuum above the liquid. Soon, however, the gauge begins to register a rising pressure. Some of the faster-moving molecules are escaping from the liquid. They become gas molecules and strike the walls of the vessel and of the gauge. Simultaneously there is a slight drop in the level of the liquid, a further indication that some evaporation is taking place. However, the pressure does not continue to rise indefinitely. At first it increases rapidly, then more and more slowly until finally it ceases to rise. From this point on the pressure will not rise any further, and the level of the liquid will remain the same.

According to the theory this is precisely what should happen. As soon as some molecules have evaporated into the space above the liquid, a few of them will begin to return, although the majority fly in other directions. As time goes on, more molecules evaporate so that their concentration in the space above the liquid increases, and hence the pressure increases. But at the same time more molecules are returning to the liquid, because there are more of them in the space above it. Thus, while the number leaving the liquid per second is the same as before, the number returning per second gradually increases. This is because the number of molecules evaporating depends on the temperature—that is, on what fraction of them have sufficient speed to escape— while the number returning depends not only on the temperature but also on how many of them are in the vapor phase per unit volume. It is easy to see what the outcome will be. The population of the gas molecules will continue to increase but only to the point at which the number returning will be equal to the number leaving the liquid at that temperature.

This final result is called a state of *dynamic equilibrium*. When this state is reached, there is no observable change. The population of the vapor molecules remains constant, because as many evaporate as condense per second. The pressure also remains constant, because the concentration of the gas molecules remains constant. Similarly and for the same reasons, the amount of liquid remains constant as well as the percent of the water in the vapor phase and in the liquid phase. Everything seems to be at a standstill. Yet, according to the theory, evaporation and condensation are still going on, but they go on at the same rates and cancel the effects of each other.

On raising the temperature we observe a rise in the pressure of the vapor above the liquid, and a greater amount of the liquid becoming a gas. To understand this the reader will recall that a rise in temperature increases the rate of evaporation, since a larger percentage of the molecules have sufficient speed to escape from the liquid. Temporarily, the number of returning molecules is the same as before and, therefore, less than the number evaporating. Soon, however, the greater rate of evaporation will increase the population of the vapor molecules and, consequently, will increase the number returning. Ultimately, when the rate of condensation is again the same as the new rate of evaporation, a new equilibrium will be established. However, at the new equilibrium there will be a greater population of the vapor molecules and a greater pressure than before.

It is now possible to explain more fully the process of boiling. As the temperature of the water is increased, the pressure of the water vapor also increases. If the vessel is rigid and the temperature is raised indefinitely, the pressure will continue to increase and the vessel will ultimately explode. If, however, there is a lid on the vessel, which is carefully counterbalanced so that it has no effective weight, boiling will occur. So long as the temperature of the water is under 100° C, the vapor pressure of water is less than that of the atmosphere, and therefore the atmospheric pressure keeps the lid in place. However, at 100° C the pressure of the steam is exactly equal to that of the standard atmosphere. Any attempt to raise the temperature, ever so slightly, by further heating will result in a pressure of steam greater than that of the atmosphere. Consequently the steam will push up both the lid and the atmosphere. Vapors will issue forth from the mouth of the vessel, pushing up the atmosphere, and bubbles will rise from the body and from the bottom of the liquid. Thus boiling takes place at the temperature at which the vapor pressure of the liquid becomes equal to that of the atmosphere (Ex. 24).

We can now understand, also, why the boiling point of the liquid is not definite, but depends on the pressure of the atmosphere. If we perform the experiment on a mountain where the pressure of the atmosphere is lower, the vapor will reach a pressure equal to that of the atmosphere at a temperature well below 100° C. Thus, on Pikes Peak water boils at 85° C. This is the reason it is so difficult to boil eggs on Pikes Peak. A more lively fire will not help. It will boil the water faster, but the temperature will not rise any higher, and cooking will not be any faster. Conversely, increasing the outside pressure on a liquid will cause it to boil at higher temperatures. This is the principle of pressure cookers. It permits the attainment of higher temperatures, and food cooks faster at higher temperatures.

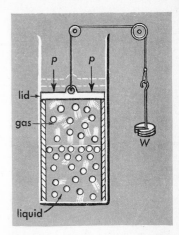

Fig. 7-11. Boiling. At the boiling point the vapor pressure of the liquid is equal to that of the atmosphere, p (black arrows).

Solids

Another important property of liquids is freezing or solidification. All liquids, without exception, become solids if the temperature is lowered sufficiently. According to the kinetic molecular theory, lowering the temperature decreases the average speed of the molecules. The molecules move over shorter and shorter distances between collisions. In continuing to cool the liquid a point is eventually reached at which the molecules do not have sufficient speed to get past their neighbors. Consequently each molecule collides only with its immediate neighbors moving around in the same small space, like a bird in a small cage. Its motion is restricted around a fixed average position. If all the molecules are thus restricted around fixed positions and no longer get past their neighbors, the mass of the material no longer flows but becomes a

a.

b.

c.

d.

Fig. 7-12. Crystalline Forms. (a) Malachite pseudomorphafter azurite. (b) Topaz. (c) Calcite, enclosing copper. (d) Quartz, long six-sided prism. The orderly large scale forms imply an orderly arrangement of the ultimate particles (atoms).

rigid structure. In this manner many liquids, such as syrup or molten glass, "thicken" on cooling, and flow less and less readily until they become solid. However, most substances, the so-called crystalline substances, freeze sharply at a definite temperature without first thickening.

Thus the kinetic molecular theory leads to an understanding of the general structure of a solid. In the solid, the molecules are still separate and still move with kinetic energy proportional to the absolute temperature, but they move in restricted regions around fixed positions. This idea also explains why a solid retains its shape. However, to understand more fully the structure of "true" or *crystalline* solids, we need another idea—the assumption that in crystalline solids the molecules are not only restricted in their motions, but that they are arranged in some regular geometric pattern.

We are led to this assumption from the fact that most liquids on freezing form crystals. The crystals have a visible regular form, such as a cube, prism, pyramid, or some other geometric form. The crystals are often large and easily visible to the naked eye. In some instances, particularly in the case of minerals, the crystals are several inches in dimensions or even larger. The faces of the crystals meet one another at definite angles and have simple geometric forms—such as triangles, squares, rectangles, parallelograms, hexagons, or similar figures. From their regularity we reason that the ultimate units making up the crystal must have corresponding regular arrangements.

The theory can now explain crystallization and the structure of crystals. When the motion of the molecules has been sufficiently restricted, the strong attraction between the molecules forces them as close to each other as possible. It is easy to see that some *orderly* arrangement would result in a more efficient packing. The exact pattern in the crystal depends upon two things: the size and shape of the molecules, and (to some extent) on which parts of the molecules the forces are the strongest.

The behavior of ice, however, needs further explanation. For most crystals, the orderly arrangement of the molecules results in a smaller volume; but in the case of ice, the angular shape of the water molecules, plus the fact that the forces are strongest at certain angles, result in ice occupying a greater volume than the same number of molecules in water. Consequently, ice is less dense than water and floats on water. Water, however, is one of the very few exceptions. Were it not for the fact that water and ice are so common and so important, we would disregard these complications. By far the majority of substances form solids that are denser than the liquids.

The arrangement of the molecules in the crystal can be deduced from a study of the visible geometry of the crystals. In larger crystals we can measure directly the angles between the various surfaces. In smaller crystals, the angles can be measured by reflection of light. Of particular importance is the method of study by using x-rays. The reader will remember that x-rays have short wavelengths, comparable to the dimensions of molecules and atoms. Consequently, layers of molecules (or atoms) forming a surface reflect x-rays. From this reflection the angles between the surfaces and the distance between the layers

Fig. 7-13. Water expands on freezing. The hexagonal arrangement of water molecules results in ice occupying a greater volume *(above)* than the same number of molecules in liquid state *(left)* and thus explains why ice is less dense than liquid water.

can be deduced. We shall not pursue the problem further at this point, except to mention that the study leads to a knowledge of the arrangement and the sizes of the molecules (and atoms). (Ex. 26).

This picture of the crystalline solid permits us to understand the opposite process of freezing—namely, *melting*. At a given temperature, the molecules of a crystal vibrate back and forth in all directions around their fixed and orderly positions. On raising the temperature, the vibrations become more and more violent. Ultimately a point is reached at which the molecules move so violently that they do not return to their average positions but move past their neighbors. Their motion is now independent and chaotic. They have become the molecules of a liquid. Thus a solid can be heated only to a temperature at which the attractive forces of the neighboring molecules are still strong enough to force a given molecule to vibrate around fixed positions. Above this temperature the molecules overcome the attractive forces of the neighbors and the solid becomes a liquid. This temperature is the melting point of the liquid (Ex. 27).

Freezing and melting can be best understood as an instance of equilibrium. We start with water in a thermos bottle at room temperature and add very cold ice—say at $-10°$ C. At first the ice will warm up and the water will cool. However, the ice cannot warm up above $0°$ C, and the water cannot cool below $0°$ C. Some of the ice will melt until the temperature of both the ice and the water is $0°$ C. No further change is observed if heat does not enter from the outside nor leave from the inside. Things appear to be at a standstill. The temperature is constant, the amount of ice is constant, and the amount of water is constant.

Yet, according to the kinetic molecular theory, both melting and

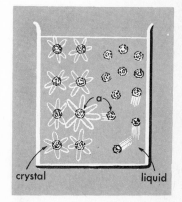

crystal   liquid

Fig. 7-14. Melting. The agitated molecules, a, leave the crystal and mingle with the other molecules of the liquid.

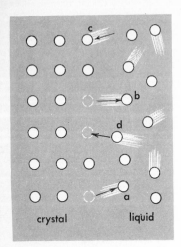

Fig. 7-15. Melting and freezing. At equilibrium, as many molecules (a and b) leave the crystal as are returning (c and d) per second.

freezing continue, but at equal rates. At 0° C, since both ice and water have the same temperature, their molecules have the same average kinetic energy. In the crystal, some molecules move faster than the average. If these fast molecules are at the surface of the crystals, they will overcome the attractive forces of the neighboring molecules and mingle with the molecules of the liquid. Consequently, some melting is going on. At the same time in the liquid some molecules are slower than the average. If these slow molecules happen to be near the surface of the crystal, they will be attracted by the molecules in the crystal and forced to take a position in the pattern. Consequently, some freezing is going on. At 0° C as many molecules leave the crystals as return to it per unit time, and hence the total quantity of ice and water remains constant.

The correctness of this explanation can be supported in many ways, but most directly by the following observation. If in an ice-water mixture at 0° C we crack some of the ice into jagged crystals, after some time the ice surface once again becomes smooth. The protrusions have melted away and the depressions have filled in. Yet, the total weight of the ice has not changed. Apparently the molecules from the protrusions escaped, while other molecules deposited at the depressions, but as many escaped as deposited per unit time.

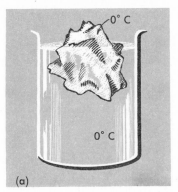 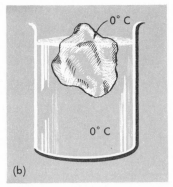

Fig. 7-16. Evidence for equilibrium. Jagged piece of ice (left) becomes smooth (right), but does not change in weight.

Solutions

A solution is defined as a uniform or homogeneous mixture of two (or more) substances. A very common type is a solution of a solid in a liquid, such as sugar in water. Also common are solutions of liquids in other liquids, such as alcohol in water, and gases in liquids, such as carbon dioxide in water. The dissolved substance, the sugar, is called the *solute* and the dissolving medium, the water, is called the *solvent*. The designation is somewhat arbitrary. A mixture of alcohol and water can be considered either as a solution of water in alcohol or as a solution of alcohol in water. Usually the substance in larger amounts is considered as the solvent.

Less usual are solutions in which the solvent is a solid and the resulting solution is solid. Thus we may have a gas, a liquid, or a solid dissolved in another solid. The remaining possibilities are not usually called solutions. A "solution" of a gas in another gas is considered as merely a mixture of gases. Similarly, solids and liquids cannot be considered as "dissolving" in gases. In order to "dissolve" in a gas, evaporation must take place, resulting in simply a mixture of gases. The suspensions of solid or liquid droplets in a gas are not true solutions and will settle sooner or later. True solutions do not settle on standing, and they appear clear and perfectly uniform even under the most powerful microscopes. For these reasons the theory explains solutions as mixtures in which the individual molecules of the solute are distributed uniformly among the molecules of the solvent.

In the most general terms the phenomena of solution imply that there are attractive forces between the molecules of the solute and the molecules of the solvent. Since sugar dissolves in water, there must be attraction between sugar molecules and water molecules. Further, this attraction must be greater than the attraction of sugar molecules for sugar molecules, and also greater than the attraction of water molecules for water molecules. For, in dissolving, sugar molecules are separated from other sugar molecules and after dissolving they separate water molecules from other water molecules. In general, if A dissolves in B, then the molecular attraction of A for B must be greater than the combined effect of the attractions of A for A and B for B. Conversely, the fact that oil does not dissolve in water implies that the attraction of water molecules for oil molecules is not as great as the combined effect of the attraction of water molecules for each other and oil molecules for each other (Ex. 28).

The solution of a solid in a liquid is in many respects similar to the melting of a solid, but, in dissolving, two substances are involved. In both processes a solid becomes a fluid. The common expression "sugar melts in water," while technically incorrect, is nevertheless basically sound. According to the theory, when sugar dissolves in water, the sugar molecules break loose from the orderly arrangement in the crystal and mingle with the water molecules. In the solution the sugar molecules move independently and haphazardly, behaving no differently from the water molecules.

The phenomena of saturation and crystallization point to a further similarity between melting and freezing on the one hand and dissolving and crystallizing on the other. Both pairs of processes are understood in terms of equilibrium. A few crystals of sugar added to some water and stirred will dissolve. As more crystals are added they continue to dissolve, but not indefinitely. Sooner or later a point is reached at which the crystals added do not dissolve. More efficient stirring does not help. The solution is saturated.

According to the theory, at saturation the fast sugar molecules still leave the crystals and the slow sugar molecules in the solution deposit on the crystal, but the two processes proceed at equal rates. We can support this explanation by observing that at saturation the crystals grow more perfect and larger as time goes on, but their total weight remains unchanged. We can also demonstrate this view in another way. If the solution stands without cover, some water evaporates, and the amount of crystals increases. Quite obviously, as the water evaporates and increases the concentration of the sugar molecules, more molecules deposit per second than dissolve and hence the crystals grow.

The dissolving of a gas in a liquid is similar to condensation. The gas in solution is in many respects similar to a liquid. The molecules move haphazardly like the molecules of the solvent. The fastest moving molecules of the dissolved gas, if near the surface, escape and equilibrium is established when as many molecules evaporate per second as dissolve (condense). The solution is saturated with the gas. Increasing the pressure over the gas causes a faster rate of dissolving until again a new equilibrium is established. At the new equilibrium more gas has dissolved than before. Thus pressure increases the solubility of gases. Similarly, raising the temperature increases the rate of escape of molecules, resulting in smaller solubility of the gas. Thus gases are less soluble at higher temperatures. In fact all the phenomena of solutions of gases can be explained by the theory, and are in every way similar to those exhibited by pure liquids.

The amount of dissolved substance at equilibrium is called the solubility, which may be expressed in several ways, such as the amount of the dissolved substance in a given quantity of the solvent, or in a given quantity of the solution. Different substances differ widely in solubility in the same medium, and the same substance differs in solubility in different media. A few general rules can be given. Substances dissolve in media in which they are similar. *Like dissolves like.* Water-like substances dissolve in water. Oillike substances dissolve in gasoline and other oillike media. Metals dissolve in molten metals. Solids and liquids in liquid solvents are more soluble at higher temperatures, although there are many exceptions. Gases are invariably less soluble at higher temperatures and more soluble at higher pressures. For any pair of substances specific information is necessary. However, in all the myriads of instances, the theory gives a complete and quantitative picture of the behavior of solutions.

Thus, with only a few assumptions the extended theory can explain the countless phenomena exhibited by matter in the gaseous, liquid, and solid states, and in solution.

4. THE KINETIC THEORY OF HEAT

In the previous discussion the phenomena of heat have been explained in terms of the ideas of motion and kinetic energy. By this time the reader has probably realized that the kinetic molecular theory is not only a theory of the structure of matter, but also a theory of heat. For instance (p. 183), for an ideal gas, the absolute temperature is proportional to the average kinetic energy of the molecules, and in a sample of gas the quantity of heat is the total kinetic energy of all the molecules. Without being entirely explicit we have extended these ideas to real gases, liquids, solids, and solutions, and in terms of them have explained heat phenomena, such as heating and cooling, boiling and condensing, melting and freezing. It is well at this point to become more explicit and organize these ideas into a coherent system.

In a nearly ideal gas, the molecules have negligible volume and there are negligible attractive forces between them. In a strictly ideal gas (which does not exist), both the volume and the attractive forces are taken as exactly zero. Consequently the molecules move unhindered throughout the whole volume occupied by the gas and exert on the wall of the confining vessel a pressure proportional to their average kinetic energy. Since the *pressure* is proportional to the absolute temperature, the average kinetic energy also must be proportional to the absolute temperature.

In real gases the volume of the molecules is still small but no longer negligible. The molecules have definite size or *extension,* like ordinary objects, and probably have parts held together by forces, much like a coiled spring. An object such as a coiled spring can have three kinds of kinetic energy. It can move as a body in a straight line and have *translational* kinetic energy; it can turn on an axis and have *rotational* kinetic energy; or its parts can vibrate and hence have *vibrational* kinetic energy. The situation is similar with molecules. But now on comparing the molecules of real gases with those of ideal gases we see that only the translational kinetic energy is involved in collisions with each other and with the wall, and hence only the translational kinetic energy is proportional to the pressure. This means, of course, that only the translational kinetic energy is proportional to the absolute temperature.

Fortunately, this complication is not too serious. From the laws of collisions obeyed by all material bodies it can be shown (though we shall not attempt it here) that after many collisions a definite fraction of the total energy is translational, a definite fraction is rotational, and a definite fraction is vibrational. Therefore the absolute temperature of a gas is still proportional to the average kinetic energy of the molecules (Ex. 18 and 29).

Even in liquids and solids the absolute temperature is proportional to the average (translational) kinetic energy of the molecules. For instance if a gas is in a glass vessel, over mercury, the molecules collide with each other and with the walls, the mercury surface being one of the walls. But the mercury surface is itself composed of molecules, and collision with the mercury surface means collision of the gas molecules with the mercury molecules. If the temperature of the mercury is the same as that of the gas, neither heating nor cooling of the gas occurs. This means that the gas molecules rebound on the *average,* with the same speed with which they strike, and implies that the average kinetic (translational) energy of the mercury molecules is the same as that of the gas molecules. The same argument holds for the molecules of the

Temperature

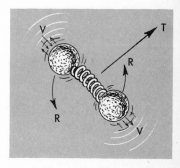

Fig. 7-17. Like a spring dumbbell, a molecule has three kinds of kinetic energy: translational, *T,* rotational, *R,R,* and vibrational, *V,V.*

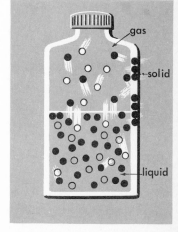

Fig. 7-18. At the same temperature the molecules of gases, liquids, or solids have the same average translational kinetic energy.

glass wall. Therefore the average (translational) kinetic energy of the molecules is proportional to the absolute temperature, whether the material is a gas, a liquid, a solid, or a mixture. More important, if two materials have the same temperature, their molecules have the same average (translational) kinetic energy, regardless whether they are gases, liquids, or solids, solutions, or any other kind of mixture.

This conception of temperature explains very clearly the process of heating a gas. The usual way of heating a gas is to apply a flame to the vessel containing the gas. At first the walls of the vessel become hot, which means that the molecules of the wall of the vessel increase in speed and have a higher kinetic energy than before. Within the vessel, the molecules of the gas collide with the faster molecules of the wall and rebound (on the average) with more energy than they strike. This means, of course, that their average speed has been increased— that is, the gas has a higher temperature than before. The heating will continue until the temperature of the gas is the same as that of the wall. At this point the molecules of the gas rebound with the same speed as they strike, and therefore the molecules of the wall have the same average kinetic energy as the molecules of the gas.

The same ideas explain the heating of a solid vessel by a flame. The molecules of the flame, having a higher kinetic energy than those of the wall of the vessel, speed up the molecules of the wall, until the molecules of the wall have the same average kinetic energy as those of the flame. The ideas can be extended to explain all cases in which one body heats another by contact. When a hot piece of iron is placed on a cold piece of copper, the molecules exchange energy at the place of contact. The molecules of the hotter iron speed up the molecules of the colder copper, until the average kinetic energy is the same for both bodies. These ideas explain further the fundamental fact that heat always "flows" from a hotter body to a colder body. As the molecules collide, the more energetic molecules of the hotter body speed up the less energetic ones of the colder body, until all the molecules have the same average kinetic energy. If the temperature of the two bodies is the same, neither body heats the other, because the average (translational) kinetic energy of the molecules is the same in both bodies.

Heat Content and Quantity of Heat

In an ideal gas the total heat energy of a sample of gas is the total kinetic energy of all the molecules. This implies that we could calculate the average kinetic energy, provided we knew the mass of each molecule and its average speed. We could further calculate the total kinetic energy in a sample, if we also knew the number of molecules present in the given sample. The total would simply be the average kinetic energy multiplied by the number of molecules. However, these quantities cannot be obtained from direct measurement on individual molecules. Nevertheless it is possible to obtain *relative* values without knowing these quantities. Thus a sample of an ideal gas at 400 degrees absolute should have twice the total heat energy as at 200 degrees absolute. Similarly, heating an ideal gas from 200 degrees absolute to 400 degrees absolute should double the total kinetic energy per gram, and heating it to 600 degrees absolute should triple it. Any heat added to the gas increases the total kinetic energy of all the molecules and registers directly as a rise in temperature.

In a real gas two complications appear. The total kinetic energy of all the molecules is now the sum of the total translational, rotational, and vibrational kinetic energy of all the molecules. A real gas at 200 degrees absolute has more total kinetic energy than an ideal gas, although its *translational* kinetic energy is the same as that of an ideal gas, for the same number of molecules, at that temperature.

In a real gas a more significant complication arises from the presence of attractive forces between molecules. As a gas expands and the molecules move further apart from one another, the molecules gain potential energy in overcoming the attractive forces. This is entirely analogous to the potential energy gained in lifting stones away from the earth's surface against the forces of gravity. Therefore, as heat is added to a gas to expand it, a small fraction of the added heat does not increase the kinetic energy but increases the *potential* energy of the molecules. This small fraction of the heat does not register as a rise in temperature, because temperature is a measure *of only* the kinetic energy of the molecules. Thus the heat energy of a gas may be *potential as well as kinetic energy* of the molecules.

Heat of Vaporization

So long as we are considering expansion of gases where the molecules are already far apart, we find that the forces are weak and the gain in potential energy is negligible. However, on considering the process of evaporation of a liquid, we find the magnitude of the forces great. The reader will recall that in the liquid the molecules are practically touching one another and are held close to one another with powerful forces. In order for a liquid to evaporate, the molecules must overcome the strong attractive forces, gaining a considerable amount of potential energy in the process.

That this energy is very high is shown by the fact that a great deal of heat is necessary to boil a liquid. Thus 540 calories are necessary to boil 1 gram of water. This quantity of heat is more than five times the amount necessary to heat 1 gram of water from $0°$ C to $100°$ C. Yet this heat does not increase the average kinetic energy of the molecules, because both the steam and the boiling water are at $100°$ C and, hence, their molecules have the same average kinetic energy. The entire amount of the heat of vaporization, therefore, becomes *increased potential* energy of the molecules (Ex. 30).

A similar phenomenon is observed in melting. On heating very cold ice, say from $-20°$ C, at first the temperature rises to $0°$ C. In this interval, the added heat becomes almost entirely kinetic energy of the molecules. However, at $0°$ C the ice melts giving water whose temperature is also $0°$ C. The continued addition of heat will not raise the temperature. The added heat, 80 calories per gram, merely changes ice at $0°$ C to water at $0°$ C. Since the temperature is the same, the average kinetic energy of the ice and of the water molecules must be the same. The added heat, therefore, increases the *potential* energy of the molecules. It is the energy necessary to overcome the forces holding the molecules in the orderly arrangement of the crystal.

Distinction between Temperature and Heat

These ideas may be summarized by drawing a sharper distinction between temperature and quantity of heat. Temperature is a measure of the average translational kinetic energy of the molecules. It is an intensive quantity. It is, in a sense, a rate—an average energy *per* molecule. Heat, on the other hand, is a total quantity. It is the total energy of all the molecules in a given sample. Moreover, heat may be kinetic molecular energy (of all three kinds) or it may be potential molecular energy. If the former, any increase of it registers as rise in temperature. If the latter, it registers as a change of state, either as melting or as boiling. A given substance, above absolute zero, will have, in general, both kinds of molecular energy. For example, a pound of steam at 120° C contains, as kinetic energy of the molecules, all the heat that is necessary to raise its temperature from absolute zero to 393 degrees absolute, and as potential energy all the heat that is necessary to melt the ice and to boil the water (and to a much smaller extent the heat necessary to expand the substance somewhat).

Interpretation of the Law of Conservation of Energy

The kinetic theory explains in a satisfactory manner the law of conservation of energy. We know in mechanics that if a moving body is suddenly stopped, the kinetic energy of the body is transformed into heat. Let us consider a box in motion containing a gas at room temperature. In this box, the molecules possess two kinds of kinetic energy. One is the average KE, corresponding to 20° C, or 293° A. This KE is due to the chaotic or haphazard motion of the molecules. But in addition, since the box with the gas in it moves as a whole, the molecules have an additional amount of KE in the direction of motion. This kinetic energy is orderly, and is superimposed on the chaotic kinetic energy. It *does not register as temperature*. If the box suddenly stops by colliding with the floor, there is, of course, no longer any orderly motion, for the box as a whole is no longer moving. What becomes of this orderly energy? In terms of the theory the molecules should collide with the walls of the box and with each other and the orderly motion should soon become *increased* chaotic motion. But increased chaotic motion means rise in temperature—the orderly KE of the body as a whole has become chaotic kinetic energy, which is heat.

From the point of view of the kinetic theory we can rewrite the law of conservation of energy as follows:

$$\text{Mechanical energy} + \text{heat energy} = \text{constant}$$

or in symbols,

$$\underset{\substack{\text{(of the bodies}\\\text{as a whole)}}}{\text{KE} + \text{PE}} \quad \underset{\substack{\text{(of the molecules}\\\text{in those bodies)}}}{+ \text{KE} + \text{PE}} = \text{constant}$$

From the example of the box of gas colliding, we can also see why, in general, mechanical energy always tends to be transformed into heat. When the box collides and stops, the orderly motion of the molecules can become chaotic. On the other hand, for the chaotic energy to become orderly very improbable events would have to occur. It would be necessary that *all* the molecules "agree" at a given instant to move in the same direction. If that should happen the box as a whole *would move* in the direction of the motion of the molecules. This is, however, highly improbable—and is not likely to happen even once in a lifetime.

Thus the kinetic theory explains the behavior of matter in the three states. It is important, however, not to miss the significant point. All the explanations have been made by a strict application of the laws of mechanics. The molecules have been treated as tiny billiard balls, having masses, momenta, accelerations, etc., and exerting forces. In other words, gases, liquids, and solids are conceived as mechanical devices. Just as Newton explained the solar system as a mechanical clock, so we have explained a gas as a *machine*. Thus, Newton's laws of motion bind together all these groups of phenomena, from the behavior of the colliding billiard balls to the motion of planets and to the behavior of gases.

5. ARE THE MOLECULES REAL?

The tremendous success of the kinetic molecular theory in explaining simply, logically, consistently, and with high precision all (or nearly all) the phenomena of gases, liquids, solids, and solutions constitutes by far the most important evidence in its favor. It would not be possible to explain the wide range of phenomena if the basic assumptions that matter consists of *molecules* in *motion* did not contain some fundamental truth. In fact, it is very difficult—if not impossible—to conceive of any other alternative. Most scientists, as well as nonscientists who examine the evidence, are quite convinced by this evidence.

Yet a hard skeptic who questions the reality of molecules, or at least insists that the case for molecules has not been conclusively "proved," has some strong points in his favor. All the explanations given thus far are in terms of these very small particles, which are individually invisible. The fact remains that no one has seen a molecule of a gas, a liquid, or an ordinary solid such as ice or sugar. Moreover, a molecule is so small it will probably never be seen. A molecule is too small to reflect ordinary light. Light waves are too long to give an outline of the shape of the molecule or even to show that it is there. To be sure, some giant molecules of certain solids, such as proteins, have been seen in the field of the electron microscope, but these "molecules" are so large that there is some question whether the term "molecule" can be applied to them without some qualifications. In the original and strict sense, a molecule is *that small particle of a gas* that has a more or less independent existence. It moves as a unit, has mass, momentum, kinetic energy, strikes a wall, and so on. Is there more direct information about these molecules?

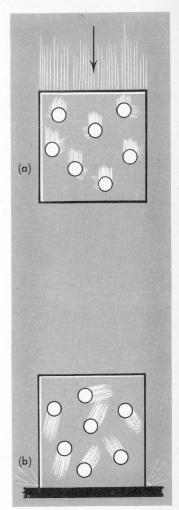

Fig. 7-19. Heat developed by friction. In a moving box (a) the molecules have both orderly and chaotic motion. When the box stops the orderly motion of the molecules becomes *increased* chaotic—hence temperature rises.

Fortunately, the kinetic molecular theory opens the way to a great deal more information about molecules and points to experiments by which we can measure their size, mass, speed, kinetic energy, and count their number in a given sample. We proceed to this goal in two more or less distinct steps. By appropriate development of the theory we can learn to measure the *relative* masses, speeds, kinetic energies, sizes, and numbers of the various kinds of molecules, under a given set of conditions. Then by appropriate experiments we can measure their *actual* sizes, masses, and other magnitudes.

The Quantitative Statement of the Theory

In order to obtain numerical measurements of either the relative or the absolute magnitudes of the molecules, the theory has to become mathematical. We shall keep the mathematics to a bare minimum here, relying as much as possible on pictorial representation and arguing logically—much as we have done so far. If the reader makes a serious effort to follow the argument, he will be rewarded with a more sound understanding. Even if he does not remember all the mathematical steps, he will gain a good insight if he follows the *trend* of the argument.

The theory can best be developed mathematically by taking a definite problem. In a box containing a gas, a good problem is to calculate the pressure, $p,$ that is exerted on the walls by the bombardment of the molecules. For the sake of simplicity, we take an ideal gas in a cubical box (Fig. 7-20), whose side is $l,$ and hence whose volume, $V,$ is l^3. Let the temperature be $T,$ and the total weight of the gas be M. It is clear that all these quantities—$p,$ $l,$ $V,$ $M,$ and T—can be measured.

To make the situation still more specific we take 1 liter of hydrogen under standard conditions and treat it as an ideal gas (which it almost is). The edge of the box, $l,$ is 10 centimeters and the area of a side, $A,$ is 10×10 or 100 square centimeters, and the volume, $V,$ is $10 \times 10 \times 10$ or 1000 cubic centimeters. The temperature, $T,$ is $0°$ C or $273°$ A; the pressure, $p,$ is 1 atmosphere or about 1,000,000 dynes per square centimeter, and the weight of hydrogen, $M,$ is about 0.09 grams. All these quantities can be readily measured with ordinary instruments.

In this specific situation, the problem is to calculate the pressure

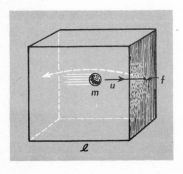

Fig. 7-20. Molecules in a cubical box. From the directly measured quantities, $T,$ $p,$ $M,$ $V,$ and $l,$ the unknown molecular quantities, **m, u,** and **N** can be calculated. Example is a liter of hydrogen at STP.

temperature, T	$= 273°$A
pressure, p	$= 10^6$ dynes/cm²
mass, M	$= 0.09$ grams
volume, V	$= 1000$ cc
length of box, l	$= 10$ cm

Unknown molecular quantities:

mass of hydrogen molecule	$=$ **m**
speed of hydrogen molecule	$=$ **u**
number of hydrogen molecules	$=$ **N**

from the bombardment of the hydrogen molecules and compare it with the measured pressure. If we knew the mass of an individual hydrogen molecule, *m*, its average speed, *u*, and the number of molecules in the box, *N*, we could calculate the pressure. Since we do not know these quantities, we treat them as "unknowns" and write them in bold type as **m, u,** and **N,** respectively to distinguish them from the quantities measurable by ordinary instruments.

1. The first step is to calculate the force exerted by a single molecule on a wall. Concentrating on the shaded wall (Fig. 7-20) whose area is *A*, we consider a molecule with average speed, headed toward that wall.

(a) Since the mass is **m,** and the average velocity **u,** the momentum of the molecule is **mu.**

> Momentum of average molecule $= \mathbf{mu}$

(b) On striking the wall the molecule rebounds elastically. Since it is moving with momentum $+$ **mu** and rebound with the momentum $-$ **mu,** it suffers a *change* in momentum by 2 **mu.** (Had it stopped dead at the wall, the momentum change would have been only **mu.**)

> Momentum change per impact $= \mathbf{2mu}$

(c) The next question is: How many times per second does this molecule strike the shaded wall? The molecule would rebound on the opposite wall, and return to strike the shaded wall again, after it has covered a distance of 2*l*. Since it travels with an average speed of **u** centimeters per second, it will strike the *shaded* wall $\dfrac{\mathbf{u}}{2l}$ times per second.

> Number of strikes per second per molecule $= \dfrac{\mathbf{u}}{2l}$

(d) Thus a single molecule changes momentum by **2mu** every time it strikes, and it strikes $\dfrac{\mathbf{u}}{2l}$ times per second. Therefore the momentum change per second for the molecule is $\mathbf{2mu} \cdot \dfrac{\mathbf{u}}{2l}$ or $\dfrac{\mathbf{mu}^2}{l}$.

> Total momentum change per molecule per second $= \dfrac{\mathbf{mu}^2}{l}$

(e) But, by Newton's second law of motion, momentum change per second is the (average) force. Therefore the force exerted by this molecule is $\dfrac{\mathbf{mu}^2}{l}$.

> $$f = \frac{\mathbf{mu}^2}{l}$$

2. The second step is to calculate the total force exerted on the shaded wall by all the molecules striking it. A few molecules strike squarely on the wall. In general, however, they strike at all angles, and many molecules strike the other pairs of sides of the box.

Although at first sight calculating the number that strike the shaded wall may appear complicated, a simple analysis gives the answer. Since the box is cubical, an equal number strike each wall per second. In the ideal case, where the molecules have no volume, all their collisions would be with the walls. Since they are moving in all directions, one sixth of their total momentum is in the direction of each wall; that is, one third of the total momentum is in the direction (toward or away from) each pair of opposite sides. The effect would be *exactly the same as if* one third of the molecules moved back and forth, one third moved up and down, and one third moved inward and outward: that is, one third of the momentum is in the direction of each of the three dimensions of the box.

Thus the number of molecules producing the force on the shaded wall is *effectively* one third of the total number in the box, or N/3. Therefore the *total* force, F, is equal to the force exerted by the average molecule *times* the number of molecules in the box.

$$F = \frac{N}{3} \cdot \frac{mu^2}{l} \tag{1}$$

3. The third step is rather simple. Since pressure is defined as force per unit area, then

$$\text{force} = \text{pressure} \times \text{area}$$

or

$$f = pA,$$

and, therefore,

$$pA = \frac{N}{3} \cdot \frac{mu^2}{l} \tag{2}$$

or

$$p = \frac{N}{3} \cdot \frac{mu^2}{l}$$

Since the shaded area times the length, l, is the volume of the gas $(A \cdot l = V)$ we obtain

$$p = \frac{N}{3V} \cdot mu^2 \tag{3}$$

This is the fundamental equation of the kinetic theory of gases. It applies strictly to ideal gases, but it is highly accurate for hydrogen and very accurate of the other gases under ordinary conditions. It expresses the pressure of a gas in terms of **N, m,** and **u,** and the volume, *V.* Since we can measure the volume, *V,* we could calculate *p,* if we knew **N, m,** and **u.** Conversely, since we can measure *p* and *V,* we could calculate any one of the unknowns, **N, m,** or **u** if we knew the other two unknowns.

Absolute Velocities of
Molecules

The velocity of the hydrogen molecules in the box can be readily calculated from the equation $p = \dfrac{\mathbf{N}\mathbf{m}\mathbf{u}^2}{3V}$. While we do not know **m** or **N** separately, we do know their product **Nm.** For, if **m** is the mass of each molecule, and **N** is the number of molecules in the box, the product **Nm** is the total weight of the gas, which can be obtained on an analytical balance. Calling the product **Nm** as *M,* the equation becomes

$$p = \frac{M\mathbf{u}^2}{3V}$$

and hence

$$\mathbf{u}^2 = \frac{3pV}{M} \tag{4}$$

In a liter of hydrogen at $0°$ C and one atmosphere, $p = 10^6$ dynes per square centimeter, $V = 1000$ cubic centimeters, and $M = 0.09$ grams. Substituting in the equation

$$\mathbf{u}_{\mathrm{H}}^2 = \frac{3.10^6 \times 1000}{0.0945} = 3.4 \times 10^{10}$$

and

$$\mathbf{u}_{\mathrm{H}} = \sqrt{3.4 \times 10^{10}} = 1.7 \times 10^5 \text{ cm per sec}$$

The speed of the hydrogen molecules, $\mathbf{u}_{\mathrm{H}}$, is more meaningful if expressed as 1.7×10^3 meters per second, or 1.7 kilometers per second, or still better as 1.2 miles per second. Thus we get the astonishing result that the hydrogen molecules at ordinary temperatures move with an average speed of more than a mile per second.

The equation can be used for all other gases. For example, a liter of oxygen weighs about 1.43 grams at $0°$ C and standard pressure. Therefore,

$$\mathbf{u}_{\mathrm{O}} = \sqrt{\frac{3 \times 10^6 \times 1000}{1.43}} = 420{,}000 \text{ cm per sec}$$

which is a little over a quarter of a mile per second.

Relative Velocities of
Molecules

If we are interested only in the relative speeds of molecules, the calculations are even simpler, by using equation (4). In comparing equal volumes at the same pressure (and the same temperature), the gases differ only in their weight. That is, the numerator would be the same for all gases and only the denominator would be different. A liter of oxygen weighs 1.43 grams at STP, while a liter of hydrogen weighs only 0.09 grams (at the same temperature and pressure). The *relative* weight of 1 liter of oxygen to 1 liter of hydrogen is 1.43 to 0.09, or very nearly 16 to 1. This means that $\mathbf{u}^2$ for oxygen is $1/16$ of $\mathbf{u}^2$ for hydrogen, or better $\mathbf{u}^2$ for hydrogen is sixteen times $\mathbf{u}^2$ for oxygen. Therefore, the average speed of the hydrogen molecules is $\sqrt{16} \cdot \mathbf{u}_0$ or four times the average speed of the oxygen molecules. In this way the relative velocities can be obtained for the molecules of any two gases at the same temperature (Ex. 35).

Relative Weights of Molecules Having obtained the *relative* speeds we can proceed to obtain the relative weights of molecules. The reader will recall that at the same temperature the average KE of all molecules is the same. In the example of oxygen and hydrogen

$$\text{average } (KE)_0 = \text{average } (KE)_H$$

Since, as shown above,

$$\tfrac{1}{2}\mathbf{m}_0\mathbf{u}_0^2 = \tfrac{1}{2}\mathbf{m}_H \cdot 16\mathbf{u}_0^2$$

on canceling,

$$\mathbf{m}_0 = 16\mathbf{m}_H$$

That is, an oxygen molecule weighs sixteen times as much as a hydrogen molecule.

Avogadro's Hypothesis The relative weights of molecules can be obtained even more simply by considering equation (3) and deriving a new principle from it. The equation may be rewritten as follows:

$$PV = \tfrac{1}{3}\,\mathbf{N}\,\mathbf{mu}^2$$

or better

$$PV = \tfrac{2}{3}\,\mathbf{N} \cdot \tfrac{1}{2}\mathbf{mu}^2 \tag{5}$$

In this equation $\tfrac{1}{2}\mathbf{mu}^2$ is the average KE of the molecules, which in turn is proportional to the absolute temperature. It is written as $\overline{KE}$.

This equation is, of course, applicable to any gas, under any conditions. Applying it to 1 liter of oxygen at $20°$ C at 1 atmosphere,

$$P_0 V_0 = \mathbf{N}_0 \cdot (\overline{KE})_0 \tag{6}$$

Similarly, for a liter of hydrogen at the same temperature and pressure,

$$P_H V_H = \tfrac{2}{3}\mathbf{N}_H \cdot (\overline{KE})_H \tag{7}$$

If we now compare the two equations (6) and (7), we obtain a most significant result. Since the pressures are the same, P_O is equal to P_H; since the volumes are the same, V_O is equal to V_H; further, since the temperatures are the same, $(\overline{KE})_O$ is equal to $(\overline{KE})_H$. Therefore, the remaining quantities must be the same, that is, N_O is equal to N_H. In other words, the number of oxygen molecules is equal to the number of hydrogen molecules. More generally, if two gases have the *same volume,* at the *same pressure,* and at the *same temperature,* then the *number* of *molecules must be the same.* This is Avogadro's hypothesis. The Italian physicist Amadeo Avogadro (1776-1850) proposed this hypothesis in 1811, not as we have derived it but as a shrewd guess in order to explain certain regularities in the volumes of gases in chemical reactions (see Chap. 8).

Using Avogadro's hypothesis it is simple to obtain the relative weights of molecules. For instance, 1 quart of oxygen and 1 quart of hydrogen in separate vessels, both at the same temperature and pressure, have the same number of molecules in each vessel. The number of molecules in each vessel is not known, and neither are the weights of the individual molecules; however, the number will be the same for each vessel. By direct weighing, the oxygen gas in the quart is found to be 16 times heavier than the hydrogen. Therefore, since the number of molecules is the same, each oxygen molecule must weigh 16 times as much as the hydrogen molecule. Thus merely comparing the weights of equal volumes of the gases at the same temperature and pressure gives the relative weights of the molecules themselves (Ex. 36).

The situation may be illustrated by a simple analogy. One truck is loaded with grapefruit and another truck loaded with the *same number* of oranges. How much any one grapefruit or orange weighs is not known, nor how many are in each truck, but the number is the same. If on weighing the grapefruit load it is found to be five times as heavy as the orange load, then *each* grapefruit must weigh five times as much as each orange. We still do not know the actual weights of either but we do know their *relative* weights.

Molecular Weights

By comparing the weights of equal volumes of gases at the same pressure and temperature, we obtain the relative weights of molecules. There is great variation in the weights. Thus the molecules of the heavy bromine gas are five times as heavy as the oxygen molecules or 80 times as heavy as the hydrogen molecules. Of all the gases, hydrogen is the lightest, and hence its molecules must be the lightest. The weights of the molecules are recorded relative to the lightest (hydrogen), giving a table of the relative weights of the molecules.

Logically the lightest molecule should be called 1, but for reasons that will become clear later, the standard is set at 2. (Briefly, the reason is that the hydrogen molecule contains 2 hydrogen atoms and it is preferable to compare both molecules and atoms to the hydrogen *atom,* which is the lightest atom.) The weight of a molecule compared to the hydrogen molecule (set at 2) is called the *molecular weight.* Thus, carbon dioxide gas is 22 times denser than hydrogen gas (under the same conditions) and, hence, its molecule weighs 22 times as much as the hydrogen molecule, giving a molecular weight of 44.

The molecular weights of liquids and solids can also be calculated provided they evaporate to form gases. Thus, liquid water and hydrogen gas are not comparable, but steam and hydrogen gas are, at some temperature such as 150° C at which both substances are gases, and at the same pressure. Under these conditions steam is 9 times as dense as hydrogen, and hence a steam molecule weighs 9 times as much as a hydrogen molecule and, therefore, has a molecular weight of 18. This topic will be expanded in Chapter 8.

The Brownian Movement

There is a very interesting phenomenon by which it is almost possible to *see* individual molecules. In 1827, the Scottish botanist Robert Brown (1773-1858) was examining under a powerful microscope some dried spores suspended in water. He was amazed to see that the tiny spores did not stand still, but executed a haphazard and irregular motion, continuously darting now in one direction, now in another. The whole ensemble executed a mad dance in the field of the microscope. At first he suspected that this motion was connected in some way with the life process. But after experimenting with suspensions of powdered salt, powdered rock, and powdered charcoal—all of which are obviously lifeless—and finding the same incessant movement, he came to the conclusion that the motion was characteristic of very small particles, suspended in water. The same phenomenon was later observed in smoke, which consists of coal particles suspended in air. This motion is now called the "Brownian movement."

The explanation of this phenomenon did not come until many years later, when it was realized that the movement was caused by the effects of molecular motion. The suspended particles are bombarded on all sides by the molecules of the water. But the bombardment is haphazard, being by pure chance—a fast-moving molecule hits the suspended particle on one side, then a fast-moving molecule hits it on another side. The result is that the particle moves in an irregular motion. The suspended particles (containing several thousand atoms) are large enough to be visible under the microscope, and yet small enough for the fast-moving molecules to move them appreciably. Thus, in the Brownian movement it is possible to see directly the *effects* of the haphazard motion of molecules on the visible particles, although, of course, the molecules themselves are not visible.

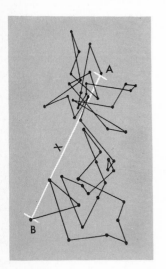

Fig. 7-21. Brownian movement. Path of a smoke particle suspended in hydrogen. The average speed of the visible smoke particle is determined from the net displacement, X, from A to B, in a given time.

Actual Weights of Individual Molecules

In 1911 Jean Batiste Perrin (1870-1942) conceived of adapting the Brownian movement experiment to measure the average kinetic energy of the suspended particle (which later leads to the calculation of the mass of an individual molecule). To find the average kinetic energy of a particle, the mass of the particle and its average speed must be known. Perrin's experiment measured both. We shall describe a variant of the experiment which is both simple in principle and easy to understand, although it requires great experimental care.

We suspend a small quantity of gambose, which is a yellow gum, in a measured quantity of water, and put the suspension under the microscope. By patient and painstaking care, we can actually count the number of particles in the field of the microscope. Knowing the volume of the solution in the field, we can calculate the total number of visible particles in the entire solution. Since we also know the total weight of gum in the solution, we can calculate the weight of the average particle. By repeating the experiments several times we can get a good estimate of the weight of these small, but still visible, gum particles.

To calculate the average speed is somewhat more difficult. We are indebted to George Gamow (1904-——) for an analogy which will help us understand this method. If we observe a drunkard around a lamp post taking irregular steps aimlessly in all directions, after some time we can calculate statistically his position. The drunkard will take some steps away from the post, some toward it, and some in other directions. From simple statistical analysis, it follows that after taking 100 steps, the drunkard will *most likely* be $\sqrt{100}$ or 10 steps away from the lamp post. After 400 steps he will be, most probably, $\sqrt{400}$ or about 20 steps. In general after *n* steps, the drunkard will be most probably somewhere on a circle which is $\sqrt{n}$ steps away from the starting point. Conversely, if the drunkard is found 60 feet away from the lamp post, he must have walked 60^2, or 3600 feet, altogether. Knowing the time since he started from the lamp post, we can calculate his average speed in feet per hour, or in feet per minute.

This method can be used directly in measuring the average speed of a suspended particle. We note the exact position of a gum particle in the crosshairs of the field of the microscope. After some time, say 10 seconds, of continuous observation, the position is again noted. The direct distance from the starting point to the finishing point in the field of the microscope is measured. Squaring the distance will give the total distance the particle moved in that time, and dividing by the time will give the average speed. Repeated observations with many particles will give a good estimate of the average speed.

Having measured the average speed and the mass of the suspended particle, we can easily calculate the average kinetic energy from the formula KE $= \frac{1}{2} \cdot mu^2$. From repeated measurements the value 6.3×10^{-14} ergs was found to be the average KE of particles at room temperature. This value has been obtained from measurements on many kinds of particles suspended in water and smoke and fog particles suspended in air, in hydrogen, and in other gases.

In the next step the average kinetic energy of individual gas molecules is deduced. The significant idea is to consider the suspended particles as giant "molecules." Since they are suspended in the medium, and collide with the molecules of the gas, they behave in every way as tiny "billiard" balls—that is, in the same manner as the molecules. This means that the average kinetic energy of the *visible* suspended particles is the same as the average kinetic energy of the *invisible* molecules of the medium.

We are now ready to calculate the mass of a single molecule. Since smoke is suspended in hydrogen at room temperature, the average KE of the hydrogen molecules is the same as that of the smoke particles, which measured 6.3×10^{-14} ergs.

Therefore,

$$\tfrac{1}{2}\, m_{\mathrm{H}}\, u_{\mathrm{H}}^2 = 6.3 \times 10^{-14} \text{ ergs.}$$

$$m_{\mathrm{H}} = \frac{2 \times 6.3 \times 10^{-14}}{u_{\mathrm{H}}^2}$$

But from earlier measurement, as shown above, u_{H}^2 is 3.4×10^{-10} cm^2 per sec^2.

Therefore,

$$m_{\mathrm{H}} = \frac{2 \times 6.3 \times 10^{-14}}{3.4 \times 10^{-10}} = 3.3 \times 10^{-24} \text{ gram}$$

which can be written as 0.000,000,000,000,000,000,000,003,3 gram—a very small mass, indeed.

We can carry out similar measurements and calculations for all other gases, and many liquids and solids, but there is no need for that. Since we know the *relative* weights of molecules, we can obtain their actual weights directly, by comparison with the hydrogen molecule. Thus, since a water molecule is nine times as heavy as a hydrogen molecule, it weighs $9 \times 3.3 \times 10^{-24}$ grams.

Number of Molecules in a Glass of Water

Knowing the weight of a single water molecule, we can calculate the number of molecules in a glass of water. A glass of water weighs about 240 grams. Since 1 water molecule weighs 30×10^{-24} grams, then in 240 grams there are $\dfrac{240}{30 \times 10^{-24}}$ or 8×10^{24} molecules, which may be written as 8,000,000,000,000,000,000,000,000 molecules.

This number is difficult to comprehend. Perhaps it can be appreciated through an imaginary experiment. We draw from a faucet a glass of water containing 8×10^{24} molecules. Suppose it were possible to label these individual molecules for future identification. (Actually this can be done by making them radioactive, but this is irrelevant to our argument.) Suppose a jet plane is commissioned to spill a few drops of the water over the Great Lakes, some into the Atlantic Ocean, some into the Pacific, and so on all over the globe. Suppose, further, that enough time elapsed for complete mixing, for evaporation and condensation—that is, for the water from the glass to mix uniformly and completely with all the waters of the globe. If a second glass of water is now drawn from the faucet, what are the chances it will contain any of the original molecules? Or how many of the original molecules will there be in the new glass of water?

The answer is about 2000—every glass of water in the globe will have about 2000 of the original molecules. This results from simple calculation. Knowing the volume of the ocean, we can easily calculate how many glasses of water there are in it (Ex. 33). We will find that there are 2000 times as many molecules in a glass of water as there are glasses of water in the ocean. This might help to give the reader an appreciation of the magnitude of the number, or the smallness of the molecules.

A rather interesting and important number to chemists is the num-   Avogadro's Number
ber of molecules in 18 grams of water. The weight of the water (18
grams) divided by the weight of the water molecules (30×10^{-24} grams)
gives 6×10^{23} as the number of molecules. This number is most significant since it also is the number of molecules in 2 grams of hydrogen,
in 32 grams of oxygen, and, in general, the number of grams equal
numerically to the molecular weight of a chemical substance. It is
known as Avogadro's number, and is often symbolized by the letter N.
The reader might recall that this number is the same as the number of
electrons in the unit of electric charge called the faraday (see Ex. 14
in Chap. 4).

Avogadro's number has been determined by many independent
methods—some more accurate than others and some more difficult to
understand than others. But all methods give essentially the same number. Thus we can speak with certainty about the weights, sizes, speeds,
and numbers of molecules (Ex. 34).

In conclusion, let us return to the question raised at the beginning   Are Molecules Real?
of the section. Are the molecules real? On the assumption that matter
consists of molecules in motion, we can explain simply, logically, and
accurately, all the properties of matter in the three states. We can
measure accurately, by many entirely independent methods, the sizes,
masses, and other dimensions of molecules. Yet molecules have never
been seen. We have *assumed* their existence. We are in the peculiar
position of saying that we are not "certain" that molecules exist, but
that if they do, we can tell *with certainty* how heavy they are, how fast
they move, and so on. Are the molecules real? From this point on the
answer to the question depends on what is meant by "real." The
answer depends on individual temperament and philosophic beliefs. The
reader can take his choice. It does not really matter. The important
thing is that he understands what is meant when molecules are said to
"exist" or on what basis an oxygen molecule is spoken of as being
16 times as heavy as the hydrogen molecule. To the chemist the
invisible microworld of molecules is almost as real as the world of
ordinary experience.

NOTES AND EXERCISES

1. Ordinarily, the definitions of solids, liquids, and gases given on
page 174 are adequate. Yet solids *flow* under high pressure. Glacial ice
flows under its own weight. In the interior of the earth rocks flow under
pressure, even though the temperature is not high enough to melt them.
Why is the earth spherical, even though it is probably solid throughout?

Even the distinction between liquids and gases is not sharp at very
high pressures and high temperatures. Liquid water above 450° C and at
very high pressures is indistinguishable from steam. If it is expanded gradually, keeping the temperature high, we end up with steam at ordinary pressures. If it is cooled keeping the pressure high, we end up with water, at
ordinary temperatures.

2. *Pressure.* A trunk 3 × 4 × 5 ft weighs 1000 lb. Calculate the pressure, on the 4 × 5 side, in pounds per square feet; in pounds per square inch. If the trunk lies on the 3 × 4 side, is the weight the same? Is the pressure the same? Explain. Ice, if not too cold, melts at high pressure, even though the temperature is below 0° C. Why do ice skates produce enough pressure to melt the ice? In skating, do you really glide on ice or on water?

3. A cubic centimeter of water weighs 1 gram. Calculate the pressure of a column of water 10 meters high.

4. Before the experiment of Torricelli, a curious phenomenon was noted with pumps. Suction pumps could not lift water higher than 33 ft. This is related to the height of mercury, which is about 2½ ft (30 in. or 76 cm). What is the density of mercury? What is the weight of a column of water 33 ft high and 1 cm in cross section? Why is mercury used in barometers?

5. A cubic inch of mercury weighs 0.491 lb. Consider a column of mercury 30 in. high, 1 sq cm in cross section. What is the total weight of the mercury? Calculate the pressure of the atmosphere in pounds per sq in.

6. It is a simple matter to calculate the total mass of the earth's atmosphere. What is the force of the atmosphere on a square foot at sea level? On a square mile? Since the area of a sphere is $4\pi r^2$, and the earth is 4000 miles in radius, what is the total area of the earth? What is the total weight of the atmosphere? What is the principal source of error in this calculation?

7. If it were not for the pressure of the atmosphere, it would not be possible to fill a fountain pen. Explain. If you have traveled in an airplane, you may have had the experience of having a pocketful of ink—explain.

8. Even though ordinarily gases are very light, appreciable weights of gases are transported in steel cylinders. A 12-qt cylinder at atmospheric pressure contains about 1 gram of hydrogen. At what pressure must the hydrogen be if it contains 25 grams of hydrogen? How much oxygen would this cylinder contain at this pressure?

9. In Figure 7.7, what is the absolute temperature when the pressure gauge reads 1? When it reads 2? When it reads 0? What is the relation between pressure and absolute temperature?

10. A gas contained in a balloon measures 30 fluid ounces at 20° C. What volume will it have if placed in boiling water, 100° C? What will its volume be if placed in ice water, 0° C? Assume the pressure to be constant.

11. The temperature of interstellar space is about −269° C. What is the temperature on the absolute scale? What is it on the Fahrenheit scale?

12. Assumptions 1 and 2 are perhaps the most fundamental. Where does the theory get its name?

13. How does the kinetic molecular theory explain qualitatively the following?

(a) Gases have mass.

(b) Gases have low densities.

(c) Gases diffuse into one another.

(d) A heavy gas diffuses upward into a lighter gas against the force of gravity.

(e) Gases do not settle on standing.

(f) Gases exert pressure.

(g) If a given quantity of gas is compressed into a smaller volume, the *pressure* exerted *by* the gas increases.

(h) If a gas is heated in a confined vessel, its pressure rises.

14. How does the kinetic molecular theory explain quantitatively the following?

(a) If a given quantity of gas is squeezed into a vessel of half the volume, the pressure necessary to do so is double. The pressure exerted by the gas is also double.

(b) If a confined gas is heated to four times the absolute temperature, the molecules must move twice as fast on the average.

(c) If the molecules move twice as fast (on the average), they exert *four* times as much pressure.

(d) If the absolute temperature of a confined gas is quadrupled, the pressure must quadruple.

(e) Diffusion is faster at lower pressures; diffusion is faster at higher temperatures.

15. *Maxwell's distribution of molecular velocities.* Maxwell put the kinetic molecular theory on a rigorous mathematical basis in 1866. Using statistical methods and analyzing the collisions in terms of Newton's mechanics, he obtained the distribution of molecular velocities shown in Figure 7-22. Most molecules have speeds (and kinetic energies) near the average. The number having speeds much smaller and much larger than the average is rapidly decreasing as we move further and further from the average. At any given instant would you expect *any* molecules to be at rest? Would you expect *many* to be at rest? Would you expect many molecules to have two times that of the average? Ten times that of the average? What is the upper limit of energy a given molecule could have? How likely is that?

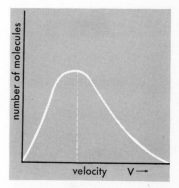

Fig. 7-22. Distribution of molecular velocities at a given temperature. The dotted line represents the average speed.

16. What happens when heat is added to a gas? How do you explain that its temperature rises? What happens when a gas is cooled? What is the lowest limit of the speed of the molecules? To what temperature does this correspond?

17. The molecules of a gas are in perpetual motion. Is this a violation of the principle that "perpetual motion is impossible"? Can you restate the principle more clearly?

18. In the derivation of the kinetic molecular theory equation, a molecule is considered as a particle whose mass is concentrated at a "point." What are the dimensions of a point? Can a point have rotation? Can it have rotational energy? Can it have parts? Can it have vibrational energy? What types of energy can a molecule of a real gas have? (See also Ex. 31.)

19. What is the evidence that there are strong attractive forces between the molecules of a liquid substance? What is the evidence that the attractive forces are greater for some liquids than for others? Are the attractive forces greater for water or for a gas such as oxygen? Why is water liquid at ordinary temperatures while oxygen is a gas? Helium is the most difficult gas to liquefy. What does this imply about the attractive forces between its molecules?

20. What is the evidence that the molecules of a gas have volume and occupy a certain small fraction of the space occupied by the gas? When 1750 cc of steam at 100° C condenses, it forms 1 cc of water at room temperature, but when 1750 cc of ether at 100° C condenses, it forms about 4 cc of ether at room temperature. Comparing steam and ether vapor at 100° C, in which case are the molecules occupying a greater space? If, in both cases, the number of molecules is the same, which molecules are larger? Roughly, how much larger?

21. What is the evidence that the molecules of a liquid (or a solid) practically touch one another, with little or no free space between them?

With some care, it is possible to make a two-layer liquid. The lower layer is a concentrated solution of copper sulfate, which is deep blue; the upper layer is pure water. At first the boundary is sharp, because the copper sulfate solution is denser than the water. However, in a few days the blue color moves slowly upward, and in about a week some of the blue color has moved to the top of the water layer. How do you explain that the heavier copper sulfate moved against the force of gravity? Why is the diffusion of copper sulfate so much slower than the diffusion of bromine in air (p. 177)? What does the experiment show about the motion of molecules in liquids?

A similar phenomenon is observed in solids. For example, gold diffuses slowly into lead if the two metals are in contact with one another (Ref. 7.7).

22. Why does a small drop of a liquid assume a sperical form?

23. A steel needle, although much denser than water, can be made to float. However, if the surface is broken, the needle will promptly sink. What holds it up above the surface? A duck with its oily surface is also held largely by surface tension. The surface of the water is continuous, because it does not "wet" the surface of the duck. If, however, the surface tension of the water is reduced by the addition of chemical soaps so that the oily surface is "wetted," the duck sinks despite its desperate efforts to keep afloat. If the water wets the duck, what happens to the surface tension?

24. That the pressure of the vapor is equal to the external pressure at boiling point can be seen by examining a bubble in a boiling liquid. The bubble is a gas, immersed in the liquid. What would happen to the bubble if the pressure of the liquid *on* the bubble were greater than the pressure of the gas *in* the bubble? In order for the bubble to retain its size, what must its pressure be? Why does the bubble rise?

25. Why is it difficult to cook hard-boiled eggs at high altitudes? What is the advantage of a pressure cooker?

26. By the study of the reflection, diffraction, and interference patterns of x-rays by crystals, it is possible to measure the distances between layers of atoms in a crystal and work out the arrangement of the atoms in the crystal (Ref. 7.3).

27. *Molecular attractions.* At the freezing point, the attraction of the molecules is sufficient to overcome the motion of the molecules. The higher the melting point, the greater the attraction. In which case is the attraction greater, in water or in quartz? In water or in oil?

28. *Like dissolves like.* Gold is insoluble in water, or in oil, but will dissolve in mercury; what can you say about gold and mercury? If you have grease in your clothing, would you use water or gasoline? Why? If you have candy (sugar) which would you use, water or gasoline? Why?

29. The actual analysis of the distribution of molecular energies, although not particularly difficult, is too complicated to discuss in this book. An excellent presentation of the theory is given by Rudolph Clausius, in the paper proposing the theory entitled "On the Nature of the Motion we Call Heat" *Philosophical Magazine*, volume **51**, pp. 108-121, 1857). A more elegant mathematical treatment is given by Maxwell in terms of the Law of Equipartition of Energy (Ref. 7.4d).

30. Suppose a molecule in a liquid is moving upward with more than enough kinetic energy to escape. What happens to its speed as it moves upward against the attractive forces? What fraction of its KE is left by the time it joins the other molecules? What becomes of the KE it lost? It is the PE which the escaping molecules gain that corresponds to the latent heat of vaporization. If a relatively slow molecule in the gas comes near the surface, what will the attractive forces do to its downward speed? Can you explain that condensation results in the release of heat?

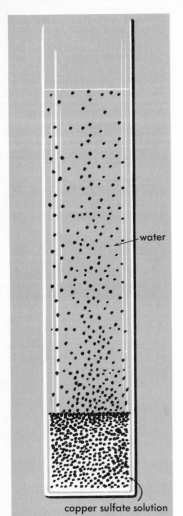

Fig. 7-23. Diffusion of copper sulfate in water. After several days some blue color has traveled to the top.

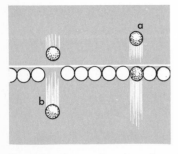

Fig. 7-24. On crossing, the surface KE becomes PE. Speed of escaping molecules (a) is reduced; that of molecule (b) is increased.

31. A molecule of a real gas has three kinds of kinetic energy. If the translational kinetic energy is a definite fraction of the total kinetic energy, and the temperature is proportional to the translational KE, then is it also proportional to the total KE?

32. It is a well-known fact that on compressing air in a bicycle pump, the air gets hotter. If the piston remains stationary, the molecules rebound with the same speed as they strike the piston. Their average speed does not change. Does the temperature change? If the piston moves down during compression, do the molecules rebound with the same, higher or lower speed? Will they have a greater average speed as a result? What will happen to the temperature? What will happen to the temperature of the gas, if it is allowed to expand—that is, to push the piston upward? (Fig. 7.25.)

33. *Volume of the ocean.* Although it sounds like a formidable task, it is rather easy to calculate fairly accurately the volume of the ocean. The area of a sphere is $4\pi r^2$. If the radius of the earth is 4000 miles or 6400 kilometers, what is it in centimeters? What is the area of the earth's surface in square centimeters? Since the ocean covers about three quarters of the earth's surface, what is the area of the surface of the ocean? The average depth of the ocean is about 2½ miles, or about 4.5 kilometers. What is the depth in centimeters? What is the volume of the ocean? How many glasses of water (250 cc each) are there in the ocean?

34. *Size of molecules.* It is rather easy to get a fairly good estimate of the size of molecules from the numbers already obtained. Since 18 grams of water occupy 18 cc, and contain 6×10^{23} molecules, what is the volume of a single molecule (assuming they touch)? If each molecule is a little sphere or a little cube, what is the diameter of the molecule?

35. A liter of helium weighs 0.18 gram, at standard conditions. Calculate the speed of the helium molecule, in kilometers per second and in miles per second.

36. A liter of carbon dioxide weighs 2.0 grams at standard conditions. How much heavier than a hydrogen molecule is a carbon dioxide molecule?

37. How many molecules are there in a pound of water?

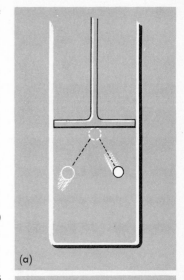

(a)

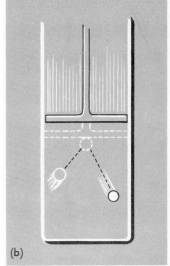

(b)

Fig. 7-25. Compression results in temperature rise. Molecule in (b) is speeded up by moving piston.

8

ATOMS AND
CHEMICAL
CHANGE

I. INTRODUCTION

In the preceding chapter we described the microworld of molecules. All material objects, whether gaseous, liquid, solid, solutions, or
of various mixtures, consist of an immense number of molecules. In a
pure substance, such as water, all molecules are alike in all respects,
but differ from the molecules of all other pure substances. In a mixture
there are two or more kinds of molecules, one kind for each substance
present. Thus in milk, there are molecules of water, molecules of milk
sugar, molecules of fat, molecules of casein, molecules of vitamin D,
and so on for every substance present in milk.

We visualize the molecules as constantly moving and explain
changes such as melting, boiling, and dissolving as processes in which
the molecules change their arrangements among themselves. In melting,
for example, the molecules break loose from the orderly arrangement
of crystals; in boiling, they break away from the strong mutual forces
and move independently; in dissolving, molecules of one substance move
between, and mix with, the molecules of another substance. Throughout all the changes so far considered, the molecules remain intact and

behave as more or less distinct and independent units. The reader will remember that all these processes are *physical changes*.

In this chapter, by considering the more drastic changes designated as *chemical reactions,* we shall delve deeper into the structure of matter and inquire into the structure of the molecules themselves. We shall consider such questions as whether the molecules consist of still smaller particles, and if so what these particles are, how many kinds there are, how many of each kind are present in a given molecule, and how they are arranged in the molecules.

We shall find that the molecules consist of smaller particles, the atoms of the elements. In a few instances, as in neon and mercury, the molecule consists of but one atom. However, in general, the molecules of the 600,000 known pure substances contain more than one atom. The molecules of many common substances contain several atoms and some contain dozens, hundreds, or even thousands of atoms.

We shall also find that there are relatively few kinds of atoms. Whereas there are hundreds of thousands of kinds of molecules (one kind for each pure substance), there are only about 100 different kinds of atoms (one basic kind for each element). These atoms combine in various proportions and in various ways to form the different kinds of molecules of each substance known, and indeed of all the substances possible. The atoms can be likened to the 26 letters of the alphabet, which can be combined in various ways to form hundreds of thousands of words. These atoms are the building blocks of the molecules and hence of the entire material world.

As already mentioned, we investigate the microworld inside the molecules—the microworld of the atoms—by studying chemical reactions. During these drastic changes, the reacting molecules disappear as structures, and new molecules appear. In some instances simple molecules containing one atom merely combine to form more complex molecules; but, in general, the molecules break up into fragments, which then recombine in other ways to form new kinds of molecules. Sometimes the fragments are the atoms themselves but usually are merely groups of atoms. Sometimes these groups of atoms are stable and can exist independently. In that event, the new fragments are the molecules of simpler substances. More often, however, the fragments are unstable under the conditions of the reaction and recombine into different stable combinations.

To the chemist the microworld of atoms is almost as real as the world of ordinary direct experience. In terms of the former, he understands the world of chemical change, which he observes in the laboratory, in industry, and in nature. The discussion will be developed with an attempt to give the reader a sense of this reality by showing how the analysis of the phenomena leads to a definite knowledge of the atoms.

Before continuing, the reader is advised to recall, and if necessary to review, the concepts developed in Chapter 6. In particular, he should have a clear idea of the meaning of the concepts: *matter, property, pure substance, mixture, physical change, chemical change, compound, element;* the distinctions between them; and the general argument that matter consists of particles.

2. CHEMICAL REACTION AND THE ELEMENTS

Let us consider in some detail the essential features of chemical change by taking a few examples. On heating a tablespoon of ordinary cane sugar, for instance, the sugar chars. If the heat is sufficiently strong and the sugar is in an evacuated tube, the entire quantity of sugar will change into charcoal and water (and small quantities of other substances, which we may disregard in our discussion).

This reaction is more instructive when carried out as follows: Three or four teaspoons of sugar are placed in a beaker to which just enough water is added to make a very concentrated solution. So far only a physical change has taken place. The sugar has only dissolved in the water, and if the beaker stands in the open, the water will evaporate and the sugar will be recovered unchanged. If, however, concentrated sulfuric acid is added to the sugar solution, a chemical reaction results. The solution begins to darken immediately, and in the course of a few seconds it becomes pitch black. In the next few seconds it froths violently and fills the entire beaker with a black spongelike mass. A great deal of heat develops—sufficient to boil some of the water, which comes off as steam. This is a very different type of change from the mere dissolving of the sugar.

Fig. 8-1. Crystalline sugar chars to give black charcoal and water. None of the properties of sugar is present either in the charcoal or in the water.

Of the many aspects of the reaction, at the moment we are interested in the fact that matter has been transformed. The experiment started with sugar, whose properties are well known. It has a sweet taste, comes in colorless crystals, has a density of 1.588 grams per cubic centimeter, is soluble in water, is a nutrient, and so on. An examination of the products will show that one of them is charcoal. It is black in color, has a density of about 2.0, has no taste, is insoluble in water— and, in short, differs from sugar in all its properties. If the experiment takes place in a closed vessel with all the products accounted for, there will be more water after the reaction than there was before it took place. In other words, water was produced in this reaction, and it is obvious that water is different from either the charcoal or the sugar. On the other hand, all the sulfuric acid can be recovered unchanged. The acid did not enter the reaction but merely facilitated the charring, and hence need not be considered further.

The fundamental change in this reaction is the destruction of the sugar and the formation of two new substances. A pure substance, sugar, with its entire set of properties has disappeared completely. It has gone *out of existence*. In place of the sugar, two other substances, charcoal and water—each with its own set of properties—have appeared. Not one of the properties of sugar is present in the charcoal or in the water. This is certainly a *change in substance*.

For the sake of clarity we summarize the reaction as follows:

sugar → charcoal + water

The arrow is to be read as "becomes" or "gives" or "changes into."

Another interesting reaction is the union of hydrogen and oxygen to form water. If approximately equal volumes of hydrogen gas and oxygen gas are placed in a bottle, a mixture of the two gases is the only result. Each of the two gases still has its own properties; for on covering the bottle with filter paper, the hydrogen diffuses more rapidly than the oxygen through the pores of the paper, and soon only oxygen remains in the bottle with some air, which diffuses into it. If, however, a lighted match is applied to the open mouth of the bottle containing a fresh mixture, a violent explosion results. Steam is produced, a part of which condenses in the bottle. If the reaction is carried out in a closed vessel, strong enough to withstand the explosion, drops of water condense on the walls of the vessel. An even simpler way of carrying out this reaction is to light with a match a stream of hydrogen as it issues from a cylinder into the air. Air contains about 20 percent oxygen, and we can show the formation of water by cooling the resulting gases with an inverted beaker. In all these instances the reaction is:

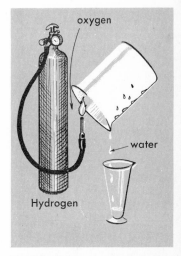

Fig. 8-2. On burning in air, hydrogen combines with the oxygen to form water.

hydrogen + oxygen → water

Here again water is a different substance from the original gases, its properties in no way resembling those of either hydrogen or oxygen.

Another reaction is the union of sodium and chlorine to give common salt. Sodium is a bright silvery metal that tarnishes very rapidly in air. In fact it tarnishes so rapidly that it is kept under kerosene as a protection against the action of air and moisture. The metal is slightly lighter than water (density 0.97) and is so soft that it can be cut with the fingernail. However, since it is corrosive to the skin, it should be cut with a knife and handled with forceps. Chlorine, on the other hand, is a green gas about 2.5 times denser than air. It has an irritating and suffocating odor, and is highly poisonous. It was the first poisonous gas used in the trenches of World War I.

Placing a freshly cut slice of sodium in a test tube, we pass chlorine over it, while heating the tube gently. A reaction immediately follows: The metallic luster of sodium disappears, the slice of sodium crumbles, and salt appears in its place. The chlorine has combined with the sodium to give sodium chloride, which is ordinary table salt.

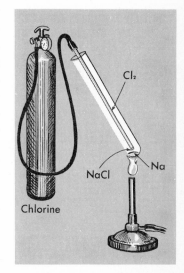

Fig. 8-3. Metallic sodium (Na) combines with chlorine gas (Cl_2) to give salt, sodium chloride (NaCl).

sodium + chlorine → sodium chloride

Another reaction of sodium may be mentioned. On dropping a piece of sodium about the size of a pea on a beaker of water, the sodium reacts violently with the water, skimming over the surface like a self-propelled rocket. A gas, hydrogen, is given off, and the sodium soon disappears. The solution tastes bitter, feels slippery on the finger, and is highly caustic. It is a solution of caustic soda or lye.

sodium + water → hydrogen + caustic soda
(sodium hydroxide)

These examples can be multiplied indefinitely. Thus hydrogen burns in chlorine with a hot, pale-blue flame, to give a gas, hydrogen chloride, which dissolves in water to give hydrochloric acid, the muriatic acid of commerce. When a solution of caustic soda is mixed with hydrochloric acid in the right proportions, both the caustic properties of the lye and the intensely sour properties of the acid disappear. The resulting solution is salty, and on evaporation of the water, crystals of ordinary table salt separate out. In the flashing of the photoflood lamp, the metallic aluminum disappears, and in its place an ashlike solid, the mineral *alumina* appears. The aluminum combines with oxygen in the bulb to form aluminum oxide.

Transformation of Substances

We are now ready to formulate the most fundamental characteristic of all chemical reactions. These changes are "drastic," not so much because they are violent and spectacular, but because matter is transformed. In each of the reactions cited, the reactants with all their properties disappear completely and new products with their own properties appear. The change is not gradual, but, on the contrary, it is sharp and discontinuous. The sugar does not lose its sweetness gradually, but whatever amount chars at any given moment loses its sweetness at that instant. Nor is the change predictable (unless, of course, someone has observed the reaction before). Who could predict that the clear and sweet sugar would become black and tasteless charcoal? That the violent caustic lye and the equally poisonous and sour muriatic acid would become ordinary salt, safe enough for table use and in every way indistinguishable from the salt obtained from the sea? Or that the gray metallic powder, silicon, would combine with the invisible gas of the air, oxygen, to give ordinary beach sand. Even when the reactions are not violent, the changes in substance are equally dramatic. Thus, plants produce colorful flowers and diverse perfumes from a few minerals, water, and the carbon dioxide of the air.

Energy Changes During Chemical Reactions

It is nevertheless true that many chemical reactions are also "drastic" in the sense that they are energetic. In the violent reactions energy is released rapidly and in large amounts. The energy may appear as heat, raising the temperature of the products. The temperature may become high enough to cause the emission of light as in the case of an ordinary fire. In other instances, particularly if the products are gaseous, the heat may develop high pressures and result in explosions. However, many chemical reactions are relatively mild, either because small amounts of energy are released or because the energy is released slowly. Careful study shows that in all reactions that take place spontaneously some energy is released. There are, however, some reactions in which energy is absorbed, and which will take place only if energy is supplied from the outside. Exhaustive study shows that in *all chemical reactions, energy is either released or absorbed.*

The fact that energy is released or absorbed in chemical reactions has far-reaching implications—the most obvious being that we can, and often do, carry out chemical reactions for the release of energy. In fact, we burn coal, oil, or gas in furnaces solely for the purpose of obtaining the energy of the reaction and not to increase the amount of carbon dioxide in the air. We burn gasoline in the cylinder of the automobile for the energy of explosion released in that reaction. Similarly, the chemical reactions in the automobile battery produce electric energy. Even the energy necessary to carry on the life processes is obtained from the chemical reactions; those taking place within the body are essentially the reactions of the "burning" of food.

Of deeper significance is the implication that there exists a new form of energy, namely, chemical energy. We have discussed kinetic and potential energy and heat and have found that for any given system the sum is constant (Chap. 4). In chemical reactions we will find that the law of the conservation of energy does not hold, unless we recognize this new form of energy. Starting with a mixture of hydrogen and oxygen in a closed vessel, we can measure the total kinetic energy, potential energy, and heat that the system contains. But if the mixture explodes, a great deal of heat is developed that *does not come* from the kinetic or potential energy of the system as a whole. This must mean that in the uncombined gases there is another type of energy that was transformed into heat during the reaction. This is chemical energy (Ex. 3).

Conservation of Energy. By a series of carefully designed experiments, the law of the conservation of energy has been extended to include chemical energy. If 1 gram of hydrogen and 8 grams of oxygen are exploded at room temperature, water is formed and 34,000 calories are released. After cooling, a comparison of the mixture of hydrogen and oxygen with the water obtained will show that the water is poorer in energy by 34,000 calories. For in order to decompose the resulting water into oxygen and hydrogen, precisely the same amount of energy must be supplied as was released in its formation. This is the amount of *chemical energy* that must have been present in the gases separately. Thus, in chemical reactions we witness another kind of energy transformation, the transformation of chemical energy into heat (or mechanical energy), and vice versa. If now we include the chemical energy in our accounting we see that

PE + KE + heat + chem. energy = PE + KE + heat + chem. energy
      (before the reaction)   (after the react⁐ n)

This is the extension of the law of conservation of energy to include chemical energy.

We emphasized that in a chemical reaction, the reactants with all their properties disappear, and nothing in the products is the same as was in the reactants. There is, however, one thing that does remain the same. The total weight (or mass) of the materials involved in the change is the same before, during, and after the reaction. It took the genius of Antoine Lavoisier (1743-1794) at about the time of the French Revolution to appreciate this fact, and to establish it firmly as a law of nature, although there were others before him who had noticed it. By careful experimentation he established that the total weight of

Conservation of Matter

all the materials before the reaction is equal to the total weight of all the materials after the reaction. He announced this fact as the "Law of Immortality of Matter." Substances, as forms of matter, may be created or destroyed during chemical changes, but matter itself is immortal—it can be altered in form, but can neither be created nor destroyed.

Today the law is known by the less imposing title as the "law of conservation of matter," and it has been amply confirmed by experiment. In all the countless chemical reactions that have been studied, no change in the quantity of matter has ever been observed. Thus, the weight of a log before burning plus the weight of the air (oxygen) that disappears during burning, will equal the weight of the ashes plus the weight of all the gases that have been produced. We can demonstrate this by burning a piece of wood in a closed vessel, and weighing before and after the burning. More conveniently, weighing a photoflood lamp before the flashing and after the flashing will show the weights to be the same, even on the most accurate analytical balance.

Yet we have reasons to believe that if we could make analytical balances millions of times more accurate, we would begin to notice small differences in mass. The reader has probably already heard that matter can be transformed into energy. Since in the flashing of the photoflood lamp, a great deal of energy was dissipated, some mass must have disappeared. But the same theory (the theory of relativity) that states that matter can be transformed into energy also provides a formula for calculating the amount of matter lost during the flashing. Calculation shows that this amount of matter is far too small to be detected by analytical balances. It is true that in extraordinary changes such as explosions of atomic or hydrogen bombs an appreciable quantity of matter does disappear, but this is a topic for another chapter (Chap. 13). Suffice it to say at this point that the most delicate measurements do not reveal any loss or gain of matter during chemical changes (Ex. 4).

Theoretical Implications   The three features of a chemical reaction considered so far give a considerable insight into the structure of molecules and the nature of chemical change. Having already shown that pure substances consist of one kind of molecule, we reason as follows: Since during chemical change the reacting substances disappear, it must mean that the molecules of these substances are destroyed. Similarly, since new substances are produced, it must mean that new molecules are produced. When oxygen and hydrogen disappear and water is produced, it must mean that the hydrogen molecules and the oxygen molecules are no longer present, and that new molecules, the molecules of steam, have been produced.

The fact that the total weight remains the same indicates that the word "destroyed" is not used in the sense that the *matter* of the molecules disappeared, but, rather, in the sense that the molecules as structures have been "disrupted" and new molecules as new structures appeared. The word "destroyed" is used in the sense that a house is destroyed, and out of the material a new structure (a gas station, for instance) has been built. The entire argument leads to the idea that molecules consist of *parts* that rearrange but are not destroyed during chemical changes. What are these parts of the molecules?

The Idea of Elements

Before proceeding to show that the parts of the molecules are the atoms of the elements, an *element* should be clearly defined. The word "element," itself, means something *simple,* something *fundamental.* Thus in "elements of geometry," "elements of accounting," or "elements of a machine," the "elements" are simple units making up the more complex structure. The evolution of the idea of "element" as a fundamental unit in the composition of matter started very early in the history of civilization.

The idea of "elements" as simple and fundamental forms of matter was introduced by the philosophers of the sixth century, B.C. One of the first men to raise and attempt to answer scientific and philosophic questions was Thales of Miletus (640-546 B.C.). Observing the immense multiplicity of forms of existence and their constant intertransformations, he raised the question, "What lies at the bottom of all this?" Confident that the world is fundamentally simple and can be understood in simple terms, he said that all the forms that exist consist of one fundamental *element* and that the element is *water.* Under the influence of certain forces, water forms other fluids; by condensation it forms ice and other solids; and by rarefaction it forms vapor or air.

Anaximenes agreed basically with Thales but proposed that the fundamental element is *air.* He went on to explain that by condensation and compaction air forms water and liquids in general, and by further condensation it forms ice and solids.

Heraclitus also agreed in principle that the world is simple, but placed his emphasis on the aspect of activity of the chemical changes. The fundamental element is *fire* in this view. By compaction and condensation fire forms air, then water (liquids), and then ice (solids). It is extremely interesting that in a hazy way he came remarkably close to the modern concept that the fundamental reality in the world is energy (fire) and that the forms of matter are merely compact forms of energy (Ex. 5).

By the fourth century B.C., "earth" was also proposed as the fundamental element (Ex. 6). By this time, it was realized that there may be more than one fundamental element. Democritus in the fourth century B.C. proposed that there are four basic elements, namely: earth, water, air, and fire. However, the philosophic arguments and the conviction remained strong that the number of elements is relatively small.

Aristotle (384-322 B.C.), who systematized all previous knowledge, accepted the four elements of Democritus, and added that these are related by the opposite "qualities": hot and cold; wet and dry. He developed a schematism in which the relations were indicated. Thus fire was hot and dry, while water was cold and wet. Unfortunately, he injected a metaphysical twist to the idea of elements, maintaining that the elements were "principles" in the sense of "qualities." Thus, water is the element of "fluidity"—water added to sugar results in a liquid, because it contains the water as an element of "fluidity" (Ex. 7). It

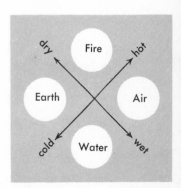

Fig. 8-4. The four Aristotelian elements related by a pair of opposite qualities, cold-hot and wet-dry. Thus water is cold and wet; fire is hot and dry.

would carry us too far afield to discuss adequately the Aristotelian notion of "elements" in its two thousand years of development. In many of their discussions it appears that by the four elements, air, water, earth and fire, the later Aristotelians meant the gaseous, liquid, and solid forms of matter, and the heat or energy that is involved in changing from one state to the other.

The tremendous authority of Aristotle exercised a stifling influence to further development of the idea of elements. In the long interval from Aristotle to the end of the seventeenth century very little progress was made. The alchemists, who were preoccupied with attempts to transform ordinary metals into gold, accepted uncritically the basic notions of Aristotle. To be sure they added (or substituted) the "elements" sulfur, mercury, and salt, and three kinds of earth, but they, too, conceived these as "principles" or "essences" *in bodies,* and not as the *bodies themselves.* Thus, when the alchemists said that a combustible substance, such as a candle, contains the element "sulfur," they did not mean that it contains the yellow substance sulfur or the brimstone of the Bible. They were rather thinking that it contains the principle, "sulfur," that gives it the property of combustibility.

A fresh and revolutionary approach was made by Robert Boyle (1627-1691) near the end of the seventeenth century. He maintained that elements should be thought of as simple *bodies*—that is, simple substances that have their own characteristic properties and that combine to form all other bodies. He theorized that the elements add their essential nature to the bodies in which they are combined. Boyle was not yet free of the Aristotelian tradition; for he doubted that pure elements can exist by themselves and thought that the only way to find out what the elements are is to study the combinations in which they are found.

It took another century and the genius of Lavoisier, to clarify the idea of Boyle's concept, "element" and to apply it to the substances we know and experiment with. Lavoisier said ". . . if we apply the term *elements or principles of bodies,* to express our idea of the last point which analysis is capable of reaching, we must admit as elements all the substances into which we are capable, by any means, to reduce bodies of decomposition." By following this idea he gave us the first list of elements.

Modern Idea of Elements

Certain facts about chemical reactions illustrate, most clearly and directly, the modern idea of the elements. We have already noted that sugar, a simple substance, undergoes charring to produce *two* other substances—namely, charcoal and water

$$sugar \rightarrow charcoal + water$$

Quite obviously, sugar, although a *simple* substance with but *one* set of properties, is not "simple" in any fundamental sense. For, by a chemical reaction, this *one* substance can be made to give *two* other bodies. Sugar, therefore, must be complex because *two* distinct *substances* come out of it. Sugar is not two substances: it is one substance but contains the ingredients from which two substances can be formed.

Similarly, water can be made to give two other substances—namely, hydrogen and oxygen—

$$\text{water} \rightarrow \text{hydrogen} + \text{oxygen}$$

and, therefore, it cannot be an element. A systematic examination of other pure substances will show the following reactions occurring under the proper conditions:

> starch → dextrine + water
> dextrine → charcoal + water
> albumin (egg white) → charcoal + water + ammonia
> ammonia → nitrogen + hydrogen
> salt → sodium + chlorine
> olive oil → oleic acid + glycerine
> oleic acid → charcoal + water + other substances
> glycerine → charcoal + water + other substances

The list can be extended almost indefinitely. Nearly all the pure substances known can be made to give *two* or more other pure substances. Obviously, therefore, these substances are not "simple bodies," but complex or *compound,* in the sense that they contain more than one ingredient in them.

There is, however, a small number of pure substances that cannot be resolved or separated into two or more other substances. No one has succeeded by means of chemical reactions (Ex. 8) in separating carbon, for instance, into two or more other bodies, say X and Y. Thus the following reaction *does not* take place:

$$\text{carbon} \nrightarrow X + Y$$

The same is true of oxygen, hydrogen, nitrogen, iron, sulfur, gold, and a small number of other substances.

This reasoning leads to the recognition of two classes of pure substances: those that by means of chemical reactions can be resolved into two or more other substances, and those that *cannot.* The first kind of substance—such as sugar or water—is a compound substance or simply a *compound;* and the second kind—such as carbon or oxygen—is an elementary substance or simply an *element.*

The soundness of the distinction between compound and elementary substances is further reinforced by consideration of the opposite chemical reactions in which *two* or more substances combine to form *one* substance. Thus hydrogen and oxygen combine to form water. Water, therefore, cannot be *simple,* because *two* distinct ingredients are contained in it. (A simple body can only have one ingredient.) The substances we have already called compound substances can be made from two or more other bodies. On the other hand for the small number of substances we call elements this is not possible. For example, no one has succeeded in combining two or more other substances to make oxygen. Oxygen, therefore, is a simple body; it is an *element.* The same kind of experimentation and reasoning establishes the simple nature of the other elements.

Further support for the nature of the elements emerges from a comprehensive comparison of a very large number of reactions. When the decomposition of compound substances is carried out to the limit of analysis, the same elements appear again and again as the ultimate products. Thus, sugar gives *charcoal* and water, but water in turn gives *hydrogen* and *oxygen*. Thousands of the substances found in living things give ultimately the same elements—*carbon, hydrogen,* and *oxygen*. Some also give, besides these three, *nitrogen, sulfur, phosphorus, iron,* and a few other elements. Over 98 percent of the weight of the rocks with the thousands of minerals contained therein can be separated into eight elements—namely: *oxygen, silicon, iron, aluminum,* and smaller quantities of *calcium, magnesium, sodium,* and *potassium*. When subjected to decomposition reactions, *all* the substances found on this planet can ultimately be reduced to the same, relatively small number of elements. In fact, chemical analysis of the planets and the stars reveals that the whole material universe can be resolved into *these same elements*.

Thus far 102 elements have been discovered. Many of them are common substances such as carbon, iron, copper, aluminum, zinc, tin, lead, silver, gold, mercury, sulfur, phosphorus, hydrogen, oxygen, nitrogen, chlorine, bromine, iodine, and others. Only a few are so rare that the average reader has not heard of them. The reader will probably recognize many more in the list on Table 10:5 (p. 303). About 90 of the elements occur naturally on the earth, the remaining having been synthesized recently in atom-building experiments.

The statement that elements have been "synthesized" seems to be a contradiction to the argument that the elements are "simple"—in a sense this is so. However, it should be remembered that the elements are the ultimate substances of *chemical analysis*. They are not destroyed or created during chemical changes. Thus, 1 pound of carbon, on being burned, will make carbon dioxide, then limestone, then acetylene, then alcohol, and a myriad of other substances. To be sure, the presence of the carbon is not apparent in the carbon dioxide or in the alcohol. The complete decomposition, however, of *any* one of the substances that comes entirely from 1 pound of charcoal will yield exactly 1 pound of carbon—no more and no less. Therefore, the carbon must be present successively in all the compounds that can be produced from it. The same is true of all the other elements. They are conserved throughout all the chemical changes. It is true that modern science has been able to change one element into another, but this is done during extraordinary changes, involving prolific amounts of energy. We shall take up these changes in Chapter 13 (see also Ex. 8). We must stress at this point, however, the fact that throughout the countless chemical changes that the elements undergo, the amount of each element remains the same. This is "the law of conservation of the elements."

It is hardly possible to overestimate the importance of the conclusion that the whole material world is made of these few elements. For example, from a storeroom with 102 bins, each containing one element, we could make, in principle, every substance that exists. If the quantity of each were sufficient, we could reproduce the entire material universe.

No other substances are necessary. These elements contain in themselves all the possibilities of material existence.

From the point of view of understanding the physical world this is a tremendous simplification, achieved by nineteenth-century science. It has gone a long way in justifying the conviction of the ancient philosophers that the world is simple and consists of a small number of simple substances. It also simplifies the study of matter. With a knowledge of all the properties of the elements, their reactions, and their structure, we could predict and understand all the phenomena exhibited by matter.

The reader has perhaps realized that the sweeping conclusions about elements and chemical changes are firmly established by experiment. No theory is necessary to establish them as facts of nature. Regardless of whether molecules and atoms do or do not exist, the following experimental facts are undeniable: pure substances are transformed into other substances; energy changes accompany chemical changes; matter is conserved and, more significantly, the elements are conserved during chemical changes; and a small number of elements make up the whole material world.

Elements Consist of Atoms

Starting with this firm experimental foundation, we can elaborate on the theories and penetrate deeper into the understanding of the ultimate structure of matter. We may raise questions such as the following: What is the structure of the elements that can explain the fact that they combine in so many diverse ways to produce all the types of materials that exist? Why are the elements indestructible during chemical changes? What parts of the elements are contained in the molecules of so many diverse substances? What are the ultimate particles of the elements?

We could develop the atomic theory by reasoning from these facts alone. Since, however, we have already developed the kinetic molecular theory, the argument can logically continue from there. According to the molecular theory, the ultimate particles of a *pure substance* are the molecules that are all alike but different from those of other substances. Since in a chemical reaction the reacting substances disappear, during a chemical change the molecules must be destroyed and new molecules produced. This, of course, implies that molecules have structure and consist of parts.

The fact that all the substances can be made from the small number of elements must mean that a part of the element is contained in each molecule of all the diverse substances that contain the element. Further, since the elements are conserved, in the sense that any element can be recovered from its compounds unchanged in quantity, must mean that those parts of the element that enter the molecules of the compound retain their essential identity. *It is these smallest parts of the element that we call atoms.*

To summarize: All these phenomena can be explained on the theory that the elements consist of atoms. These atoms are not destroyed during chemical changes. They combine to form molecules of all the compounds that exist. They may also combine with atoms of the same kind to form the molecules of the elements. Thus, a small number of substances can combine to form the diverse substances that exist. Only a few, but well-established, experimental facts thus lead to a qualitative statement of the atomic theory. This, however, is merely the beginning. In the next section we will discuss the atom in more detail.

3. THE ATOMIC THEORY

The most convincing evidence that elements consist of atoms is derived from certain remarkable and rather unexpected numerical relations, observed during chemical changes. In fact, it was these quantitative relations that led Dalton and other chemists in the beginning of the nineteenth century to transform the qualitative atomic theories of the Greeks into a firm and convincing quantitative theory. Not only the reality of the atoms was firmly established, but it became possible to measure the relative weights of the atoms of the elements, to determine how many of them combine with each other to form a molecule of a given substance, to derive many of their other properties, and ultimately to estimate their actual weights and sizes.

The Law of Definite Proportions   Among the several important contributions of Lavoisier, the law of definite proportions is certainly one of the greatest. His emphasis on the weights of reacting substances during chemical reactions led him to recognize that when two elements combine to form a distinct compound, they do not combine indiscriminately but in a definite weight ratio that is characteristic of the elements and of the compound which they form. Thus when 1 gram of hydrogen is burned in air, it combines with 8 grams of oxygen to give 9 grams of water, despite the fact that the amount of oxygen in the air is practically unlimited. If 1 gram of hydrogen is burned in pure oxygen, it still combines with 8 grams of oxygen. On exploding a mixture of 1 gram of hydrogen and 10 grams of oxygen, only 8 grams of oxygen combine, and 2 grams of oxygen remain *uncombined*. On mixing 1 gram of hydrogen with only 4 grams of oxygen, $\frac{1}{2}$ gram of hydrogen will combine with the 4 grams of oxygen, leaving $\frac{1}{2}$ gram of hydrogen uncombined. Again the weight ratio of hydrogen to oxygen that have combined is $\frac{1}{2}:4$, or still 1:8 (Ex. 9).

Another way of stating this law is that water always contains $\frac{1}{9}$ (or 11.1 percent) hydrogen and $\frac{8}{9}$ (or 88.9 percent) oxygen, no matter what its origin. Regardless of the source of water—whether it is from the ocean, from the ice caps of Greenland, from rain water, from wells, or whether it is made by any of the numerous chemical ways, such as the burning of gasoline or the charring of sugar—it always has the constant composition of $\frac{1}{9}$ hydrogen and $\frac{8}{9}$ oxygen, by weight. For this reason the law is often called the *law of constant composition.*

This is not an isolated case of the elements hydrogen and oxygen or of the compound water. *Every chemical compound has a definite composition, by weight.* Thus, salt, regardless of its origin or mode of formation, always contains 23/58.5 sodium and 35.5/58.5 chlorine. More generally, in every chemical reaction the ratio of the weights of any given reactant to that of any other reactant or any product is constant. Thus, when a piece of marble is dissolved in hydrochloric acid, the same quantity of carbon dioxide is always obtained, regardless of the amount of acid added, provided it is enough to react with all of the marble.

This law is of great importance in manufacture, in industry, in the arts, and, of course, in chemical experiments. It permits the use of the right quantities in making any substance without wasting materials. It further permits the recording of the formula of any compound. We use here the word "formula" in the original sense of a "recipe," as indicating what materials the substance contains, and how much of each. Thus the "formula" for water is 1/9 hydrogen or 8/9 oxygen, by weight. The law of definite proportions is the basic principle upon which all chemical analysis depends.

It was John Dalton (1766-1844) in 1802 who first clearly recognized the theoretical significance of the law of constant composition. He saw that the fact that elements combine in definite weight ratios implies that the elements consist of definite packages—that is, they consist of particles or "atoms." How else is it possible to explain that every sample of water contains the same ratio of hydrogen and oxygen? On the other hand, a simple rationale of this fact can be given on the assumption that hydrogen consists of particles of definite weight, and oxygen consists of particles of definite, but different, weight, and that these atoms combine in some simple ratio such as 1:1, or 1:2, or 1:3, or perhaps 2:1, or 3:1, or 2:3. On this assumption, every particle of water contains the same weight ratio of the elements and, therefore, every sample of water has the same ratio. To be concrete, *if* an oxygen atom weighs 8 times as much as an hydrogen atom, *and if* one atom of oxygen combines with one atom of hydrogen to form a water molecule, then the weight ratio of oxygen to hydrogen is 8:1 (Ex. 10).

Theoretical Implications

This reasoning further implies that water, which is a compound, also consists of packages. Dalton called these particles "atoms" of water, but we now call them molecules. He reinforced his argument from certain simple relations he observed in the pressure and in the solubility of gases. He was not entirely clear about the distinction between atoms and molecules. The kinetic molecular theory was not yet developed. In fact, it was Dalton's ideas that helped in part to ultimately develop the molecular theory by the middle of the nineteenth century.

Fig. 8-5. Dalton. Originator of the modern idea of atoms explaining weight relationships in chemical reactions. *(The Bettmann Archive.)*

Since we have already developed for the reader the kinetic molecular theory by a different line of reasoning, we shall avoid some of Dalton's confusion and present a simple and very convincing argument for atoms. Since all the molecules of water are alike, each molecule of water must contain the same amount of oxygen-matter and hydrogen-matter. This implies that the hydrogen-matter and the oxygen-matter must consist of packages—a package of each element per molecule. Examination of all the other oxygen compounds, each of which, of course, contains a definite percentage of oxygen, shows that all their molecules contain definite packages of oxygen-matter. The same conclusion can be reached about hydrogen by examining hydrogen compounds, and similarly for the other elements. In other words, all the elements enter into the molecules in packages of definite weights. This is a strong argument for the corpuscularity of the elements, but does not yet prove that the *same packages* of a given element—for instance, of oxygen—are present in the molecules of all the oxygen compounds.

Law of Multiple Proportions   Dalton soon thereafter discovered another experimental law of weight relationships that convinced even his most skeptical opponents of the essential correctness of the atomic theory. This is his famous law of *multiple proportions*. It had been known for some time that many elements combine with one another in more than one ratio to form different chemical compounds. Each of the compounds has a definite weight ratio, but the ratio of the elements is different in any two compounds. For example, hydrogen and oxygen besides water form another compound between them—namely, hydrogen peroxide. The ratio of hydrogen to oxygen in this compound is 1 gram of hydrogen to 16 grams of oxygen. In tabular form

	hydrogen	to	oxygen
water	1	:	8
hydrogen peroxide	1	:	16

The existence of the two compounds is not a contradiction of the law of definite proportions—each compound has its own definite composition—but rather leads to an additional and new relationship. The law of multiple proportions refers to the weight of oxygen in the two compounds. For the same quantity of hydrogen (1 gram in both cases) the amount of oxygen in hydrogen peroxide is *twice* the amount that is in water.

Why should the amount of oxygen in one compound be exactly twice what it is in the other? Does it not mean that oxygen comes in packages? The amount of hydrogen is the same in both cases; in each water molecule a certain amount of oxygen combined with so much hydrogen; now, in a hydrogen peroxide molecule there is not merely more oxygen but *twice the amount*. Thus, there must be twice as many packages of oxygen. In other words, oxygen does come in packages.

If this were true only of water and hydrogen peroxide, it might be a mere accident. However, all elements show this behavior. For example, nitrogen and oxygen form no less than six compounds, with the following weight ratios given in Table 8:1.

In all these nitrogen compounds of oxygen, for the same weight of one element (14 grams of nitrogen in each case), the weights of

TABLE 8:1

Compound	Weight ratio nitrogen:oxygen
A	14:8
B	14:16
C	14:24
D	14:32
E	14:40
F	14:48

the other element (oxygen) are either 8 grams or multiples of 8. The weights of oxygen could have been 9, 17, 33, 45, or some other number of grams, but they are not. They are all multiples of 8. This cannot be due to chance. It must mean that oxygen comes in atoms and enters the molecule in units. The least amount that can enter a molecule must be one atom. If there is to be more oxygen in another molecule, there must be two atoms, or three atoms, and so on, but not a fraction of one atom. We come to the same conclusion about hydrogen or nitrogen by restating the ratios. With additional data we conclude that each of the elements consists of a "package" (Exs. 11 and 12). It is this package that is called the *atom*.

This is one of the strongest arguments for the existence of atoms. The reader may appreciate its force by considering an analogy. In ordinary experience, sugar comes either as granulated sugar or in cubes. At this level of experience, granulated sugar represents *continuity,* while cube sugar represents *packages;* that is, granulated sugar is available in any amount, within the accuracy of ordinary measurements. But cube sugar is available only as 1 cube, 2 cubes, and so on, not 7/8, or 1.35 cubes, or any other fraction.

Suppose that there is a tea party in the next room, and the guests refuse to tell whether the sugar used is in granular form or in cubes. Is there a way of finding out? Indeed there is and without looking at the dispenser or asking any guest. Suppose we take some cups, evaporate the tea, and weigh the sugar found in each cup. What would our conclusion be if we found the following amounts of sugar in the various cups?

Cup 1	2.44 grams	Cup 6	4.88 grams
Cup 2	1.22	Cup 7	1.22
Cup 3	1.22	Cup 8	2.44
Cup 4	3.66	Cup 9	1.22
Cup 5	6.10	Cup 10	1.22

Obviously, the conclusion is that the sugar comes in cubes, and each cube probably weighs 1.22 grams. This is analogous to the situation of elements exhibiting the law of multiple proportions. With the same quantity of one element (per cup, in the analogy), the amount of the second element combined in the various compounds is either the same weight or a whole-number multiple of it. Therefore, the element oxygen enters the molecules in packages. The smallest of these packages is called the *atom*.

Formal Statement of the Theory

From this type of reasoning Dalton was led to propose and defend the atomic theory. We shall take the liberty of altering somewhat his original wording and bypassing some of the difficulties that he and his followers cleared up later. By 1860 the basic assumptions of the theory could be stated as follows:

(1) The elements consist of very small ultimate particles of finite size which are called "atoms."

(2) The atoms do not divide and are in no way destroyed during chemical changes.

(3) The atoms of a given element are exactly alike—particularly in weight—but they differ from the atoms of any other element.

(4) Atoms combine with other atoms to form molecules. Atoms of one element combine with atoms of another element to form molecules of compounds. Atoms of the same element combine to form molecules of a pure elementary substance.

The theory can now be used to explain the phenomena associated with chemical changes. It gives to the chemist a consistent mental picture by which he can understand, explain, and often predict the countless chemical changes that go on in nature, in manufacturing, or in the laboratory.

Thus, to the question, "How is it that all the substances that exist can be made from a small number of elements?" the theory answers, "The elements consist of atoms, one kind for each element, and the atoms can combine in many ways to form molecules of the various substances." To the question, "Why is matter conserved during chemical changes?" the theory answers, "because in chemical changes the atoms are not destroyed—the same atoms merely rearrange in different combinations." To the question, "Why are the elements conserved and why can they be recovered from their compounds in full amounts?" the answer is, "The number of atoms of any one element are still present in the compound and can be separated by appropriate reactions." To the question, "What is the difference between elements and compounds?" the theory answers, "The molecules of an element have only one kind of atom, while the molecules of a compound have two or more kinds of atoms in them." To the question, "Why are energy changes observed in chemical reactions?" the theory answers, "There must be forces of attraction between atoms, and their actions result in energy changes."

The theory can also explain with great clarity the quantitative relations observed during chemical changes. Thus, the law of definite proportions is explained as follows: Since the atoms of a given element are all alike in weight, and since the same number of atoms of a given element are present in a molecule of a given compound, then there is a definite percentage of weight of this element in each molecule. Hence, for any number of molecules of the compound—that is, for any quantity of the material—the percent of the elements is the same. To take water as a specific example, which experimentally has the weight ratio of 1 part hydrogen to 8 parts oxygen, the reasoning is as follows: In every molecule of water there is a certain number of oxygen atoms and a certain number of hydrogen atoms. The exact number of each is not yet known, but that does not matter at the moment. The total weight of the oxygen atoms per molecule must be 8 times as great as the total weight of the hydrogen atoms. Since every sample of water is merely an assemblage of many molecules, then every sample must have the weight ratio of hydrogen to oxygen, $1:8$.

The law of multiple proportions can be explained equally directly. In hydrogen peroxide, which contains more oxygen for the same number of hydrogen atoms, there must be twice as many oxygen atoms per molecule as there are in water. Hence the weight ratio is $1:16$. It is also explained that for all the instances of compounds formed by any two elements, for a fixed weight of one element—that is, for a given number of atoms of one element in a molecule—the number of atoms of the other element must be a whole-number multiple of the smallest number found in one of the compounds. These and many other questions can be answered by the theory. The reader is advised to try some of the exercises at the end of the chapter (Exs. 13 and 14).

Until it is developed further, however, the theory cannot give the relative weights of atoms, nor state how many atoms of each element are present in the molecule. In fact, these two quantities are related and depend on one another. Using water as an example in which the experimental weight ratio of oxygen to hydrogen is $8:1$, the following possibilities exist. *If* the oxygen atom weighs 8 times as much as the hydrogen atom, then in water there is 1 oxygen atom to 1 hydrogen atom. *If,* on the other hand, the oxygen atom weighs 16 times as much as the hydrogen atom, then there is 1 oxygen atom for every 2 hydrogen atoms; for then the ratio would be 16 to 2×1 or again $8:1$. Further, if the oxygen atom weighs 24 times as much as the hydrogen atom, there must be 3 hydrogen atoms per oxygen atom, the weight ratio being 24 to 3×1 or still $8:1$. (For other possibilities see Ex. 10.)

Conversely, knowing the number of atoms of each kind that are in a molecule of water would give the relative weights of the atoms. Thus, if a water molecule contains 1 hydrogen and 1 oxygen atom, then the oxygen atom must weigh 8 times as much as the hydrogen atom. If on the other hand, a water molecule contains 2 hydrogen atoms and 1 oxygen atom per molecule, the oxygen atom must weigh 16 times as much as the hydrogen atom. Other possibilities are obvious.

Thus, from the weight ratio alone, there is no way of telling what the relative weights of the atoms are without knowing how many of each combine in a molecule, or *vice versa*. This problem occupied the minds of the leading scientists of the early part of the nineteenth century, and cannot be answered without obtaining additional and *independent* information. Several ways of obtaining independent information were developed (Ex. 15), but the best and easiest to understand came about 1860, when the molecular theory was sufficiently developed. Since we already have developed the kinetic molecular theory (Chap. 7), we shall proceed to show how the problem was solved.

Relative Weights of the Atoms

Fig. 8-6. Avogadro. His famous hypothesis permits the determination of relative weights of molecules and atoms. *(The Bettmann Archive.)*

Number of Hydrogen Atoms in a Hydrogen Molecule

The reader will recall from Chapter 7 (p. 210) that the kinetic molecular theory gives an extremely simple method for determining the *relative weights* of *molecules*. In this method the all-important principle is the hypothesis of Avogadro, which states that *equal volumes of any two gases under the same conditions of pressure* and temperature *contain the same number of molecules*. If we weigh samples of two gases, *equal in volume* and under the *same conditions,* then the ratio of the weights of the samples (determined on the balance) is the same as the ratio of the weights of the molecules themselves. Thus, since at STP (standard temperature and pressure) 1 liter of oxygen weighs 1.43 grams and 1 liter of hydrogen weighs 0.09 gram, then an oxygen molecule weighs 1.43/0.09 or almost exactly 16 times as much as the hydrogen molecule.

The reader must note that from this reasoning, 16 to 1 is the ratio of the weights of the molecules, and *not necessarily* the ratio of the weights of the atoms. For we have not yet discussed how many hydrogen atoms are in a hydrogen molecule, nor how many oxygen atoms are in an oxygen molecule. (The fact that there are two atoms per molecule in each of these two gases, as we shall show presently, is purely accidental in this argument.)

It is possible, however, to go from the relative weights of the molecules to the relative weights of atoms. With the help of the theory and a few additional experiments, we can find out how many atoms are in a molecule of pure hydrogen gas and, in fact, how many hydrogen atoms are in the molecule of any hydrogen compound. We proceed as follows:

By actual weighing, 1 liter of hydrogen chloride gas weighs 1.63 grams at standard conditions. By chemical analysis the hydrogen chloride contains 2.95 percent hydrogen. From these two measurements, it follows that 1 liter of hydrogen chloride contains $1.63 \times 2.95/100$ or 0.045 gram of combined hydrogen. This number is most significant. We recognize that 0.045 gram of hydrogen is exactly one half of the amount found in 1 liter of pure hydrogen (which is 0.090 gram). Since there are as many molecules in 1 liter of hydrogen chloride as there are in 1 liter of hydrogen gas, there is half as much hydrogen-matter in a molecule of hydrogen chloride as there is in a molecule of pure hydrogen. In other words, a hydrogen molecule contains at least two packages of hydrogen-matter. Since the smallest package of hydrogen-matter that can exist is the hydrogen *atom,* then a molecule of hydrogen gas contains at least two atoms (Ex. 16).

Similar investigations of other hydrogen compounds will reveal whether the hydrogen gas molecules contain only two atoms (only two packages) or more; that is, whether the hydrogen package found in hydrogen chloride is the smallest hydrogen package. A liter of ammonia weighs 0.76 gram, and analysis shows it to contain 18.3 percent hydrogen. Therefore, the amount of hydrogen in a liter of ammonia is $0.76 \times 18.3/100$ or 0.135 gram. This is exactly 3×0.045. Thus the amount of hydrogen-matter in an ammonia molecule is 3 times as much as in a hydrogen chloride molecule or $1\frac{1}{2}$ times as much as in a molecule of pure hydrogen gas. These results further support the idea that in hydrogen chloride the hydrogen package is the atom.

Extending this investigation to a large number of other compounds of hydrogen, we find the following results:

TABLE 8:2

Substance	Amount of hydrogen per liter, in grams
Pure hydrogen	0.090
Hydrogen chloride	0.045
Ammonia	0.135
Chloroform	0.045
Methane	0.180
Methyl chloride	0.135
Hydrogen bromide	0.045
Water	0.090
Any other hydrogen compound	$n \times 0.045$

This list is only partial. Literally thousands of hydrogen compounds have been analyzed. In all cases the amount of hydrogen per liter is either 0.045 gram or some multiple of it: in the molecules of each of these substances the amount of hydrogen-matter comes in packages that are either half of that found in a molecule of pure hydrogen or else a multiple of it. This smallest package of hydrogen-matter is called the *atom* of *hydrogen*. Therefore the hydrogen atom weighs half as much as a hydrogen molecule, or a molecule of hydrogen contains two hydrogen atoms. (How many hydrogen atoms does a molecule of methyl chloride contain? See Ex. 16.)

An exactly similar situation exists for oxygen. Analysis of a large number of oxygen compounds shows the results given in Table 8:3.

Number of Oxygen Atoms in an Oxygen Molecule

TABLE 8:3

Substance	Amount of oxygen per liter, in grams
Oxygen	1.43
Ozone	2.04
Water	0.715
Wood alcohol	0.715
Formaldehyde	0.715
Carbon monoxide	0.715
Carbon dioxide	1.43
Glycerine	2.04
Osmium oxide	2.86
Any other compound of oxygen	$n \times 0.715$

Here, too, the amount of oxygen per liter of any gaseous compound is either 0.715 gram or some whole-number multiple of it. It is never less than 0.715 gram and never anything other than a whole-number multiple of 0.715. Thus oxygen-matter also enters in the molecules in packages—one package (the *smallest* package) in water and one in wood alcohol, two packages in pure oxygen, three in ozone, and four in osmium oxide. Of special interest is that the oxygen gas *molecule* contains two of the smallest oxygen packages—that is, two atoms.

Atomic and Molecular Weights

These data permit comparison of the weight of one atom relative to the weight of any other atom or any molecule. Thus the hydrogen molecule weighs twice as much as the hydrogen atom since it weighs 0.090/0.045 or twice as much. Similarly, the oxygen molecule weighs twice as much as the oxygen atom, since it weighs 1.43/0.715 times as much. Further the weight of the oxygen molecule is 1.43/0.090 or 16 times as much as the hydrogen molecule, or 32 times as much as the hydrogen atom. Finally, the oxygen atom weighs 0.715/0.045 or 16 times as much as the hydrogen atom. All this information can be tabulated as follows:

hydrogen atom	1
hydrogen molecule	2
oxygen atom	16
oxygen molecule	32

where the weights of the particles are expressed in terms of the weight of the hydrogen atom, which is the lightest of these four particles.

This table can be extended to include the atoms of all the other elements and the molecules of all substances. The method and the reasoning is exactly the same for all substances that form gases. However, a new factor emerges on extension of the table—all the atoms and all the molecules of the other substances are always heavier than the hydrogen atom. Analysis shows that there is always more than 0.045 gram of any element (other than hydrogen) in 1 liter of that element or its compounds. In other words, *the hydrogen atom is the lightest atom*.

Thus a table containing the weights of all the particles of the microworld of atoms and molecules can be expressed in terms of the weight of the hydrogen atom. *Atomic weight* designates how many times an *atom* of an element is heavier than the *hydrogen atom*. *Molecular weight* designates how many times a *molecule* of a substance is heavier than the *hydrogen atom*. In both cases the unit is the weight of the hydrogen atom.

The reasoning in this section has been complicated and the reader is advised to reread it carefully. The main points of the argument are as follows:

Since there are the same number of molecules in a liter of any gas (at STP), the hydrogen molecule is the lightest molecule. The weight of any molecule, *A,* relative to the weight of the hydrogen molecule, is obtained by comparing the weight of a liter of gas *A* to the weight of a liter of hydrogen (0.090 gram at STP).

Extensive investigation of numerous hydrogen compounds reveals that the amount of combined hydrogen per liter is either 0.045 gram or some whole-number multiple of it. This smallest weight (0.045 gram) is exactly one half of the weight of hydrogen in 1 liter of hydrogen gas. Since a liter (under the same conditions) contains the same number of molecules, the smallest amount of (combined) hydrogen per molecule of the compound is one half of the amount of hydrogen in a molecule of pure hydrogen gas. The smallest amount of hydrogen found in a molecule of a hydrogen compound is defined as the hydrogen atom. It weighs one half as much as the hydrogen gas molecule.

Similar investigations on all available compounds of any other element *E* reveal that the weights of combined *E* per liter are all multiples of a smallest weight. The smallest weight of *E* found per liter must correspond to the smallest weight of *E* per molecule, and hence the weight of an atom of *E* (Ex. 18).

Taking the weight of the hydrogen atom as the unit, the atomic weight of element *E* is defined as the number of times an atom *E* is heavier than the hydrogen atom (Exs. 19 and 20). Experimentally it is determined by dividing the smallest weight of *E* found per liter by the smallest weight of hydrogen found per liter (0.045 gram). Similarly, the molecular weight of any substance *A* is the number of times a molecule is heavier than the hydrogen atom. Experimentally the molecular weight of *A* is the weight of a liter of *A* (STP) divided by the smallest weight of hydrogen per liter (0.045 gram).

4. WEIGHING AND COUNTING ATOMS AND MOLECULES

The preceding section discussed the experiments leading to the idea that the elements consist of atoms. It also gave the basic reasoning for determining the relative weights of atoms and molecules as well as the number of atoms in a molecule. Application of these ideas to all substances and reactions permits the visualization of these submicroscopic units and the processes they undergo. For any given element we know what its atoms weigh relative to the hydrogen atom. For any given substance we know how many atoms its molecule contains. For any given reaction we know what molecules break up and what new molecules are formed from the fragments, and thus visualize the course of chemical reactions. This knowledge gives to the microworld a reality that is scarcely less convincing than the reality of ordinary experience. However, in order to obtain this sense of reality, we will repeat the reasoning in several examples, and amplify some of the implications of these ideas.

The Gram-molecular Volume

The central point in the reasoning will be to compare equal numbers of molecules by comparing weights found in equal volumes of gases under the same conditions. The reasoning can be simplified considerably if instead of using 1 liter as the volume of comparison, the volume selected makes the numerical relations easier to comprehend and to interpret.

For reasons that will become apparent later, the volume is chosen to contain 1 gram of hydrogen, *in those compounds of hydrogen in which the amount of hydrogen is the smallest.* Hydrogen chloride is such a substance, since it contains only 0.045 gram of hydrogen per liter. Therefore, the volume of hydrogen chloride that will contain 1 gram of hydrogen is 1/0.045 or 22.4 liters.

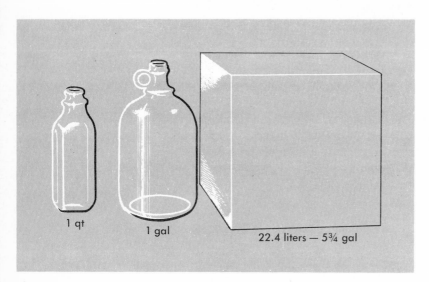

1 qt

1 gal

22.4 liters — 5¾ gal

Fig. 8-7. The gram-molecular volume at STP is 22.4 liters—about 5¾ gallons. When filled with hydrogen chloride at STP it contains 1 gram of combined hydrogen.

This volume, 22.4 liters of a gas at STP, will play a very important role in the following discussion. It is equal to about 23 quarts, or almost 6 gallons, and is called the *gram-molecular volume,* again for reasons that will become apparent.

The theoretical significance of this volume emerges on further analysis. At STP, 22.4 liters of hydrogen chloride contain 1 gram of hydrogen, and also the *smallest* amount of hydrogen (found in the volume); 6 gallons of all other hydrogen compounds contain either 1 gram or a whole-number multiple of 1 gram. Hydrogen chloride, therefore, contains the least amount of hydrogen per molecule, which means one *atom* per molecule. (See below for further discussion of this point.) Thus, in this volume there is one hydrogen atom per molecule, and the total number of hydrogen atoms weigh 1 gram.

Avogadro's Number

The number of hydrogen atoms in 1 gram of hydrogen is defined as Avogadro's number, and symbolized by the letter N. (This is the fundamental definition of N.) The numerical value of N, determined by various experimental methods, is 6×10^{23}. However, for this discussion it is sufficient to know that N is some very large, but definite, number.

Several implications follow immediately from this definition of N. Since each hydrogen chloride molecule contains one atom of hydrogen, we must have N molecules of hydrogen chloride in 22.4 liters of the gas. That means that the total weight of 22.4 liters (STP) of hydrogen chloride is the actual weight of N molecules of hydrogen chloride; that is, N molecules of hydrogen chloride weigh 36.5 grams. It follows, therefore, that Avogadro's number N has already four meanings:

(a) It is the number of *hydrogen atoms* in 1 gram of hydrogen (so defined).

(b) It is the number of *hydrogen atoms* in 22.4 liters of hydrogen chloride.

(c) It is the number of *hydrogen chloride molecules* in 22.4 liters of hydrogen chloride.

(d) It is the number of *hydrogen chloride molecules* that weigh 36.5 grams.

If now we take 22.4 liters of any other gas at STP, it will also contain N molecules. This result follows from Avogadro's hypothesis, which states that equal volumes of gases contain the same number of molecules. Therefore any gaseous compound of hydrogen contains N molecules per 22.4 liters at STP. The number N now takes on an additional and more general meaning. It is the number of molecules in 22.4 liters of *any* gas at STP, whether the gas contains hydrogen or not.

The weight of 22.4 liters of a gas at STP is, therefore, the weight of N molecules. Thus N molecules of hydrogen chloride weigh 36.5 grams; N molecules of hydrogen gas weigh 2 grams; N molecules of ammonia weigh 17 grams; and so on. The weight of N molecules is defined as the gram-molecular weight, or *mole* for short. From this definition follows a very convenient method of finding the weight of N molecules of any gas. All that is needed is to fill a 6-gal can with the gas (at STP) and put it on the balance. Or any convenient volume can be weighed and the weight of 22.4 liters calculated from it. In fact, a sample of the gas can be weighed at any convenient pressure and temperature and the weight of 22.4 liters at STP calculated, using the gas laws, thus obtaining the gram-molecular weight.

One step further will give the gram-molecular weight of a substance even though the substance *is not a gas* at STP. By weighing a given sample of the substance at a temperature and pressure at which *it is* a gas, we can calculate the weight it *would have if it were a gas at STP*. Thus 22.4 liters of steam at 273° C and standard pressure weigh 9 grams. Therefore, at 0° C, 22.4 liters would weigh $9 \times \dfrac{273 + 273}{273} = 9 \times 2$ or 18 grams. Therefore N molecules of water vapor weigh 18 grams (Exs. 23 and 24).

The next step is to determine the weight of a molecule of any gas relative to the weight of the hydrogen *atom*. The weight of the molecule is to the weight of the hydrogen atom, as the weight of the N molecules is to the weight of N hydrogen atoms. For example, since N molecules of hydrogen chloride weigh 36.5 grams (by experiment) and N hydrogen atoms weigh 1 gram (by definition of N), one hydrogen chloride molecule weighs 36.5 times as much as a hydrogen atom. This weight of a molecule relative to the weight of the hydrogen atom is called the *molecular weight*. It is numerically equal to the gram-molecular weight.

Number of H Atoms in Molecules of Hydrogen Compounds

Application of these ideas permits us to see more clearly the atomic nature of hydrogen and to find the number of hydrogen atoms in the molecules of any hydrogen compound. We take 22.4 liters (STP) of gaseous substances containing hydrogen and determine the weight on a balance. Chemical analysis will give the percentage of hydrogen in the compound. Simple multiplication gives the amount of hydrogen in 22.4 liters. For example, 22.4 liters of ammonia weigh 17 grams. By actual chemical analysis 17.7 percent of ammonia is hydrogen. That is, decomposing 100 pounds of ammonia gives 17.7 pounds of hydrogen. Therefore, the amount of hydrogen in 17 grams of ammonia is 17 × 17.7 percent or 3.0 grams.

This procedure applied to several substances containing hydrogen gives Table 8:4.

TABLE 8:4

Substance	Weight of 1 liter (STP)	Weight of 22.4 liters (STP)	Percent hydrogen	Weight of hydrogen is 22.4 liters (STP)
Hydrogen chloride	1.63 grams	36.5	2.65	1.0 grams
Hydrogen bromide	3.62	81.0	1.24	1.0
Chloroform	5.03	119.5	0.87	1.0
Hydrogen gas	0.09	2.0	100.	2.0
Ammonia	0.76	17.0	17.7	3.0
Water (vapor)	0.805	18.0	11.1	2.0
Wood alcohol	1.43	32.0	12.5	4.0
Formaldehyde	1.34	30.0	6.67	2.0
Grain alcohol	2.05	46.0	13.0	6.0
Ether	2.05	46.0	13.0	6.0
All other hydrogen compounds ——	——	——	$n \times 1.0$	

One of the most significant facts is brought out in the last column of the table. In the substances compared here, the weight of hydrogen found per 22.4 liters at STP is either 1 gram or a whole number of grams. It is not surprising for hydrogen chloride, of course, for we chose the volume 22.4 liters precisely because it will contain 1 gram of hydrogen. But it is indeed surprising for all the other substances. In all the hydrogen compounds that have been analyzed (and they include many thousands), the amount of hydrogen per 22.4 liters is always a whole number of grams—never less than 1 gram; never anything other than a whole number of grams. This is the strongest experimental evidence that hydrogen comes in packages or "atoms," and that the smallest package is that found in hydrogen chloride. That is, a hydrogen chloride molecule contains only one atom of hydrogen.

A further implication is that we can tell the number of hydrogen atoms in any molecule containing hydrogen. Thus in hydrogen chloride there is one atom of hydrogen per molecule, and also one in chloroform and one in hydrogen bromide. In hydrogen gas (or water vapor or formaldehyde) there are two hydrogen atoms per molecule. That is, there are N molecules containing 2 grams of hydrogen, which means $2N$ atoms of hydrogen, and hence two hydrogen atoms per hydrogen molecule. In ammonia, N molecules contain 3 grams of hydrogen which means $3N$ hydrogen atoms, and hence 3 hydrogen atoms per molecule. In general, the number of atoms of hydrogen in a molecule is equal to the number of grams of hydrogen contained in 22.4 liters of the gaseous substance at STP.

The critical reader will realize that these conclusions depend on the assumption that there is one hydrogen atom per molecule in hydrogen chloride. He may feel that there is some uncertainty in this assumption. "How do you know," he may object, "that in the future we shall not find a hydrogen compound containing less than 1 gram of hydrogen per 22.4 liters?" The frank answer is that we do not know. However, in all the thousands of hydrogen compounds, it has not been found. Further, all the hydrogen compounds contain whole-number multiples of 1 gram, which means that all the molecules contain whole-number multiples of the package found in a hydrogen chloride molecule. If the hydrogen atom were smaller than that found in a hydrogen chloride molecule, long ago someone would have discovered some substance containing less than 1 gram or a fractional number of grams in 22.4 liters. Therefore, we are confident that a hydrogen chloride molecule contains the smallest package, which must be *one* atom.

The same answer results from a logical analysis of the concept, the hydrogen "atom." We called the hydrogen atom the smallest package of hydrogen found in a molecule. That package is found in a hydrogen chloride molecule. All other molecules contain either this package, or else two, three, and so on, times that package. If now the reader insists that this package may contain, say five, hydrogen atoms, and there is one such package in a hydrogen chloride molecule, two packages in hydrogen gas, and so on, and that it enters the molecules *always* in packages of five, the answer would be, "That package which you call a "package of five" is what we call *one atom*. For it is senseless to say that you have a package of five, and that the package never, *never,* splits up." Since all the phenomena ever observed are explainable by assuming that the hydrogen atom is that package of hydrogen found in a hydrogen chloride molecule, and since it never has been necessary to assume that it is anything smaller than this, we say that this *is* the *hydrogen atom*. Should phenomena ever indicate that the atom is smaller than now assumed, we will revise our ideas accordingly. However, that situation is extremely unlikely to arise in this case.

Oxygen and Its Compounds

The same reasoning can be applied to oxygen and its compounds. An analysis of many oxygen compounds results in Table 8:5.

Here again all the oxygen compounds contain either 16 grams of oxygen or a multiple of it per 22.4 liters. The logical conclusion, there-

TABLE 8:5

Substance	Weight per liter (STP)	Weight per 22.4 liters (STP)	Percent oxygen	Weight of oxygen in 22.4 liters (STP)
Oxygen	1.43 grams	32 grams	100.00	32.0 grams
Ozone	2.14	48	100.00	48.0
Water (vapor)	0.81	18	89.90	16.0
Formaldehyde	1.34	30	53.50	16.0
Wood alcohol	1.43	32	50.00	16.0
Carbon monoxide	1.25	28	57.30	16.0
Carbon dioxide	1.96	44	72.90	16.0
Grain alcohol	2.05	46	34.80	16.0
Osmium oxide	10.30	254	25.20	64.0
All other oxygen compounds ——	—	——	$n \times 16.0$

fore, is that substances such as water, or wood alcohol, containing the least amount of oxygen per N molecules, must contain one atom per molecule. Similarly, oxygen gas contains two oxygen atoms per molecule, ozone three, and osmium oxide four.

The only new thing that emerges from consideration of oxygen is that we can now find the weight of the oxygen *atom* relative to the hydrogen atom. Perhaps, we can see at a glance that the oxygen atom weighs 16 times as much as a hydrogen atom. Should it be necessary to reason more explicitly, the argument is as follows: Since 22.4 liters of formaldehyde gas contain the smallest weight of oxygen—namely, 16 grams—there is one oxygen atom per molecule. Further, since 22.4 liters of formaldehyde contain N molecules, there are N oxygen atoms in this volume. Thus N oxygen atoms weigh 16 grams. Since N hydrogen atoms weigh 1 gram (by definition), then one oxygen atom weighs 16 times as much as a hydrogen atom.

Other Elements

A similar situation is found for all the other elements. For example, Table 8:6 is computed from the analysis of several compounds of carbon:

TABLE 8:6

Substance	Weight per liter (STP)	Weight per 22.4 liters (STP)	Percent carbon	Weight of carbon in 22.4 liters (STP)
Wood alcohol	1.43	32	37.5	12.00
Formaldehyde	1.34	30	40.1	12.00
Carbon monoxide	1.25	28	42.70	12.00
Carbon dioxide	1.96	44	27.3	12.00
Grain alcohol	2.05	46	52.2	24.00
Glycerine	4.11	92	39.3	36.00
Ether	3.30	74	65.0	48.00
All other carbon compounds	—	—	—	$n \times 12.00$

From these data the carbon atom weighs 12 times as much as a hydrogen atom; wood alcohol contains one carbon atom per molecule, grain alcohol two, glycerine three, and ether four.

The weight of an atom relative to the hydrogen atom is called the *atomic weight* of the element. It is found by analysis of as many compounds of the element as possible, and by noting the *smallest* weight found in 22.4 liters. This weight expressed in grams is called the *gram-atomic weight* or the *gram-atom*. It is the actual weight of N atoms of the element. Since the weight of N hydrogen atoms is 1 gram, the atomic weight of the element is numerically equal to the *least number of grams* of the element found in 22.4 liters (gaseous at STP).

By applying this procedure to all the other elements, a list of atomic weight is obtained. These are given in Table 10:5, page 303.

Atomic Weights and Gram-atomic Weights

The reader has probably realized that the procedure we have outlined is a method for obtaining the number of atoms of an element in a molecule of any substance that contains that element. We have already concluded that a molecule of hydrogen gas contains two hydrogen atoms; an oxygen molecule, two oxygen atoms; and an ozone molecule, three oxygen atoms. This can be applied equally well to any compound. Thus, water contains 2 grams of hydrogen per 22.4 liters, which means *two* hydrogen atoms per molecule. It also contains 16 grams of oxygen per mole, which means one oxygen atom per molecule. Hence, the formula for water is two hydrogen atoms and one oxygen atom, per molecule. If H stands for a hydrogen atom and O for an oxygen atom, the water molecule is symbolized: H_2O. This is the basic reasoning behind the use of H_2O as the formula for water.

The method may be illustrated by another example. In grain alcohol 22.4 liters at STP contain 46 grams of alcohol. By actual analysis this amount of alcohol contains 24 grams of carbon, 6 grams of hydrogen, and 16 grams of oxygen. Comparing these values with the atomic weights (determined previously) shows that there are 2 carbon atoms, 6 hydrogen atoms, and 1 oxygen atom per molecule. Therefore, the formula is C_2H_6O (Ex. 31).

Formulas of Substances

Chemical symbols help greatly in visualizing the microworld. Symbolism has had a long and interesting history. In ancient times the planets were represented by distinctive symbols. In the period of astrology and alchemy, certain metals were associated with each planet and the alchemists used the same symbol for both the planet and the metal. Thus, gold was associated with the sun, because it is the "king of metals" and also has the color of the sun. Both were represented by ⊙. Silver was the metal of the moon. We still say the "silver moon," and the old name "lunar caustic" is still used for silver nitrate. Iron was the metal of the red and fiery Mars, named after the God of War. Copper was the metal of Venus, the Goddess of Beauty, for it served her as a mirror. The alchemists used the symbols primarily to conceal information and as an abbreviation for the name of the metal (Fig. 8.8).

When Dalton developed his atomic theory, he drew figures to

Chemical Symbolism

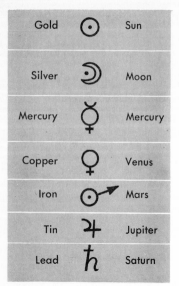

Gold	☉	Sun
Silver	☽	Moon
Mercury	☿	Mercury
Copper	♀	Venus
Iron	♂	Mars
Tin	♃	Jupiter
Lead	♄	Saturn

Fig. 8-8. Alchemical symbols for the seven metals and the seven heavenly bodies associated with them.

represent the atoms of the elements, as an aid in visualization. He represented an atom of oxygen with an open circle, and an atom of hydrogen with a circle having a dot in the center. He represented a molecule of water as follows: ⊙◯. (He thought that water contained only one hydrogen atom and one oxygen atom.) For carbon he used a black circle to suggest the color of charcoal. Soon, however, he ran out of distinctive figures, so he used a circle with the initial of the element. Thus, Z was the symbol for an atom of zinc.

The famous Swedish chemist Berzelius took the next logical step. He dropped the circle and used only the initial letter. Dalton insisted on retaining the circle, partly on the ground that it suggests the spherical atom and thus acts as a visual aid. However, Berzelius won out. The chemists soon learned to visualize the atom from the letter alone, although admittedly Dalton's scheme is more meaningful to beginners, as seen by a comparison of the two schemes (Fig. 8-9).

Today we use essentially the scheme of Berzelius. For many elements the initial capital letter of the name is taken to represent an atom of the element. Thus H stands for hydrogen, O for oxygen, N for nitrogen, and C for carbon. However, since the names of many elements begin with the same letter, a second letter is often added, usually a distinctive letter in the name of the element. The second letter is never capitalized. Thus, while C is the symbol for carbon, it is Ca for calcium, Cd for cadmium, Cl for chlorine, Cr for chromium, and Co for cobalt. In a few instances the symbols are derived from the Latin name of the element. Thus, the symbol for gold is Au (Aurum); for silver it is Ag (Argentum); and for sodium it is Na (Natrium).

A molecule of any substance can be represented symbolically, provided the atoms it contains are known. The symbols of the atoms in the molecule are written together as one word. This representation is called the *formula* of the substance. For example, knowing from the data on Tables 8.5 and 8.6 that a molecule of carbon monoxide contains one carbon atom and one oxygen atom, the formula becomes CO. If more than one atom of an element is present in the molecule, then a subscript is used. Thus the formula CO_2 for carbon dioxide indicates that there is one carbon atom and two oxygen atoms per molecule. Similarly the formula of hydrogen gas is H_2, of oxygen gas is O_2, of ozone is O_3, and of grain alcohol it is C_2H_6O. Thus, the information in Tables 8:4, 8:5, and 8:6 can be represented effectively by the formulas.

Quantitative Meaning of Chemical Symbolism

Originally, chemical symbolism was meant to serve merely as a pictorial aid in representing atoms and molecules. However, with the growth of chemical knowledge, the symbols took on quantitative meaning. The extension was natural because a formula implies certain weight relationships. An atom in a molecule represents a certain fraction of the weight of the molecule. Thus in the formula H_2O, each H represents a hydrogen atom, each weighing one unit, and O represents an oxygen atom, weighing 16 units—that is, 16 times as much as the hydrogen atom. The whole molecule weighs $2 \times 1 + 16$ or 18 units, that is 18 times as much as the hydrogen atom. Therefore, the oxygen atom accounts for 16/18 of the weight of the water molecule and the two hydrogen atoms account for 2/18 of it. This consideration makes it clear that symbols H and O, as well as the formula H_2O, have quantitative meanings.

Symbols. There are quantitative meanings for symbols. To the chemist the symbol, O, is not only an abbreviation of the name of the element oxygen, but also stands for an atom of oxygen. This, however, implies further meanings. The symbol, O, stands for that particle of oxygen which is 16 times heavier than the hydrogen atom. Thus, the symbol is associated with the atomic weight of oxygen. Finally, the symbol O implies that 16 grams of oxygen is the actual weight of N oxygen atoms. All this information is carried by the symbol O.

Thus the symbol carries the following information:

(a) An abbreviation of the name of the element.
(b) An atom of the element.
(c) The weight of the atom relative to the hydrogen atom.
(d) The least weight (in grams) of the element found in 22.4 liters.
(e) The weight of N atoms of the element.

Meaning of Formulas. The quantitative meanings of symbols become even clearer by considering the meanings of the formulas in which they are used. The formula for water, H_2O, is not only an abbreviation for water, but stands for a molecule of water. It states that a molecule of water contains two hydrogen atoms and one oxygen atom. Since each hydrogen atom weighs 1 unit and the oxygen atom weighs 16 units, the entire molecule weighs 18 units.

The formula can give the weight composition of a water molecule. Of the total weight of the molecule, 2/18 is hydrogen and 16/18 is oxygen. Since any sample of water is merely an assemblage of so many water molecules, the percent of any sample is also 2/18 or 11.1 percent hydrogen and 16/18 or 88.9 percent oxygen. Thus, the formula of H_2O is a "formula" in the sense of a "recipe" in that it tells what constituents the substance contains and how much of each constituent.

Further meaning can be derived from the formula, by considering how it is determined experimentally. The formula H_2O implies that 22.4 liters of water vapor at STP contain 2 grams of hydrogen and 16 grams of oxygen. In other words, in 1 gram-molecular weight of water there are 2 gram-atoms of hydrogen and 1 gram-atom of oxygen; also that 22.4 liters of water vapor contain 18 grams of water, and that N molecules of water weigh 18 grams.

All this information is contained in the formula H_2O (Ex. 32).

Chemical Equations. Chemical symbolism was developed further to represent chemical reactions. If we take the reaction

$$\text{hydrogen} + \text{oxygen} \rightarrow \text{water}$$

and write the formula of each substance, we get

$$H_2 + O_2 \rightarrow H_2O$$

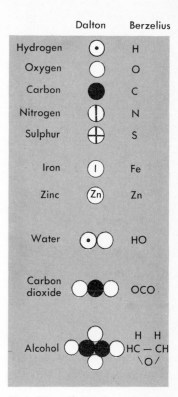

Fig. 8-9. Chemical symbols of Dalton and Berzelius.

	Dalton	Berzelius
Hydrogen		H
Oxygen		O
Carbon		C
Nitrogen		N
Sulphur		S
Iron		Fe
Zinc		Zn
Water		HO
Carbon dioxide		OCO
Alcohol		HC — CH

If the formulas had only qualitative meaning, the symbolic representation would have been satisfactory. It would simply read: hydrogen reacts with oxygen to give water. However, H_2 stands for a molecule of hydrogen, containing two hydrogen atoms. Similarly, O_2 stands for a molecule of oxygen, containing two oxygen atoms, and H_2O stands for a water molecule, containing two hydrogen atoms and one oxygen atom. Thus quantitatively the representation of the reaction is not correct; for it implies that we started with an oxygen molecule having *two* atoms and ended with a water molecule having only *one* oxygen atom—it implies that an oxygen atom was lost in the reaction. This situation is remedied by the realization that one oxygen molecule would form two water molecules. Therefore,

$$H_2 + O_2 \rightarrow 2H_2O$$

One hydrogen molecule, however, cannot give two water molecules; for before the reaction there were only two hydrogen atoms instead of four. This situation is easily corrected by writing 2 in front of H_2, finally obtaining

$$2H_2 + O_2 \rightarrow 2H_2O$$

The resulting symbolic expression is called a chemical equation. Qualitatively, it states that hydrogen combines with oxygen to form water. All the quantitative meanings of symbols and formulas, however, are now carried over to the equation. The equation contains a wealth of information, some of which follows:

(a) Two hydrogen molecules combine with one oxygen molecule to give two molecules of water.
(b) Two moles of hydrogen combine with one mole of oxygen to give two moles of water.
(c) Four gram atoms of hydrogen combine with two gram atoms of oxygen to give two moles of water.
(d) Four grams of hydrogen combine with 32 grams of oxygen to give 36 grams of water.
(e) One gram of hydrogen combines with 8 grams of oxygen to give 9 grams of water.
(f) Two times 22.4 liters of hydrogen combine with 22.4 liters of oxygen to give 2×22.4 liters of water vapor at STP.
(g) $2 \times 6 \times 10^{23}$ hydrogen molecules combine with 6×10^{23} oxygen molecules to form $2 \times 6 \times 10^{23}$ water molecules.
(h) Two gallons of hydrogen combine with 1 gallon of oxygen to give 2 gallons of steam, under the same conditions.

This and a great deal more information is contained in the symbolic expression of the equation, which is extremely useful to the chemist (Ex. 33).

We need not dwell too long on the techniques of deriving formulas, or balancing equations. There are, however, certain principles of fundamental importance that should be emphasized. The entire system of chemical symbolism has been devised to describe chemical phenomena.

Symbols have only the meanings assigned to them. However, the meanings must be consistent and also should represent the phenomena—otherwise, they become meaningless jargon. The symbolism on the one hand helps in the visualization of the microworld. At the same time it is based on experiments, and it is a symbolic record of experiments.

A *symbol* represents an atom of the element and also its weight relative to the hydrogen atom. The atomic weight can be obtained only by experiment—by finding the least weight of the element in 22.4 liters (or by similar *experimental* methods).

A *formula* represents a molecule of the element. However, the formula is determined *experimentally* by finding the percentage composition and the weight of 22.4 liters at STP. We cannot write a formula by simply putting symbols together.

A *chemical equation* represents what molecules react and what molecules are produced. Again, the chemical equation represents a chemical reaction that has actually been observed to take place. Each of the substances reacting and each of the substances produced must be observed. Moreover, for each of the substances the formula must be determined, sometime or other, by experiment. An "equation" cannot be written by simply putting together formulas and trying to "balance" them.

Seeing it from this light, chemical symbolism is a powerful instrument in describing the world of everyday experience, in visualizing the microworld, and in explaining the world of ordinary experience in terms of the microworld.

Valence

The symbolic expression of the formula makes it easy to recognize a most fundamental property of the atom that might have remained obscure in the mass of data. This property is the *combining capacity* of atoms, called "valence." On determining the formulas of several common substances by the method already described, we get the following:

hydrogen chloride	HCl
hydrogen bromide	HBr
hydrogen iodide	HI
water	H_2O
hydrogen sulfide	H_2S
ammonia	NH_3
phosphine	PH_3
marsh gas	CH_4
silane	SH_4

Inspection of this table reveals that atoms of different elements have a *different* capacity of holding hydrogen atoms. Thus, an atom of chlorine (or bromine, or iodine) holds one hydrogen atom. An atom of oxygen (or sulfur) holds two hydrogen atoms; a nitrogen (or phosphorus) atom holds three, and a carbon (or silicon) atom holds four.

The capacity of an atom to hold hydrogen atoms is called the valence of the element. Thus, the valence of oxygen in water is 2, meaning that one oxygen atom is combined with two hydrogen atoms. If an element combines with hydrogen, the valence of the element in the compound can be determined by simple inspection of the formula, *after the latter has been determined experimentally.*

This definition of valence is limited, in that it is applicable only to elements that form compounds with hydrogen. However, many elements, notably the metals, do not combine with hydrogen, or do so only under unusual conditions. These elements, on the other hand, do combine with other elements. For example, sodium combines readily with chlorine, bromine, iodine, oxygen, and sulfur, forming compounds with the following formulas:

$$NaCl \quad NaBr \quad NaI \quad Na_2O \quad Na_2S$$

Comparison of the sodium compounds with the hydrogen compounds reveals a simple correspondence. The compounds of sodium are similar to the hydrogen compounds, with the sodium atom corresponding to the hydrogen atom. Thus a comparison of HCl with NaCl shows that the Na atom, like the H atom, combines with one atom of chlorine. Similarly comparing H_2O and Na_2O shows that two sodium atoms combine with one oxygen atom just as two hydrogen atoms do. Accordingly, we say that the hydrogen atom and the sodium atom have equal capacity for holding a chlorine atom, and extend the idea of valence to apply to sodium that has *replaced* hydrogen, saying that the *valence* of sodium is the same as that of chlorine or of hydrogen; that is, the valence of sodium is 1.

A similar situation exists with magnesium, which forms the following compounds:

$$MgCl_2 \quad MgBr_2 \quad MgI_2 \quad MgO \quad MgS \quad Mg_3N_2$$

Here the magnesium atom is equivalent to *two* hydrogen atoms. In $MgCl_2$ the magnesium atom holds two chlorine atoms, doing "the same job" as two hydrogen atoms. A comparison of MgO and H_2O shows that a magnesium atom takes the place of the two hydrogen atoms. Therefore, the valence of magnesium is *two*.

Similarly from the formulas

$$FeCl_3 \quad Fe_2O_3 \quad AlCl_3 \quad Al_2O_3 \quad PbCl_4 \quad PbO_2 \quad PbCl_4$$

the valence of iron (Fe) is three, that of aluminum (Al), also three, that of lead (Pb) four.

Positive and Negative Valence. In further developing the idea of valence, it becomes useful to distinguish between the elements that replace hydrogen from those that combine with it, calling the valence of the former positive, and that of the latter negative.

Accordingly, by definition:

Positive valence is the number of hydrogen atoms which an atom of the element *replaces.*

Negative valence is the number of hydrogen atoms which an atom of the element *combines with.*

These definitions imply that the valence of hydrogen is defined as +1. Thus from the formula, NH_3, the valence of nitrogen is −3, and from the formula, $AlCl_3$, the valence of aluminum is +3.

The concept of valence gives a further insight into the relationship among the elements. For example, the nonmetals, as a rule, have negative valences, since they combine with hydrogen. The metals (as well as hydrogen), on the other hand, have positive valences since they replace hydrogen (or, what amounts to the same thing, they combine with the nonmetals). Thus, the distinction between metals and nonmetals, originally made on obvious and purely physical properties, seems to be much deeper. It is a distinction in at least one fundamental chemical property of the atom.

Valence, as a fundamental property of the atoms, is capable of further development. From the definitions, it is a numerical property and it is a whole number. However, a complication arises from the fact that some atoms show different valences in different compounds. Thus, iron forms $FeCl_2$ and $FeCl_3$. In the first compound the valence of iron is +2, in the latter it is +3. Nearly all elements show more than one valence. Thus, carbon forms carbon monoxide, CO, carbon dioxide, CO_2, methane, CH_4, carbon tetrachloride, CCl_4, and many other compounds. Applying the definitions to these compounds we find the following valences for carbon:

in CO   the valence is +2
in CO_2 "   "   " +4
in CCl_4 "   "   " +4
in CH_4 "   "   " −4

There is no contradiction here, except to recognize that an element may have more than one valence. We must keep clearly in mind that the valence of an atom is the number of hydrogen atoms that it *has* combined with or replaced, *in a given compound*. In any given compound the valence of an element is definite. We should not speak of the valence of carbon, but rather of the *valence of carbon in a given compound*. In carbon monoxide the valence of carbon is definitely +2; carbon tetrachloride is definitely +4, in methane it is definitely −4. In uncombined carbon, the valence is zero since the atom has neither combined nor replaced hydrogen. It is clear, therefore, that the valence of any element in the free or uncombined state must be zero (Ex. 34).

Despite this complication, a given element shows only a few valences. In general, a given element exhibits one valence most prominently and most often, and this is called the *principal* valence. The complication, instead of being a troublesome detail, is really an opportunity to explore further the combining power of the atom and its structure, as we shall see later (Chap. 10).

In this section we have shown how to enter the microworld and describe it quantitatively. We have shown how to find the relative weights of atoms and molecules, the combining capacity of the atoms, the number of atoms of each element in a given compound, the number

Recapitulation

of molecules of each substance reacting and being formed in a given reaction. While the reasoning may appear complicated at first, it is important to realize that all this information is obtained directly from experiments.

In particular we must distinguish between what is observed experimentally, and what are theoretical conclusions, drawn from the experiments. The former knowledge is firm and definite. The latter are interpretations that may change, although that is highly unlikely for the ideas presented in this section. The former is a description of the world. Whether atoms and molecules exist or not, it is an experimental fact that the amounts of each element in 22.4 liters of all its thousands of compounds are simple multiples of the smallest amount found in that volume; that any given compound contains per 22.4 liters the smallest amount of each element found in that volume, or else a whole-number multiple of it; that the "formula" of any substance can be given very simply by stating its composition in terms of the smallest packages of weight (gram-atoms) found in 22.4 liters; that all substances, and the elements containing them, react in these weight packages. Theories may change, but these facts cannot change.

Perhaps we can best highlight the distinction between observation and theory by giving the experimental and theoretical definitions of the various concepts side by side.

TABLE 8:7

	Experimental (Operational)	Theoretical
Gram-atomic weight (gram atom)	The smallest number of grams of an element found in 22.4 liters	The weight of N atoms of the element (in grams)
Atomic weight	The ratio of smallest weight of an element found in 22.4 liters to the smallest weight of hydrogren found therein	The weight of an atom relative to the hydrogen atom
Gram-molecular weight (mole)	The weight of 22.4 liters of the substance (STP)	The weights of N molecules (in grams)
Molecular weight	The ratio of weight of 22.4 liters of the substance (STP), to the smallest weight of hydrogen found in that volume	The weight of a molecule of the substance relative to that of the hydrogen atom
Valence	The number of grams of hydrogen combined with (negative) or replaced by (positive) a gram atom of the element	The number of atoms of hydrogen combined with (negative) or replaced by (positive) an atom of the element
Chemical equation	The number of gram-atoms (or gram-molecules) of each substance reacting and being produced in the reaction	The number of atoms (or molecules) of each substance rearranging in the reaction

While we admit as a matter of pure logic that the theoretical conclusions are interpretations subject to change, we are quite confident that any essential change in the theory presented in this section is extremely unlikely. The evidence is much too strong to be doubted. Any change in the theories will be in the direction of giving greater detail. Moreover, if we accept the theories we are able to visualize the microworld, and to understand, predict, and control the phenomena. The theories of the microworld are not only intellectually necessary and esthetically satisfying, but they are also of immense practical value. They help in the understanding, prediction, and control of the countless chemical reactions that go on in the physical world.

NOTES AND EXERCISES

1. In the reaction of sodium and chlorine to give salt, list all the properties you know of each substance. Are any of the properties of sodium present in salt? Are any of the properties of chlorine present in the salt? How fundamental is the change?

2. Enumerate the various characteristics of a chemical reaction and show that they are exhibited in the reaction of sodium and chlorine to form salt.

3. *Chemical Energy.* In order to admit chemical energy as a form of energy and to demonstrate that the law of conservation of energy holds, it is necessary to show that whatever amount of energy is released in a reaction, the same amount is necessary to produce the opposite reaction. How much energy would be necessary to decompose 9 grams of water? And if by experiment this is found to be so, how does this prove that the law of conservation of energy holds when chemical energy is included? What makes us think there is such a thing as chemical energy and how do we define it?

4. When 1 gram of hydrogen and 8 grams of oxygen combine, 34,000 calories are released. Since a calorie is 4.2 joules and a joule is 10,000,000 ergs, how many ergs are released? From the theory of relativity, $E = mc^2$ or ergs $=$ grams $\times$ $(3 \times 10^{10}$ cm per sec$)^2$. Calculate the weight loss corresponding to the loss of 34,000 calories. Is this weight measurable on an analytical balance?

5. It is interesting that in a hazy sort of way Heraclitus came close to the modern concept that energy is the basic reality and that the various forms of matter are more "compact" forms of energy. If by his "fire," we understand him to mean "energy," then energy in certain packages becomes photons, electrons, neutrons, and so on, and these become atoms, and then molecules of gases, liquids, and solids. However, we must not ascribe to Heraclitus the clarity of the concepts as now held, or their experimental verification.

Assuming that energy is the fundamental entity, how much energy does an electron represent? (The mass of the electron is 9×15^{-28} gram and $c = 3 \times 10^{10}$ cm per sec.) How much energy does a proton represent? How much energy does a water molecule represent? How much energy does a pound of water represent? A pound of rock? How would you describe, in general terms, the difference between matter in the form of a pound of water and matter in the form of a pound of rock?

6. Again, we must not read into the word "earth" the more precise or definite meanings that have developed since it was first used. From the general observation that all things, living and nonliving, come from the ground, the idea developed that there is a fundamental "principle" in the ground, underlying all things and constituent of many. Ashes and bones contain "earth." A piece of wood contains ashes (earth), fluids (water), exhalations (air), and fire (when it burns).

That the earth is a fundamental element is related to the myth of Antaeous. This giant was the son of the Earth. Hercules noticed, when he wrestled with Antaeous, that the giant regained strength whenever he touched the earth. Hercules therefore lifted him high out of contact with the earth and slew him in midair.

In what sense does an animal contain "air, water, fire, and earth"? Identify each element in the animal. In what sense are the "four elements" different from the chemical elements?

7. According to the Aristotelian view, a melted substance contains "water." A solid can be "melted" either by adding water (dissolving) or by heating (driving other elements out and leaving the water). What is the implication in the name "quicksilver" or "liquid silver" (Greek— *Hydrargyrum*).

8. *Circularity.* Unless careful, we may become involved in logical circularity. "An element does not alter during chemical reactions" and "A chemical reaction is a change in which the elements do not alter." The terms "element" and "chemical reaction," devoid of their connotations and their meaning derived from the immense empirical knowledge, are indeed circular. However, a chemist has no difficulty in recognizing the elements and the chemical reactions and in distinguishing the latter from the "nuclear" reactions, during which the elements are transformed. One basis is the fact that nuclear reactions involve extraordinarily large amounts of energy, compared to chemical reactions.

It is indeed possible to break up carbon into two or more other substances, and it is also possible to synthesize carbon from other elements (see Chap. 13). However, the reactions are very different from the countless reactions that carbon compounds undergo in living things and in manufacturing processes.

The distinction between "chemical and nuclear" changes is definite, but very complicated. The theory (ultimately based on experiments) makes this distinction clear. Operationally an element may be defined as a material having one set of characteristic x-ray spectra (see Chap. 11), and a chemical reaction as a change that does not involve changes in these spectra. Is the formation of water from hydrogen and oxygen a chemical reaction? Is the formation of helium from hydrogen a chemical change? Is the formation of lead, helium, and radium from uranium a chemical change?

9. The law of definite proportions is illustrated in this question. If you mix 3 grams of hydrogen and 40 grams of oxygen and explode them, how much water would you form? What else, if anything, would you have?

10. What would be the formula for water, and how many atoms of hydrogen and oxygen would be in a molecule *if* the oxygen atom weighed: (a) 4 times as much as the hydrogen atom; (b) 8 times as much as the hydrogen atom; (c) 16 times as much as the hydrogen atom; (d) 24 times as much as the hydrogen atom; (e) 32 times as much as the hydrogen atom? What other simple possibilities can you think of?

11. Suppose that the nitrogen atom weighs 14 times as much as the hydrogen atom and the oxygen atom 16 times as much as the hydrogen atom. Write the formulas of the oxygen compounds of nitrogen A, B, C,

D, E, and F on page 235. Repeat, assuming that the oxygen atom weighs 8 times as much as the hydrogen atom.

12. Another interesting relation was soon discovered, known as the "law of reciprocal proportions." The weight ratio in water is hydrogen 1.00 to oxygen 8.00; the weight ratio in hydrogen chloride is hydrogen 1.00 to chlorine 35.46. When a compound of oxygen and chlorine was discovered and analyzed, the weight ratio was found to be: oxygen 8.00 to chlorine 35.46. This is most intriguing! How can this fact be used as an argument for the existence of atoms?

13. How does the atomic theory explain that:

(a) The weight ratio of hydrogen to oxygen in water is always 1:8.

(b) The weight ratio of hydrogen to oxygen in hydrogen peroxide is 1:16, and that in hydrogen peroxide the weight of oxygen is twice that in water for the same amount of hydrogen.

(c) The composition of a compound is always constant.

(d) From only a few elements a very large number of substances can be produced.

(e) Oxygen and ozone are two different substances and yet the same element.

14. How do the atomic and molecular theories explain the difference between

(a) Mixtures and pure substances

(b) Elements and compounds

(c) Physical and chemical change

Define each of the terms and show the differences by taking specific examples.

15. *Atomic weights from specific heats.* (See first Chap. 3, p. 80.) We could estimate the relative weights of atoms if we had any means of weighing *equal numbers* of atoms. The kinetic theory provides these means. On adding heat to a solid metal, we raise the temperature—that is, the average KE of the atoms. Of the total heat added, a certain portion goes to each atom (or particle) in the solid, on the average. Taking two metals, say lead and copper, we can easily find a block of each metal such that will require the same amount of heat to raise its temperature by 1 degree. We would then know that the two blocks contain the same number of atoms. Why? Then by comparing the weights of the blocks would we have the relative weights of the atoms?

Specific heat of lead is 0.0306 calories per gram per degree. How many calories would raise the temperature of 1 gram of lead from 20° C to 21° C? With 6.2 calories how much lead can you heat from 20° C to 21° C?

The specific heat of copper is 0.0921 cal per gram deg. With 6.2 calories, how much copper can you heat from 20° C to 21° C? What can you say about the block of copper and the block of lead requiring the same amount of heat (6.2 calories) to heat them 1 degree? What is the ratio of the weights of an atom of lead to an atom of copper?

16. How many atoms of hydrogen are there in a molecule of hydrogen chloride? What justification is there for your answer? How many hydrogen atoms are there in a molecule of chloroform; water; hydrogen gas; ammonia; methane?

17. How many oxygen atoms are there in a molecule of water? What justification is there for your answer? How many oxygen molecules are there in a molecule of wood alcohol; water; glycerine; osmium oxide?

18. Why do we say that the oxygen compounds containing 0.715 grams

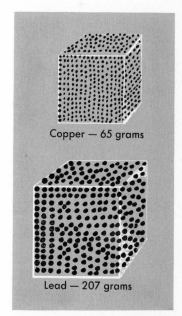

Copper — 65 grams

Lead — 207 grams

Fig. 8-10. Atomic weights from specific heats. Each of these cubes requires 6.2 calories to rise in temperature by 1° C; hence they contain the same number of atoms.

per liter (STP) *most probably* contain one atom per molecule? Two positions can be taken. Is this an empirical generalization? If so, what does "most probably" mean? On the other hand, what *is meant* by an "oxygen atom"? From this point of view, what does the statement mean?

19. The molecular weight of oxygen is 32. An oxygen molecule is how many times as heavy as a hydrogen molecule? How do we know this? An oxygen molecule is how many times as heavy as an oxygen atom? How do we know this? An oxygen molecule is how many times as heavy as an hydrogen atom? How do we know this?

20. An atom of oxygen is 16 times as heavy as a hydrogen atom: How do we know this?

21. A quart of nitrogen at STP weighs about 1.22 grams. What does 1 gallon of nitrogen weigh? What is the weight of 6 gallons (about 22.4 liters)? What is the approximate molecular weight of nitrogen? Using the more accurate figure (5.75 gallons = 22.4 liters) calculate the molecular weight of nitrogen.

22. At STP 5.75 gallons of ammonia weigh 17 grams. What is the molecular weight of ammonia? How many ammonia molecules are there in 5.75 gallons? Express it in terms of N or numerically as a product of 6×10^{23}. How much do 6×10^{23} molecules of ammonia weigh? If you want to take 3×10^{23} ammonia molecules, how much ammonia would you need? Express it both in volume and in weight.

23. By analysis, 5.75 gallons of ammonia is found to contain 3 grams of hydrogen. How many atoms of hydrogen is this? How many hydrogen atoms per molecule of ammonia?

24. A 22.4-liter vessel filled with steam at 273° C (546° A) and 1 atmosphere, contains 9 grams of steam. If the vessel were filled with steam at 100° C, would it contain more or less steam? Using the gas laws, calculate the weight of the steam the vessel would contain at 100° C, and 1 atmosphere. If steam were a gas at 0° C (273° A), what would 22.4 liters weigh? What is the molecular weight of steam? If you want $10 \times 6 \times 10^{23}$ molecules of water, how much water would you take?

25. If you are still troubled by the fact that steam is not a gas at 0° C, consider this reasoning. At STP, 22.4 liters of hydrogen chloride weigh 36.5 grams, contain 1 gram of hydrogen, and contain N atoms of hydrogen and N molecules of hydrogen chloride. If you raise the temperature to 273° C (546° A), keeping the pressure constant, what *volume* would you have? How many grams of hydrogen would you have? How many hydrogen atoms would you have? How many hydrogen molecules would you have?

If now 22.4 liters of steam at 273° C weigh 9 grams, what would 44.8 liters weigh? How many steam molecules would you have? What is the weight of a steam molecule compared to the hydrogen atom?

Still another way of looking at it may help further. At 273° C (546° A), 22.4 liters contain a certain number of molecules which weigh 9 grams. If you cool the steam, more weight could be contained and more molecules. If you cool it to 0° C, the absolute temperature drops to 1/2. How much steam would the vessel contain? How many molecules. How much do N steam molecules weigh?

26. Develop the argument that a hydrogen chloride molecule has only one atom of hydrogen. Continue the argument to show that a molecule of hydrogen gas has two hydrogen atoms.

27. If you have 22.4 liters of a series of oxygen compounds at STP, which of the following weights of oxygen could any of them contain? 8, 9,

16, 19, 25, 32, 35, 36, 48, 50, 64, 70, 80, 90, 100, 120. In what sense are some of these numbers "impossible"?

28. Why do we say that the atomic weight of hydrogen is 1? Is it a matter of experiment or is it a matter of definition? How do we know that the atomic weight of carbon is 12? That the atomic weight of oxygen is 16? (See also Ex. 29.)

29. *Exact atomic weights.* The discussion is based on the use of approximate data. For example, it is only approximately true that all oxygen compounds contain 16 grams of oxygen or a multiple of it. Due to different amounts of deviation from the ideal gas laws, the weight of oxygen hardly ever comes out *n* times exactly 16.00000, for any compound. However, when appropriate corrections are made, they do.

Exact atomic weights may be obtained, using the weight ratios determined by careful experiments and using accurate analytical balances. The weight ratio of hydrogen to oxygen is found to be 1.000:7.94. Since the atomic weight of oxygen is about 16 (or since water contains two hydrogen atoms and one oxygen atom), what is the exact atomic weight of oxygen compared to hydrogen as 1.000? Now for various reasons, historically because the weight ratios were determined by analysis of oxides, it was decided to use oxygen as exactly 16.00000. What is the atomic weight of hydrogen on this basis? The atomic weight found on lists of atomic weights is $0 = 16.00000$. How do we know this? Do we define it so, or is it a matter of experiment. Discuss, and see Exercise 28.

30. The formula of water is H_2O. What do we mean by this statement? How do we know this. Define each term in your argument and cite the experiments that justify the statement.

31. Let us illustrate how a formula is determined. Ethane gas weighs 1.25 grams per liter at STP and by analysis is found to consist of 80 percent carbon and 20 percent hydrogen. What is the weight of 22.4 liters of this gas at STP? What is the molecular weight of this gas? How much carbon does a mole of this gas contain? How many gram-atoms of carbon is this? How many carbon atoms per molecule of ethane are there?

How much hydrogen does a mole of ethane contain? How many gram-atoms of hydrogen is this? How many atoms of hydrogen per molecule of ethane are there? What is the formula of ethane?

32. Consider the fuel gas, butane, found in "bottled gas," and in the little bombs of some cigarette lighters. If you know its formula to be C_4H_{10} and that the atomic weight of carbon is 12, what can you tell about it?

(a) How many carbon atoms and how many hydrogen atoms per molecule?

(b) How much heavier is a butane molecule than a hydrogen atom? A hydrogen molecule? An oxygen molecule?

(c) How much does 22.4 liters of butane weigh at STP? How much does a quart weigh (approximately)?

(d) How much of that is carbon? How much is hydrogen? What percent of butane is carbon? hydrogen?

(e) Volume for volume, under the same conditions, which is heavier, butane or oxygen; how much heavier?

(f) If you have a 3-gallon cylinder at a pressure of 300 pounds per square inch, what weight of butane does it contain (approximately)?

(g) If you burn a mole of butane, [(c) above] and all the hydrogen becomes water, how much water will you get?

33. *Meaning of chemical equations.* Consider the burning of butane gas, which proceeds according to the equation

$$2C_4H_{10} + 13O_2 \longrightarrow 8CO_2 + 10H_2O$$

(a) Calculate the molecular weight of each of the substances.

(b) Complete this sentence: In this reaction, _____ grams of butane combine with _____ grams of oxygen to form _____ grams of carbon dioxide and _____ grams of water.

(c) Complete this sentence: In this reaction, 44.8 liters of butane combine with _____ liters of oxygen to form _____ liters of carbon dioxide and _____ of steam. (Same conditions.)

(d) If you burn 2 gallons of butane, what volume of oxygen do you need? What volume of *air* (20 percent oxygen) do you need? What volume of carbon dioxide is produced. (Same conditions.)

(e) If you have 100 molecules of butane, how many molecules of oxygen do you need? How many molecules of CO_2 do you make?

34. By inspection of the formula find the valence of each element in the following compounds by starting with the definition that the valence of hydrogen is $+1$: H_2O, NH_3, $NaBr$, $FeCl_2$, $MnCl_4$, Pb_2O_3, MnO_2, SiO_2, SO_2, SO_3, H_2SO_4, HNO_3, H_3PO_4, H_2, O_2, Mg.

35. The atomic weight of bromine is 80. What does this mean theoretically? What does it mean experimentally?

36. A mole of hydrogen sulfide (22.4 l at STP) weigh 34 grams. The atomic weight of sulfur is 32. How many gram-atoms of hydrogen per gram-atom of sulfur are there in this compound? What is the valence of sulfur in this compound? How does the valence of sulfur compare with those in question 34?

9

TWO CHEMICAL REACTIONS

1. BURNING AS A CHEMICAL CHANGE

By studying the common features of chemical change, we have been able to penetrate deeply into the structure of matter. The material world is made up of atoms, which combine and recombine in various ways to form the molecules of all substances; and all chemical reactions can be visualized, explained, and described quantitatively by means of the atomic and the molecular theory.

The number of chemical reactions are countless. Surprisingly enough, however, most of them can be understood in terms of a few simple types. Actually, an understanding of what goes on when a candle burns in air and what happens when an acid stomach is "alkalized," are a good basis for an understanding of the great proportion of the chemical reactions of all the elements. The burning of a candle is an example of what is called an oxidation-reduction reaction, while the "alkalizing" is an example of the acid-base reaction. In this chapter we shall consider these two types of reaction.

The burning of a piece of wood in an ordinary fire is a common chemical reaction. It has been observed from the earliest times and has excited the interest of many an observer. During combustion the phenomena are striking enough. A great deal of heat is given off, the flame seems to consume the material, and soon the wood disappears, leaving only a small quantity of ashes. In some instances, as in the case of the

An Early Theory of Combustion

candle, hardly anything is left. Observing a flame flickering and altering in shape as though it were alive, consuming the material and going out when the material is used, has led to many a speculation on the nature of fire, of matter, of life, and of death. It is not surprising that fire has played a central role in many religions and early philosophies.

The Phlogiston Theory. Throughout the centuries there have been many attempts to explain combustion. The first theory of any scientific value was proposed by Joseph Becher (1635-1682), and elaborated by his student George Stahl (1660-1734) around 1670. It became known as the phlogiston theory. According to Stahl, a combustible substance contains a "principle," which he called *phlogiston.* The presence of this constituent imparts to the substance the ability to burn. During burning, the phlogiston disengages itself from the rest of the substance, and the violence of the disengagement produces the fire and often a flame.

According to this theory, wood is a composite of ashes and phlogiston. During the burning the following reaction takes place:

$$\text{wood} \rightarrow \text{phlogiston (escaping)} + \text{ashes}$$

A candle is nearly all phlogiston, so that the burning of a candle is merely a violent release of phlogiston,

$$\text{candle} \rightarrow \text{escaping phlogiston}$$

The theory explained also calcination of metals, a phenomenon associated with burning. When metals are heated in air, they lose their metallic character and are transformed into powdery substances of various colors. Thus, iron is changed into a reddish substance which is iron rust. Tin is transformed into a white ashlike substance. Copper is transformed into a black rust. Mercury under the proper conditions is transformed into a rust of brick-red color. These powdery substances were called "calxes," though more properly they could be called "rusts."

According to the phlogiston theory, a metal is an intimate combination of an ash (or calx) and phlogiston. When a metal is heated in air the phlogiston escapes and the ash is left.

$$\text{metal} \rightarrow \text{phlogiston (escaping)} + \text{ash}$$

Thus, a metal is analogous to wood, and the calcining of a metal is similar to the burning of wood.

The theory was generally accepted for over a century and was extended to explain many other phenomena that were recognized as similar to burning. There were, however, a few contradictions which the critics pointed out from time to time. Burning, as well as calcination of metals, takes place only in the presence of air; it does not take place in a vacuum. If the amount of air is limited, then burning or calcining proceeds only for a while but soon stops.

This difficulty was disposed of rather easily, or so the phlogistonists thought. They advanced the notion that air is necessary for burning in order to absorb the escaping phlogiston. If the supply of air is limited,

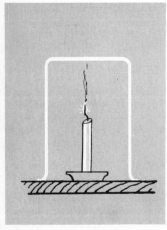

Fig. 9-1. A candle burning in a limited quantity of air soon goes out.

the air soon becomes so saturated with phlogiston that the burning stops. The defenders of the theory pointed to the similar situation of trying to boil a liquid in a closed vessel. The space above the liquid is soon saturated with the vapor and boiling stops.

Another difficulty was somewhat more serious. It had been known for some time that when a metal is heated in air, the resulting rust weighs more than the original metal. This difficulty is not encountered in the burning of wood or coal. In these instances the ashes always weigh less than the burning material. But in the case of the metals, the ashes weigh more. "How then," the critics pointed out, "could a metal be a composite of ashes *plus* plogiston, and *after losing* the phlogiston, weigh more?"

It is a curious historical fact that even this objection did not disturb the defenders of the theory too much. Perhaps the basic reason was that the early chemists did not recognize the importance of weight. We must remember that these ideas were held before Lavoisier had formulated the law of conservation of matter. Those who were impressed by the objection attempted to meet it by assuming that phlogiston was very light. It made the substance with which it combined lighter, much as a life preserver makes the weight of a drowning person "lighter," even though it adds to his weight. These people were obviously confusing weight with density, and did not understand the meaning of buoyancy. Those who recognized this error went even further astray and assumed that phlogiston is a substance that has a *negative weight*. This would mean that phlogiston is repelled by the earth (Ex. 1).

Fig. 9-2. Lavoisier—father of modern quantitative chemistry—established the law of conservation of mass, developed the concept of elements, and explained combustion as union with oxygen. (The Bettmann Archive.)

Lavoisier's Theory of Combustion

These explanations did not impress Antoine Lavoisier (1743-1794). He had studied Newton and was convinced that weight is a fundamental property of matter. Nowhere in Newtonian mechanics is matter found repelling other matter. Negative weight does not make sense. Air was known to have weight, and by this time other gases or "airs" had been studied and weighed. Nor could he dismiss so easily the fact that air is necessary for burning, for calcining of metals, and for the sustenance of life. Lavoisier was groping for an explanation, along the lines that burning instead of being *loss* of something (phlogiston) was *union with* something in the air.

At this time there occurred one of those happy accidents in science that mark the great milestones in its progress. Joseph Priestley (1733-1804) discovered what we now call "oxygen." On heating red rust of mercury he obtained an unusual gas which had the properties of air to a remarkable degree. Combustible substances burned in it much more vigorously than in air, and metals calcined in it much more readily. A mouse placed in a bottle of this "air" continued to live much longer than in ordinary air. Having tried it on another mouse with apparently no ill effects, Priestley tried it on himself. He described his experience as an exhilarating effect. "Thus far two mice and myself have breathed this gas; who knows that in the future this may not become an article of luxury." These words were prophetic of the modern use of oxygen in hospitals and in high altitudes. Because of its properties, this "air" was called "fire air" or "life air."

On hearing of this discovery and reading the reports, Lavoisier sought Priestley out. While dining with him in Paris, he asked for details of the experiment. In particular he wanted to know what else besides this gas Priestley had obtained. The answer was *mercury*. The second question was, how did he obtain the red rust of mercury in the first place? The answer here was, by heating mercury with a "burning" lens, in the presence of air. Does this not mean, argued Lavoisier, that when mercury is heated with a burning lens in the air, the mercury combines with *something in the air* to form the red rust? Then, on heating the red rust to a higher temperature, the mercury is recovered as well as the gas that was extracted from the air in the first place? This substance extracted from the air is now pure, and that explains why it supports combustion more vigorously. It must be this substance in the air that is responsible for burning in an ordinary fire.

Priestley was unconvinced, but Lavoisier went on to develop his own ideas. In a series of brilliant experiments he collected evidence that he marshalled against the phlogiston theory and in support of his own theory. Most of his contemporaries were convinced. A notable exception was Priestley himself. It is ironical that the discoverer of oxygen went to his grave, some twenty years later, a confirmed phlogistonist.

The main support of Lavoisier's argument was obtained from his celebrated "twelve-day experiment." It is a classic example in the method of science. He used the apparatus shown in Figure 9-3. He put some mercury in the retort, the outlet of which communicated with a jar containing a measured quantity of air, over mercury. On prolonged heating, there gradually appeared particles of red rust floating over the surface of the mercury in the retort. The quantity of rust increased on succeeding days for about a week, after which no further change was evident. On the twelfth day, he allowed the apparatus to cool. He found that about one fifth of the air had disappeared.

On heating the red rust to a temperature higher than that of the furnace, he obtained Priestley's "fire air." Combustible substances burned in it vigorously; metals calcined readily, and mice lived in it longer than in an equal volume of ordinary air. He called the "fire air" *oxygen* which means "acid former," because it combined with many substances to form acids. On the other hand, the residual air in the jar did not behave like air. Lighted candles immersed in it went out; metals did not rust in it, and mice placed in it promptly died. He called the residual air *azote,* meaning "not supporting life." We now call it nitrogen, because it is a constituent of niter, or saltpeter, which is used to make gun powder.

Thus, Lavoisier proved that air consists of two parts. One part, about one fifth, is the active part, responsible for burning. The other, the remaining four fifths, is inactive. He clinched the argument by decomposing a weighed quantity of the red rust and measuring the amount of gas given up. By simple calculation he showed that the amount of gas, combined with all the red rust in his experiment, was exactly the amount lost by the air. Thus, all the oxygen in the rust came from the air. As a final proof, he mixed one volume of the "fire air" with four

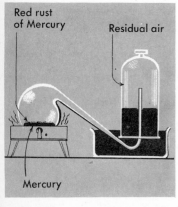

Red rust
of Mercury

Residual air

Mercury

Fig. 9-3. Lavoisier's twelve-day experiment. By the twelfth day, on cooling, one fifth of the air in the bell jar had disappeared and some red rust of mercury had collected at the surface of mercury.

volumes of the residual air and obtained ordinary air, in every respect indistinguishable from the air in the atmosphere.

The proof for the theory was now complete. Air consists of one-fifth oxygen and four-fifths nitrogen. Oxygen is the active component responsible for burning. When combustible substances burn in pure oxygen, they combine chemically with the oxygen. When they burn in air, they still combine with oxygen. The reaction in air is slower, because the concentration of oxygen is only 20 percent.

The important part of Lavoisier's reasoning is that it explained **Oxidation** burning as a chemical reaction. Since he had pure oxygen, the burning of an element in it can only be a direct chemical *union* of the element with oxygen. This point is further confirmed by the fact that the weight of the product is the sum of the weights of the oxygen and the element burning in it. For example, when carbon burns in pure oxygen, it combines chemically with the oxygen to form "carbonic acid gas," now called carbon dioxide. We can now record this reaction more clearly by using the equation

$$C + O_2 \rightarrow CO_2$$

which shows that a certain quantity of carbon (12 grams) combines with a certain quantity of oxygen (32 grams) to give a quantity of carbon dioxide (44 grams), which is the sum of the weights of the reactants. We can go even one step further and visualize the carbon atoms combining with the oxygen molecules to form molecules of carbon dioxide.

Many other elements burn in pure oxygen, forming chemical compounds with it. For example, sulfur, phosphorus, hydrogen, iron, and magnesium burn in oxygen giving off a great deal of heat and forming the corresponding oxygen compounds. Moreover, many metals when burned (or calcined) in pure oxygen, change into the calxes, which can only be compounds of the metal with oxygen. Further, when exposed to oxygen over long periods of time, these same metals rust, forming essentially the same compounds. All these are instances of chemical union with oxygen. The essential identity of these processes can be seen more clearly by writing the chemical equations for the reactions.

$$S + O_2 \rightarrow SO_2$$
$$4P + 5O_2 \rightarrow 2P_2O_5$$
$$2H_2 + O_2 \rightarrow 2H_2O$$
$$4Fe + 3O_2 \rightarrow 2Fe_2O_3$$
$$2Mg + O_2 \rightarrow 2MgO$$
$$2Hg + O_2 \rightarrow 2HgO$$
$$2Cu + O_2 \rightarrow 2CuO$$

Lavoisier gave the name *oxidation* to the chemical union of a substance with oxygen; and the name *oxide* to the compound that is produced in the process. Thus, when iron burns in oxygen, it *oxidizes,* forming *iron oxide*. When iron is calcined in oxygen, it is still oxidized, forming the iron oxide. When iron rusts slowly in oxygen, again it oxidizes, forming the oxide of iron. The idea of oxidation, so clearly conceived, was destined to serve as the prototype in the understanding of all chemical reactions, as we shall proceed to show.

The immediate extension of the idea of oxidation is almost too obvious. Not only elements, but also compounds, burn in oxygen, forming the oxides of the elements in the compound. Thus when an oil, which is a compound of carbon and hydrogen, burns in oxygen, it forms the oxide of carbon and the oxide of hydrogen (which is water).

$$C_{17}H_{36} + 26O_2 \rightarrow 17CO_2 + 18H_2O$$

Similarly, when iron pyrite ("fools' gold"), which is a compound of iron and sulfur, is heated in air, it forms the oxide of iron and the oxide of sulfur,

$$4FeS_2 + 11O_2 \rightarrow 2Fe_2O_3 + 8SO_2$$

Thousands upon thousands of chemical compounds burn in oxygen or react more slowly with it, in each case forming the oxides of the elements in the compound. All these reactions are instances of oxidation or chemical union with oxygen.

Lavoisier argued that when *air* instead of pure oxygen is used, the processes are essentially the same. The reactions are slower, to be sure, due to the fact that air is only 20 percent oxygen, but otherwise they are in no way different. The phenomena are entirely similar in all the outward appearances, and more significantly, the same compounds, the oxides of the respective elements, are formed in all cases. (The fact that in some cases different oxides of the elements are produced under different conditions does not invalidate the truth of this statement.) Therefore, burning, calcining, or rusting in *air* are all instances of oxidation.

The systematization of chemical knowledge resulting from this idea can hardly be overestimated. A number of diverse and rather distinct phenomena are understood to be essentially the same chemical process. Moreover, countless substances are now shown to be related. Thus water, instead of being a fundamental element is merely one of the oxides. Sand is the oxide of silicon; rust is the oxide of iron; red rust of mercury is the oxide of mercury. Many other minerals hitherto known by names in no way indicative of their natures have been found to be merely oxides of the elements (Ex. 4). More important, the way was paved to an understanding of the composition of still other minerals. Many minerals are either more complicated combinations of oxides, or they are compounds of other elements, analogous to the oxides, such as sulfides, chlorides, tellurides, and bromides. For example, galena, the common mineral of lead, is lead sulfide, PbS. The mineral horn silver is silver chloride, AgCl. Rock salt is sodium chloride, NaCl. We shall return to the generalization to other elements presently.

Meanwhile, Lavoisier extended the idea of oxidation to the explanation of other phenomena. He recognized that respiration of living things also involves oxidation. The similarity was suggested by the fact that air is necessary for life. The complete proof is not too complicated. When carbon burns in pure oxygen, it combines with the oxygen to form carbon dioxide. The product is a gas that reacts with limewater to form a milky suspension, which soon settles as a sediment of calcium carbonate or limestone. Thus carbon dioxide can be easily detected by bubbling it through limewater. The same gas, CO_2, is produced when carbon or its compounds burn in air. We know this because the same milky suspension results on bubbling the resulting gases through limewater. Breathing involves taking in oxygen. When the exhaled breath is bubbled through limewater it gives the same milky precipitate, showing that it contains carbon dioxide. Therefore, in the body the essential reaction is oxidation of the carbon compounds in the food to form carbon dioxide, among other substances (Ex. 5).

Another interesting extension of the idea of oxidation is the explanation of the souring of wines. It had been known that wines sour when exposed to air, but keep well if air is excluded. Wine contains alcohol, CH_3CH_2OH, and when it sours it becomes vinegar, which is a dilute solution of acetic acid, CH_3COOH. It is clear, therefore, that the souring is essentially the oxidation of alcohol to acetic acid. The equation makes it even more clear.

$$CH_3CH_2OH + O_2 \rightarrow CH_3COOH + H_2O$$

In this reaction we may note two additional points. When alcohol is oxidized, it forms an acid. Other substances similarly give acids on reacting with oxygen. It was instances of this sort that led Lavoisier to give the name *oxygen* to the "fire air" of Priestley, the word "oxygen" meaning "acid former." The other point is that oxidation need not be complete turning to carbon dioxide and water. As long as the substance reacts with oxygen it is *oxidized*. Many other changes in nature— for example, the decay of dead plants and animals—were soon discovered to be instances of oxidation. Thus, Lavoisier extended the concept of oxidation to explain a wider and wider range of phenomena.

One very important extension of the idea is the recognition that substances can be oxidized even when they combine with the oxygen present in oxygen compounds. If a jet of burning hydrogen is inserted into a flask of nitric oxide gas, NO, the hydrogen continues to burn in the nitric oxide, with a hot flame, producing water and nitrogen gas.

$$2H_2 + 2NO \rightarrow 2H_2O + N_2$$

In this case, the oxygen, although already combined with the nitrogen, oxidizes the hydrogen to form water. Similarly, an ignited piece of wood continues to burn in the nitric oxide very much the same as in air. In fact, a great many substances "burn" in nitric oxide much the same as if the latter were free oxygen and form their oxides in the process.

Nitric oxide is not unique in its resemblance to oxygen. A great many oxygen compounds behave similarly. For example, a piece of excelsior immersed suddenly in a flask of nitric acid vapor above its boiling point (say 120° C) bursts into a flame and burns vigorously. Similarly, a piece of copper immersed in hot nitric acid gas reacts violently, forming the oxide of copper. Many other gaseous compounds of oxygen support combustion. An interesting example is steam itself. If a ribbon of magnesium metal is lighted in air and then immersed in steam, the magnesium continues to burn vigorously, extracting the oxygen from the steam, and forming magnesium oxide.

$$Mg + H_2O \rightarrow MgO + H_2$$

Thus the similarity of the phenomena leads us to recognize that oxidation can take place not only in pure oxygen but also in compounds containing oxygen.

Having extended the idea of oxidation this far, it is possible to go one step further. The substances that furnish oxygen need not even be in the gaseous state. Thus copper reacts with liquid nitric acid or with a solution of nitric acid, giving essentially the same products that it gives with the vapor of nitric acid. Moreover, many other substances, liquids as well as solids, furnish oxygen and oxidize combustible substances. A good example is saltpeter, or potassium nitrate, KNO_3, used in gun powder. Gun powder is a mixture of powdered charcoal and sulfur, mixed with potassium nitrate. When gun powder explodes, the carbon and the sulfur are "burned" to carbon dioxide and sulfur dioxide by the oxygen in the saltpeter. In the more recent development of the solid rocket fuels, the oxygen is furnished by the solid compounds of oxygen.

The substances that furnish oxygen, as well as oxygen itself, are called *oxidizing agents*. A great many oxidizing agents are known. Thus in addition to those mentioned, the list includes: hydrogen peroxide, H_2O_2; manganese dioxide, MnO_2; potassium chlorate, $KClO_3$; potassium dichromate, $K_2Cr_2O_7$; potassium permanganate, $KMnO_4$; and many others. Some of these oxidizing agents are more powerful than oxygen itself. Thus hydrogen peroxide is one of the most powerful oxidizing agents known and is used to oxidize the fuel in rockets. Other oxidizing agents are relatively mild. Thus, the bright-red compound in the blood, called oxyhemoglobin, oxidizes the food in the tissues.

We need not be disturbed by the fact that some of these reactions mentioned are complicated. The important thing is that all these reactions are instances of *oxidation*—that is, union with oxygen. Thus, the initial concept of Lavoisier has been extended to include a very wide range of phenomena and to serve as the organizing principle in the understanding of a large body of chemical knowledge.

Reduction Lavoisier's principle of oxidation, however, was destined to receive a still further extension. A group of phenomena at first sight unrelated to burning were soon understood to be merely processes *opposite to that of oxidation*. For centuries metals have been obtained from their ores by a process that was termed "reduction of an ore to the metal." Since many ores are oxides (or complicated combinations of oxides), the process of "reduction" is merely the *removal* of oxygen from the ore. For example, iron ore is reduced to metallic iron by mixing it with charcoal and heating:

$$2Fe_2O_3 + 2C \rightarrow 4Fe + 3CO_2$$

In this reaction the carbon removes the oxygen from the iron oxide, leaving the metal free. Reduction, therefore, is merely the opposite of oxidation. It could be called "deoxidation."

A great many substances can be used to reduce the oxides to the respective metals. For example, hydrogen, carbon monoxide, or even other metals are widely used in metallurgical processes. We list a few of those reactions:

$$Fe_2O_3 + 3H_2 \rightarrow 2Fe + 3H_2O$$
$$Fe_2O_3 + 3CO \rightarrow 2Fe + 3CO_2$$
$$Fe_2O_3 + 3Zn \rightarrow 2Fe + 3ZnO$$
$$Fe_2O_3 + 2Al \rightarrow 2Fe + Al_2O_3$$
$$CuO + H_2 \rightarrow Cu + H_2O$$

In all these reactions the ore (oxide) is reduced to the metal.

A careful examination of these reactions shows that the substances reducing the ores have one thing in common. They all remove the oxygen, and for this reason they are called *reducing agents*. And in addition these substances remove the oxygen *by combining with it*. Hence, the reducing agents must be substances that have a great affinity for oxygen. Thus, among the reducing agents there are hydrogen and combustible substances in general and, very significantly, the metals as a class.

Comparison of oxidation with the opposite process, deoxidation or reduction, discloses another important relation between them. Both take place in the same reaction. We can see this relation by examining the reduction of iron oxide to iron.

$$2Fe_2O_3 + 3C \rightarrow 4Fe + 3CO_2$$

In this reaction the iron oxide, Fe_2O_3, is reduced to the metal, Fe; but at the same time the *carbon* is *oxidized* to carbon dioxide. It is clear that in all these reactions, there can be no *reduction* of an oxygen-containing substance unless at the same time another substance combines with the oxygen and is itself *oxidized;* in other words, *oxidation and reduction take place simultaneously*. During an oxidation-reduction reaction, the oxidizing agent (the ore) is reduced, while, at the same time, the reducing agent (the substance that combines with the oxygen) is oxidized. Thus oxidation and reduction are inseparable, like the opposite sides of the same coin.

Chemistry has come a long way since Lavoisier formulated the concept of oxidation as union with oxygen. With each extension an ever-widening range of phenomena were understood. A vast number of the reactions of oxygen and its compounds are oxidation-reduction reactions, and as they were studied and explained in terms of the extended concept, they became a part of the growing body of chemical knowledge. Moreover, in the same studies, the chemical reactions of those substances which react with oxygen or from which oxygen is removed were understood and incorporated into the body of chemical knowledge.

Extension of the Concept of Oxidation-Reduction to Other Elements

The reader will recall (p. 266) that the explanation of ordinary burning was to serve as the model for the understanding of the chemical reactions of all elements. This was achieved by a further extension of the concept oxidation-reduction, using analogical reasoning. As a first step, the concept of oxidation-reduction as the chemical union or removal of *oxygen* was extended to other elements showing a chemical behavior similar to that of oxygen. A good example is chlorine, which may be obtained from sea water. Chlorine is a greenish-yellow gas, with a pungent and suffocating odor. It is about $2\frac{1}{2}$ times denser than air and is somewhat soluble in water. It has a formula, Cl_2, indicating that, like many other common gases, it has two atoms per molecule.

Chlorine behaves in many ways like oxygen. For example, a jet of hydrogen lit in the air and then inserted into a bottle of chlorine continues to burn in the chlorine with a hot pale-blue flame, forming hydrogen chloride. When hydrogen burns in oxygen, it forms the oxide; when it burns in chlorine, it forms the chloride. Not only are the phenomena entirely similar in the two cases and the products analogous, but the chemical equation describing the phenomena are also entirely analogous. Comparison of the two equations emphasizes the similarity.

$$2H_2 + O_2 \rightarrow 2H_2O + \text{heat}$$
$$H_2 + Cl_2 \rightarrow 2HCl + \text{heat}$$

Again this is not an isolated instance. Many substances burn in chlorine to form chlorides. In fact most substances burn even more vigorously in chlorine than in oxygen. Thus, when a piece of copper foil is dropped into a bottle of chlorine, it ignites spontaneously forming copper chloride, $CuCl_2$. When powdered antimony is sprinkled into a bottle of chlorine, it reacts with it giving off sparks and forming antimony chloride, $SbCl_3$. These examples can be multiplied almost indefinitely.

The similarity of chlorine to oxygen is also observed in the opposite process. Just as oxygen can be removed from oxides, so chlorine can be removed from chlorides by reducing agents, and the free metal be produced in each case. For example, when hydrogen is passed over heated copper chloride, $CuCl_2$, hydrogen chloride is formed and the copper compound is reduced to the metal. This reaction is perfectly analogous to the reduction of copper oxide by hydrogen, as seen by a comparison of the two reactions.

$$CuO + H_2 \rightarrow Cu + H_2O$$
$$CuCl + H_2 \rightarrow Cu + 2HCl$$

These similarities in the chemical reactions of oxygen and chlorine led chemists to recognize that the processes are fundamentally similar. Accordingly, they applied the term "reduction" to the removal of either oxygen *or* of chlorine, and "oxidation" to the union with oxygen *or* with chlorine. It may seem somewhat illogical to call a reaction with chlorine *oxidation* when oxygen is not involved, but the use of the same term emphasizes the essential similarity of the two reactions.

The extension of the concept of oxidation to chlorine was but the first step in the extension to other elements that behave like oxygen. Among these elements are bromine, iodine, fluorine, sulfur, and nitrogen. Thus hydrogen will burn in *bromine* vapor—giving hydrogen bromide, and copper will burn in bromine vapor to form copper bromide. Similarly, hydrogen and many metals will burn in *fluorine* gas, forming the fluorides, in *iodine* vapor forming the iodides, or in *sulfur* vapor forming the sulfides. A few active elements will even burn in nitrogen. Thus magnesium metal will burn in *nitrogen* to form magnesium nitride. The following equations show the similarity of the reactions.

$$2Cu + O_2 \rightarrow 2CuO$$
$$Cu + Cl_2 \rightarrow CuCl_2$$
$$Cu + Br_2 \rightarrow CuBr_2$$
$$Cu + I_2 \rightarrow CuI_2$$
$$Mg + F_2 \rightarrow MgF_2$$
$$Cu + S \rightarrow CuS$$
$$3Mg + N_2 \rightarrow Mg_3N_2$$

Again this is only a partial list of such reactions. Thus several elements are similar to oxygen and their reactions are similar to those of oxygen. Hence, by analogy, all these reactions are called *oxidation* reactions.

Inspection of these reactions brings out one of the most important generalizations in chemistry. Oxygen is, of course, a nonmetal. But all the elements that behave like oxygen are also nonmetals. Accordingly, the concept of oxidation is extended to mean chemical union with *any nonmetal.* The nonmetals as a class are oxidizing agents.

The extension of the concept of oxidation is further justified by considering the opposite process—that is, the *removal* of nonmetals from their compounds by reducing agents. Thus, hydrogen will reduce to copper a large number of compounds of copper, as shown by the following equations.

$$CuO + H_2 \rightarrow Cu + H_2O$$
$$CuCl_2 + H_2 \rightarrow Cu + 2HCl$$
$$CuBr_2 + H_2 \rightarrow Cu + 2HBr$$
$$CuI_2 + H_2 \rightarrow Cu + 2HI$$
$$CuS + H_2 \rightarrow Cu + 2H_2S$$

Compounds of other metals may be given as further examples. Accordingly, the term *reduction* is extended to mean *removal of any nonmetal from a compound.*

We may now summarize the discussion by restating the generalized definitions of oxidation, reduction, oxidizing agents, and reducing agents.

Oxidation is the *union* with oxygen or any other nonmetal.

Reduction is the *removal* of oxygen or any other nonmetal.

Oxidizing agents are oxygen or any other nonmetal.

Reducing agents are hydrogen, carbon, and the metals in general.

The reader can hardly fail to notice the magnitude of the achievement that resulted from generalizing these concepts. They led to the realization that oxidization and reduction are fundamental reactions of all the elements, and that the metals as a class are reducing agents, while the nonmetals as a class are oxidizing agents—an important relation among the elements. Thus, the distinction between metals and nonmetals is not merely one of appearance and physical properties; it is deeper than that. It involves a distinction between the *chemical properties* of these two types of elements. In the subsequent discussion we shall show in greater detail how the concept of oxidation-reduction helps in the organization and understanding of chemical behavior of all the elements and their compounds.

Correlation of Oxidation-Reduction with Valence

An unexpected outcome of the generalization of the concepts of oxidation and reduction is that they lead into a correlation with valence, which is a property of the atoms. In Chapter 8 (p. 252) the valence of an element was defined as the number of hydrogen atoms an atom of the element combines with or replaces. The distinction between positive and negative valence was also made. If the atom combines with hydrogen, it has a negative valence; if it replaces hydrogen, it has a positive valence. Thus, from the formula H_2O, we deduce that the valence of oxygen in water is -2; from the formula Fe_2O_3, we deduce that the valence of iron in this compound is -3. Similarly the valence of carbon in CO is -2; in CO_2 is $+4$; in free C it is zero.

Examination of an oxidation-reduction reaction always indicates a change in valence, with the oxidation part of the reaction always showing an increase in positive valence. For example, when carbon burns in a *limited* amount of air carbon monoxide is formed.

$$2C + O_2 \rightarrow 2CO$$

In this reaction the carbon has been oxidized, and its valence has increased from 0 to $+2$. Burning the carbon in plenty of air oxidizes the carbon to carbon dioxide, CO_2. In this case the valence is increased from 0 to $+4$. Burning the carbon monoxide, CO, further to carbon dioxide,

$$2CO + O_2 \rightarrow 2CO_2$$

again increases the valence of carbon, this time from $+2$ to $+4$. These examples are sufficient to show that whenever any element is oxidized, its valence increases—that is, becomes more positive.

The opposite relation exists in reduction. In this case the element reduced decreases in valence. For example, in the reduction of copper oxide to copper

$$CuO + H_2 \rightarrow Cu + H_2O$$

the valence of copper decreases from +2 to 0. If copper chloride, $CuCl_2$, is reduced to Cu, again the valence decreases from +2 to 0. From these examples it is clear that the element undergoing reduction always decreases in valence (Ex. 15).

Another useful idea in further organizing chemical knowledge is the concept of oxidizing and reducing power. Some nonmetals are better oxidizing agents than others. We have already pointed out that chlorine is a more powerful oxidizing agent than oxygen itself. Qualitatively, the oxidizing power of an element can be described by the vigor with which it reacts. Quantitatively, the oxidizing power of two elements may be compared by the amount of energy given off during corresponding reactions. Thus, burning 1 gram of hydrogen in oxygen releases (gives off) 18,000 calories; burning 1 gram of hydrogen in chlorine releases 47,000 calories:

$$2H_2 + O_2 \rightarrow 2H_2O + heat \quad 17,000 \text{ cal (per gram of hydrogen)}$$
$$H_2 + Cl_2 \rightarrow 2HCl + heat \quad 47,000 \text{ cal (per gram of hydrogen)}$$

A comparison of these two reactions shows that chlorine is a more powerful oxidizing agent than oxygen, because it gives off more heat than oxygen in burning 1 gram of hydrogen. Chlorine, therefore, is more *active* than oxygen as an oxidizing agent. From such measurements the nonmetals are arranged in a series in the order of decreasing oxidizing activity. Thus, in Table 9:1, fluorine is the most powerful oxidizing agent and nitrogen the least powerful.

A similar situation exists with the reducing power of the metals. On burning in the same quantity of oxygen (or chlorine) the more active metals give off more heat than the less active ones. As an example, a comparison of the amounts of heat given off on burning aluminum and iron in pure oxygen is listed below.

$$4Al + 3O_2 \rightarrow 2Al_2O_3 + heat \quad 9000 \text{ calories (per gram of oxygen)}$$
$$4Fe + 3O_2 \rightarrow 2Fe_2O_3 + heat \quad 4200 \text{ calories (per gram of oxygen)}$$

These reactions indicate that aluminum is a more powerful reducing agent than iron, and is, therefore, the more *active* metal. From such measurements the metals are arranged from the more powerful to the least powerful reducing agents (Table 9:2). This is the *activity series* of the metals.

It would carry us too far afield to discuss all the information contained in these tables. Some conclusions are, however, obvious. In the activity series of the metals, the more active elements are at the top,

Oxidizing and Reducing Power of the Elements

TABLE 9:1
Activity Series of Nonmetals

Fluorine
Chlorine
Oxygen
Bromine
Iodine
Sulfur
Nitrogen

TABLE 9:2
Activity Series of Metals

Sodium
Magnesium
Aluminum
Iron
Tin
Lead
Hydrogen
Copper
Silver
Gold

and the least active at the bottom. This means that the free metals at the top oxidize or rust with great vigor—they give off a great deal of energy in being oxidized. This explains why sodium, for example, must be kept under kerosene—it oxidizes too rapidly in air. On the other hand, the metals in the middle of the series rust rather slowly, while those at the bottom rust with great difficulty, or not at all. Thus, copper rusts more slowly than iron, silver with difficulty, and gold not at all.

The position of the metal in the activity series also determines the ease or difficulty in obtaining the metals from their ores. These two properties are, of course, related. The more active the metal, the more heat it gives off in combining with oxygen, and the more difficult the reduction of its oxide. This explains why gold and silver are found free in nature; why copper is sometimes found native, but more often combined. This is why copper ore is reduced rather easily, iron ore with greater difficulty, while aluminum ores require the powerful means of electric currents. It is not an accident that gold and silver were known from remote antiquity, that the bronze age (copper and tin) preceded the iron age, and that the active light-weight metals such as aluminum and magnesium have been obtained from their ores only in recent times. These and many more conclusions now become evident from the tables of activities (Exs. 12-15).

Chemistry has traveled a long road since Lavoisier first gave a clear conception of burning as chemical union with oxygen. We have gone into considerable detail in this section primarily to illustrate the evolution of a scientific concept and to indicate the scope of its usefulness, and the reader should not feel obliged to memorize all the facts that have been presented. With each extension of the concept of oxidation an ever-widening range of phenomena were understood and became part of an organized body of chemical knowledge. The oxidation and reduction reactions are fundamental reactions of all the elements and their compounds. A large fraction of all chemical reactions are oxidation-reduction reactions. Moreover the correlation of oxidation and reduction with valence constitutes a big step toward understanding the properties of the atoms, and ultimately the structure and nature of all matter.

2. ACIDS AND BASES

The oxidizing property of nonmetals is related to another fundamental property, namely,·the acid-forming property. We have already hinted at the relation between union with oxygen and the formation of acids. The very name "oxygen," meaning "acid former," was given by Lavoisier to Priestley's "fire air," because the element in many instances forms acids. The relation, however, needs clarification, and extension to other nonmetals. As might be suspected, the metals have properties opposite to those of the nonmetals. The metals form *bases,* which, as will be shown presently, have properties opposite to those of the acids.

From time immemorial, a number of materials were recognized as having a characteristic sour taste. Among those were unripe grapes and other fruits, lemons and other citrous fruits, vinegar, apple cider, rhubarb, and milk that has been left in a warm place for some time. In the course of centuries, the substances responsible for the sour taste have been isolated. Thus, acetic acid was isolated from vinegar; citric acid from citrous fruits; tartaric acid from wine tartar and grapes; oxalic acid from rhubarb; and lactic acid from milk. These substances were early recognized as belonging to a class and were called acids, from the Latin *"acidum,"* meaning "sharp."

Acids and Their Properties

During the middle ages, the alchemists discovered several mineral acids, which are not normally found in nature. Four of these are the most important. Sulfuric acid or vitriolic acid was produced from sulfur or brimstone. Nitric acid was produced by mixing sulfuric acid with saltpeter (potassium nitrate), and distilling. Muriatic acid, or "marine" acid (hydrochloric acid), was produced by adding sulfuric acid to sea salt and distilling. Phosphoric acid was produced by burning phosphorus and dissolving the resulting white smoke in water. The mineral acids are far stronger than the acids found in nature, possessing the property of acids to a very marked degree.

The acids as a class, whether mineral or of life origin, have the following characteristic properties in common.

Sour Taste. This is, of course, the most obvious property. In fact a substance is classified as an acid if it exhibits this property.

Effect on Indicators. It was noticed during the middle ages that the dye of the litmus plant (a plant of the cabbage family) always assumes a characteristic red color in the presence of acids. Many other dyes have since been found to assume distinctive colors in the presence of acids. For example, the dye, methyl orange, normally of orange color, turns bright pink in the presence of acids. Methyl violet (the dye found in indelible pencils) is yellowish green in strong acid solutions. The reader may have had the unfortunate experience of spilling lemon juice or vinegar on colored clothes, and been dismayed by the change in color, although the cloth was apparently not injured. These dyes are called indicators, for they indicate the presence of acids. A practical outcome of this observation is the use of indicators to detect the presence of acids without the necessity of tasting them and running the risk of destruction of a part of the tongue, or of fatal poisoning.

Reaction with Active Metals. Acids react with active metals, to give off hydrogen. A number of active metals—such as iron, zinc, and aluminum—react with acids. The metal disappears and at the same time the characteristic properties of the acid vanish. We say, somewhat improperly, that the metal dissolves in the acid. It is not a simple dissolving, however. If the solution is evaporated, the metal is not recovered, but a solid, called the salt of the metal (see below), is obtained, usually in the form of crystals. For example, if iron is placed in hydrochloric acid, hydrogen bubbles off and iron chloride is formed in solution.

$$Fe + 2HCl \rightarrow H_2 + FeCl_2$$

On evaporation of the solution, pale-green crystals of iron chloride are obtained.

This reaction of the acids is especially significant because it indicates that all acids contain hydrogen, which may be replaced by a metal. In the example cited, the hydrogen of the hydrogen chloride has been replaced by iron forming iron chloride. Therefore, acids characteristically contain hydrogen.

This characteristic is brought out most clearly by the formula which is determined by the methods described in Chapter 8. The formulas of the acids mentioned are as follows:

hydrochloric acid	HCl
nitric acid	HNO_3
sulfuric acid	H_2SO_4
phosphoric acid	H_3PO_4
acetic acid	$H \cdot C_2H_3O_2$
oxalic acid	$H_2 \cdot C_2O_4$
tartaric acid	$H_2 \cdot C_4H_4O_6$
citric acid	$H \cdot C_3H_5O_3$
lactic acid	$H_3 \cdot C_6H_5O_7$

All acids, therefore, contain hydrogen. However, the converse is not necessarily true. Many substances containing hydrogen do not react with metals nor show the other properties of the acids. These are not acids. For example, sugar, $C_{12}H_{22}O_{11}$, contains hydrogen, but it is not an acid. It does not have a sour taste, nor does it give up any of its hydrogen when in contact with an active metal. *Acids, therefore, are substances containing hydrogen, which they give off on reacting with active metals.*

Conduction of Current. Acids conduct the electric current, liberating hydrogen at the negative pole. It is significant that acids give off hydrogen not only on reacting with active metals but also during the passage of current. Moreover, if we recall that negative electric charges attract their opposite, the fact that hydrogen is liberated at the negative pole implies that the hydrogen of the acids carries a positive electric charge in solution. It is written H^+ and is called the hydrogen ion. We shall take up this point in greater detail later.

Reaction with Bases. Perhaps the most important property of acids is their reaction with another class of substances called *bases* or *alkalis,* to form a third class of substances called *salts.* For example, all acids react with lime (calcium hydroxide) which is a typical base. The acids are thoroughly destroyed in the process, and form salts of calcium.

While all the acids show the characteristic properties of the class, they vary considerably among themselves in the intensity with which they show these properties. Some acids are more intensely sour than others. For example, the taste of many fruit acids is pleasantly sharp; vinegar is edible but only in dilute solutions; oxalic acid is intensely sour and hydrochloric acid is unbearably so, even in extremely dilute solutions. Similarly, acids vary in the vigor with which they react with metals. For example, iron dissolves slowly in vinegar, but very rapidly in hydrochloric acid. Likewise, acids vary in their ability to conduct electric current. Thus acetic acid is a rather poor conductor, while hydrochloric acid and sulfuric acid are excellent conductors. *Strong acids* are those that show the acid properties to a marked degree and *weak acids* are those that show the properties to a slight degree.

In principle, the strength of an acid may be measured by any of the characteristic properties. However, some of these are not subject to accurate experimental measurement, or entail other difficulties. The intensity of the sour taste, for example, is too subjective to be reliable, besides being dangerous. The effect on the color of indicators requires considerable knowledge of the subject and special care in carrying out experiments. The completeness of reaction with bases is also quite complicated. The rate of reaction of an active metal could be used, and at times is used to obtain rough quantitative comparisons.

By far the simplest and most accurate method of comparison of the strength of acids is the measurement of their electrical conductivity. The stronger the acid, as roughly indicated by the intensity of its properties, the better the conductor. Hence the electrical conductivity of solutions is used as a measure of acid strength. However, in order that the comparisons be strictly valid, comparable concentrations must be used. By "comparable" concentrations we mean equal amounts of replaceable hydrogen per liter of solution. Thus, a comparison of hydrochloric acid, HCl, with acetic acid, $H \cdot C_2H_3O_2$, requires the use of 36.5 $(1 + 35.5)$ grams of hydrochloric acid, HCl, and 60 grams $(1 + 24 + 3 + 16)$ of acetic acid, $HC_2H_3O_2$—each dissolved in 1 liter of solution. Each of these amounts of the acids contains 1 gram of replaceable hydrogen, which means equal numbers of replaceable hydrogen atoms. (In $HC_2H_3O_2$ only one of the four hydrogen atoms is replaceable by a metal, and also one atom from each molecule is liberated at the negative pole on electrolysis.) Of course, valid comparisons could be made by using half, or any other proportional part of these amounts, respectively. Solutions containing the same amount of replaceable hydrogen per liter are called *equivalent* or more technically "equinormal" solutions.

A comparison of equivalent solutions of hydrochloric acid and acetic acid finds the former about 100 times more conducting than the latter. (The exact value depends on concentrations, but we need not go into that complication.) Hydrochloric acid, therefore, is about 100 times stronger than acetic acid. By similar measurements boric acid, HBO_3, is about 100 times *weaker* than acetic, or 10,000 times weaker than hydrochloric acid.

Thus a comparison of the various acids shows that hydrochloric acid is one of the strongest acids; nitric acid is about equally strong; sulfuric acid almost as strong; and phosphoric acid about two thirds as strong. Several other mineral acids are also very strong. There are also, however, many weak mineral acids. Thus boric acid, HBO_3, is so weak it makes a safe eye wash, and carbonic acid, H_2CO_3—soda water (carbon dioxide dissolved in water)—is so weak it hardly tastes sour. Acetic acid is intermediate in strength, being only about 100 times weaker than the strongest mineral acids. Interestingly enough, most of the acids from the plant and animal world are either about as weak as acetic acid or weaker.

Acids and Nonmetals

The reader has no doubt noticed that all the acids mentioned are compounds of nonmetals. All acids contain hydrogen, of course, but beyond this fact, all acids contain a nonmetal. Thus there are acids of chlorine, sulfur, phosphorus, bromine, carbon, and the other nonmetals. Lavoisier noticed that many of the acids are produced by reaction of nonmetallic oxides with water. Thus, sulfuric acid is produced by reaction of sulfur trioxide with water,

$$SO_3 + H_2O \rightarrow H_2SO_4$$

carbonic acid, by a reaction of carbon dioxide with water,

$$CO_2 + H_2O \rightarrow H_2CO_3$$

nitric acid by reaction of nitrogen pentoxide with water,

$$2N_2O_5 + H_2O \rightarrow 2HNO_3$$

and phosphoric acid by reaction of phosphorus pentoxide with water,

$$2P_2O_5 + 3H_2O \rightarrow 2H_3PO_4$$

The reaction is perfectly general. Nonmetallic oxides react with water to form acids. However, there are many acids that are not formed from the oxides and in fact contain no oxygen. For example, hydrochloric acid, HCl, hydrobromic acid, HBr, and thioarsenic acid, H_3AsS_4, contain no oxygen; nevertheless, all these acids are compounds of nonmetals. Therefore, non-metallic character and acid-forming properties are intimately associated.

The relation of the acid properties of nonmetals to their oxidizing properties goes even deeper than this. There is a general relation between the oxidizing power of a nonmetal and the strength of the acids it forms. In deriving this relation, however, the comparison must be between similar acids; otherwise it becomes too complicated by other differences and obscurity results. For example, on comparing chlorine, sulfur, and phosphorus, we find chlorine the most powerful oxidizing agent, sulfur intermediate, and phosphorus the least powerful. Correspondingly, chloric, $HClO_3$, is the strongest acid; sulfuric, H_2SO_4, is intermediate; and phosphoric, H_3PO_4, is only moderately strong. Another valid comparison is between HCl and H_2S; both are acids but hydrochloric acid is far stronger than hydrosulfuric acid.

Having discovered an association between nonmetals and acids, we might inquire into a possible association between metals and substances that are the opposite of acids. Such substances were known in early times and were called *bases*. They were recognized as belonging to a class, long before the ideas presented above had been developed.

Bases and Their Properties

The earliest known base is lime, obtained from limestone. When limestone is heated in a kiln, it produces quicklime, CaO, which reacts with water violently to give slaked lime, $Ca(OH)_2$. The caustic qualities of lime were observed very early. It is highly corrosive to flesh and to animal matter in general. It was used, and it is still used, to dehair hides. It was also observed very early that lime "sweetens" acids, destroying their sour properties and forming solids, which came to be known as *salts*.

The alchemists discovered bases even more powerful than lime. By reacting lime with wood ash and soda ash, they obtained caustic potash, KOH, and caustic soda, $NaOH$, respectively. Caustic soda is the "lye" used to clean drains and to make soap, and caustic potash is used in making liquid soaps. These substances, often called alkalis, are similar to lime in that they have the property to "sweeten" acids to form salts.

In the course of centuries other substances became recognized as bases; for example, magnesia alba (milk of magnesia), though not caustic, sweetens acids to form salts of magnesium. The formation of salts came to be recognized as a property of the class, and the substances were called bases in the sense that they are the "bases" from which solid salts can be made.

A number of properties were found to be characteristic of the class. The properties are in some respects analogous, but in some respects opposite to those of the acids. A listing of the properties and a comparison with the acids will illustrate these relationships.

Taste. The characteristic taste of bases is bitter. Except in very dilute solutions, however, they are corrosive to the taste buds, and should not be tasted. Many weak organic bases on the other hand can be tasted and are intensely bitter; a good example is quinine.

Effect on Indicators. The bases affect the color of indicators, the effect being opposite to that of the acids. For example, litmus, which is red in acid solutions, turns blue in basic solutions. Methyl orange, which turns pink in acid solutions, turns back to orange in basic solutions. Whatever change the acids produce on the color of an indicator, the bases produce the opposite effect.

Conduction of Current. The bases conduct electric current and in this respect they are similar to the acids. The common characteristic of the bases, however, is the fact that they give off *oxygen* at the *positive* electrode. What happens at the negative electrode depends on the particular base and upon the specific conditions.

Reaction with Acids. As mentioned already, bases react with acids, destroying the characteristic of the acids in the process and forming salts. We shall return to this property presently.

Formulas of Bases. When the formulas of bases are determined by the usual methods, it is found that many are hydroxides of metals. Thus,

caustic soda is sodium hydroxide—NaOH

caustic potash is potassium hydroxide—KOH

slaked lime is calcium hydroxide—$Ca(OH)_2$

milk of magnesia is magnesium hydroxide—$Mg(OH)_2$

In general, metallic hydroxides are bases, containing a metal atom and one or more hydroxide groups. A hydroxide group is a unit containing one hydrogen and one oxygen atom. As will be shown later, this group has a semi-independent existence as a single particle and carries a negative charge; it is written OH^-.

There are many bases, however, which are not hydroxides of metals. Thus the "volatile alkali," ammonia, in water solution has the formula, NH_4OH, and quinine has the formula $(C_{16}H_{26}ON_2) \cdot (OH)_2$. Nevertheless, all bases contain the characteristic group OH^-, in water solutions.

Strong and Weak Bases. As in the case of acids the strength of bases ranges from the powerful and caustic alkalis, such as NaOH and KOH; to the mild magnesium hydroxide, which is safe enough to take internally; and to aluminum hydroxide, which is so weak that it hardly affects any indicator. Indeed many bases or hydroxides of metals are so weak they react only with the stronger acids.

The strength of bases is determined by electrical conductivity, as in the case of acids. Sodium and potassium hydroxides are excellent conductors and are two of the strongest bases that exist. Ammonium hydroxide is about 100 times weaker, magnesium hydroxide 10,000 times weaker, and aluminum hydroxide 100,000 times weaker than sodium hydroxide, respectively.

Bases and Metals

The base-forming properties of the metals is further related to another characteristic property of the metals—namely, the reducing property. The general relationship holds that the more active the metal (as a reducing agent) the more strongly basic its hydroxide. Thus sodium and potassium, which are among the most active metals, form the strongest bases. Calcium, which is somewhat less active, forms a weaker base. Magnesium, which is still less active than calcium, forms a still weaker base. The less active metals, such as iron or copper, form very weak bases.

Neutralization

As already mentioned, the most important property of the acids and of the bases is their mutual destruction and formation of salts in the process. This reaction is called neutralization. On mixing a solution of sodium hydroxide with a solution of hydrochloric acid, in the "right" proportions, the properties of both the base and the acid disappear. By right proportions, this means equal numbers of available hydrogen and hydroxide ions. The resulting solution tastes salty, and on evaporation gives ordinary salt. On carefully measuring the amount of water in the solutions, we find that water is formed in the reaction. The equation for the reaction is as follows:

$$NaOH + HCl \rightarrow NaCl + H_2O$$

The reaction is a general one. For example, magnesium hydroxide reacts with sulfuric acid to form magnesium sulfate (epsom salt) and water.

$$Mg(OH)_2 + H_2SO_4 \rightarrow MgSO_4 + 2H_2O$$

In all cases, water is formed; in addition another substance is formed, consisting of the metallic part of the base and the nonmetallic part of the acid. The name "salts" was given to this class of substances because of their analogy to table salt.

In the neutralization reaction a fundamental relationship is exhibited between the three classes of substances. The acids—characteristically compounds of nonmetals—destroy the bases, which are characteristically compounds of metals, to form salts, which are compounds containing both metals and nonmetals. These three classes of substances make up the majority of the chemical compounds in the mineral world and a great many of the compounds found in living matter.

A great advance in the understanding of acids, bases, and salts was provided by the theory of ionization proposed by Svante Arrhenius in 1883. It would carry us ahead of our story to give a full account of the development of this theory at this point. We shall do so in Chapter 11. Nevertheless, we can use some of the results of the theory of ionization to summarize the phenomena described in this section, as well as to visualize them.

The Theory of Ionization

According to the theory of ionization an acid is a substance which in water solution forms hydrogen ions. The hydrogen ion is a hydrogen atom carrying a positive charge, (H^+), the charge being equal to the smallest charge found by Millikan on an oil drop (p. 98). In water, a "molecule" of an acid—for example, hydrochloric acid, HCl—breaks up into two electrically charged particles, a hydrogen ion, H^+, and a chloride ion, Cl^-. Similarly, molecules of acetic acid, $HC_2H_3O_2$ separate into H^+ and $C_2H_3O_2^-$ ions. All acids give H^+, the other ion being characteristic of the particular acid. According to the theory, the H^+ is responsible for the acid properties.

The ionization theory also gives a simple explanation of the difference between strong and weak acids. In a strong acid a high *percentage* of the molecules are broken up into ions, while in a weak acid only a small percentage of the molecules are ionized.

The theory explains *bases* on a similar pattern. Bases are substances whose water solutions contain OH^-. The positive ion is usually a metal ion. Thus NaOH consists of Na^+ and OH^- ions. In a strong base a high percentage of the molecules are ionized; in a weak base a small percentage of the molecules are ionized.

The theory explains the neutralization reaction very directly. Since both the acid and the base properties disappear during the reaction, it must mean that both the H^+ ions and the OH^- ions disappear in the process. Accordingly, a neutralization reaction is the union of the H^+ ion and the OH^- ion to form water. Simultaneously the positive metallic ion of the acid and the negative nonmetallic ion of the base remain, constituting a solution of a salt. The reaction may be visualized by the equation.

$$H^+Cl^- \;+\; Na^+OH^- \;\rightarrow\; HOH \;+\; Na^+Cl^-$$
$$\text{acid} \qquad \text{base} \qquad \text{water} \qquad \text{salt}$$

These reactions and the evidence for the theory will be presented more fully in later chapters.

Conclusion   Thus, beginning with a study of the common phenomena of burning, we have developed the ideas of oxidation and reduction which explain a wide range of the reactions of the elements and their compounds. Correlated with oxidation reduction are the phenomena of acids and bases. These two reactions form the most fundamental reactions of the elements and their compounds, which is to say, the reactions of all matter.

More significantly, we have laid the ground work for the understanding of the elements. The distinction between metals and nonmetals, made at first on purely physical grounds, has been shown to have chemical significance. The chemical properties, oxidation-reduction reaction, positive and negative valence, and acid-base reaction are fundamental properties that will be used to classify and to clarify the behavior of all the elements. We shall turn to this study in the next chapter.

NOTES AND EXERCISES

1. On *a priori* grounds, there is nothing wrong with the idea of *negative* weight. There are positive and negative electric charges, and north (positive) and south (negative) poles. However, negative weight would mean a kind of matter that *repels* ordinary matter. Whether such matter exists or not can be discovered only by experiment. Those who proposed this hypothesis could not know whether such matter exists; from Newton's laws of gravitation, we do not expect it to exist, and in all subsequent experience this kind of matter has never been observed. However, recent discovery of "antimatter" may alter the situation (Ref. 9.7).

If matter with negative weight did exist, would the analogy between matter and electric charge have to be altered? Would like matter attract or repel like? Can you state the kind of law of attraction repulsion you would expect?

2. The confusion between absolute "levity" and relative levity or buoyancy, was fully sensed and clarified by Jean Ray. According to the views current in the thirteenth century, fire (hot gases) and light gases rise in air because they are *attracted toward* (or seek) the place of lightness above the air. Jean Ray said that hot gases rise because they are *less dense* than an equal volume of air and are *pushed* up, in accordance with Archimedes' principle. A light piece of wood, immersed in water is *pushed* up by the denser water. If a piece of wood is attached to a piece of iron immersed in water, does the wood add to the weight of the iron? Why then does the combination tend to rise?

3. Calling (defining) "oxygen," the gas obtained from heating the red rust of mercury, show by a series of experiments that the burning of a candle in air is union with oxygen. Show similarly that the rusting of iron in air is union with oxygen.

4. Lavoisier's systematic naming of compounds reveals their composition. Look up the chemical names, and if possible the formulas of the following substances. Water, sand, hematite, quicklime, corundum, chrome green, magnesia, pyrolusite, cuprite, melaconite, cassiterite, rutile, thorianite, pitchblende. Do the common names reveal any relationships among these substances? Do the chemical names reveal any relationships? To what class of substances do all these materials belong?

5. What substances are formed when sugar, $C_{12}H_{22}O_{11}$, is burned in air? Write a balanced equation for the reaction. What substances are produced when sugar is "burned" in the body? Can you devise experiments to show that sugar (and food in general) when burned in the body give essentially the same main products?

6. Gunpowder is a mixture of charcoal, C, sulfur, S, and potassium nitrate, KNO_3. Which of these substances are the fuel and which is the oxidizing agent? What happens to the carbon and the sulfur during the explosion?

7. An explosive may have both the fuel and the oxidizing agent in the same molecule. A good example is nitroglycerine, $C_3H_5(NO_3)_3$, the active ingredient of dynamite. What are some of the substances formed during the explosion? Why is the explosion an "oxidation" reaction?

8. Give several examples of oxidation not mentioned in the text.

9. Write the equation for the burning of hydrogen in chlorine. Why is this reaction called "oxidation" even though oxygen is not involved.

10. Write the equation for the reduction of hematite, Fe_2O_3, with hydrogen gas. What happens to the hematite? What happens to the hydrogen? Is it oxidized or reduced?

11. Classify the following elements as oxidizing or reducing agents. Oxygen, chlorine, iron, hydrogen, bromine, magnesium, zinc, aluminum, fluorine. To what class of elements do the oxidizing agents belong? To what class of elements do the reducing agents belong? Is hydrogen an exception?

12. A heated piece of magnesium "burns" in steam or in boiling water, extracting the oxygen to form magnesium oxide

$$Mg + H_2O \rightarrow MgO + H_2$$

In this reaction, which is the reducing agent? Which is the oxidizing agent? What happens to the reducing agent during the reaction? What happens to the oxidizing agent? Is it clear why oxidation must be accompanied by reduction and vice versa?

13. Why do we say that magnesium is more active than iron? More active than hydrogen?

14. During World War II, magnesium bombs were used extensively. Magnesium burns with the evolution of large quantities of heat. Why is it difficult or impossible to put out a magnesium fire with water?

15. A thermite mixture contains powdered aluminum and iron oxide.

On ignition the more active aluminum replaces the less active iron

$$Fe_2O_3 + 2Al \rightarrow 2Fe + Al_2O_3$$

Which is the reducing agent? Is it oxidized or reduced? What happens to its valence?

Which is the oxidizing agent? Which element is reduced? What happens to its valence?

16. A piece of red litmus paper will remain red in pure water, and a piece of blue litmus paper will remain blue. Therefore water is neutral. What color changes would you expect if you put a piece of red and a piece of blue litmus paper in water solutions of the following: hydrochloric acid, vinegar, salt, slaked lime, milk of magnesia, lemon juice, sugar, soda water, boric acid, lye.

17. What will happen if you put a piece of iron in sulfuric acid? Write the equation for the reaction and name the products.

18. Which is a better conductor of electricity in comparable (equivalent) concentrations. Hydrochloric acid or vinegar? Vinegar or boric acid? Ammonia water or lye (sodium hydroxide)? Ammonia water or vinegar? Hydrochloric acid or sodium hydroxide?

19. Why does an acidic solution which is a good conductor of electricity show the characteristic properties of acids to a pronounced degree?

20. Why do you take milk of magnesia for an "acid" stomach? Write the equation for the reaction. What two products are formed in the stomach? Could you use lime instead of milk of magnesia? Why or why not?

21. If you spilled sulfuric acid on your skin, what would you use to neutralize it? Would you use lye to neutralize it? Why or why not? If you spill lye on your hand, what would you use to neutralize it?

22. What ions do you expect to find in solutions of the following substances? Hydrochloric acid, nitric acid, sodium hydroxide, calcium hydroxide, sodium chloride, sulfuric acid, copper sulfate.

23. Acids are compounds of nonmetals. The oxides of nonmetals react with water to form acids. Starting with phosphorus, how would you make phosphoric acid. How would you make sulfuric acid from sulfur?

24. Starting with metallic sodium, how would you make sodium hydroxide.

25. Which of the following will form acids and which bases, by the proper reactions? Write the formulas of typical acids or bases of these elements. Sodium, calcium, phosphorus, bromine, chlorine, magnesium, iron, copper, boron, carbon.

26. Sodium is more active than calcium. Which is the stronger base, NaOH or $Ca(OH)_2$? Aluminum hydroxide, $Al(OH)_3$ is much weaker than lime, $Ca(OH)_2$. Which is the more active metal, aluminum or calcium?

27. Bromine is a more active nonmetal than phosphorus. Which is the stronger acid, bromic acid, $HBrO_3$ or phosphoric acid, H_3PO_4?

28. An element (now well known) was reported by its discoverer as a typical very active metal. Without further information what properties would you expect? Will it be a reducing or an oxidizing agent? It is a powerful one? Will it form acids or bases? Strong or weak? Will it have a positive or a negative valence? Had he reported it as a very active nonmetal what properties would you expect?

10

THE PERIODIC
CLASSIFICATION
OF THE ELEMENTS

1. INTRODUCTION

One of the most important contributions of chemistry to the philosophy of nature is the experimental establishment of the fact that the entire material universe is made up of a small number of simple substances, the elements. This fundamental truth emerged gradually during the early part of the nineteenth century. Following the acceptance of Lavoisier's clear conception of "element," several common substances were recognized as elements and a number of new ones were discovered. Although Lavoisier's original list of about 35 elements had grown to about 60 by the middle of the nineteenth century, and there was an occasional discovery of a new and rare element, it became increasingly evident that the number of elements is small. Today about 100 elements are known. This handful of simple substances contain in themselves all the possibilities of material existence.

Since it was realized that the elements hold the key to the understanding of the chemical behavior of all matter, it became the main concern of the chemists to study their physical and chemical properties, and to investigate the ways in which they react, the conditions under which they react, the kinds of compounds which they form, and the physical and chemical properties which their compounds exhibit. A wealth of chemical knowledge was accumulating, and this knowledge was organized around the elements. For in the final analysis all the properties and the reactions of the myriads of substances are the reactions and properties of the elements.

The reduction of the multitude of substances to a few elements was an achievement of the first magnitude. The long quest for simplicity in nature was at least partially fulfilled. However, the very wealth of information was becoming increasingly a burden. The reduction to simplicity had not gone far enough. The ancient hope was revived, that further reduction may yet be possible. Accordingly, the properties of the elements and their compounds were compared in the search for relations among the elements, which may reduce the number of fundamental entities still further.

The problem of finding relations among many objects is essentially a problem of classification. It involves, by examining similarities and differences, the comparison of the objects to be classified. In the case of the elements it was not difficult to find similarities and differences; with such a large number of elements and their diverse properties, innumerable relations suggested themselves. The problem was, rather, to find the relations that are general, fundamental, and significant.

Of the many attempts and partial successes in correlating the elements, the most successful and comprehensive classification was achieved by the brilliant Russian chemist, Dmitri Mendeleev (1834-1907), around 1868. He arranged the elements in a system now known as the periodic table. In this table, innumerable relations among the elements became apparent. In fact, all the properties of the elements, and hence of all matter, were reduced to a system. Moreover, the classification pointed the way to deeper penetration into the structure of the atoms. Next to the atomic theory, the periodic classification of the elements is the most important contribution of nineteenth-century chemistry.

Fig. 10-1. Mendeleev arranged the elements in a system showing periodicity. *(The Bettmann Archive.)*

In this chapter we shall present the method of reasoning that led to the periodic classification. Mendeleev used the immense body of chemical knowledge known in his day and took advantage of the partial success of his predecessors. However, it is possible to understand his reasoning, by using only the knowledge gained in the preceding chapters. We have already selected and studied in some detail four chemical properties of the elements: first, the *oxidizing* or *reducing* power of the element and its compounds; second, the *acid-* or *base-*forming properties of the element and its compounds; third, the *valence* of the element (the capacity of its atom to "hold," or unite with, atoms of other elements); fourth, the *atomic weight* (the weight of the atom of the element relative to the weight of the lightest atom, hydrogen). The reader will recognize that according to the atomic theory these four properties, and especially the last two, are the properties of the atoms themselves. We shall present the reasoning, using only these four chemical properties and a few obvious physical properties. To make the task still easier, and without sacrifice in logic, we shall use all the elements now known, thus avoiding the difficulties caused by the absence of those elements not yet discovered at the time of Mendeleev.

2. CLASSES AND FAMILIES OF ELEMENTS

The significance of the periodic classification can be best understood by recognizing three fairly distinct steps in its development. The first is the classification of the elements into metals and nonmetals. The second is the recognition that elements form natural families. The third and most comprehensive is the correlation of the families, and hence of all the elements, into a single system.

Metals and Nonmetals

The most fundamental idea in the classification of the elements is the distinction between metals and nonmetals. Historically the elements were first classified as metals and nonmetals, on the basis of obvious appearance and physical properties. The metals possess a characteristic luster, which differentiates them from all other substances. Equally characteristic of the metals is their electrical conductivity, a property which explains their use in electric systems. The metals are also good conductors of heat. If one end of an iron rod is placed in the fire, heat is conducted so rapidly that the other end soon becomes too hot to handle. In contrast, a stick of wood or sulfur can be held by one end while it burns at the other end.

The properties often associated with metallic character are high tensile strength, toughness, hardness, high density, high melting point, and ability to be drawn into wires or hammered into thin sheets. However, not all the metals possess all these properties, nor do they exhibit them to the same degree. Thus, while most metals—for example, iron and nickel—are hard, tough, and strong, other metals—copper, lead, and aluminum—are rather soft and weak, and sodium is so soft that it can be pulled apart like putty. Similarly, most metals are dense materials, but aluminum is light and lithium is only about half as dense as water. The melting point of most metals is high, but lead melts rather easily and mercury is a liquid at room temperature. Copper and gold can be drawn into fine wires and pressed into exceedingly thin foils, but bismuth is brittle and breaks on being hammered. Nevertheless, many metals exhibit several of these properties, and in a rough sense, these properties are associated with metallic character.

The nonmetallic elements, as the name implies, lack the properties of the metals. They do not have a metallic sheen, either in the solid or in the liquid state. They do not conduct electric current, and at least one, sulfur, is often used as an insulator; carbon is an exception, being a fair conductor in the form of graphite, although a nonconductor in the form of diamond. The nonmetals are also poor conductors of heat, as mentioned earlier. They lack tensile strength and are brittle in the solid state. On the whole, they melt and boil at low temperatures. Many of them are gases at room temperature, one (bromine) is a liquid, and the few that are solids melt easily. Carbon is again a striking exception; it has the highest melting point of all the elements, melting at about 3500° C.

The distinction between metals and nonmetals might have remained relatively unimportant were it not for the discovery that each of these classes possesses distinct chemical properties, defining it as a class and setting it against the other class. This fact was pointed out in the study of oxidation reduction, acid base, and valence (Chapter 9). As a class the metals are reducing agents, form bases, and show positive valence. In contrast, the nonmetals are oxidizing agents, form acids, and show negative valence. In all these chemical properties the metals are opposite to the nonmetals. Had the study been extended to other chemical properties additional support for the distinction would have been found. Thus, a constellation of properties almost always goes together and in a sense defines "metallic" character. A constellation of the opposite properties again goes together and defines "nonmetallic" character.

The concepts "metallic character" and "nonmetallic character," and the related concepts "typical metal" and "typical nonmetal" play a very important role in the classification of the elements. A typical metal is not an "average" metal, but one that possesses the metallic properties to the highest degree. A typical metal is a powerful reducing agent, forms strong bases, exhibits positive valence exclusively, is an excellent electric conductor, and has a pronounced metallic luster. Sodium and potassium are among the most typical metals. In contrast, a typical nonmetal is a powerful oxidizing agent, forms strong acids, exhibits negative valence exclusively, is a good insulator, and is completely devoid of metallic luster. Fluorine, chlorine, and oxygen are among the most typical nonmetals. We may note that chemically speaking, "nonmetallic" character is not the mere *absence* of the metallic properties, but is the *presence* of definite and related properties.

In attempting to classify all the elements on the basis of "metallic" and "nonmetallic" character, we find contrary to expectation that they fall into four classes, instead of two. One group of elements possesses distinctly metallic properties. It is interesting that the majority of the elements—about 75 of the 102 known—are metals. A much smaller group, about 10, are distinctly nonmetallic. There is, however, a third group of elements that is intermediate between the metals and the nonmetals. These elements either possess both weak metallic and weak nonmetallic properties, or else they possess some, but not all, the properties of the metals and again some, but not all, the properties of the nonmetals. These elements are called metalloids. Finally, there is a group of elements, the inert gases, which possess neither the properties of the metals nor the properties of the nonmetals.

The failure to classify unambiguously all the elements into metals and nonmetals may appear, at first sight, as a weakness in the distinction. However, the difficulty is inherent in any scheme of classification of natural objects. In any attempt to classify a large number of natural objects into two classes, we almost invariably find all four logical possibilities. Some objects fall distinctly into one class, some fall into the other class, some belong to both classes, and some belong to neither. Recognizing this fact, we continue the classification by making use of the *degree* to which they show these properties.

This procedure is perhaps obvious and well known, but is worth noting, for it is an important part of the method of modern science. Once the characteristics of a class are formulated more or less distinctly, further progress is made by shifting the approach. The *variation* in the characteristic is used as the basis for *relating* the objects, and ordering them according to the degree with which they exhibit the characteristic. In Chapter 3 this element of the scientific method was pointed out discussing how the distinction between "hot" and "cold" was transformed into a distinction between the "hotter" and the "colder," ultimately leading to the development of a temperature scale. A similar situation arises in the case of "metallic" and "nonmetallic" character.

In the case of the elements we find wide variation in the "typical" properties in each class. Thus, while all the metals are reducing agents, they range widely in their reducing power. Sodium and potassium are powerful reducing agents, iron and zinc are only moderate, while gold and platinum are so inactive they exhibit their reducing power only toward the very active oxidizing agents. Similarly, the base-forming power varies between wide limits. The hydroxides of sodium and potassium are strong bases, while the hydroxides of iron and copper are very weak. A similar situation is found with the nonmetals. Fluorine, chlorine, and oxygen are powerful oxidizing agents, but sulfur is a weak oxidizing agent, and nitrogen does not support combustion of ordinary fuels—it oxidizes only the most active metals. Similar variations are observed in all the other "typical" properties.

Using the range in the properties we have two alternatives if, after this discussion, we are still interested in classes. One alternative is to subdivide the metals into active, moderately active, and inactive metals and to subdivide the nonmetals into active and inactive nonmetals. However, this subclassification has limited value. The subclasses are not very distinct, for the differences in activity are differences in degree and not in kind. The subclasses are useful in general discussions, but they necessarily overlap and even the distinctions of the major classes fail in several cases. Thus, carbon is nonmetallic in appearance and forms a weak acid —which would lead to its classification as a nonmetal. On the other hand, carbon, in the form of graphite, has a distinct luster, conducts electric current, and is a powerful reducing agent—properties that are characteristic of the metals.

A more fruitful alternative is to arrange the elements according to the *intensity* of their properties, from the most distinctly metallic to the most distinctly nonmetallic. This shift in the method of approach results in a shift in the kinds of questions asked and answered. The question is no longer whether a given element is or is not a metal, but whether it is more metallic or less metallic than another element. The question whether an element is or is not a reducing agent becomes how good a reducing agent it is, and whether it is a better or a poorer reducing agent than another element. The question whether a given substance is or is not a base, becomes how strong a base it is and whether it is stronger or weaker than another base. Thus the emphasis becomes a matter of *degree* and *relative* character.

Families of Elements

The second step in the classification of the elements is the discovery that certain elements fall into well-defined groups, in the sense that the elements within a group resemble one another more than they resemble the other elements in the same class or in the same subclass. These groups are known as *families* of elements. Within each family, the physical and chemical properties of the elements are strikingly similar. We shall take four families to illustrate this fact. In doing so we shall mention a great number of facts, but these are not meant to be memorized, being illustrative examples so that the reader may appreciate the factual background from which the reasoning is developed.

The Alkali Metals

The alkali metals can be used as a good example of a family of metals. Early in the last century it was noticed that the three metals, sodium, potassium, and lithium, resemble one another far more than the rest of the metals. About 1860 rubidium was added to the family, then cesium, and recently (1940) francium. In physical properties these metals are soft, have low densities, low melting points, high silvery luster, and are excellent electric conductors. Chemically they are powerful reducing agents and form the strongest of bases. All six exhibit the valence +1. While a few other metals may have one or another of these properties, no other metal has the entire set.

The similarities in their properties may be illustrated by a few examples. Just as sodium reacts violently with chlorine to produce salt, NaCl (see p. 223), all the other elements react similarly to form the chlorides whose formulas are similar to sodium chloride.

$$LiCl, NaCl, KCl, RbCl, CsCl, \text{ and } FrCl$$

The metals react with fluorine even more violently, forming the fluorides,

$$LiF, NaF, KF, RbF, CsF, \text{ and } FrF$$

and somewhat less violently with oxygen forming the oxides,

$$Li_2O, Na_2O, Rb_2O, Cs_2O, \text{ and } Fr_2O$$

The oxides, in turn, react with water to form the hydroxides,

$$LiOH, NaOH, KOH, RbOH, CsOH, \text{ and } FrOH$$

The metals corrode very rapidly on exposure to air and moisture; they are kept under kerosene for this reason. We have already seen that sodium reacts with water to form sodium hydroxide and liberate hydrogen,

$$2Na + 2\,HOH \rightarrow 2NaOH + H_2$$

All the alkali metals react similarly. In countless of other reactions they also behave in the same way, forming similar compounds. If the reactions of one of the members, say sodium, are known the reactions of all the elements in the family are also known.

The similarities of the formulas of their compounds are, of course, due to the fact that all the elements have the same valence, namely, $+1$. In fact the identity in valence results in the formation of analogous compounds with similar formulas. Thus all chlorides have the general formula, MeCl, where Me may be any one of the six metals. Similarly the fluorides have the general formula, MeF, the oxides Me_2O, the hydroxides MeOH, the sulfates, Me_2SO_4, the phosphates Me_3PO_4, and so on. If the formula of a sodium compound is known, the formula of the corresponding compounds of the other alkali metals can be written by analogy.

However, the similarity is much more than formal. The physical and chemical properties of the compounds themselves are strikingly similar. All the chlorides resemble table salt, NaCl, the best-known member. They are crystalline transparent substances, soluble in water. As already noted, all the oxides react with water forming the hydroxides, which are very strong and very soluble bases. In their thousands of compounds and their reactions, one metal may be substituted for another and still give compounds that are similar. For example, when a fat is boiled with NaOH, soap is produced, having the formula $NaC_{17}H_{35}CO_2$; if KOH is substituted for NaOH, a soap, $KC_{17}H_{35}CO_2$, is also obtained, the only difference being that the latter is liquid soap. Another example is the formation of glass. Ordinary glass is obtained by heating a mixture of sodium oxide, Na_2O, sand, and lime; if K_2O is used instead of Na_2O, again a glass is obtained, only it is a harder glass. The oxide of any alkali metal may be used and still give a glass. This is not true of the oxides of the other metals not in this family, as for example silver or iron.

The degree of similarity of the elements within the family may be brought out more forcibly by contrasting them with the other elements. While a few other elements may have one or a few properties similar to the alkali metals, no other element has all the properties of this family. For example, silver has a highly reflecting surface (hence, is used in mirrors), is an excellent electric conductor, and has a valence of $+1$. However, the similarity to the alkali metals ends here, essentially. Silver is a heavy metal, and is so unreactive it does not rust in air, nor does it react with water or simple acids. To be sure the oxide has the formula Ag_2O (since its valence is also $+1$), but it reacts with water only to a slight extent and its hydroxide, AgOH, is an insoluble and extremely weak base. The chloride has the formula, AgCl, but unlike NaCl and the other alkali chlorides, it is very insoluble and darkens on exposure to light (hence is used in photography). The oxide, Ag_2O, cannot be substituted for Na_2O, to give glass, nor does AgOH form soaps with fats. In the countless of properties and reactions of the element and its compounds, silver is unmistakably different from the alkali metals. On comparing any other element with the alkali metals, we find similar and even greater differences—as with silver. If the

TABLE 10:1

The Alkali Metals

Element symbol	Lithium Li	Sodium Na	Potassium K	Rubidium Rb	Cesium Cs	Comparison
PROPERTIES						
Qualitative						
Metallic luster	high	high	high	high	high	similar
Electric conductivity	high	high	high	high	high	similar
Chemical activity	high	high	high	high	high	similar (increasing)
Reducing power	high	high	high	high	high	similar (increasing)
Strength of base	high	high	high	high	high	similar (increasing)
Quantitative						
Atomic weight	6.94	23.0	39.10	85.48	132.91	increasing
Density	0.53	0.97	0.86	1.53	1.90	increasing
Melting point, °C	186	97.5	62.5	38.50	26.50	decreasing
Boiling point, °C	1200	880	760	700	670	decreasing
Valence	+1	+1	+1	+1	+1	identical
Formula of chloride	LiCl	NaCl	KCl	RbCl	CsCl	similar
Formula of oxide	Li_2O	Na_2O	K_2O	Rb_2O	Cs_2O	similar
Formula of hydroxide	LiOH	NaOH	KOH	RbOH	CsOH	similar

reader contrasts the alkali metals with any nonmetal, or any metal he may know, such as iron, gold, aluminum, or lead, he will be impressed by the magnitude of the differences.

Thus, the alkali metals form a well-defined family. Although the most important single characteristic of the family is the identity in valence, equally important is the striking similarity of the physical and chemical properties of the elements and their compounds.

The third important characteristic of the family is the regular manner in which the properties vary. The properties are very similar, but they are not identical (except for the valence); within more or less narrow limits, there is a *range* in the properties. All the alkali metals are excellent electric conductors, but potassium is a better conductor than sodium, and sodium is better than lithium. All react violently with water, but potassium is more reactive than sodium and sodium is more reactive than lithium. Similar variations are found in all the other properties.

As early as 1817, Johann Döbereiner (1780-1849) discovered that the variation in the properties is related to the atomic weight. He noticed that the elements, lithium, sodium, and potassium, are closely related and form a "triad." Here the atomic weight of sodium (23) is intermediate between that of lithium (7) and potassium (39.1); in fact, it is close to the average of the other two—that is, $(7 + 39.1)/2 \doteq 23$.

The significant fact is that the elements in the triad form a sequence. All the properties of sodium, the middle member of the triad, are intermediate between those of lithium and potassium. Thus, potassium is the best reducing agent, sodium next, lithium the poorest of the three. Potassium is the best electric conductor, sodium next, lithium the poorest. Potassium is the densest element, sodium next, lithium the lightest. Whatever property of potassium (or its compounds) selected, the property of sodium (or its corresponding compound) will be either more pronounced or less pronounced. If it is more pronounced, then the property for lithium (or its compounds) will be more so. If it is less pronounced, then the property for lithium will be less so. In other words, the properties vary (increase or decrease) in the same direction as the atomic weight. The exceptions to this regularity are few and far between.

The regularity holds for all six members of the alkali family. Thus rubidium (atomic weight 85) is a better reducing agent than potassium; cesium (atomic weight 133) still better; and francium (atomic weight 223), the best reducing agent of the alkali metals. The additional properties listed in Table 10:1 are sufficient to show that the change in properties is in the same direction as the atomic weight.

The alkaline earth metals form another well-defined family. Döbereiner in 1817 recognized that calcium, strontium, and barium form another "triad," with calcium the lightest (lowest atomic weight) and barium the heaviest member. Later, the still lighter magnesium was recognized as belonging to the family, and Mendeleev added beryllium as the lightest member. At the turn of this century, Pierre and Madame Curie discovered radium, the heaviest member of the family.

Alkaline Earth Metals

These elements have all the characteristics of a family. They have the same valence (+2), and their physical and chemical properties, as well as those of their corresponding compounds, are very similar. The elements exhibit the typical metallic properties to a high degree, although not so high as the alkali metals. As a group they are somewhat denser and harder, have higher melting points, and are somewhat poorer conductors than the alkali metals, even though there is some overlapping between the two families. Chemically, they are active reducing agents, react vigorously with chlorine and oxygen, and their oxides react with water to form hydroxides, which are strong bases. They react with cold or hot water to give off hydrogen. Again in chemical properties they are somewhat less "metallic" than the alkali metals.

What distinguishes these elements from the alkali metals the most is their valence. They all exhibit the principal valence +2. Consequently, all their compounds have similar formulas, but different from those of the alkali metals. For example, the formula of calcium chloride is $CaCl_2$, and all the chlorides have corresponding formulas. The oxides have the general formula, MeO; the bromides, $MeBr_2$; the sulfates, $MeSO_4$; the carbonates, $MeCO_3$. In properties, too, the compounds are similar. Thus, just as limestone, calcium carbonate ($CaCO_3$), is insoluble in water, so are all the carbonates. Similarly, just as calcium sulfate (gypsum) is insoluble, so are all the sulfates.

The typical variation in the properties, according to atomic weight, is likewise observed. Thus radium, the heaviest member of the family, is the most powerful reducing agent and forms the strongest base, while beryllium, the lightest member, is the poorest reducing agent and forms the weakest base. All the carbonates of these elements are insoluble, but calcium carbonate is less insoluble than magnesium carbonate, and the trend continues to radium carbonate. All the sulfates are likewise insoluble and become less soluble with increasing atomic weight of the metal. Thus, calcium sulfate (gypsum) is sparingly soluble, strontium sulfate is less soluble, barium sulfate still less soluble, and radium sulfate is the most insoluble of the sulfates. All the properties of numerous compounds follow these trends, almost without exception.

The Halogens

Among the nonmetals, the elements, fluorine, chlorine, bromine, and iodine, form the most clearly defined family. More recently (1940), astatine was added to the family. These elements are called "halogens," meaning "salt formers," from the fact that they form compounds similar to ordinary salt, NaCl, with a great number of active metals, particularly the alkali metals. They all exhibit the valence of −1. They are powerful oxidizing agents and form the strongest acids.

TABLE 10:2
The Halogens

Element symbol	Fluorine F	Chlorine Cl	Bromine Br	Iodine I	Comparison
Atomic weight	19.0	35.46	79.92	126.91	increases
Valence	−1	−1	−1	−1	identical
Formula of molecules	F_2	Cl_2	Br_2	I_2	similar
Boiling point, °C	−187	−35	+59	+184	increases
Melting point, °C	−223	−103	−7.2	+114	increases
Color	light yellow	greenish yellow	orange red	violet	deepens
Chemical activity	extremely active	very active	active	moderately active	decreases
Silver salts					
Formulas	AgF	AgCl	AgBr	AgI	similar
Solubility in water (g per 100 cc)	182	.0001	.0000084	.0000003	decreases
Hydrogen compounds					
State	gas	gas	gas	gas	similar
Solubility in water	very soluble	very soluble	very soluble	very soluble	similar
Acidity	strong	very strong	very strong	very strong	similar

A few examples will illustrate the family resemblances of these elements. All the halogens react quite violently with sodium, forming the following compounds: NaF, NaCl, NaBr, and NaI, respectively. These compounds are all saltlike substances, similar to sodium chloride, the most familiar member. The halogens form similar saltlike compounds with the other alkali metals, and corresponding compounds with the alkaline-earth elements. For example, with calcium, they form CaF_2, $CaCl_2$, $CaBr_2$, CaI_2, respectively. The halogens combine directly with hydrogen, forming HF, HCl, HBr, and HI. These compounds are gases with a sharp, pungent odor, and are very soluble in water, forming strong acids. The oxides, Cl_2O_5, Br_2O_5, and I_2O_5, react with water, forming another series of strong acids, $HClO_3$, $HBrO_3$, and HIO_3. In thousands of reactions of the elements and their compounds, the striking family resemblances are exhibited.

The typical variations of the properties, according to the atomic weight, are likewise exhibited. The oxidizing power increases with *decreasing* atomic weight. Thus, iodine is a good oxidizing agent, bromine a better one, chlorine a very powerful one, and fluorine—the lightest member of the family—is the most powerful oxidizing agent of all the elements. In their physical properties, similar relations are observed. Thus, fluorine is a gas, boiling at $-187°$ C; chlorine is also a gas, boiling at $-35°$ C; bromine is a liquid, boiling at $59°$ C; and iodine is a solid, boiling at $184°$ C. Even in depth of color, the trend is evident, becoming darker with increasing atomic weight. Thus, fluorine is a light-yellow gas, chlorine a greenish-yellow gas, bromine a wine-colored liquid (orange red as a vapor), and iodine is a steel-gray solid (deeply violet in the vapor state). As we might expect in a typical family, all the properties of the halogens and their compounds vary according to atomic weight. In Table 10:2 a few additional properties are listed. The table can be extended almost indefinitely.

The Inert Gases

A very interesting family, not known to Mendeleev at the time of the discovery of the periodic law, are the inert gases: helium, neon, argon, krypton, xenon, and radon. These elements are gases, their boiling point increasing with increasing atomic weight. Helium boils at -268, barely 4 degrees above absolute zero, while radon boils at $-38°$ C.

The most striking fact about these elements is the complete lack of chemical properties. The elements are neither reducing nor oxidizing agents. They form neither acids nor bases. In fact they do not form any compounds whatsoever; hence, their valence is 0. They are a class by themselves. They are not metals, since they have none of the properties of the metals. However, they are not "nonmetals," either; for they do not have any of the chemical properties of the nonmetals.

Several other families were known to Mendeleev, and still other families have been recognized since. In all instances the family relationships are exhibited—namely, identical valence, similarity in physical and chemical properties of the elements and their compounds, and variation of the properties according to atomic weight.

3. MENDELEEV'S PERIODIC LAW

Most of the foregoing information and a great deal more was known at the time of Mendeleev. Families of elements had been recognized for a long time, and the chemical reactions of oxidation-reduction and acid-base were fairly well understood. To be sure, some of the elements had not yet been discovered, but the chemists had at their finger tips a great deal more chemical knowledge than we thought prudent to include in our discussion.

There was, however, one development which immediately preceded Mendeleev's classification, and which was a necessary precursor of it. In 1860 the method for determining atomic weights without ambiguity was clearly formulated by Cannizzaro. This method has been explained in Chapter 8. Briefly, the atomic weight of an element is determined by finding the smallest number of grams of that element in 22.4 liters at STP. From this the valence is calculated by further determining the number of gram-atoms of hydrogen combined with (or replaced by) a gram-atom of the element. As a result of this development the chemists had for the first time a dependable set of atomic weights and valences of the elements. With this information many chemists began to recognize relationships among the elements, which had been only dimly perceived earlier.

Mendeleev, more clearly than any of his contemporaries, recognized that both the atomic weight and the valence are fundamental properties of the atoms themselves and strongly suspected that these two properties in some way determine all the other physical and chemical properties of the elements. It is no accident, he reasoned, that all the elements of the same family have the same principal valence and the same secondary valences. Nor is it an accident, that within a family the properties vary according to the atomic weight. The atomic weight, therefore, must be the fundamental property that determines all other properties and perhaps the valence as well.

Mendeleev's great idea resulted from his firm belief that the atomic weight relates not only the elements within a family, but also the families to other families, and thus correlates all the elements. After much groping, he hit upon the remarkably simple idea of arranging the elements in the increasing order of their atomic weights and discovered that the properties of the elements vary *periodically*. We shall explain this idea, following Mendeleev's reasoning. We shall, however, use all the elements now known, although this will simplify the reasoning somewhat, and anticipate some of the discoveries made by Mendeleev and his immediate successors.

On arranging the elements according to increasing atomic weight, we obtain a list from the lightest, hydrogen, to the heaviest, nobelium. We may put this list on a long tape, a part of which is reproduced in Figure

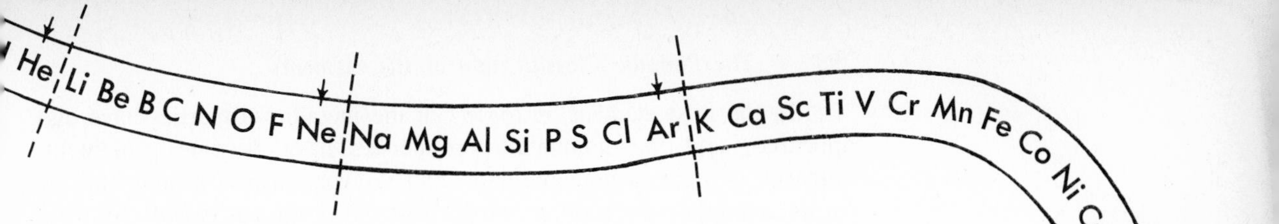

Fig. 10-2. Elements arranged in order of increasing atomic weight.

10-2. The serial number of the element is the *atomic number*. Thus, the atomic number of hydrogen is 1, the atomic number of helium is 2, and so on. The atomic number of chlorine is 17, meaning it is the seventeenth lightest element in atomic weight. The atomic number (to be defined more precisely later) is the best way of specifying an element. Thus, element 17 *means* chlorine. The atomic number is often written in parentheses following the name or symbol (for example, chlorine (17) or Cl (17) to facilitate its location in the list of the elements; see Tables 10:4 and 10:5).

An examination of the elements—not merely as symbols, but as chemical individuals, with all their physical and chemical properties—discloses a remarkable sequence. We will develop the sequence, describing each element in sufficient detail to show its character.

The first and lightest element is the familiar hydrogen. It is a gas, burning in oxygen and in the halogens. It is a constituent of all acids. Physically it is a nonmetal; yet it is a reducing agent, and like the metals it has a positive valence of +1. (It also has a valence of −1 in certain compounds, and has some similarity to the halogens, but we shall not pursue this point much further.)

The next heavier element is helium. It is an inert gas. It has no chemical properties and forms no compounds whatsoever. Hence its valence is 0.

The next heavier element is lithium. It is an alkali metal. It is an excellent conductor of electricity. It is a powerful reducing agent and forms a strong base, LiOH. Its valence is +1.

The next element is beryllium. It is a fairly "typical" metal, but distinctly less metallic than lithium. It is a good conductor, but not so good as lithium. It is not as good a reducing agent as lithium, and its hydroxide, $Be(OH)_2$, is a much weaker base than LiOH. Its valence is +2.

The next element is boron. It is not a typical metal. It is only a fair conductor of electricity. It is a reducing agent, but not a powerful one. Its oxide reacts with water but instead of forming a base, it forms boric acid, which is a very weak acid. Compared to the preceding elements, the metallic properties have been subdued, and the nonmetallic properties begin to make their appearance. Its valence is still that of a metal, namely, +3.

On moving to the next element, carbon, the trend becomes unmistakable. Carbon is not a metal, although it has some vestiges of metallic character. In the form of graphite, it has a peculiar luster and is a fair electric conductor. However, in the form of diamond it is a nonconductor and is nonmetallic in appearance. The element does not form bases, but carbonic acid, which is a weak acid. It has a valence of +4 as in CCl_4, but also −4, as in CH_4.

In the next element, nitrogen, all the metallic properties have disappeared, and the nonmetallic properties have become prominent. Nitrogen is a gas, a nonconductor, and in every respect a nonmetal. It forms strong acids, such as nitric acid. It even has some oxidizing properties, although these are not too pronounced. Active metals, such as magnesium, burn in it, but ordinary fuels do not. It exhibits a valence of $+5$, as in HNO_3, but also -3, as in NH_3.

The next element, oxygen, is a "typical" nonmetal. It is a powerful oxidizing agent, and forms numerous acids, as Lavoisier noted long ago. It does not exhibit positive valence, but only the negative valence -2, as in H_2O or MgO.

The nonmetallic properties become even more pronounced in the next element, fluorine. It is the most typical of all the nonmetals. It is the most powerful oxidizing agent of all the elements and forms several series of strong acids. Its valence is -1.

On going to the next element, neon, we encounter our first surprise. Instead of a further increase in the nonmetallic character and activity, here is a complete and abrupt disappearance of all chemical activity. For neon has no chemical properties, forms no compounds, and its valence is 0. It is an inert gas, reminiscent of helium.

Another surprise immediately follows. The next element, sodium, is very active, but its activity is that of a metal. It is remarkably similar to lithium, and belongs with lithium in the alkali family, as already noted. Sodium is a more powerful reducing agent, forms a stronger base, and is a better electric conductor than lithium. However, it has the same valence as lithium, namely $+1$.

On moving to the next heavier element, the surprises continue. This element, magnesium, is an alkaline-earth metal very similar to beryllium. Its valence is $+2$. It is less metallic than sodium. Magnesium hydroxide, $Mg(OH)_2$ (milk of magnesia), is a very weak base.

The next element, aluminum, is similar to boron, and its valence is $+3$. But the chemical metallic properties have already decreased markedly. The hydroxide of aluminum, $Al(OH)_3$, is an extremely weak base and, curiously enough, it is also a very weak acid, sometimes written as H_3AlO_3. The next element, silicon, is semimetallic, of valence $+4$, forming a weak acid, silicic acid. It is in many respects similar to carbon. Next comes phosphorus, distinctly nonmetallic and similar to nitrogen. Then comes sulfur, in many respects similar to oxygen, showing a valence of -2, and finally chlorine, so similar to fluorine, that it is difficult at times to tell them or their compounds apart. The two elements are in the same halogen family.

Following chlorine, and again without any forewarning detectable in the trend, we encounter argon, an inert gas. Immediately following, comes potassium, an alkali metal like sodium; and, in turn, calcium, which is an alkaline-earth metal similar to magnesium.

It is not necessary to dwell on all the remaining elements, for by this time the trend and the pattern are evident. Following calcium, the general trend continues. The metallic properties decrease more or less regularly, and the nonmetallic properties appear, faint at first and then more pronounced until bromine is reached, which is a halogen, similar to chlorine. Then comes argon, an inert gas, followed by the alkali-metal potassium, and in turn by the alkaline-earth metal, strontium. This remarkable sequence from metallic to nonmetallic character is repeated several times to the very end of the list of the elements.

This is the essence of Mendeleev's discovery, which he called the *periodic law*. It may be stated as follows: If the elements are arranged in the order of their atomic weights, from the lightest to the heaviest, a *repetition of a sequence of properties* is observed. The sequence is a stepwise change in properties from strongly metallic, to weakly metallic, to intermediate, to weakly nonmetallic to strongly nonmetallic, followed by an abrupt and complete disappearance of all chemical properties. This sequence is repeated several times on going down the list until all the elements are exhausted. Every so often—that is, *periodically*—the same sequence of properties is repeated. *Periodically,* similar elements are found in the same place in the sequence. In Mendeleev's words, "The properties of the elements are a *periodic function of their atomic weights.*"

The periodicity is detected most easily by spotting the inert gases, which punctuate the list. Periodically—that is, every so many elements —an inert gas appears. Immediately preceding each inert gas there is a halogen (except before helium, Exs. 15 and 16). Immediately following the inert gas there is an alkali metal, followed in turn by an alkaline-earth metal. Between the alkaline-earth metal and the next halogen, there is a general stepwise decrease of the metallic properties and a simultaneous increase in the nonmetallic properties.

Using the inert gases as markers, we may consider each inert gas as the end of a sequence, or as the beginning of the next sequence. Either way has its advantages. Adopting the first alternative, we find seven sequences or periods. The first ends with helium, the second with neon, and so on. The seventh is apparently incomplete, for nobelium is a metal and not an inert gas.

The reader will note that the periods contain different numbers of elements. The first contains only 2; the second and third, 8 each; the fourth and fifth 18 each; the sixth, 32; and the incomplete seventh, only 16. Apparently there must be other undiscovered elements beyond nobelium. The number of elements in each period is given in Table 10:3.

TABLE 10:3

Period	Number of elements	Description
1	2	hydrogen to helium
2	8	lithium to neon
3	8	sodium to argon
4	18	potassium to krypton
5	18	rubidium to xenon
6	32	cesium to radon
7	16 (known)	francium to ? (incomplete)

The most important aspect of the periodic law is that elements of the same family occupy the same relative position in each period. Thus the first element in each period is an alkali metal, the second is an alkaline-earth metal, the last is an inert gas, the one before the last is a halogen. The relations become somewhat less clear in the middle of the period, owing to the fact that the periods contain different numbers of elements. However, on comparing periods with the same number of elements such as the second and third, or the fourth and fifth, we find that the similarities of corresponding elements are maintained throughout the periods. The most troublesome is the first period with hydrogen, which we shall discuss later. Nevertheless the periodicity in the properties holds in a general way throughout the list of elements (Exs. 18-25).

The periodicity is not limited to the few properties already mentioned, but is found in all the properties of the elements and their compounds. This, of course, is implied in the statement that elements of the same family (that is, having strikingly similar properties) appear periodically and in the same part of each period. Thus not only the reducing properties appear most prominent at the beginning of each period, but also the base-forming properties, electric conductivity, and all the other properties characteristic of the metals. Similarly, not only the oxidizing properties, but all the properties of the nonmetals appear near the end of each period. Valence itself shows an interesting periodicity. In each period, it starts as $+1$ and increases stepwise to $+2$ to $+3$, becomes difficult to characterize by the middle of the period, but by the end of the period again becomes distinct and decreases from -3 to -2 to -1 and finally to 0 in the inert gases at the end of the period. All the other properties—such as density, melting point, atomic volume, hard-

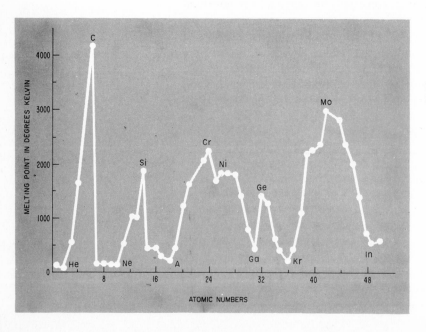

Fig. 10-3. Periodicity in the melting points of the first 50 elements.

ness, solubility of compounds and countless of other properties—show the same periodicity (Ex. 17).

Thus, without any additional principles, the periodic law places the elements in their proper families. This can be shown most clearly by arranging the periods in a *table*. The simplest way of achieving this would be to use the type listing of elements previously suggested (Fig. 10-2), cutting the ribbon after each inert gas, then attempting to arrange the strips under each other so that elements of the same family fall in the same column. There is no difficulty at the beginning and at the end of the periods. The alkali metals fall into the first column, the alkaline earths into the second column, the inert gases into the last column, and the halogens into the column before the last.

Periodic Tables

However, considerable difficulty is encountered in the middle of the table. As mentioned earlier, this is due to the fact that the periods have different numbers of elements. So long as the periods contain the same number of elements—such as the second and third, or the fourth and the fifth—similar elements fall under each other without any difficulty. But between periods having different numbers of elements—such as the third and fourth—no simple matching is possible. Since the third period has only 8 elements, and the fourth has 18, some elements in the third period are related to more than one element in the fourth period. The most troublesome is the first period, with only two elements. Helium is at the head of the inert gases, without question, but hydrogen is difficult to place. It is related to the alkali metals, in showing a valence of +1, but it is also related to the halogens in that it shows a valence of −1 and forms hydrides that are similar to salts. In a sense the single element hydrogen is the entire first period, outside of the inert gas. But hydrogen, the simplest of the elements, is unique, both for this and for many other reasons, as we shall see later (Ex. 15 and Chap. 12).

Literally hundreds of tabular arrangements have been proposed in attempts to bring out the diverse relations among the elements. Mendeleev himself proposed several arrangements. All of these are called "periodic tables." Each of these forms of the table emphasizes some relationships but necessarily deemphasizes or ignores others. Even three-dimensional arrangements have been constructed. No single table however, does justice to all the multitudinous relations that exist among the elements.

One of the most common and most useful forms of the periodic table is shown in Table 10:4. It is an extremely good compromise. The beginning and the end of the table contain the most well-defined families, and these appear in the full columns. However, the middle of the first three periods had to be separated, resulting in shorter columns. Even with this separation, parts of the extra-long periods had to be placed as footnotes at the bottom to avoid extreme separation. In this form the inert gases sometimes appear both at the extreme left and the extreme right, to emphasize the continuity of the atomic numbers (in Table 10:4 they appear only on the right). The reader will notice that hydrogen appears in two places, showing relations to both alkali metals and to the halogens (see Exs. 15 and 16).

TABLE 10:4
Periodic Chart of the Elements

SHELL	IA	IIA	IIIB	IVB	VB	VIB	VIIB	VIII			IB	IIB	IIIA	IVA	VA	VIA	VIIA	INERT GASES	
1	1 **H** 1.0080																	2 **He** 4.003	2
2	3 **Li** 6.940	4 **Be** 9.013											5 **B** 10.82	6 **C** 12.011	7 **N** 14.008	8 **O** 16.000	9 **F** 19.00	10 **Ne** 20.183	2 8
3	11 **Na** 22.991	12 **Mg** 24.32											13 **Al** 26.98	14 **Si** 28.09	15 **P** 30.975	16 **S** 32.066	17 **Cl** 35.457	18 **Ar** 39.944	2 8 8
4	19 **K** 39.100	20 **Ca** 40.08	21 **Sc** 44.96	22 **Ti** 47.90	23 **V** 50.95	24 **Cr** 52.01	25 **Mn** 54.94	26 **Fe** 55.85	27 **Co** 58.94	28 **Ni** 58.71	29 **Cu** 63.54	30 **Zn** 65.38	31 **Ga** 69.72	32 **Ge** 72.60	33 **As** 74.91	34 **Se** 78.96	35 **Br** 79.916	36 **Kr** 83.80	2 8 18 8
5	37 **Rb** 85.48	38 **Sr** 87.63	39 **Y** 88.92	40 **Zr** 91.22	41 **Nb** 92.91	42 **Mo** 95.95	43 **Tc** (99)	44 **Ru** 101.1	45 **Rh** 102.91	46 **Pd** 106.4	47 **Ag** 107.880	48 **Cd** 112.41	49 **In** 114.82	50 **Sn** 118.70	51 **Sb** 121.76	52 **Te** 127.61	53 **I** 126.91	54 **Xe** 131.30	2 8 18 18 8
6	55 **Cs** 132.91	56 **Ba** 137.36	57 ***La** 138.92	72 **Hf** 178.50	73 **Ta** 180.95	74 **W** 183.86	75 **Re** 186.22	76 **Os** 190.2	77 **Ir** 192.2	78 **Pt** 195.09	79 **Au** 197.0	80 **Hg** 200.61	81 **Tl** 204.39	82 **Pb** 207.21	83 **Bi** 209.00	84 **Po** (210)	85 **At** (210)	86 **Rn** (222)	2 8 18 32 18 8
7	87 **Fr** (223)	88 **Ra** (226)	89 †**Ac** (227)																

*LANTHANUM SERIES

57 ***La** 138.92	–	71 **Lu** 174.99

†ACTINIUM SERIES

89 †**Ac** (227)	–	102 **No** (253)

TABLE 10:5
International Atomic Weights

THE ELEMENTS, THEIR SYMBOLS, ATOMIC NUMBERS, AND ATOMIC WEIGHTS

Name of element	Symbol	Atomic number	Atomic weight	Name of element	Symbol	Atomic number	Atomic weight
Actinium.......	Ac	89	227	Mercury.......	Hg	80	200.61
Aluminum......	Al	13	26.98	Molybdenum...	Mo	42	95.95
Americium.....	Am	95	[243]	Neodymium....	Nd	60	144.27
Antimony......	Sb	51	121.76	Neon..........	Ne	10	20.183
Argon..........	Ar	18	39.944	Neptunium.....	Np	93	[237]
Arsenic.........	As	33	74.91	Nickel.........	Ni	28	58.71
Astatine........	At	85	[210]	Niobium.......	Nb	41	92.91
Barium........	Ba	56	137.36	Nitrogen.......	N	7	14.008
Berkelium......	Bk	97	[249]	Nobelium......	No	102	253
Beryllium......	Be	4	9.013	Osmium........	Os	76	190.2
Bismuth........	Bi	83	209.00	Oxygen........	O	8	16
Boron.........	B	5	10.82	Palladium......	Pd	46	106.4
Bromine........	Br	35	79.916	Phosphorus.....	P	15	30.975
Cadmium......	Cd	48	112.41	Platinum.......	Pt	78	195.09
Calcium........	Ca	20	40.08	Plutonium......	Pu	94	[242]
Californium.....	Cf	98	[251]	Polonium......	Po	84	210
Carbon.........	C	6	12.011	Potassium......	K	19	39.100
Cerium.........	Ce	58	140.13	Praseodymium..	Pr	59	140.92
Cesium.........	Cs	55	132.91	Promethium....	Pm	61	[147]
Chlorine........	Cl	17	35.457	Protactinium ...	Pa	91	231
Chromium......	Cr	24	52.01	Radium........	Ra	88	226.05
Cobalt.........	Co	27	58.94	Radon..........	Rn	86	222
Copper........	Cu	29	63.54	Rhenium.......	Re	75	186.22
Curium........	Cm	96	[247]	Rhodium.......	Rh	45	102.91
Dysprosium	Dy	66	162.51	Rubidium......	Rb	37	85.48
Einsteinium....	E	99	[254]	Ruthenium.....	Ru	44	101.1
Erbium........	Er	68	167.27	Samarium......	Sm	62	150.35
Europium......	Eu	63	152.0	Scandium......	Sc	21	44.96
Fermium.......	Fm	100	[253]	Selenium.......	Se	34	78.96
Fluorine........	F	9	19.00	Silicon.........	Si	14	28.09
Francium.......	Fr	87	[223]	Silver.........	Ag	47	107.880
Gadolinium.....	Gd	64	157.26	Sodium........	Na	11	22.991
Gallium........	Ga	31	69.72	Strontium......	Sr	38	87.63
Germanium.....	Ge	32	72.60	Sulfur..........	S	16	32.066
Gold..........	Au	79	197.0	Tantalum......	Ta	73	180.95
Hafnium.......	Hf	72	178.50	Technetium.....	Tc	43	[99]
Helium.........	He	2	4.003	Tellurium......	Te	52	127.61
Holmium.......	Ho	67	164.94	Terbium.......	Tb	65	158.93
Hydrogen......	H	1	1.0080	Thallium.......	Tl	81	204.39
Indium.........	In	49	114.82	Thorium.......	Th	90	232.05
Iodine.........	I	53	126.91	Thulium.......	Tm	69	168.94
Iridium........	Ir	77	192.2	Tin............	Sn	50	118.70
Iron...........	Fe	26	55.85	Titanium......	Ti	22	47.90
Krypton.......	Kr	36	83.8	Tungsten.......	W	74	183.86
Lanthanum.....	La	57	138.92	Uranium.......	U	92	238.07
Lead..........	Pb	82	207.21	Vanadium......	V	23	50.95
Lithium........	Li	3	6.940	Xenon..........	Xe	54	131.30
Lutetium.......	Lu	71	174.99	Ytterbium......	Yb	70	173.04
Magnesium.....	Mg	12	24.32	Yttrium.........	Y	39	88.92
Manganese.....	Mn	25	54.94	Zinc............	Zn	30	65.38
Mendelevium...	Mv	101	[256]	Zirconium......	Zr	40	91.22

A value given in brackets denotes the mass number of the isotope of longest known half-life.

Because of natural variations in the relative abundance of the isotopes of sulfur the atomic weight of this element has a range of ± 0.003.

The columns are called groups. The long columns are the main groups, and the shorter ones are the subgroups. The main groups are numbered I-A to VII-A, the inert gases having no designation. The subgroups are numbered I-B to VIII-B, indicating secondary and less well-defined relations. The groups and subgroups contain, of course, the elements of the same family.

General Relations in the Periodic System

Some of the important relations in the periodic system may now be summarized. Ignoring for a moment the inert gases, we find the metals on the left side of the table and the nonmetals on the right side. The most typical metals are on the extreme left. The metallic properties decrease and the nonmetallic properties increase at the same time, going across a row or period. In a given row, the most nonmetallic element is on the extreme right.

Equally important are the vertical relations, which are now prominently displayed. These are the relations of the elements in the same family, and are simplest in the main groups. Going down a given column, the atomic weight increases, and a regular change, in properties occurs. On the left side (the metal side) the metallic properties—more powerful reducing agents, stronger bases, better electric conductors—increase on going *down* the table. On the right side (the nonmetal side) the nonmetallic properties—better oxidizing agents, stronger acids, better insulators—increase on going *up* the table. At first sight, this reversal in the trend (*down* for the metals, *up* for the nonmetals) may appear as a contradiction until we remember that the nonmetallic properties are opposite to the metallic properties. Looking on the table as a whole, we may summarize the general trends as follows: Metallic properties increase toward the left and down the periodic system; nonmetallic properties increase toward the right and up the periodic system. Thus, the most metallic element is francium at the lower left corner and the most nonmetallic element is fluorine at the upper right corner. All other elements lie between these two extremes.

These trends hold in a general way throughout the periodic system. In the main groups the simple rules of steady increase or decrease of a property hold strictly and almost without exception. However, in the subgroups the relations are somewhat more complicated. Sometimes the general trends are not evident over a limited region, and in a few instances they are even reversed (Ex. 26). The relations are just as definite, however, even in the subgroups. They merely require more complicated rules to express them. We shall limit ourselves to the main groups, in which the rules are simpler.

The most important and perhaps the simplest numerical property is the valence. It is always a small whole number. In all the groups, including the inert gases, the principal valence and the secondary valences are the same for the elements of the same group. However, on closer inspection of the table other interesting relations appear; these are most evident in the main groups. On the metal side, in going from left to right, the valence increases stepwise from 0 to +1 to +2 to +3 to +4; that is, elements of group zero have the valence 0, elements of group I have the valence of +1, and so on. In other words, the valence is the *same as the group number.* On the right side of the table, in going from right to left, the valence decreases from 0 to −1 to −2 to −3; that is, elements of the last group have a valence of 0, those of group VII a valence of −1, those of group VI a valence of −2. In other words, on the right-hand side of the table the principal *valence is equal to the group number subtracted from 8.*

In the middle of the main groups the relations are more complicated. On approaching the middle groups from either end and applying the rules, we get +4 and −4 for the valences of the elements of group IV, and +5 and −3 for the elements of group V. In each case both answers are correct and these elements show multiple valence. The rules may be simplified still further by selecting only the positive valence. Thus, all seven elements of the third row combine with oxygen, forming the following series of oxides:

$$Na_2O, \ MgO, \ Al_2O_3, \ SiO_2, \ P_2O_5, \ SO_3, \ Cl_2O_7$$

In this series the valence increases stepwise from +1 to +7. Similar but more complicated rules apply to the subgroups.

We must not leave the reader, however, with the impression that the rules are indefinite or that the general trends in the properties hold only in a broad sense. The rules and relations may be complex but they are definite. On measuring quantitatively any property—such as valence, electric conductivity, density, reducing power, solubility of sulfates, or any other numerical property—the trend and the changes from one element to the next can be described accurately. These trends are so definite and so well known that it is possible to predict the properties of an element from the properties of the elements surrounding it. If, for example, we do not happen to know the density of an element, we can predict it quite accurately from the density of the elements before it, after it, above it, and below it, using the general trends.

As a matter of historical fact, this regularity in the trends has been used to predict the existence of elements, yet unknown, and to prescribe their properties. The reader will recall that at the time of Mendeleev a number of elements had not yet been discovered. From the general trends Mendeleev placed the then known elements in their proper families, but noticed several gaps. For example there was no element between zinc and arsenic known at the time. Mendeleev unhesitatingly concluded that there must be two elements yet undiscovered, one similar to aluminum and the other similar to silicon. He courageously went further and predicted the properties of these elements.

Most interesting is the prediction of the existence and properties of the element between silicon and tin which Mendeleev called Eka-silicon. He predicted that the element should have a valence of +4, which of course he based on the fact that it should be a member of group IV. However, he predicted with unusual insight many other properties. Soon afterwards the element was discovered and was called *germanium*. The agreement between the predicted and the observed properties is indeed remarkable as shown in Table 10:6.

The prediction of other elements was also fully borne out. More recently the general trends in the periodic system have been of inestimable value in predicting the properties of the elements beyond uranium. The chemical reactions of these elements were known fairly definitely before the elements were synthesized in atom-smashing and atom-building experiments. Today scientists know fairly definitely the properties of elements yet undiscovered beyond mendelevium. This is made possible only by the knowledge of the general relationships in the periodic system (Ex. 27).

It is hardly possible to overstate the importance of the periodic law. It reduces the entire set of elements to a *system*. All the chemical and

TABLE 10:6
The Properties of Element 32

	Predicted	Found
Atomic weight	72.0	72.32*
Specific gravity	5.5	5.47
Atomic volume	13.0	13.22
Valence	4	4
Specific heat	0.073	0.076
Specific gravity of dioxide	4.7	4.703
Molecular volume of dioxide	22.0	22.16
Boiling point of tetrachloride	under 100°C	86°C
Specific gravity of tetrachloride	1.9	1.887
Molecular volume of tetrachloride	113.0	113.35

* Most recent value of atomic weight is 72.60.

physical properties of the elements, and hence of all matter, can now be systematized and understood. To the chemist and to the scientist in general, whether practical or theoretical, this is of inestimable value. He can study and record all knowledge of the elements systematically and efficiently. Using the periodic system as a guide in research, he can explore and discover new compounds, new properties, and new reactions. The periodic system contains all the information of all the materials possible of existence. It is all there if we can but learn to read it.

The very existence of this natural system raises some fundamental questions. The interrelations among the elements suggest strongly that the chemical elements are not "elements" in the sense that they are "simple" and ultimate. For "simple" things have no parts and are not related to other things. Things are related to other things because they have *parts in common*. A bus and a car (or an ice box) are related to the extent that they have in common similar parts as well as similar structures. The suggestion is strong that the chemical elements must be complex and must be made of more fundamental stuff. The atoms of the elements are not the ultimate particles of matter. They must have parts and they must have structure. We shall take up the question of the structure of atoms in the next chapter.

NOTES AND EXERCISES

1. What are the physical characteristics of metals? What are their chemical characteristics? What are the physical characteristics of the non-metals? What are their chemical characteristics?

2. Using physical and chemical properties, classify the following as metals or nonmetals, looking up the information, if necessary: aluminum, iron, copper, sulfur, oxygen, carbon, gold, mercury, arsenic, silicon, helium, chlorine, boron, neon, phosphorus. Why is it necessary to have two additional classes? What elements belong to each of the additional classes?

3. What is a "typical" metal? Give three examples. Is gold a typical metal? Why or why not?

4. What is a typical nonmetal? Give examples. Is nitrogen a typical nonmetal? Why or why not? Is helium a typical nonmetal? Why or why not?

5. Which is the most "metallic" of the alkali metals? Which is the least "metallic"?

6. The formula of sodium sulfate is Na_2SO_4. What is the formula of francium sulfate? What regularity permits you to answer this question?

7. Family relationships are exhibited even in unusual properties. In the photoelectric cell (Chap. 5) blue light ejects electrons from the sodium surface, but red light does not. Light of wavelength shorter than blue can eject photoelectrons from potassium. What element would you try to construct a photoelectric cell sensitive to red light?

8. Strontium-90, a radioactive species of ordinary strontium, is one of the most detrimental substances to human health. Can you explain this in terms of family relationships? Why does strontium-90 concentrate in milk? Why does it concentrate in human bones?

9. Astatine, the heaviest halogen (atomic weight 210) was recently produced artificially. It is not listed in Table 10:2. Add astatine to the table as column 6, predicting as many properties as you can. Look up the information and check the accuracy of your predictions.

10. Make a table of the inert gases, similar to Table 10:2. Include the following among the properties: boiling point, melting point, density, solubility in water, valence. What chemical properties and what compounds can you list? Explain.

11. Why did Mendeleev consider the atomic weight and the valence as "properties of the atoms themselves"? Consider graphite and diamond. What element is present in both? What is the atomic weight of carbon? What is its valence? What is the color of graphite? What is the color of diamond? What is the color of "carbon"? What is the color of carbon atoms? Is color a property of the atoms or a property of the substances in bulk? Is color different from atomic weight in this respect?

12. What is atomic number? What is meant by "element 8"? What is the name of the element? What is element 92?

13. Describe the sequence of properties from one element to the next, in the fifth period, starting with rubidium (element 37) and ending with xenon (element 54). Relate each element to the corresponding element in the preceding period, from potassium (19) to krypton (36).

14. How many elements would you predict the seventh period to have, when completed?

15. Hydrogen is in many respects a unique element. Physically, it is a nonmetal. Yet it is a reducing agent. The most common valence is +1, as in hydrochloric acid, HCl. However it also combines with the alkali metals forming salt like substances called hydrides. An example is lithium hydride, LiH. If the valence of lithium is +1, what is the valence of hydrogen in this compound?

16. The first period contains only hydrogen besides the inert gas helium. Hydrogen therefore plays many roles. If hydrogen is considered the first member of the period, which elements should it resemble? Does its valence +1 bear this out? If hydrogen is considered as the element immediately preceding the inert gas, what elements should it resemble? Does the formation of lithium hydride, LiH, bear this out?

17. One of the most interesting properties varying periodically is the gram-atomic volume. This is defined as the volume of a gram-atom of the element. Thus, the atomic volume of gold is the volume of 197.2 grams of gold. When the gram-atomic volume is plotted against the atomic number the following plot is obtained.

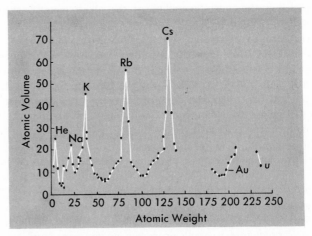

Fig. 10-4. Periodicity in the atomic volumes of the elements.

Since the gram-atoms of the elements contain the same number of atoms (6×10^{23} atoms) the *relative* gram-atomic volumes are in the same ratio as the (average) volumes of individual atoms. If the volume of 6×10^{23} atoms of gold is 10.2 cc, what is the average volume of a single gold atom? What is the average volume of a single sodium atom? Which atom is larger, a sodium atom or a silver atom?

18. What is a group in the periodic system? What is a main group? What is a subgroup? What is a period?

19. Sulfur (16), selenium (34), and tellurium (52) are in the sixth main group of the periodic system. If the formula of sulfuric acid is H_2SO_4 what is the formula of selenic acid? Of telluric acid? Why are the formulas of corresponding compounds similar for the elements in the same group?

20. The halogens decrease in nonmetallic character from fluorine (9) to iodine (53). In fact iodine has a steel-gray luster, although not distinctly metallic. Would you expect astatine (85) to be metallic or nonmetallic?

21. Show that the increase in metallic character from top to bottom is illustrated by the elements of group V (from nitrogen to bismuth).

22. Which is the better reducing agent: Sodium (11) or magnesium (12); potassium (19) or calcium (20); magnesium (12) or calcium (20)?

23. Which is the stronger base: Sodium hydroxide, NaOH; or magnesium hydroxide, $Mg(OH)_2$?

24. Which is the stronger acid: Phosphoric acid, H_3PO_4, or arsenic acid, H_3AsO_4? phosphoric acid, H_3PO_4, or sulfuric acid, H_2SO_4?

25. Which is the better electric conductor, boron (5) or carbon (6); carbon or nitrogen?

26. Consider the elements of subgroup IB, copper (29), silver (47), and gold (79). Which rusts the most easily? Which is the most active of the three? Which is the least active? Is this the trend exhibited by the alkali metals (main group I)? Is there a reversal for the elements in the subgroups?

27. The regularity in the trends is even more fundamental than atomic weight. Look up in the periodic table the atomic weights of tellurium (52) and iodine (53). Are they placed in the right order, from lighter to heavier? Mendeleev unhesitatingly placed tellurium before iodine, even though this violated the very basis of the arrangement. Why did he do that? Can you find any other similar "irregularities" in the table? Would Mendeleev consider atomic volume "a property of the atoms themselves"? Explain.

11

ATOMS AS MINIATURE SOLAR SYSTEMS

1. PRELIMINARY SURVEY

Throughout the whole span of the nineteenth century the atoms of the elements were regarded as the ultimate particles of matter. The very word "atom" means something that "cannot be cut," and thinkers throughout the centuries conceived of matter as consisting of ultimate "noncuttable" particles. In 1802, Dalton gave a concrete meaning to the idea, and pointed to experimental methods for establishing the atomicity of the elements. As the century rolled on, experimental methods were developed which permitted the measurement of the relative weights of the atoms, their combining capacity, and their number in a given molecule. Some experiments even provided an estimate of their actual weights, sizes, and numbers. The atoms became more and more real. They were used freely to explain and visualize chemical reactions, and, conversely, the chemical reactions were studied to discover the properties of the atoms. Up to nearly the end of the century the atoms were conceived as ultimate tiny spheres, all alike for a given element, but differing in sizes and weights from the atoms of the other elements. They were thought of as perfectly solid, hard, and indestructible particles, retaining their identity unaltered in combining and re-combining with other atoms.

This picture of the atom was destined to alter radically during the present century. While in its main features the picture of the atom is still the same, it differs greatly in the amount of detail. Today we conceive of the atom as an elaborate structure, consisting of still smaller and more fundamental particles. These subatomic particles are particles of positive and negative electricity, particles of neutral matter, and particles of energy. In general structure, the atom consists of a very small and very dense core, the *nucleus,* which is positively charged and is surrounded by negative electrons vibrating in concentric shells around it. The atom resembles a solar system in three dimensions. The atoms of a given element are not necessarily all alike in all respects; they may vary somewhat in weight, but all the atoms of a given element have the same positive charge on the nucleus and have identical arrangements of the electrons. In combining with other atoms, the atoms of an element do alter in their periphery but they remain essentially unaltered in their interior and particularly in their central cores—their nuclei. Although they are not *destroyed* during chemical changes, they are not *indestructible.* During drastic *nuclear changes,* atoms can be smashed, and broken up into lighter and smaller atoms, or they may fuse to form heavier atoms. The reader may refer to Chapter 6, to review a more extensive presentation of this picture.

The change from the simpler picture to the more elaborate did not take place all at once, although the most rapid changes occurred in the first two decades of this century. There were many indications of the complexity and electrical structure of the atoms throughout the nineteenth century. As already noted, the remarkable regularities in the periodic system strongly suggested that the atoms have complex structures. Structure implies *parts,* and specifically that there exist particles still smaller than atoms, from which the atoms are built. The similarities in the properties of the elements suggest that atoms of similar elements have similar structures. This further implies that the structure of the atoms in some way determines their properties.

Long before the periodic system was developed however, there were other specific indications of the constitution of the atoms, although their full significance was but dimly appreciated at the time. As early as 1817, Prout, observing that the atomic weights of many elements are nearly whole numbers (that is, their atoms are a whole number of times heavier than hydrogen atoms), proposed the hypothesis that all the atoms are complex "combinations" of hydrogen atoms. However, the idea was abandoned after the atomic weights were determined more accurately and were found not to be whole numbers for many elements. For example the atomic weight of chlorine is 35.46, almost halfway between whole numbers.

Another indication came from the association of valence and combining power with electric attraction and repulsion. The mysterious nature of valence persistently excited much speculation. Valence is always a small whole number and, like electricity, may be positive or negative. In a series of experiments around 1835, Faraday demonstrated that the correspondence between valence and electricity is more than a formal analogy. By studying the electric conduction of acids, bases, and salts, he found that the metals (and hydrogen) not only show a positive valence in these compounds, but that their atoms carry a positive *electric* charge. Similarly the nonmetallic atoms not only show the opposite valence but carry a negative electric charge. However, the full import of these experiments was not realized until some forty years later.

More direct indication of the electrical nature of matter came toward the end of the century from a series of experiments on the electric conduction of gases in partially evacuated tubes. The first great event was the discovery of cathode rays by Crookes in 1878. He produced these rays by passing a high-voltage current through highly evacuated tubes. Cathode rays are now familiar in television sets; it is the beam of cathode rays in the evacuated picture tube that produces the image on the screen. Around 1890, J. J. Thomson (1856-1940) demonstrated that cathode rays are a swarm of *material particles* moving at high speeds and carrying a negative electric charge. By measuring their mass he found that these particles are some 2000 times lighter than the hydrogen atoms, which are the lightest atoms. The particles in the cathode-ray beam were named electrons. Apparently, under the high voltages in the tube, the electrons are torn off from the neutral atoms of the materials in the tube and fly at very high speeds from the cathode (or negative pole) toward the positive pole. Since the same electrons are obtained regardless of the materials in the tube, the conclusion is inescapable that the negative electrons are present in the atoms of all the elements.

Soon afterward positive rays were discovered in a modified version of the cathode-ray tube. These rays move in the opposite direction—that is, *toward* the cathode. This discovery explained the fate of the neutral atoms in the tube after the negative charges were detached from them. They become positively charged particles and move as a beam toward the cathode. On measuring their masses, however, they are found to be positively charged atoms of the very tenuous gas still remaining in the tube. These observations confirm the conclusion that the atoms contain positive electricity, too.

Meanwhile, additional evidence for the presence of electricity in atoms was gathering from an apparently unrelated field—the study of light. After the discovery of spectra, around 1860, it was found that each element has a distinct spectrum. In fact, the spectrum of each element is so characteristic that it may be used to identify the element. With this added knowledge and some further developments in electricity, James Maxwell in 1864 formulated the electromagnetic theory of light, as discussed in Chapter 5. The essential part of the theory is that light is produced by oscillating electric charges and that the wavelength depends on the rapidity of oscillation. From measurements of the wavelengths of the emitted light and from the fact that the wavelengths are different for different elements, it became evident that light originates *within the atoms*. This implies that within the atoms there are electric charges, oscillating in powerful electric fields, and that the strength of these fields is different in the different atoms.

These two lines of evidence—from light and from electricity—were brought closer together by the discovery of x-rays. In 1897, Wilhelm Roentgen discovered that a beam of cathode rays falling upon a metal target produces highly penetrating rays; not knowing what these were, he called them "x"-rays. They proved to be of the same nature as light, but of extremely short wavelength. This discovery and its explanation were a powerful confirmation of the electromagnetic theory of light. The theory explained the production of x-rays as follows. On hitting the metal target the high-speed electrons are stopped suddenly; that is, they experience a high (negative) acceleration. Hence they emit radiation of extremely short wavelength. This confirmation of the electromagnetic theory in turn strengthens the argument that light originates within the atoms by electrons oscillating in powerful electric fields.

Thus, by the end of the nineteenth century the general outline of the new picture was taking form. Atoms contain both positive and negative electricity in packages of electric charge, each package equal in quantity to the charge on the electron. It was not clear what else the atom might contain, but, of course, it does contain matter. The negative electrons themselves are in the atom, and they contribute to the mass. But, most of the mass of the atom must be associated with the positive charge. It was not clear what material particles are associated with the positive charge. Up to that time the smallest particle known to carry a positive charge was the positively charged hydrogen atom, which was named the *proton* (Ex. 1). It was not clear whether neutral particles are also present in the atom, how many electrons and protons are in it, or what the general structure of the atom is. Many speculations and many theories were proposed, but all were rather vague.

Around 1910 Ernest Rutherford (1871-1937) formulated a definitive picture of the atom, basically as it is accepted today. His theory synthesized all the conclusions discussed above and answered most of the questions raised in the preceding paragraph. However, two additional series of experiments not yet discussed were essential to his theory. One series is the discovery of radioactivity by Henri Becquerel (1852-1908) in 1896, and its subsequent interpretations. Uranium and other related elements, spontaneously and without any prompting, give off three kinds of rays: alpha rays (α), which were identified as helium atoms carrying a double positive charge (He^{++}), identical with some of the positive rays obtained in those cathode-ray tubes that contain helium; beta rays (β), identical with high-speed cathode rays; and gamma rays (γ), which are very penetrating x-rays. Rutherford interpreted the emission of the α, β, and γ rays as being due to the disintegration of the atoms of the radioactive elements into atoms of smaller atomic weight. He correctly concluded that the atoms contain in their structure the materials of these rays and perhaps other particles, in strong electric fields, and disintegrate releasing large amounts of energy in the process.

The second series of experiments led directly to Rutherford's theory. These were certain experiments on the penetration and scattering of

Fig. 11-1. Rutherford was the originator of the concept that the atom is a miniature solar system. *(The Bettman Archive.)*

β rays and α rays when shot through very thin metal foils. In one of the experiments, Rutherford directed a beam of α particles at a thin gold leaf. To his surprise, most of the rays went through the leaf unhindered and undeflected, as though the leaf did not contain any matter. However, an extremely small fraction of the α particles did suffer a deflection and a few of them were deflected very sharply. Apparently the matter of the leaf is concentrated at certain *centers* or *nuclei*. These centers of mass must also be strongly charged, because they deflect sharply the positively charged α rays. Since the atoms of gold in the leaf essentially touch one another, this must mean that the mass of the atom is concentrated in a nucleus and the rest of the atom is essentially empty space, having little or no matter. (That the atoms in the gold leaf "touch" one another follows from the experimental fact that solid gold is practically incompressible.)

From these and related experiments, Rutherford proposed the theory that the atom consists of a very small, positively charged nucleus which contains nearly all the mass of the atom and is surrounded by negatively charged electrons. To account for the positive charge and for the mass of the nucleus, Rutherford assumed that it contains heavy protons and perhaps some electrons. To account for the neutrality of the atom as a whole, he assumed that in the relatively vast space outside the nucleus there is a sufficient number of electrons to counterbalance the positive charge. This is the basic outline of Rutherford's theory, which excellently accounts for many of the experiments.

At this stage, however, the theory left one broad question unsettled. What is the arrangement, if any, of the electrons outside the nucleus? In terms of volume, the part of the atom outside the nucleus is nearly the whole atom. The electrons in this region vibrate to give the characteristic spectra and the electrons detached from the atom or extra electrons attached to it produce the charged atoms or ions found in acids, bases, and salts. In 1913, Niels Bohr, a student of Rutherford, applied the electromagnetic theory of light to explain the spectra, and came to the conclusion that the electrons are arranged in intricate patterns of concentric shells. In his theory Bohr took a courageous step in modifying drastically the electromagnetic theory of light. We shall discuss this point further in Chapter 12. The theory is now capable of explaining not only the spectra, but also the regularities in the periodic system and all the chemical behavior of the elements.

This is the modern picture of the atom in outline form. We shall present the picture in greater detail and give it a deeper meaning, by describing the essential experimental evidence and the reasoning that led to it. To make the discussion understandable, however, it is necessary to strip it of its immense mathematical complexity and present it in terms that can be visualized. We believe this can be done without losing the essential points of the argument in the simplification; but it will be necessary for the reader to review and to keep in mind a few of the basic ideas in electricity, light, and chemical reactions. We shall call attention to the concepts as needed and refer the reader to their more detailed discussion in other sections.

2. EVIDENCE THAT MATTER CONTAINS ELECTRICITY FROM ELECTRICITY, CHEMISTRY, AND LIGHT

Many relations between electricity and matter were known for a long time, and several of them have already been mentioned. Electricity was discovered and first studied as a peculiar behavior of matter. Some kinds of matter can be electrified and some cannot. Some kinds of matter, notably the metals and certain types of solutions, conduct electric current, and others do not. Certain materials in a battery produce electric currents by undergoing chemical reactions, others do not. These simple but basic phenomena raise the question: What is the relation between kinds of materials and their electrical properties?

A more intimate relation between electricity and matter was obtained by Michael Faraday around 1835 in a series of experiments on the conduction of acids, bases, and salts, in solution as well as in the molten state. These liquid conductors differ markedly from the metallic conductors in several important particulars. First, the liquid conductor is *permanently decomposed* during the passage of electric current. For example, when a direct current is passed through a solution of hydrogen iodide, hydrogen is given off at the negative pole and iodine is deposited at the positive pole. If the passage of the current is continued long enough, all the hydrogen iodide is decomposed, leaving only water, which is a very poor conductor. Water itself can be *electrolyzed* —that is, decomposed by the current. If a few drops of sulfuric acid are added to make the water a conductor, all the water is decomposed into hydrogen and oxygen, leaving behind only the few drops of sulfuric acid added. On electrolyzing a solution of copper bromide the compound is decomposed into its elements, the copper depositing at the negative pole and the bromine at the positive. In all conducting solutions, the conductor is permanently decomposed. For this reason acids, bases, and salts are called *electrolytes,* meaning they can be decomposed by electric current.

Thus, the behavior of liquid conductors is very different from that of metallic conductors. A copper wire after conducting a current is as good as before (unless the heat developed is sufficient to melt it or to oxidize it in the air); but in the case of electrolytes, decomposition takes place. Decomposition, of course, implies chemical reactions. These reactions are observed taking place right at the electrodes. A further relation is noted: hydrogen and the metals in general are liberated at the negative pole, while the nonmetals are liberated at the positive pole. Often more complicated reactions take place at the electrodes, but these may be disregarded at the moment.

The second important difference between metallic and electrolytic

Faraday's Experiments on Electrolysis

Fig. 11-2. Faraday related atoms of matter with quantity of electric charge. *(The Bettmann Archive.)*

conductors is that, in the latter, *matter actually moves toward the electrodes* during the passage of the current. This movement of matter takes place not only near the electrodes, but also throughout the solution. It can be demonstrated with the apparatus in Figure 11-3. With careful manipulation of the stopcocks at A and B, and some cotton wads, it is possible to put copper chloride solution in the middle section, and sulfuric acid in the right and left compartments. If with the stopcocks closed the levels are adjusted equally, and then the stopcocks are opened, no detectable flow or mixing of the liquids at A or B will take place. The middle solution is blue, a characteristic of chemically combined copper in many of its compounds. The other two solutions are colorless, for sulfuric acid has no color.

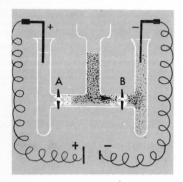

Fig. 11-3. Migration of matter during electrolytic conductivity. Blue color, due to copper, enters right arm and moves toward the negative electrode. Chlorine (colorless) moves toward the positive electrode.

If now a direct current is passed in the direction indicated in Figure 11-3, the blue color moves very slowly into the right compartment and away from A. Since the color is due to the copper in the compound, it is evident that the copper moves toward the negative pole. If the passage of the current is continued long enough, all the blue color will enter the right compartment and eventually the copper will reach the negative pole and deposit on it as metallic copper. Meanwhile, the (chemically combined) chlorine has been moving toward the left compartment. We cannot see this, of course, for chlorine has no color in the combined state, as in ordinary salt (NaCl). But we can test for combined chlorine very easily. On adding silver nitrate to the left compartment, the chlorine unites with silver to give a white cloud of the insoluble silver chloride, becoming milkier as the current continues. Alternatively (without adding silver nitrate) after the chlorine reaches the positive pole, it will be liberated as free gaseous chlorine which can be recognized by its characteristic pungent odor.

This experiment can be performed with other electrolytes. In all cases, we observe migration of matter. The conductivity of electrolytes is very different from metallic conductivity in this respect. On passing a current through a junction of two metals such as copper and iron, neither the iron migrates toward the copper nor *vice versa*. But in the conduction of acids, bases, and salts, the constituents of these substances migrate. In general, hydrogen and the metals migrate toward the negative pole and eventually deposit there; the nonmetals migrate toward the positive pole and deposit there. In some instances, additional chemical reactions may take place at the electrodes, but, again, these specific complications should not obscure the main point.

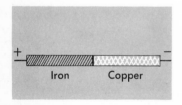

Fig. 11-4. In metallic conductivity the metals do not penetrate into one another at the junction.

The explanation of these experiments now appears rather easy. Since particles of matter migrate during the passage of the current, they must carry an electric charge while in solution. In fact the motion of the charged particles *is the current,* for as we have seen an *electric current is a charge in motion.* These charged particles are called ions, meaning "travelers," to indicate that they migrate in electric fields (in this case in the electric field set up by the battery). The hydrogen ions and the metal ions must be positively charged atoms, since they are attracted by, and migrate toward, the negative pole. On reaching the negative pole they are neutralized and become ordinary uncharged atoms of the metals (or hydrogen), and if enough of them collect the deposited free metal (or bubbles of hydrogen gas) are visible. Similarly, the nonmetallic ions must be negatively charged, since they migrate toward the positive pole, where they are neutralized forming the free nonmetals.

Easy though it may seem, the foregoing explanation was not formulated until about 50 years after Faraday first observed these relations. In 1883, Svente Arrhenius (1859-1927) proposed his theory of ionization, explaining conductivity in terms of the motion of ions. From this and other evidence, he went even further and demonstrated that acids, bases, and salts in solution consist of positively and negatively charged ions. These ions are present in the solutions even *before* the current is turned on. The electric field merely causes the ions to migrate toward the poles, but the ions are present in solutions all the time. The charge cannot be detected in these materials under ordinary conditions, only because the total positive charge is equal to the total negative charge in a given sample.

A deeper insight into the nature of the ions is obtained by considering certain measurements made by Faraday, which revealed some intriguing relations, now known as Faraday's laws. The most fundamental of these is the relation between the quantity of electricity passing through the solution and the weight of matter liberated at the electrodes. For a given element, the weight of that element liberated during electrolysis depends entirely on the quantity of electric charge passing through the solution, and on *nothing else*. For example, in order to obtain 1 gram of hydrogen by the electrolysis of acids, 96,500 coulombs must pass through the solution. (The coulomb is a unit of electric *charge,* not to be confused with volts, amperes, or other electrical units; see Chap. 4). The amount of charge necessary to discharge 1 gram of hydrogen is always the same, regardless of conditions. Whether we use high or low voltages, large or small currents, large or small electrodes, hot or cold solutions, concentrated or dilute acids, strong or weak acids, or even water, or whether we vary the conditions in any other way, we invariably find that 96,500 coulombs are required to liberate 1 gram of hydrogen. The different conditions may result in liberating the hydrogen faster or slower, but the weight of hydrogen is proportional only to the number of coulombs. The same situation is found with the other elements but, of course, the weight of each element liberated per 96,500 coulombs is different for the different elements. (In elements having more than one valence we obtain two or three *sets* of weights, one for each valence, as will become clear presently. See also Ex. 4.)

It is a surprising fact that this experiment did not lead immediately to the obvious conclusion that electricity is corpuscular in character, but, of course, hindsight is better than foresight. In 1874, George Stoney (1826-1911) argued as follows. A given weight of an element consists of a definite number of atoms. Since a definite quantity of charge liberates a definite number of atoms of a given element, each atom on discharging, must absorb a definite fraction of the total charge. Therefore, *before* discharging, the ion must carry the same amount of the opposite charge. In other words, if matter consists of atoms (packages of matter), electricity must also come in packages, at least when found on atoms. Since a given quantity of electricity discharges the same

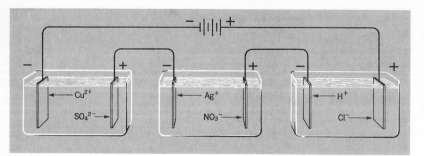

Fig. 11-5. The same quantity of electricity is passed through several solutions, by connecting them in series. Although the actual weights of elements liberated vary greatly, in all cases 96,500 coulombs liberate a gram - atomic weight of each element divided by a whole number.

weight (that is, same number of atoms) of a given element from its various compounds, each atom of that element must carry the same package of electricity in all its compounds.

The "package" structure of electricity is further and more strikingly demonstrated by another law discovered by Faraday in his experiments. The weight of the various elements liberated by a given quantity of charge is related to their atomic weights. As already stated, 96,500 coulombs liberate 1 gram of hydrogen. Investigation of several other elements shows that this same quantity of charge liberates at the positive pole 35.5 grams of chlorine, 80 grams of bromine, and 127 grams of iodine, and at the negative pole 23 grams of sodium, 39 grams of potassium, or 108 grams of silver. We see at once that these weights are the gram-atomic weights of these elements, each containing the *same number of atoms,* namely Avogadro's number, *N.* Therefore, each atom of any of these elements carries the same quantity of charge and this quantity is the same as that carried by the hydrogen atom. The charge may be positive or negative, but it is equal in amount per atom of any of these elements.

Before jumping to conclusions, however, it is prudent to investigate a few other elements. By actual experiment, we find that 96,500 coulombs liberate only 8.0 grams of oxygen, 12.1 grams of magnesium, 20.0 grams of calcium, 32.7 grams of copper, and 103.6 grams of lead. These weights are one half of the gram-atomic weights of the respective elements; also, these elements have a valence of 2. Quite obviously, the same quantity of electricity liberates one half as many atoms in this group of elements. This can only mean that each atom of these elements carries twice the charge, as compared to the hydrogen atom. Continuing the experiments, we find that 96,500 coulombs liberate only 9 grams of aluminum, which is one third of 27, the atomic weight of aluminum. Therefore, the aluminum ion carries three units of charge just as its valence is three. Similarly, this quantity of electricity liberates 18.6 grams of iron, from $FeCl_3$, which is one third of 55.6. The law now becomes clear. The amount of the element liberated by 96,500 coulombs is either 1 gram-atomic weight, or one half, or one third, depending on whether the valence is one, two, or three. (Exs. 3 and 4.) In other words, to obtain 1 gram-atom of an element by electrolysis we need

96,500 coulombs per each *unit* of valence. The quantity of charge, 96,500 coulombs, is a new unit of charge and is called the *faraday*.

Thus, these experiments and their interpretations explain valence in electrical terms and provide a method for determining it experimentally, at least for those elements found in acids, bases, and salts. Valence is the charge on the ion, expressed in units of the charge found on the hydrogen ion. If the element has a valence of one, its ions carry one unit charge. It may be positive or negative, but it is equal in amount to the charge on the hydrogen ion. If the valence is two, the ion carries exactly twice that charge. If the valence is three, the ion carries three units of charge. Experimentally, we can determine the charge on the ion by merely noting how many faradays of electric charge are required to liberate 1 gram-atomic weight of the element. From these experiments we come to the significant conclusion that electricity comes in packages, and the smallest package is that found on the hydrogen ion. All other charges found on other ions are either equal to that or are small whole-number multiples of it. In 1874, Stoney, who formulated much of the above reasoning, called this package of charge the *electronic* charge, or the *electron*.

Although a little ahead of our story, we can draw at this point some extremely interesting conclusions. We can measure the charge on the hydrogen ion and express it in ordinary electrical units. Since a faraday (96,500 coulombs) liberates 1 gram of hydrogen, and since 1 gram of hydrogen contains N atoms (Avogadro's number), a faraday contains N units of this smallest charge—*one for each atom*. In other words, there *are as many electronic charges in a faraday as there are atoms in 1 gram of hydrogen*. But we have measured N by several and independent methods and found it to be about 6×10^{23}. Therefore a faraday contains 6×10^{23} electronic charges (Ex. 5).

A somewhat different way of looking at this relation brings out another interesting result. Since a faraday liberates 6×10^{23} atoms of hydrogen, each hydrogen ion carries $\dfrac{1}{6 \times 10^{23}}$ of a faraday. This is 96,500 times $\dfrac{1}{6 \times 10^{23}}$ or 1.6×10^{-19} coulombs. Since a coulomb is 3×10^9 electrostatic units, the charge on the hydrogen ion is 1.6×10^{-19} times 3×10^9 or 4.8×10^{-10} electrostatic units. This amount of charge is the same as the smallest charge found by Millikan on an oil drop in his famous experiments of 1911 (Chap. 4). In other words, the smallest charge on the ions in electrolysis *is the same as the smallest charge on an oil drop* (Ex. 7).

If Avogadro's number had not been determined by other methods, we could turn the reasoning around and calculate it, using Faraday's experiments and Millikan's experiment. A faraday of charge is 96,500 coulombs, and a coulomb is 3×10^{10} electrostatic units. From Millikan's experiment, an electrostatic unit is 2×10^9 electronic charges. Therefore a faraday contains

$$96,500 \times 3 \times 10^{10} \times 2 \times 10^9 = 6 \times 10^{23} \text{ electronic charges}$$

If we now assume that each hydrogen atom carries one of these charges, then 1 gram of hydrogen contains 6×10^{23} atoms. In other words there are as many electrons in a faraday as there are atoms in 1 gram of hydrogen. More generally, there are as many electrons in a faraday as there are atoms in 1 gram-atom of any element. This is one of the most accurate methods for counting the number of atoms in a gram-atom (Ex. 5).

Even in the absence of Millikan's experiment, however, the experiments of Faraday permit us to penetrate deeply into the electrical structure of matter. Let us summarize the significant conclusions. Electricity consists of packages or ultimate units. The charged atoms of the electrolytes carry one or more of these units. The number of these charges on a given ion is numerically equal to the valence. In the electrolytes at least, combining power is due to the mutual attraction of the opposite charges. The evidence is direct that these units are on the charged atoms, but the suggestion is strong that they are part of the constitution of the neutral atoms as well. For it is evident that the ions are formed from neutral atoms at the time the atoms combine, as, for example, when ordinary sodium and ordinary chlorine combine to form salt. How else could a neutral sodium atom and a neutral chlorine atom become charged ions during the reaction, if they did not have electric charges to begin with, in their neutral state?

The Discovery of the Electron

The next development in establishing the electrical nature of matter came in the last quarter of the nineteenth century from a series of experiments on the conduction of electricity through gases. The signal discovery in this series was the discovery of the cathode rays. Interpretation of the nature of these rays resulted in further confirming the "package" nature of electricity and the discovery of the *electron* as a *material particle,* having both mass *and* charge. The charge and mass of the electron were measured and the evidence became strong that these electrons are part of the constitution of all atoms. We shall describe the experiments leading to these conclusions.

Under ordinary conditions gases are not conductors of electricity. We know this from many every-day observations. Live wires are exposed to the air without fear of conduction. The power companies transmit currents at high voltages, 22,000 volts or higher, over the countryside, using bare wires. If air were a conductor, the electricity would be conducted to the ground. There is, however, a small leak through the air, and the leak increases at higher voltages, resulting in some losses. In lightning, where the voltages are very high, air becomes temporarily a conductor, the spark being the conducting path of the discharge. But the voltages must be very high in order to produce a lightning discharge; it takes about 50,000 volts for a spark of 1 inch in air.

Conduction of gases at low pressures. The situation is surprisingly different at low pressures. Gases become conductors under these conditions. This can be demonstrated by a glass tube about 20 inches long and 2 inches in diameter, containing ordinary air, and connected to a voltage source of a few thousand volts, say 10,000 volts. An ammeter

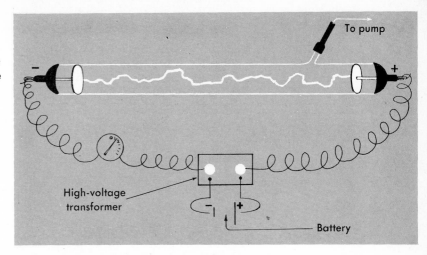

Fig. 11-6. Conduction of electricity through rarefied gases. Early stage at moderate evacuation.

in the line will measure the current, if there is any. At ordinary pressures no spark is observed and the ammeter shows no current. However, on connecting the tube to a pump and evacuating it, at some stage of the evacuation a zig-zag discharge is observed in the tube, streaming from one terminal to the other. At the same time the ammeter registers a current (Fig. 11-6).

As evacuation is continued the spark gradually straightens and thickens more and more, until it fills the entire tube. The tube now glows with a pale pink color. This is the "neon-sign" stage. In fact, if instead of air, the experiment started with neon in the tube, the result would be a neon sign with the characteristic neon light; other gases give different colors. As this stage is approached the ammeter shows a larger and larger current. Apparently, the air at low pressures becomes a conductor and the conductivity increases with evacuation.

We can explain this stage by merely extending the ideas that explain lightning. The molecules of the air apparently behave like tiny pith balls. At the positive pole the neutral molecules acquire by contact a positive charge, and then are repelled toward the negative pole or cathode. Similarly, at the cathode they acquire a negative charge and are repelled toward the positive pole. Many of them acquire these charges, even without touching the electrodes. Throughout the tube, under the severe tension of the high voltage, the molecules are charged by induction. As a result in their collisions with other molecules they lose or gain charges and become ions. Once they have acquired a charge, they surge toward the oppositely charged pole. *The current is nothing other than their motion.*

The conductivity of gases is similar to that of the electrolytes with one notable exception. In the electrolytes, the atoms are *already and permanently* charged, *before* the passage of the current. In the gases, the molecules become charged only under the influence of the high voltages and may lose the charge on colliding with other molecules. An individual molecule never gets very far. It collides many times per second with other molecules, losing its charge in the collision. Soon thereafter, of course, it may acquire another charge of the same kind, or of the opposite kind, and resume its motion toward the electrode of the opposite charge. Incidentally, the light is emitted at the instant the ions become *discharged,* as we shall see later. In fact, the continuous glow is evidence that the molecules acquire and lose charge repeatedly. There is, however, enough over-all motion of the ions toward the opposite poles during the time they are charged to account for the current (Ex. 8).

The most direct evidence for these explanations comes from observing the ammeter. At first the current is rather small, meaning that most of the ions produced do not get very far. As the evacuation is continued, the current increases. This means that the ions can now move further before colliding. With further evacuation, the current continues to increase. However, after a point of high evacuation the current begins to *decrease* and the glow in the tube becomes fainter. This reversal may appear surprising at first, but should be expected. In carrying the evacuation to the point of removing the few molecules still remaining in the tube, we are removing the very particles that form the ions. Low pressures are needed to permit the ions to move without too much hindrance, but not so low that there are not enough molecules to form the ions. With still higher evacuations, the glow disappears, the tube becomes quite dark, and the current drops to a very low value.

Cathode rays. It is at this stage that the cathode rays appear. Everything up to this point has been preliminary to the experiment and to an understanding of what is to follow. The current is now very small, *but it is not zero.* Further evacuation down to the best possible vacuum does not reduce the current any further. There is no glow inside the tube, and calculations will indicate that the ions still remaining are too few to carry the current registered on the ammeter. *And yet the current flows.* How does it flow without the benefit of a conductor? Is it electricity, free of matter, flowing through the vacuum? Although the glow inside the tube disappears, a new type of glow appears. The *entire wall* of the glass tube now glows with a soft, greenish fluorescence. Rather significantly, the glow is somewhat brighter on the wall of the tube opposite the cathode.

Further experiments suggest that within the dark tube there are "rays" of some kind. These mysterious rays are invisible, but produce a fluorescent glow on striking the glass wall; their presence is suggested by several simple experiments. A solid obstacle, such as a metal cross, placed in the middle of the tube, casts a *shadow* on the wall opposite the cathode. Apparently these rays originate from the cathode and travel in straight lines, away from the cathode. The motion in a straight line is further confirmed by another simple experiment. If a metal disk with a slot across the center is placed near the cathode, most of the fluorescent glow on the glass beyond the disk disappears. But opposite the slot a bright band is cast on the glass wall. Apparently these mysterious rays originate around the cathode and travel in straight lines. The rays going through the slot constitute a beam and cast an image of the slot on the wall of the tube. They are invisible within the tube, but become visible on striking the glass wall. Since they originate in the cathode, the rays were called "cathode rays."

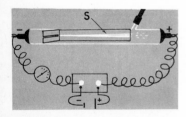

Fig. 11-7. Cathode rays rendered visible. The rays originating at the cathode are invisible until they strike a screen, S, coated with zinc sulfide paint.

A great help in studying these rays is to render them visible. The rays may be located roughly by observing the fluorescent spot on the glass, but a much better method was developed subsequent to the early experiments. It was soon found that other glasses and other materials placed in the tube also fluoresce. Some minerals give brilliant colors when the rays strike them. For example, the mineral zinc sulfide, which has a dull gray color under ordinary light, glows with a brilliant purple color when placed in the path of the rays. Accordingly, a metal screen coated with zinc sulfide paint is inclined to the path of the rays, as shown in Figure 11-7. A brilliant ribbon, from the slot at the cathode to the opposite end, marks the path of the rays.

A great controversy arose about the nature of these rays. William Crookes (1832-1919), who discovered them, thought at first that the material in the tube was in a "fourth state of matter," far more rarefied than in the gaseous state. This idea was soon abandoned, as it became evident that something moves from the cathode to the anode. The German investigators thought that these were "true" rays—that is, some kind of light similar to ultraviolet rays. The British physicists, on the other hand—notably J. J. Thomson—maintained that they were electrified particles moving from the cathode at high speeds. In a series of well-planned experiments and with simple logic, J. J. Thomson proved his point. His investigations constitute one of the most brilliant chapters in the history of science. We shall condense and present his argument, departing only slightly from the exact historical sequence, but without altering the essential points of his reasoning.

Fig. 11-8. Thomson identified the electron as a material particle and measured the ratio of its mass to charge. *(The Bettmann Archive.)*

The first point in Thomson's argument is that the beam consists of *negative charges in motion.* This is revealed by three experiments: their deflection in an electric field; their deflection in a magnetic field; and their ability to charge an electroscope.

The deflection in an electric field is shown by the following experiment. Two metal plates are inserted in the cathode-ray tube, with sealed connections through the glass, one above the beam and the other below it (Fig. 11-9). On connecting the upper plate to the positive pole and the lower to the negative pole of an auxiliary battery, the beam is bent upward. This is exactly what may be expected if the beam consists of negative charges. The positive upper plate attracts the charges and the negative lower plate repels them, causing an upward deflection. Reversing the charges on the plates deflects the beam downward.

The deflection in a magnetic field is even easier to carry out. On placing the S pole of a magnet *behind* the tube and the N pole of a similar magnet in *front* of it, the beam is deflected *downward.* The deflection is at right angles to the field. It is the same as would be experienced by a rather limber wire connected between the cathode and anode (see Chap. 4). In other words, the beam is a *current,* but without a conductor. The negative charges move freely from the cathode to the anode.

The electrical nature of the beam was even more directly proved by J. J. Thomson by the following experiment. He attached a glass tube with a small hole at A'. Inside this hole he sealed into the glass a wire

Ratio of Mass to Charge of Cathode Rays

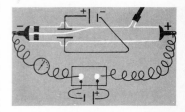

Fig. 11-9. Bending of the cathode rays by an electric field. The upward bending demonstrates that they have a negative charge.

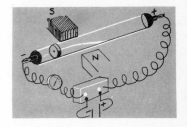

Fig. 11-10. Bending of the cathode rays by a magnetic field. Evidence that the beam consists of negative charges in motion.

which he connected to an electroscope. On bending the beam with a magnet, so that it fell into the hole at A′ and hit the wire, he observed a large charge on the electroscope. The charge proved to be negative— that is, the same kind as found on an electrified amber rod. When the charge missed the hole, hardly any charge appeared on the electroscope. Thus, from this and the other two experiments Thomson concluded that the beam consists of negative charges in motion.

The next point in Thomson's argument was that these charges consist of *material particles* carrying the charge. In other words, the charges have matter associated with them. At the time this idea was revolutionary. Hitherto, the electrolysis experiments (and even Millikan's oil-drop experiments) showed that electricity comes in "packages" of charge, but gave no hint or evidence that the charges are *material* packages.

The evidence for the materiality of the charges came from several experiments. First, the fact that the beam travels in straight lines suggested that the charges have matter; for by Newton's first law of motion, material bodies move in a straight line. Further evidence came from the following experiment. A delicate paddle wheel, placed in the path of the beam, rotates when the beam strikes the blades. This implies that the charges have momentum (mv), and momentum implies mass. A beam of light does not rotate the wheel. (The pressure of light, discovered later, is far too small to affect the wheel.) Additional evidence comes from the experiments that show that the beam has energy. A strong beam directed on a piece of silver quickly heats it to the melting point. Apparently the charges have kinetic energy, $\frac{1}{2}mv^2$, and this again implies that they have mass.

Thomson had the insight to recognize that these experiments with the proper measurements can yield numerical values for the mass, charge, and speed of these particles, and thus prove the reality of the electrons by the consistency in the measurements. The interested reader may consult reference 11.4 d for the fuller mathematical argument. However, we shall discuss here the principles involved, which will provide a good understanding of how the various properties of these particles are measured. We shall analyze these principles in some detail, because they constitute a very powerful method for the study of atomic and subatomic particles in general. The reasoning is as follows.

Assuming that the cathode rays are a swarm of submicroscopic particles, the problem is to determine their mass, **m**, charge, **e**, and velocity, **v**. These quantities will appear in bold face type in the following discussion as a reminder that they cannot be measured directly, but must be calculated from other direct measurements.

First the charge on the beam is measured. Taking a beam of a given duration, say 10 seconds, we bend it by means of a magnet into an electroscope in order to measure the charge collected (Fig. 11-11).

Suppose that in a given tube, of definite voltage, the measured charge is Q coulombs. If **n** is the number of particles in the 10-second beam, then the total charge is **n · e,** and it must be equal to Q

$$\mathbf{n \cdot e} = Q \qquad (1)$$

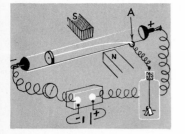

Fig. 11-11. Measurement of charge of a cathode - ray beam. The beam is bent into the receptacle, A, which contains the metallic terminal of an electroscope (or electrometer).

We do not know **n** or **e**, of course, but we can measure Q with the electroscope or more accurately with an electrometer.

The next step is to measure the energy of the beam. We lead a 10-second beam from the same experiment into a calorimeter. This device is merely another attachment at a point near A containing a small piece of silver of known weight, and a delicate electric thermometer. From the rise in temperature, the weight of the silver, and the specific heat of silver, we can measure the heat produced in the stopping of the rays. Let us say that W calories have been developed. This heat must be the total kinetic energy of the particles in the 10-second beam. Since the kinetic energy of each particle is $\frac{1}{2}$ **mu**^{2}, and there are **n** particles, the total kinetic energy is **n** $\cdot \frac{1}{2}$**mv**^{2}, and this is equal to the measured energy, W calories.

$$\mathbf{n} \cdot \tfrac{1}{2}\mathbf{mv}^2 = W \qquad (2)$$

Again, **n**, **m**, and **v** are not known, but we can measure W by the calorimeter.

Third, consider the bending of the beam in a magnetic field of known strength, say H. If the field is uniform, the beam is bent into an arc of a circle. Let us consider the factors involved.

The bending is produced by the force of the magnetic field on the current. The current is produced by the moving charges. For each charge the strength of the current is the charge multiplied by the velocity, **e**$\cdot$**v**. Since the force on the current depends on the strength of the field and on the strength of the current, we have, for the force on each particle of the beam,

$$f = H\mathbf{ev} \qquad (3)$$

and this force is bending the particle in a circle—that is, accelerating it.

Now, if the particle is a material particle—that is, if it has mass—it is resisting the acceleration in proportion to its mass. According to Newton's first law, the particle "wants" to go in a straight line. The reader will recall that in mechanics (p. 85) the force necessary to bend it is proportioned to the mass and to the acceleration ($f = m \cdot a$ by Newton's second law of motion), and that acceleration in a circle is $\frac{v^2}{r}$. Therefore, the force necessary to bend the particle in a circle of radius r is

$$f = \frac{\mathbf{mv}^2}{r} \qquad (4)$$

But from Newton's third law of motion, the magnetic force bending the particle is equal to the inertial force resisting the bending. Therefore, from equations 3 and 4,

$$\frac{\mathbf{mv}^2}{r} = H\mathbf{ev}$$

Cancelling the **v**'s and rewriting the equation

$$\frac{mv}{e} = Hr \qquad (5)$$

As before, **m**, **v**, or **e** are not known, but we can measure the strength of the field, *H*, and we can measure *r*, from the geometry of the apparatus.

This is the complete analysis of the factors and the principles involved. We have obtained three equations 1, 2, and 5, which contain the mass, charge, and velocity of the particles, **m**, **e**, and **v** respectively. These are expressed in terms of the quantities *Q*, *W*, *H*, and *r*, which can be measured directly. From here on it is mathematics—rather simple algebra, and the reader is advised to try to follow it.

By combining the equations mathematically we obtain an expression for the speed of the particles, as follows:

Dividing equation 2 $\qquad$ **n** · ½**mv²** = *W*

by equation 1 $\qquad\qquad$ **n** · **e** = *Q*

we get $\qquad\qquad\qquad \dfrac{mv^2}{e} = \dfrac{2W}{Q} \qquad (6)$

Now, dividing equation 6 $\quad \dfrac{mv}{e} = Hr$
by equation 5

we get $\qquad\qquad\qquad \mathbf{v} = \dfrac{2W}{QHr} \qquad (7)$

Equation 7 expresses the velocity of the particles in terms of *W*, *Q*, *H*, and *r*. As pointed out above, we can measure all these quantities by ordinary methods, and calculate the speed of the particles.

When Thomson carried out the measurements and the calculations, he found the speeds to range from about 3×10^9 to about 6×10^9 centimeters per second, or of the order of 30,000 to 50,000 miles per second.

These extraordinary speeds are a good fraction of the speed of light, which is 3×10^{10} centimeters per second (186,000 miles per second). Hitherto the speeds of molecules were considered high. But the fastest of them, the hydrogen molecule, moves with a speed of only about a mile per second at room temperature. These particles move with speeds tens of thousands times higher. Thomson found further that the higher the voltage, the greater the speed. With 100,000 volts a speed three quarters that of light is attained. Incidentally these results confirm, in an extraordinary way, that the cathode beam is not like x-rays or light. If the beam were an electromagnetic radiation, the speed should be exactly the speed of light.

m/e Ratio $\qquad$ The next goal is to seek an expression for the mass and the change. The reader with some training in mathematics will quickly see that it is not possible to obtain from equations 1, 2, and 5 an expression either for the mass or the charge separately. However, it is possible—in fact, rather easy—to obtain an expression for the *ratio* of the mass to the charge (or the inverse). We proceed as follows:

Taking equation 5, $\qquad\qquad \dfrac{\mathbf{mv}}{\mathbf{e}} = Hr$

and dividing by equation 7 $\qquad \mathbf{v} = \dfrac{2W}{QHr}$

we get $\qquad\qquad\qquad \dfrac{\mathbf{m}}{\mathbf{e}} = \dfrac{QH^2r^2}{2W}$ $\qquad$ (8)

The ratio, $\mathbf{m/e}$, the ratio of mass to charge, is the unknown quantity. All the quantities on the right-hand side of the equation can be measured directly. Expressing all the quantities in the appropriate units, we obtain the ratio of mass to charge, $\mathbf{m/e}$, in grams per faraday.

On carrying out the calculations from his measurements, Thomson found the ratio $\mathbf{m/e}$ to be equal to about 0.0005 grams per faraday. This means that if he continued a given experiment until 96,500 coulombs collected on the electrometer, the total mass entering the electrometer would be about 0.0005 grams, or about 1/2000 gram. Rather significantly, he found the same number in all the experiments with cathode rays.

The most astonishing part of this result is the smallness of this ratio. This can be brought out most clearly by comparing it with the values obtained in electrolysis. In the case of hydrogen it is 1 gram per faraday. With all the other elements larger numbers are obtained, namely, 1 gram-atomic weight divided by the charge on the ion, per faraday. For example, for silver it is 108 grams per faraday; this means that the silver atom is 108 times as heavy as the hydrogen atom, but carries the same charge. In the case of oxygen, 8 grams per faraday are obtained, meaning that the oxygen atom weighs sixteen times as much as the hydrogen atom, but carries twice the charge; hence, the ratio of mass to charge is 16/2 or 8 grams per faraday.

The smallness of the $\mathbf{m/e}$ ratio in the cathode rays implies either that the particles in the beam are thousands of times lighter than atoms, or that the charges are thousands of times greater than those found on atoms (or some combination of the two). In all the electrolysis experiments the charges are of the same order of magnitude as found on the hydrogen atom—possibly twice or three or a few times that, but certainly not thousands of times that. If the charges on the cathode-ray beam are equal to the smallest charge found on ions (that is, the same amount as on the hydrogen or the chloride ion), then the mass of the particles in the cathode ray must be 2000 times smaller than the mass of the hydrogen atom and 70,000 times smaller than that of the chloride ion. In Thomson's words, "There is no escape from the conclusion that we are dealing here with particles far, far lighter than atoms." These are the experiments which led to the "discovery" of the electron. *The electron is the particle* in the cathode-ray beam, having a charge equal to that on the hydrogen ion.

These experiments have far-reaching implications about the structure of the atoms. The same electrons are found in all the cathode-ray experiments. Whether the beam is strong or weak, the voltage high or low, the tubes of different kinds of glass, the electrodes of different materials, or the gases in the tube are different, ratio **m/e** is the same. Whether the electrons come from the atoms of the gas in the tube, or the glass, or the electrodes, they are the same electrons. Apparently the same electrons are constituents of all the atoms.

The Discovery of Positive Rays   The following simple argument demonstrates that the atoms also contain positive electricity. Since the uncombined elements under ordinary conditions are neutral, their atoms, as a whole, must be neutral. Since the atoms contain negative electrons, they must also contain equal amounts of positive electricity in order to be neutral.

More direct evidence came from the discovery of positive rays by Eugen Goldstein in 1886 in a modified version of the cathode-ray tube. By extending the cathode-ray tube in the opposite direction from the cathode, Goldstein constructed a "dumbbell"-shaped tube (Fig. 11-12). For a cathode he used a metal plug having several holes, or "canals," running through it. On operating the tube in the usual way, he observed a faint beam in the *left* section of the tube. Unlike the cathode beam, this beam is visible, without fluorescent materials. Suspecting that the beam is charged, Wilhem Wien, in 1897, tried the effect of a magnet. As expected, the beam was deflected, but the deflection was opposite to that observed for the cathode-ray beam. Apparently, this beam consists of *positively* charged particles, moving in the opposite direction from the cathode—that is, toward the left.

On further study, other differences between the positive beam and the cathode beam have been found. The same magnet produces a much smaller deflection on the positive rays than on the cathode rays. This means that the particles in the positive ray either are much heavier, or move more slowly, or have smaller charges. All three factors may be involved, but it is possible to untangle them. By using a stronger magnet

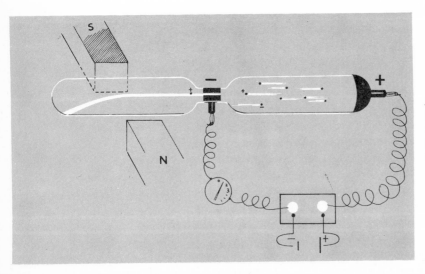

Fig. 11-12. Positive rays. Originating in the right compartment they travel through the perforations of the cathode emerging into the left compartment.

and carrying out the same measurements as for cathode rays, the velocity, **v**, and the **m/e** ratio for these rays can be calculated. Indeed, the velocities are smaller, but not small enough to explain the very weak deflection. The important part of the story must lie in the **m/e** ratio—that is, in the amount of mass associated with the charge.

The calculations from these measurements show that the **m/e** ratio for positive rays is thousands of times larger than for the electrons. Significantly, the ratios are comparable to those found in electrolysis of chemical compounds. If the *charges* on the positive rays are comparable to those found in cathode rays or in electrolysis, then the *masses* must be very large and indeed comparable to the masses of the atoms. This suggests that the particles in the beam are atoms or groups of atoms carrying one or a few units of positive charge.

This is confirmed by still another difference between the positive rays and the cathode rays. Whereas the **m/e** ratio is the same for all the cathode rays, the **m/e** ratio of the positive rays is different for the different gases. This follows from the fact that the rays of different gases are bent in magnetic fields by different amounts, under conditions that otherwise are the same. Moreover, for the same gas in the same experiment the beam splits into two or more beams in the same magnetic field. Thus different **m/e** ratios are obtained for the same gas, and this implies that some of the particles in the rays have either different masses or different charges (or both). All this evidence points to the conclusion that the positive-ray beams consist of atoms or molecules of the gas carrying one or more positive charges.

More extensive experiments and more accurate measurements reveal the nature of the particles in the beam—that is, their masses and their charges. If the initial gas in the tube is hydrogen, the beam, when bent in a magnetic field, gives an **m/e** ratio equal to 1 gram per faraday. This ratio is identical to that found in the electrolysis of acids. We cannot escape the conclusion that hydrogen ions are present in the beam.

Where and how were the hydrogen ions formed? Apparently some of the hydrogen atoms in the *right-hand side* of the tube, under the tension of the high voltage, are stripped of an electron and become positive hydrogen ions. On acquiring a positive charge, they are strongly repelled by the positive pole and are attracted by the cathode; hence they rush at high speed toward the latter. Many of them, perhaps most of them, hit the cathode and are neutralized, and then wander in the tube until they again lose an electron. But some of them miss the cathode as they rush toward it at high speeds, and because of their high momentum go through the "canals" and emerge on the other side. It is these positive ions that constitute the positive-ray beam (see Ex. 16).

A similar situation exists starting with helium in the tube. This time, however, the beam is separated by the magnetic field into two beams. Both beams are more difficult to bend than the hydrogen beam. The more difficult to bend is the brighter beam, and has the **m/e** ratio of 4 grams per faraday. Quite obviously, this beam consists of helium atoms carrying a single positive charge. Since, from chemical evidence, the helium atom weighs 4 times as much as the hydrogen atom, it must

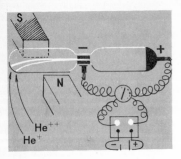

Fig. 11-13. Positive rays from helium. In the magnetic field, the beam bends and separates into two beams, identified as He⁺ and He⁺⁺.

carry the same charge as the hydrogen ion to give an **m/e** ratio 4 times greater than hydrogen. The fainter beam is more easily bent and gives a ratio of 2 times that of hydrogen. It must consist of helium atoms carrying a *double* positive charge, He^{++}.

This is explained as follows: since the mass is 4 times that of hydrogen and the charge is +2, the **m/e** ratio is ½ or 2 times that of hydrogen.

Similar phenomena are observed with the other gaseous elements, except that, in general, several beams are obtained. For example, with oxygen in the tube, one of the beams gives a ratio of 16 grams per faraday. This beam obviously consists of oxygen atoms carrying a single *positive* charge. A fainter beam gives 8 grams per faraday and a still fainter one gives 16/3 grams per faraday. These must be oxygen atoms carrying double and triple *positive* charges, respectively. Such oxygen ions are not known in electrolysis. All the oxygen ions in electrolysis carry *negative* charges (Ex. 17).

Thus, by measuring the deflection of the positive rays in a magnetic field and calculating the **m/e** ratio, we can identify the particles in the beam. They are all atoms (or groups of atoms) carrying one or more *positive* charges. All the elements, whether hydrogen, metals, or non-metals, give positive rays. This implies that all the atoms contain positive electricity, and these are in multiples of the charge on the hydrogen ion.

The Discovery of X-rays

The third great discovery in the cathode-ray tube was the discovery of x-rays by Roentgen in 1897. X-rays have been discussed in Chapter 5, and the reader is referred to that section. However, we shall repeat here the salient points that have a bearing on the structure of matter.

X-rays are produced when a cathode beam is directed against a thick metal target. They radiate from the target in all directions and are highly penetrating. They are of the same nature as light, as proved by the fact that they are diffracted by crystals of salt and other minerals. From measurements of their wavelengths x-rays are found to be extremely short ultraviolet rays.

The immediate contribution of the x-ray experiments to the structure of matter was at first indirect. They provided further experimental support to Maxwell's electromagnetic theory of light. According to this theory (Chap. 5), radiation is emitted by accelerating electric charges. In the cathode-ray tube the electrons are fast-moving charges that are suddenly stopped. The energy of the electrons is radiated as x-rays. Further proof on this point is obtained from the fact that the faster the electrons that are stopped, the shorter the wavelength of the x-rays produced. This means greater frequency of the x-rays, greater energy, and greater penetrating power. These conclusions reinforced the idea that light is emitted by accelerating electric charges in atoms, oscillating in powerful electric fields. However, the information from x-ray experiments became more direct after Rutherford formulated the basic ideas of the structure of the atom, as we shall discuss in detail in the next section.

3. RUTHERFORD'S THEORY OF THE NUCLEAR ATOM

At the turn of the century the accumulated evidence from studies in chemistry, electricity, and light pointed unmistakably to the conclusion that atoms have complex structures and that electricity is an integral part of that structure. The discovery of the electrons and the measurement of their charge and mass made it clear that these light and negatively charged particles are constituents of the atom. The discovery of the positive rays, and particularly the fact that all the elements can form positive ions (including the nonmetals, which ordinarily form only negative ions), provided the most direct evidence that all the atoms contain positive electricity as well.

Many speculations were advanced at that time in an effort to construct a more definitive theory of the structure of the atom. Perhaps the most interesting of these is the so-called "jelly" theory of Thomson. According to this theory, the atom is a jellylike smear of matter, distributed more or less uniformly throughout the whole volume of the atom. Embedded in this jelly are a number of positive charges of electricity, tightly bound to matter in some unspecified manner. Each charge is equal to the charge on the hydrogen ion. The atom also contains negative electrons—as many as there are positive charges. If an atom loses one or more electrons, it becomes a positive ion; if it gains one or more extra electron, it becomes a negative ion.

The theory summarized fairly well the phenomena known at that time and explained them in a general sort of way. However, the theory lacked definiteness. The idea of the presence of the electrons in the atoms as negatively charged particles was definite enough. However, the theory was vague regarding the way the positive charge was present in the atom. It was not clear how many positive charges are imbedded in the "jelly" of a given atom nor how much matter is associated with a unit positive charge. It seemed reasonable that the more matter in the atom, the greater the number of positive charges. The smallest particle of matter known at that time to carry a positive charge was the hydrogen ion. The disproportionate amount of matter associated with positive electricity, compared with the amount of matter associated with the electron, was in itself a puzzle. Nevertheless it was generally assumed that the atoms contained positive hydrogen ions. The hydrogen ion was named "proton," meaning "primary" in a revival of the ancient idea of "primary matter," from which the other atoms are built (Ex. 1). The atom contained enough protons to account for the positive charge and for nearly all the mass, and an equal number of electrons to render the atom neutral without appreciably adding to its mass.

Considerable detail of the structure of the atom was obtained from the newly discovered phenomena of radioactivity and their subsequent

Radioactivity

interpretation. In 1896, Becquerel discovered that uranium minerals emit spontaneously a very penetrating radiation. The discovery was quite accidental. He had been studying the phosphorescent properties of uranium minerals and had put away in a drawer a sealed package of unexposed photographic film. On returning to his experiments some time later, he developed one of the plates as a routine check on the quality of the film. To his surprise the plate showed a picture of a key, or rather a shadowgram very similar to that produced by the then recently discovered x-rays. On investigating what might be the cause of the picture, he recalled that a key had been placed on top of the package and over it some of the uranium minerals. Apparently, the uranium minerals emit some kind of rays that penetrate through the thick wrapping of the film, but are stopped or weakened by the metal key.

Pursuing this lead, Becquerel found that all uranium minerals, whether phosphorescent or not, emit this mysterious radiation. He assigned to Marie Sklovoda, one of his research students, the problem of investigating this new phenomenon further. In collaboration with Pièrre Curie, to whom she was later married, she found that other substances present in uranium minerals are also radioactive. In 1898, the Curies isolated two new elements, polonium and radium, both of which are more radioactive than uranium. It is interesting that both of these elements fitted very well into the blank spaces of the periodic system, and in fact polonium was one of the elements whose existence had been predicted by Mendeleev. Other investigators found that several other elements of high atomic weight, notably thorium, are also radioactive.

Considerable insight into the phenomenon was gained by the study of the emitted rays themselves. Three distinct types of rays were soon recognized, and were christened alpha (α), beta (β), and gamma (γ) rays, in the order of their discovery. All three rays effect the photographic plate, but they differ markedly in penetrating power. The alpha rays are easily stopped by a piece of paper or by a few centimeters of air. The beta rays go through the thickness of a book to darken a photographic plate on the other side. The penetrating power of the gamma rays is fantastic. They go through hundreds of feet of air, or several inches of solid lead, to darken a photographic plate beyond.

Another important property of the rays is their ability to discharge an electroscope. As the rays go through the air, they produce charged ions, apparently by tearing through the molecules of the air and stripping them of electrons. The molecule that has lost an electron becomes a positive ion, and the molecule to which the electron attaches itself becomes a negative ion. The electroscope becomes discharged by attracting and neutralizing the ions that happen to have the opposite charge. The rays differ in their ability to ionize the air. The alpha rays produce heavy ionization and quickly discharge the electroscope; the beta rays produce much less ionization, and the gamma rays a very weak one, discharging the electroscope very slowly.

The ability of the rays to ionize the air led C. T. R. Wilson of the Cavendish Laboratory in England to develop a remarkable instrument for the study of these rays. This instrument is now called the Wilson cloud chamber (Fig. 11-14). In its simplest version, it is essentially a glass vessel a few inches in diameter, containing some water over mercury. Under these conditions the air space above the water is saturated with water vapor at this temperature. If the mercury is allowed to drop suddenly, the air cools by the expansion and becomes supersaturated with water vapor. The extra water will condense, but not immediately, unless the air contains discontinuities, such as dust particles, droplets already formed, or ions. If at the instant of the expansion some rays are sent through the chamber, water droplets will condense around each ion, along the path of the ray. The track is visible as a white streak and can be easily photographed. The alpha rays produce short heavy tracks, the beta rays thin long tracks, and the gamma rays very faint tracks from one end of the chamber to the other.

In the cloud chamber the rays can easily be identified by their tracks. More remarkable is the fact that by means of this instrument individual particles in the rays can be observed. Each track is the path of a single particle in the ray.

Each type of ray has other individual characteristics. When the alpha rays impinge on a surface coated with zinc sulfide paint, they produce tiny sparks, which are visible as individual sparks under a good magnifying glass. Each spark is presumably produced by a single particle in the ray hitting the screen. In many early experiments a low-power microscope, called the spinthariscope, was used to count individual particles. On striking a zinc sulfide screen the beta rays produce a glow remarkably similar to that produced by cathode rays, and the gamma rays produce a fluorescence very similar to that produced by x-rays.

The nature of the rays was established by studying their behavior in strong magnetic fields. A beam of rays from a radioactive source can easily be produced by taking a block of lead several inches thick, drilling a hole in it, and placing some radioactive materials in it. The rays are absorbed by the lead, except those coming out in the direction of the hole. If a strong magnetic field is placed above the hole at right angles to the beam, the beam is resolved into the three types of rays. The alpha rays are bent moderately in one direction, the beta rays are bent strongly in the opposite direction, and the gamma rays continue undeflected. From the direction of the bending we conclude that the alpha rays are positively charged, the beta rays are negatively charged, and the gamma rays are uncharged.

The charged rays were definitely identified by measuring the amount of bending in strong magnetic fields, using exactly the same methods which were used to identify the rays in evacuated tubes. The alpha rays give an m/e ratio of 2.00 grams per faraday, and hence are identical with the weaker band of positive rays found in highly evacuated tubes containing helium. Therefore, the alpha rays are helium atoms carrying a double positive charge, He^{++}. The only difference is that their speeds are very high, being of the order of one twentieth that of the speed of light (Ex. 21). The beta rays give an m/e ratio of 0.0005 grams per faraday, and are, therefore, high-speed electrons, ϵ. Again their speeds are very high, being of the order of 0.95 of the

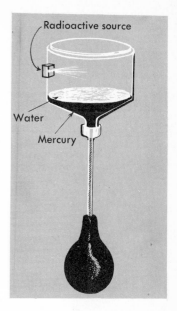

Fig. 11-14. Wilson Cloud Chamber. Water droplets condense marking the path of the ray as a fog track.

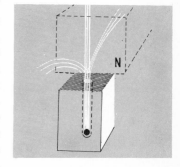

Fig. 11-15. Rays from radioactivity. A magnetic field separates them into α, β, and γ rays.

speed of light or higher. The gamma rays are identified as very penetrating x-rays—that is, x-rays of very short wavelength. It is interesting
that the radioactive materials behave like evacuated tubes at very high
voltages. They produce the same three types of rays as the evacuated
tubes, except that they produce them spontaneously. Apparently the
atoms are the seats of extremely strong electric fields, much higher than
the fields used in evacuated tubes at that time.

To Rutherford, the more significant aspect of the phenomenon was
the implication of what happens to the atoms that emit these rays. The
emission of material particles from the atom, and especially the emission
of the heavy alpha particles, implies that the atom loses an appreciable
part of its mass in the process. Consequently the atom must become
lighter, and perhaps become an atom of a different and lighter element.

This conclusion was confirmed by investigating another group of
phenomena associated with radioactivity. It was known by this time
that all uranium minerals contain polonium, radium, lead, and perhaps
other elements, in addition to the helium which they emit. All the
atoms of these elements are lighter than the uranium atoms, the latter
being the heaviest known at that time. Consequently, Rutherford conceived the idea that in the emission of these rays, the uranium atoms
disintegrate into lighter atoms, which in turn disintegrate into still lighter
atoms. The end product appeared to be lead, which is not radioactive
and hence does not disintegrate. The net result of these successive and
complex changes is the transformation of uranium into lead and helium.

$$U \rightarrow Pb + 8He$$

This was a revolutionary idea. In all the hitherto observed phenomena of physical and chemical changes, the elements retained their
identity. Apparently, in radioactivity, however, the changes are of a
more drastic character, the elements being transmuted into other elements. This implies the breakdown of the atoms themselves. The old
idea of the alchemists of transmuting base elements into gold, which
was completely abandoned during the nineteenth century, was again
revived. Not only can the elements be transmuted into other elements;
it is happening spontaneously.

By isolating the elements found in uranium minerals and investigating the types of rays each atom emits, Rutherford was able to
reconstruct the course of disintegration. Pure uranium with an atomic
weight of 238 emits alpha particles only. Since each alpha particle is
a helium ion, He^{++}, the remaining atom must weigh four atomic units
less and contain two positive charges less. In other words, the resulting
atom must have an atomic weight of 234, and contain two less positive
charges. Radium with an atomic weight of 226 emits an alpha particle
to become the inert gas radon, with an atomic weight of 222. Polonium
with an atomic weight of 210 likewise emits an alpha particle to become
lead, with an atomic weight of 206. There must be other intermediate
elements that give off alpha particles. If radium comes from uranium,
there must be two more intermediate elements that emit alpha particles.

In addition, there must be other elements that give off beta particles and gamma rays.

The emission of beta particles is in itself interesting. Since these electrons are emitted with very high speeds, they apparently do not come from the outskirts of the atoms as do the electrons that result in ordinary ionization. They must come from the deep interior where there are strong electric forces. Moreover, the atoms emitting them do not lose any appreciable part of their mass (only about 1/500,000), but they do lose a negative charge from the deep interior. Do they then become atoms of different elements? Rutherford suspected so, and by chemical separations he was able to isolate several other elements emitting beta rays. By the same reasoning atoms emitting gamma rays lose neither mass nor charge, but they lose energy which goes off as "super x-ray" radiation.

By isolating the various elements emitting the radiations and correlating the results of many experiments, Rutherford reconstructed the following course of disintegration.

TABLE 11:1

Uranium I $\xrightarrow{\alpha}$	Uranium $X_1 \xrightarrow{\beta}$	Uranium $X_2 \xrightarrow{\beta}$	Uranium II $\xrightarrow{\alpha}$	Ionium $\xrightarrow{\alpha}$
238	234	234	234	230
4.4×10^9 years	24.5 days	1.14 minutes	3×10^5 years	8×10^4 years
Radium $\xrightarrow{\alpha}$	Radon $\xrightarrow{\alpha}$	Radium A $\xrightarrow{\alpha}$	Radium B $\xrightarrow{\beta}$	Radium C $\xrightarrow{\beta}$
226	222	218	214	214
1,590 years	3.82 days	3.05 minutes	26.8 minutes	19.7 minutes
Radium C' $\xrightarrow{\alpha}$	Radium D $\xrightarrow{\beta}$	Radium E $\xrightarrow{\beta}$	Polonium $\xrightarrow{\alpha}$	Radium Lead
214	210	210	210	206
10^{-6} seconds	22 years	4.9 days	140 days	not radio-active

By similar experiments, Rutherford reconstructed a similar course of disintegration for two other series. Thorium, having the atomic weight of 232, gives a similar series of products, ultimately ending with lead of atomic weight 208. Actinium, atomic weight 231, gives a third series, ending with lead of atomic weight 207. An interesting sidelight is that these three kinds of lead are chemically indistinguishable from each other and from ordinary rock lead. We shall return to this point presently (p. 345 and Ex. 22).

In the reconstruction of the course of disintegration, the study of the *rate* of decay of the atoms was a great help. It was soon established that each element gives off these rays at a definite rate, characteristic of the element. For a given quantity of an element, a definite number of particles are emitted per second, meaning that a definite fraction of the atoms decay per second. The rate of decay is independent of any external condition. It does not matter whether the element is in the free state or in any of the compounds; the rate of emission of decay particles depends only upon the number of atoms of that element in the sample. Moreover, the rate is the same whether the element is subjected to high or low pressures, high or low temperatures, strong or weak magnetic or electric fields, to violent chemical reactions, or to any other treatment, however drastic. Apparently the rate of decay is a property of the atoms of a given element and the decay must be due to instability deep within the atom. At any given instant, a certain fraction of the atoms present in the sample become unstable enough to decay, just as in any given day a certain fraction of a population dies. The decay rate, like the death rate, may be studied statistically.

A meaningful way of expressing the rate of decay is to state the time in which half of the atoms decay. This is called the *half life*. Thus, the half life of radium is 1590 years. This means that starting with 1 gram of radium, there will be only half a gram left after 1590 years. After another 1590 years there will be one half of one half or one quarter of 1 gram remaining. Another 1590 years will leave one eighth, and so on (Exs. 23 and 24). The rates of decay of the various elements vary enormously. Thus uranium has a half life of 4.6 billion years and radium C' about one millionth of a second. The half lives of the uranium series are given in Table 11:1.

Let us now summarize some of the important conclusions to which the phenomena of radioactivity point. The atoms of the radioactive elements are unstable, and decompose giving off alpha particles, beta particles, and gamma rays, becoming lighter atoms in the process. They must contain these particles or at least the materials from which these particles are formed. Moreover, the structures of the atoms must be very complex. The emitted particles must be present in very powerful electric fields. To Rutherford, the simple picture of a smear of "jelly," fairly uniformly distributed, was too simple to account for these phenomena. There must be some sort of "bunching" of the matter and of the electric charge in the atom.

Rutherford's Scattering Experiments

The concept of the atom as a minute solar system was suggested directly from a series of historic experiments on the penetrability of matter by alpha and beta particles. We have already mentioned, but dismissed without comment, that the rays from radioactivity go through considerable thicknesses of solid matter. The beta rays go through $\frac{1}{8}$ inch of solid aluminum without appreciable absorption. The alpha rays are completely stopped by a metal plate about 0.005 inch thick, but they do go through thinner foils of gold and silver.

This phenomenon becomes significant on closer examination. There is every reason to believe that in solids the atoms are virtually in contact with one another. Just as we conclude that there are large spaces between molecules of gases from the fact that gases are so highly compressible, so we conclude that there is very little "free" space between the atoms of solid metals from the fact that the metals are practically incompressible. In fact, on the assumption that the atoms in metals "touch" one another, it is possible to estimate their size, knowing

Avogadro's number and the density of the metals (Ex. 25). The sizes of the atoms thus obtained are in good agreement with those obtained by other methods. Realizing that even the thinnest foils contain hundreds of thousands of layers of atoms, we cannot escape the conclusion that the alpha and beta particles go right through the interiors of the atoms.

The German physicist Phillip Lenard was the first to investigate the penetration and absorption of thin metallic foils by beta rays. Quite unexpectedly he found that most of the rays go through the foils without suffering any appreciable slowing down or deflection. He did notice, however, that a small fraction of the rays *are* deflected, and some of them are deflected very sharply. On reading the reports of these experiments Rutherford had the insight to sense that these experiments provide a method for probing into the interior of the atom.

Rutherford repeated Lenard's experiments using alpha particles from polonium. He chose alpha particles for several reasons. In the first place, alpha particles are whole ions, having a mass of 7500 times that of the beta rays, and since they move at about 10,000 miles per second, they have enormous kinetic energies. Moreover, alpha particles are relatively easy to observe. Each alpha particle produces a tiny spark on hitting a zinc sulfide screen and, therefore, can be observed individually by a low-power microscope, called the spinthariscope. Furthermore alpha particles go through very thin foils, but are stopped by thicker foils. Therefore it should be relatively easy to count the number of alpha particles that penetrate the foil, the number that are absorbed, the number that are slowed down by various amounts, and the number that are deflected by various angles. This information should give a good idea of the structure of the atom.

In a typical experiment, Rutherford directed at a gold leaf about 0.0005 inches thick a beam of alpha particles from polonium (Fig. 11-16). He measured the kinetic energy of the particles and counted the number of particles in the beam. Then he proceeded to count the number of particles at various distances and angles, after they had hit the foil. To his surprise, even the heavy alpha particles behaved like Lenard's beta rays. The vast majority of the alpha particles went through undeflected and unretarded as though the leaf were not there. The leaf behaved like a ghost. Since the alpha particles go through several hundred thousand atoms, the atom appeared pretty empty. Where was the matter of the leaf? Where was the matter of the atom?

The key to this puzzle lay hidden in the small number of particles that *were* deflected. Considering only the particles that were deflected, he found a good fraction of them deflected by *very large* angles. In fact some particles were deflected by more than 90° and appeared on the same side of the foil as the incident beam. A few were even deflected by nearly 180°. Apparently these particles hit something hard and massive; for it takes a considerable mass to deflect such a heavy projectile moving at these high speeds. Here then was the elusive matter of the leaf. Apparently the mass of the leaf—and therefore the mass of *each atom* in the leaf—is concentrated in certain *centers* or *nuclei,* leaving the rest of the space quite empty.

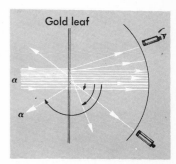

Fig. 11-16. Scattering of alpha rays on going through a thin gold leaf. The vast majority of the rays go through the leaf without deflection. A few suffer large deflections.

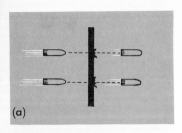

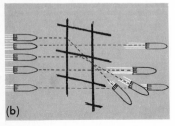

Fig. 11-17. Two types of iron "fence." (a) All bullets are slowed down by moderate amounts; none is deflected. (b) Bullets deflect only on hitting the wire.

The significance of these results may be appreciated by a simple analogy. If a contractor has 500 pounds of iron for the purpose of enclosing an open side of a room, he can make the wall in two distinct ways. He can hammer the iron into a thin sheet and cover the space with it, or he can cast the iron into a stout wire and make a fence to cover the same area. If the contractor covers the wall with wallpaper on both sides before anyone else sees it, would it be possible to find out which way the wall was made?

A very simple method would be to shoot some bullets straight at the wall and observe them on the other side. If the wall is a sheet of iron, all the bullets will be slowed down by the same moderate amount and none will be deflected. If, on the other hand, the wall is a wire fence, most of the bullets will go through the spaces between the wires, practically unaffected. In the latter case, however, a small percentage of the bullets will hit the wire and be deflected; and most of those deflected will be deflected sharply. Rutherford had the same situation with the alpha particles going through the gold leaf.

The analogy can be carried one step further. By counting the percentage of the bullets that are deflected it is possible to estimate the ratio of the area covered by the wire to the total area. If, for example, 6 percent of the bullets are deflected, 6 percent of the area is iron wire and the rest of it is empty space between the wires. Continuing the analogy, if the fence has two layers, one in front of the other with little or no overlapping of the wires, in each of the fence layers the area of the wire is about 3 percent of the total area of the fence.

Reasoning in this manner Rutherford proceeded to estimate the size of the nucleus relative to the size of the atom. Knowing the thickness of the gold leaf, he could calculate rather accurately the number of layers of atoms (the number of fences in the analogy). Then, by actual counting he could estimate the percentage of alpha rays that were deflected, and thus calculate the ratio of the cross-sectional area of the nuclei relative to the total area of the layer, per single layer. This ratio must also be the ratio of the cross-sectional area of a single nucleus to that of the whole atom. On carrying out the counts and the calculations, Rutherford obtained a ratio of one to about 100 million. This makes the diameter of the atom about 1/10,000 that of the atom, and the volume of the nucleus *one millionth of a millionth* of the volume of the atom. Yet this small nucleus contains nearly all the mass of the atom (Ex. 26).

Rutherford then went on to investigate whether the nucleus was merely a minute ball of mass or whether it had an electric charge. The key to this problem lay in a finer analysis of the nature of the collisions causing the deflections. What was the nature of the collisions? Was the collision like a bullet hitting the wire (or a billiard ball hitting another billiard ball), or was the deflection due to electric forces? He knew, of course, that the alpha particle had a double positive charge. If the nucleus had no charge, the deflection would be like a billiard-ball collision. Most of the alpha particles would pass, on the average, in the vast spaces between the nuclei and be entirely undeflected. Only a direct hit on the nucleus would cause a deflection. Moreover, a small

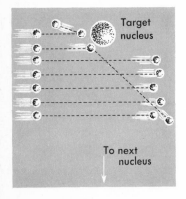

Fig. 11-18. Billiard-ball type of collision. Only a grazing collision would result in a small deflection. The next nucleus is 10,000 diameters—about 300 feet on the scale of the diagram.

deflection could result only from a glancing collision. If the alpha particle came even a little closer to the nucleus than a bare glance, it would be deflected sharply. Since the alpha particles in the beam are quite far apart, the chances are extremely unlikely that many of them would come at the exact distance from the nucleus to cause a glancing collision. In other words, a billiard-ball type of collision would produce very few small deflections. Most of the deflections would be large.

If, on the other hand, the nucleus had a charge, say positive, then the deflecting forces would be effective at relatively larger distances from the center of the nucleus. Of course these forces would become weaker rapidly, decreasing as the square of the distance, but they would still be strong enough at several diameters from the nucleus to produce noticeable deflections. This would not alter the ratio of those deflected to those undeflected to any extent, since the distances between the nuclei are some 10,000 nuclear diameters. But it would alter radically the ratio of small to large deflections. A charged nucleus would result in many small deflections, fewer large deflections, and only occasionally a complete turning back of those alpha particles that happen to aim directly at a nucleus. If the nucleus happened to have a negative charge, exactly the same situation would exist, with one exception. The deflections would be due to attraction toward the nucleus, rather than repulsion away from the nucleus, but the percentage of deflections at various angles would be exactly the same.

Rutherford carried out the above argument, using rigorous mathematics, the laws of motion, and Coulomb's law of force between charged bodies. The problem is identical in form to the problem of comets coming toward the sun; for in both cases the force decreases as the square of the distance. From this analysis he calculated the number of deflections to be expected at the various angles. He then patiently counted the number of sparks at various angles and found them as predicted for a charged nucleus. He found a great number of small deflections and, more significantly, the predicted proportions for each angle. He therefore concluded that the nucleus had an electric charge (Refs. 11.3 and 11.7). However, this experiment did not settle the question whether the charge was positive or negative.

Rutherford concluded that the charge in the nucleus is positive from other considerations. First, the electrons that have a negative charge are associated with negligible mass, while all positive rays are associated with practically the whole mass of the atom. The smallest particle carrying a positive charge is the proton, and this is 2000 times as heavy as the electron. The alpha particle itself, which has positive charge, has a mass 7500 times that of the electron. The alpha particle may very well be the nucleus of the helium atom. In fact these very experiments provide further support on this point. The experiments indicate not only that the mass of the target atom is concentrated, but also that the mass of the projectile (that is, the alpha particle) itself is concentrated. Rutherford obtained such an excellent agreement with experiment by assuming the alpha particles to be extremely small in size relative to an atom. This argues that all the atoms are built on the same plan and that the charge on all the nuclei is positive.

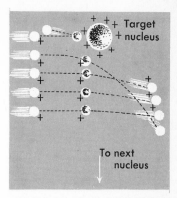

Fig. 11-19. "Collision" by electric forces. Many small deflections due to electric forces acting at a distance. The next nucleus is 10,000 diameters.

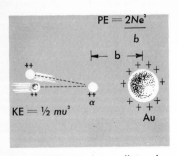

Fig. 11-20. Head-on collision between an alpha particle and a gold nucleus, Au. The distance b is considered to be the "radius" of the gold nucleus.

Further analysis of this experiment permitted Rutherford to obtain a rough estimate of the amount of charge on the target nucleus. If an alpha particle happens to be aimed directly at a nucleus, it will be slowed down by the repulsion, until it stops at some distance b, and then be accelerated back in the opposite direction (Fig. 11-20). At the distance b, all the kinetic energy of the alpha particle becomes potential energy of repulsion. The original kinetic energy is $\frac{1}{2}mv^2$, where m is the mass of the alpha particle and v is its velocity. The potential energy at b can be calculated as follows: If the nucleus has a charge of N positive units, its total charge is $+Ne$, and since the charge of the alpha particle is $+2e$, the potential energy is $\frac{Ne \cdot 2e}{b}$. Furthermore, since all the kinetic energy of the alpha particle has now become potential energy,

$$\frac{1}{2}\,mv^2 = \frac{Ne \cdot 2e}{b}$$

and solving for N,

$$N = \frac{mv^2 \cdot b}{4e^2}$$

All the quantities on the right-hand side of the equation are known accurately except b. This distance b is in itself interesting in that it represents the closest approach to the nucleus and may be considered as the "radius" of the nucleus (see Ex. 27). An estimate of b from the percentage of deflections (as done above in the bullet-fence analogy) results in a rough estimate of N. For gold Rutherford obtained about 100 for the value of N. This means that the charge on the nucleus of the gold atom is about 100 times that of the hydrogen atom or about 50 times that of the alpha particle. Repeating the experiments for other metals he found N to be about 50 for silver and about 30 for copper.

These numbers, although only approximate, are highly suggestive in that they are roughly half of the respective atomic weights. Thus gold, with the atomic weight 197, behaves as though it contains about 49 alpha particles. This would give it an atomic weight of 196 and a charge of +98. The situation is similar for silver, copper, and the other elements. The alpha particle itself has a weight of four times that of the hydrogen atom and a charge of only twice that of the hydrogen ion. Also significant is the fact that during radioactivity, alpha particles do come out from the atom. They can only come from the nucleus, since only the nucleus has so much mass; moreover, only the nucleus has a positive charge. All these considerations point to the conclusion that all the atoms are built on the same plan and Rutherford proceeded to uncover it.

The Rutherford Theory

By synthesizing the evidence from scattering experiments and from radioactivity, by 1911 Rutherford had worked out the general pattern of the atom. From these phenomena he had firmly established that the atom consists of two parts: a very small, extremely dense nucleus containing nearly all the mass and all the positive charge; and a tenuous envelope making up the rest of the volume, and consisting of negatively charged electrons of negligible mass. He then proceeded to investigate further each of these parts.

The scattering experiments indicated that the nucleus has a charge roughly equal to half of the atomic weight. As a first approximation, the nucleus appeared to consist of alpha particles; or at least to contain the materials from which the alpha particles themselves are made, and in about the same proportions. The radioactivity experiments provided supplementary evidence consistent with this picture. A dozen or more radioactive elements emit alpha particles. The alpha particles can only come from the nuclei, since only the nucleus contains the bulk of the mass and the positive charge. Moreover, since the alpha particles are emitted with high energies, only a nucleus with considerable mass and a positive charge can propel them with these high speeds. Further, the decaying atom, after losing four units of mass and two units of charge, must result in an atom that again has a mass to charge ratio of about 2 to 1.

However, the idea that the nuclei consist only of alpha particles could not be the entire story. The charge on the nucleus was at best estimated only roughly. Also, several radioactive elements emit negatively charged beta particles, and since these particles emerge with stupendous speeds, they, too, in all probability, come out of the nucleus. An emission of a beta particle would leave the nucleus with a charge *greater by one positive unit*. Therefore, not all nuclei could have charges multiple of the alpha particle. Moreover, the atomic weights of most elements are not multiples of four, and hence could not contain only alpha particles.

Other considerations indicated that the nuclei contain protons. So many atomic weights are very nearly whole numbers, that is, whole number of times that of hydrogen. The frequency of whole numbers in the atomic weights is far greater than would be expected by pure chance. More significantly, the smallest particle carrying a positive charge is the proton, which is a positively charged hydrogen ion. All these considerations inevitably suggested that the heavy positive particles in the nucleus are protons and that the proton is itself a nucleus—*the nucleus of the hydrogen atom.*

The structure of the alpha particle itself provided the key to the further development of the theory. The alpha particle weighs four times as much as the hydrogen atom, but has a charge of only twice that of the proton. If the helium nucleus contained four protons, the mass could be accounted for, but not the charge. All efforts to find an alpha particle with a charge of +3 or +4 or to obtain a positive-ray beam from helium with more than two charges had failed. Furthermore, the size of the alpha particle is so small compared to the whole helium atom as to preclude the possibility that it has any extranuclear electrons. The only other reasonable alternative was to assume that the alpha particle is itself a nucleus, and that in this nucleus there are two electrons in *close association* with two of the protons. Thus, two of the charges are neutralized in the nucleus, leaving only *two* net positive charges.

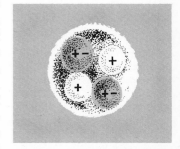

Fig. 11.21. The helium nucleus contains two protons (white with +) and two neutrons (dark with + and −).

From this reasoning Rutherford concluded that besides protons, there must exist in the nucleus, particles that are essentially neutral, each consisting of a close association of a proton and an electron. This particle was named the *neutron*. It should have a mass about equal to the mass of the hydrogen atom (or of the proton), but it should have no charge. Years later, in 1933, the neutrons were observed outside the nucleus as the result of the breaking up of nuclei of beryllium. Outside the nucleus the neutron is unstable and decays into a proton and an electron, with a half life of about 12 minutes. Normally, the neutron is stable inside the nucleus, but presumably it is unstable within the nuclei of those radioactive atoms that emit beta rays. Thus Rutherford was able to explain at the same time the origin of the beta particle. It results from the decay of a neutron into a proton (which remains in the nucleus) and an electron (which is ejected) (Exs. 29 and 35). The neutrons may be symbolized as ($\pm$) or (pe), signifying that it contains both a positive and a negative charge. Nevertheless, it should be thought of as a single neutral particle.

With this development, the Rutherford theory assumed more nearly its modern form. There are three fundamental particles as ultimate building blocks of the atoms. They are listed as follows:

Particle	Symbols	Charge	Mass	
		(electronic charge = 1)	(0 = 16.0000)	
			approx.	exactly
proton	p, p^+	+1	1	1.00813
neutron	n, n^0	0	1	1.00893
electron	e, e^-	−1	~0	0.00055

According to the theory, the nucleus contains protons and neutrons. These two particles taken together are collectively called *nucleons*. The total number of nucleons account for the weight of the nucleus, and of the atom to the nearest whole number. The charge of the nucleus is due to the protons, and is numerically equal to the number of "free" or "net" protons—that is, those not "bound" with electrons in the neutrons. Outside the nucleus are the electrons. In a neutral atom the number of extra nuclear electrons is numerically equal to the number of nuclear protons or, what is the same thing, to the charge on the nucleus expressed in electronic units.

It is a simple task to write the structure of any atom, knowing how many protons, neutrons, and electrons it contains. However, this raises the more fundamental problem. How "count" the number of each of these particles in a given atom? In the case of hydrogen the problem is simple. Since the atom weighs about the same as the proton, the nucleus can only consist of a single proton. Consequently, there is one electron surrounding the nucleus. In the case of helium, the nucleus must contain two protons to account for the charge of +2, and two neutrons to account for the total weight, which is 4 atomic units. Is this method applicable to other atoms? Is there a pattern, a regularity that governs the structure of the atoms in the periodic system? Are

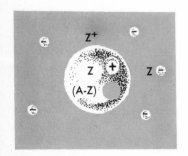

Fig. 11-22. Blue print of all atoms:
A = atomic weight = total number of nucleons
Z = atomic number = number of protons
A-Z = number of neutrons
Z is also equal to nuclear charge and to number of planetary electrons.

there any simple and reliable methods for the determination of the numbers of protons, neutrons, and electrons in a given nucleus?

As already implied, the *total number of nucleons* (protons plus neutrons) in an atom can be obtained directly from the *atomic weight* of the element. The atomic weight can be determined by any of the several methods discussed in Chapter 8. The atomic weight is numerically equal to the sum of protons and neutrons. Thus, since the atomic weight of aluminum is 27, as determined by chemical methods, the aluminum nucleus must contain 27 nucleons. The number of nucleons is called the *mass number* and is symbolized by the letter A. It signifies the atomic weight of the nucleus—or of the atom—to the nearest whole number. Thus, the total number of nucleons in an atom can be readily determined if the atomic weight is near a whole number. (We shall take up presently the case of these elements whose atomic weights differ markedly from a whole number.)

To find the number of *protons* in a given nucleus a new idea is required—the idea of *atomic number*. The reader will recall that the periodic system was obtained by arranging the elements in the increasing order of their atomic weights. The atomic number was defined provisionally as the serial number of the element, from the lightest to the heaviest. The numerous and complex regularities excluded the possibility of the existence of unknown elements between *adjacent* columns of the periodic system. Therefore, the atomic numbers represented the "natural" order of the elements without any gaps.

Rutherford had the inspiration to postulate that the atomic number represents the positive charge on the nucleus of the element. The idea that each element had a nuclear charge one unit greater than the immediately preceding lighter element had a strong appeal. Thus helium, the second lightest element, has twice the nuclear charge of hydrogen; lithium, the third element, has three times the nuclear charge of hydrogen; uranium, the ninety-second element has 92 positive charges on its nucleus.

That the "serial number" of the element gives the charge on the nucleus was strikingly confirmed in 1913 by Robert Moseley, a student of Rutherford. A short time earlier it had been discovered that an x-ray tube emits two kinds of x-rays. One kind is a band of continuous wavelengths (or frequencies), the shortest of which depends on the speed of the electrons hitting the target. This in turn depends only on the voltage of the tube and not on the nature of the target element. The other kind of x-rays consists of two lines—two distinct wavelengths. The wavelengths of these two lines are characteristic of the metal used as the target. The same two lines are obtained from a given metal regardless of the voltage, provided it is sufficiently high.

Suspecting that the characteristic x-rays are produced by the strong electric fields near the nucleus, Moseley reasoned that by comparing the characteristic wavelengths of two elements an indication of the *relative strengths of the fields* around their nuclei could be obtained. The strength of the fields, in turn, would give an idea of the relative amount of charge on the respective nuclei. He photographed and compared the characteristic x-rays of several elements as they appear in

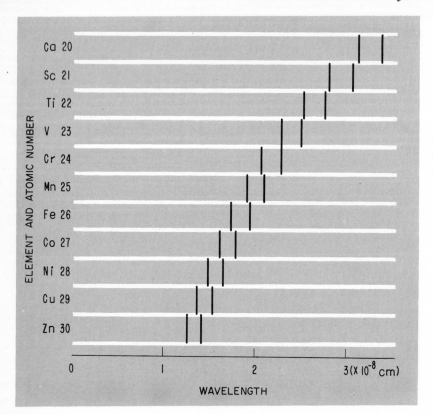

Fig. 11-23. Moseley's relationship. The wavelengths of the characteristic pair of x-ray lines decrease stepwise with increasing atomic number of adjacent elements.

sequence in the periodic system. As expected, the wavelengths were shorter for elements of greater atomic weight. Shorter wavelength means greater frequency, and indicates a stronger field and a greater charge around the nucleus. More significantly, the decrease in wavelength was stepwise for adjacent elements, indicating an increase of charge by a single whole positive unit. Soon afterwards, Bohr's newly developed theory of spectra (to be discussed in the next chapter) permitted the accurate calculation of the charge on the nucleus. The charge was found equal to the atomic number times the charge on the hydrogen atom, as expected from the theory.

We may summarize the points developed so far and repeat them for clarity. With these two numbers, the *atomic weight, A,* and the *atomic number, Z,* both of which are experimentally determined, the full structure of any atom can be written. The atomic number gives the number of protons in the nucleus. It also gives the charge on the nucleus, relative to the charge on the hydrogen atom, which is the smallest charge ever observed. Furthermore, this number gives the number of electrons outside the nucleus in a neutral atom. The atomic weight on the other hand, gives the total number of protons and neutrons in the nucleus. The difference between the atomic weight and the atomic number (that is $A-Z$) is the number of neutrons in the nucleus. Thus the theory explains simply and clearly the structure of the atom of any element that has an atomic weight near a whole number.

As pointed out earlier, the atomic weights of several elements are markedly different from whole numbers. A good example is chlorine, with an atomic weight of 35.46. The Rutherford theory does not provide for fractional nucleons; this posed a basic problem and seriously threatened his theory. The reader will recall that the existence of fractional atomic weights dealt a deathblow to Prout's hypothesis (that the elements are made of hydrogen, p. 311) nearly a century earlier.

This time, however, the difficulty was removed by new experimental discoveries, leading to a new idea: *isotopes*. This idea not only resolved the difficulty but added strength to the theory. In the discussion of radioactivity, we mentioned that the end product of the disintegration of uranium is lead, but that the atomic weight of this lead is 206. The thorium series ends with lead of atomic weight 208, and the actinium series with lead of atomic weight 207., These atomic weights are different from 207.2, which is the atomic weight of ordinary lead obtained from lead mines. All these kinds of lead are indistinguishable from one another in their chemical properties and, except for very slight differences, in their physical properties as well.

The existence of various types of lead suggested the revolutionary idea that the atoms of an element are not necessarily "exactly" alike, but may differ somewhat in weight. However, they can only differ by a whole weight unit. Each kind of lead atom had to have a weight near a *whole number* if it consisted of a whole number of nucleons. If this interpretation was correct, then the atomic weight of ordinary lead could easily be explained as merely the *average* of the weights of various kinds of lead atoms it happened to contain.

Incidentally, this was the first time it was realized that the atomic weights obtained by any of the chemical methods are only averages. It is a curious fact that Dalton's assumption that the atoms of an element are all exactly alike so predisposed the thinking of the chemists that the possibility of the atomic weights being mere averages did not occur to most and had never been seriously considered by many of them. To be sure, the atomic weights of the elements from widely different sources are remarkably constant, but that merely indicates that the proportions of the atoms of different atomic weight are constant, possibly because they have been thoroughly mixed in the material that originally formed the earth (see Chap. 15).

Fortunately, the then recently discovered positive rays provided a new method for the determination of atomic weights. This method does not measure mere averages. As explained on page 328, the amount of bending of a positive-ray beam in a magnetic field depends on the mass and on the charge of the particles in the beam. If two ions *(of the same speed)* have the same charge, but different masses, then the heavier particle will be bent less. The bending force is the same since it depends on the charge, but the heavier particle resists the bending more, in proportion to its mass. We have reasoned to this conclusion in detail on page 329, in explaining that in a given tube the cathode rays are bent much more easily than the positive rays. To be sure, in a given tube and at the same voltage, the speeds are not quite the same. The

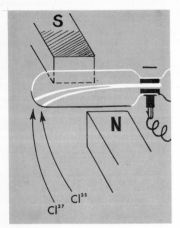

Fig. 11-24. Chlorine atoms differ in weight. A positive-ray beam from chlorine gas separates into two beams with atomic weights 35 and 37.

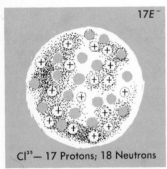

Cl^{35}— 17 Protons; 18 Neutrons

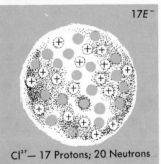

Cl^{37}— 17 Protons; 20 Neutrons

Fig. 11-25. Two isotopes of chlorine, Cl^{35} and Cl^{37}. Both have the same number of protons (17) but different number of neutrons (18 and 20, respectively).

heavier particles do move somewhat slower, but not slow enough to compensate for their greater mass. (Exs. 17 and 18.)

The reader will recall that the positive rays from a given element are separated into two or three beams. For each beam, the m/e ratio corresponds to the atomic weight, or to a half or a third of it, depending on whether the charge on the ion is one, two, or three units. Frederick Soddy and Francis Aston, two colleagues of Rutherford, reasoned that if any one of these beams is subjected to still *stronger* magnetic fields, the beam should separate further according to the mass of the particles, *if the masses are indeed different.* They tried first neon and then chlorine, whose chemical atomic weight is 35.46. The strongest beam of chlorine did separate into two closely placed beams, one corresponding to an atomic weight of 35, and the other to 37. Obviously, therefore, there are two kinds of chlorine atoms, one weighing 35, the other weighing 37 times as much as the hydrogen atom. Other elements gave similar results. In all cases the elements consist of atoms, which weigh a whole number of times as much as hydrogen. A few elements consist of only one kind of atoms, but most of them consist of two or more kinds, and some of them of as many as a dozen or more kinds. These various kinds of atoms of the same element, differing only in weight, are called *isotopes.*

According to Rutherford's theory, the heavier chlorine isotope contains 37 nucleons, and the lighter, 35. A number of questions immediately arise. Why are both of these atoms of chlorine? In what respects are they alike and in what respects are they different? Specifically, how many protons and how many neutrons are there in each kind of atom? The answer to the last question came directly from the examination of the characteristic x-ray spectra. Chlorine (and every element) gives *but one pair* of characteristic x-ray lines. Since the wavelength of these lines depends on the electric field around the nucleus, each kind of atom of chlorine must have the same charge on the nucleus and, hence, the same number of protons (Ex. 32). Since chlorine is the seventeenth element on the list, either atom must have 17 protons. Now, since the two kinds of atoms have different weights, they must have a different number of neutrons. The heavier atom (37), therefore, must have 20 neutrons and the lighter (35) must have 18 neutrons (Ex. 33). Thus, the isotopes of a given element have the same number of protons in their nuclei, but different numbers of neutrons.

One question still remains to be answered. Why are both of these atoms *chlorine* atoms? Both kinds of atoms are present in ordinary chlorine, and their chemical properties are identical, so far as can be determined by the usual chemical observations. Both form the same compounds with equal ease, and without any other detectable difference. Throughout all the chemical reactions of ordinary chlorine, both remain in the same proportions: all the samples of chlorine from diverse sources have the same proportions of the isotopes. The physical properties of the isotopes are also extremely similar, if not identical: both are gases, are green, are soluble in water and so on; and, hence, cannot be separated by the usual methods employed to separate dissimilar substances. Apparently the fact that they differ in mass (because they contain different numbers of neutrons in their nuclei) is not too significant (Exs. 22 and 36).

The identity in chemical (and physical) properties must be sought in the respects in which the two kinds of atoms *are* identical. Both kinds of chlorine atoms have identical numbers of protons (17) in their nuclei, and this identity results in identical nuclear charges and identical numbers of planetary electrons. These factors are related, and their identity in the two kinds of chlorine atoms in some way results in identity in chemical properties, the implication being that the chemical properties are determined either by the number of nuclear protons, or by the charge on the nucleus, or by the number of planetary electrons, or by the arrangement of the planetary electrons. This conclusion is further confirmed by the fact that each element has a unique nuclear charge and also a unique set of chemical properties.

We are now in a position to recapitulate the main points of the Rutherford theory. The atom consists of two quite distinct parts. The central part is the nucleus. We have been able to determine its size, its charge, and the number of protons and neutrons it contains. Rather significantly, the nucleus of an atom remains unaltered during the countless ordinary physical and chemical changes. It is altered only during the extraordinary changes, called nuclear changes, in which elements are transmuted into other elements. We shall return to consider this part of the atom in further detail in Chapter 13.

The other part of the atom is the outer envelope, containing negatively charged electrons. It is this part of the atom that determines the physical and chemical properties. It is this part of the atom that alters during the physical and chemical changes. We shall turn to the consideration of this part of the atom in the next chapter.

NOTES AND EXERCISES

1. The name "proton" was given to the hydrogen ion in a revival of the ancient idea that it represents "primary matter" ($\pi\rho\acute{\omega}\tau\eta$ $\overset{\shortparallel}{\upsilon}\lambda\eta$). All the other atoms appeared to be assemblages of protons, sometimes neutralized by electrons and sometimes not. Why was not the electron considered "primary matter"? In what respects are the two particles similar? In what respect are they different? After the discovery of the neutron and the positron, could the neutron be considered as "primary matter"?

2. Contrast metallic and electrolytic conductivity. Contrast the electrical properties of the metals and the nonmetals, as revealed during electrolytic conductivity. Is the statement "an electric current is a flow of electrons" always true? How would you modify the statement?

3. What is the experimental evidence that in blue vitriol (copper sulfate, $CuSO_4$), the copper atom is really an ion, carrying a positive charge? What is the evidence that the charge is twice that of the hydrogen ion? Twice that of the electron, but opposite in sign?

4. How many coulombs are required to liberate 1 gram-atom of iron (atomic weight, 55.84) from ferrous chloride, $FeCl_2$? From ferric chloride, $FeCl_3$? How many faradays in each case? What is the valence of iron in each case? Is the valence the same in both cases?

5. To "count" the number of hydrogen atoms in 1 gram of hydrogen is essentially the problem of determining Avogadro's number, *N*. It takes 1 faraday of electric charge to liberate 1 gram of hydrogen. How many coulombs are in a faraday? How many electrostatic units of charge in a coulomb? How many electrostatic units in a faraday? How many electrons in an electrostatic unit? How many electrons in a coulomb? How many electrons in a faraday? If it takes one electron to liberate a hydrogen atom, how many atoms in 1 gram of hydrogen? How many atoms in 1 pound of hydrogen?

6. Similarly it is possible to "count" the number of molecules in a glass of water. How heavy is the water molecule, compared to the hydrogen atom (see Chap. 8)? How much do N (6×10^{23}) molecules of water weigh? If a glass of water weighs 250 grams, how many molecules does it contain? How many molecules of sugar in a pound of sugar, $C_{12}H_{22}O_{11}$?

7. The charge on the hydrogen ion can be calculated by reversing the reasoning in Exercise 5. It takes 96,500 coulombs to liberate 1 gram of hydrogen from an acid solution. If 1 gram of hydrogen consists of 6×10^{23} atoms, how many coulombs are carried by a hydrogen ion? How many electrostatic units of charge? How does this compare with the smallest charge on an oil drop?

8. Assuming that the molecules of air act like tiny pith balls, how do you explain the formation of an electric spark, such as lightning? How does this explain the action of a neon sign? Why does the low pressure in a neon sign permit the flow of the current at much lower voltages? How is the current "carried" in a neon sign? In what respects is this similar to electrolytic conductivity? In what respects is it different? In what respects is it different from the conduction of electric current by a wire?

9. What is the evidence that at the "cathode-ray stage" of evacuation an electric charge is flowing through the tube? That the charge is *not* carried by the ions in the near vacuum? What is the evidence that the charge originates from the cathode?

10. How did Thomson prove that the "rays" in the highly evacuated tube are electrically charged? That the charge is negative? That the charge is associated with mass? That the beam is a swarm of material particles carrying the charge? That these particles have momentum? Kinetic energy?

11. Several factors influence the motion of the electrons in the magnetic field. Consider the effect of each factor, assuming all others to remain constant. What is the effect on,

(a) The speed, if the voltage is increased?
(b) The current (due to the motion of the particles), if the speed is increased?
(c) The amount of bending, if the mass were greater?
(d) The amount of bending, if the charge were greater?
(e) The amount of bending, if the speed were greater?
(f) The amount of bending, if the field were stronger?
(g) The m/e ratio, if the voltage were greater?
(h) The m/e ratio, if the field were stronger?

12. Using the equation, $v = \dfrac{2W}{QHr}$, Thomson calculated the speed of the electrons, from the quantities he could measure in the laboratory. What does W stand for, and how is it measured? What does Q stand for, and how is it measured? What does H stand for and how is it measured? What does r stand for and how is it measured? Is it fair to say that Thomson *measured* the speed of the particles? Explain.

13. What is meant by m/e ratio? During the electrolysis of hydrochloric acid, what is the value of m/e for H^+ ions? Express it in grams per faraday. What is the value of m/e for Cl^- ions? What is the value of m/e for electrons? What is the "atomic weight" of the electron?

14. Using the equation, $\dfrac{m}{e} = \dfrac{QH^2r^2}{2W}$, Thomson calculated the ratio of mass to charge, for the electron. What does Q stand for and how did he measure it? What does H stand for and how did he measure it? What does r stand for and how did he measure it? What does W stand for and how did he measure it? Is it fair to say that Thomson *measured* the m/e for the electron?

15. Assuming that the charge, e, on the cathode-ray particle is the same as the smallest charge found by Millikan on an oil drop, calculate the mass of the electron.

16. How are the positive rays produced in the evacuated tube? What is the evidence that they are *positive* rays? Why do they bend much less than the cathode rays, in the same magnetic field? How do the m/e values for positive rays compare with those of cathode rays? How do they compare with those found in electrolysis? What is the evidence that the positive rays are atoms or molecules of the gas, carrying one or more charges?

17. By measuring the deflection of the positive beams and calculating the m/e ratio, it is possible to identify the particles in the beam. They are atoms or groups of atoms carrying one or more positive charges.

With oxygen in the tube several beams are obtained. The m/e of one of the beams is 16 grams per faraday. What are the particles in this beam? Another beam has an m/e of 16/3 grams per faraday. What are the particles in this beam? A third beam has an m/e of 32 grams per faraday. What are the particles in this beam?

The positive-ray tube has been developed into an instrument called the mass spectrograph, which measures atomic weights with an accuracy of parts per million. Is this a method independent of chemical methods for determining atomic weights?

18. What is the evidence that chlorine consists of two isotopes, of mass 35 and 37, respectively?

19. What is the evidence that all the atoms contain the same negative particles (that is, electrons)? What is the evidence that atoms differ in the amount of positive charge they contain?

20. Make a table listing the mass and the charge of the alpha, beta, and gamma rays. Identify the particles in each of these rays. In what sense is a radioactive material similar to an evacuated tube under very high voltage? What rays in the evacuated tube correspond to alpha rays? To beta rays? To gamma rays? How is the correspondence proved?

21. That alpha particles are helium ions, He^{++}, was proved conclusively using the apparatus in Figure 11-26. The inner vessel had extremely thin walls through which alpha rays could penetrate, but ordinary gases, including helium, could not. Some radioactive material was placed in the inner vessel. After several months, the spectrum of helium was detected in the gas between the inner and the outer vessel. How was the helium produced in the outer vessel? How does this prove conclusively that alpha rays are helium ions? Why could not the fact that helium is associated with radioactive materials be considered sufficient evidence?

22. Lead samples from different radioactive sources may have atomic weight 206, 207, or 208. What are these "types" of lead called? The

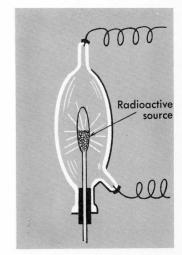

Fig. 11-26. Alpha rays are helium nuclei. Alpha rays from a radioactive source penetrate a thin glass wall. The spectrum of helium is observed in the outer vessel.

atomic weight of lead from lead mines is 207.21. Why are all these materials called "lead"? What is the probable constitution of ordinary lead?

23. The half life of uranium-238 is 4.6 billion years. Starting with a pound of uranium, how much will be left after 4.6 billion years? After 9.2 billion years? After 46 billion years? How much time is needed for all of it to disintegrate?

24. Another way of understanding the meaning of "half life" is the following. Suppose we are observing a single radium atom. A half life of 1590 years means that if we continue to observe it for 1590 years, the chances are fifty-fifty that it will have disintegrated in that time. What are the chances that it will disintegrate in 3180 years? In 4770 years? How long must we observe it to be certain that it will disintegrate? Might it disintegrate in the first year? What are the chances?

25. The size of the gold atom can be calculated fairly closely from the density, the atomic weight, and Avogadro's number, all of which have been measured. One cubic centimeter of solid gold weighs 19.3 grams. Since the atomic weight of gold is 197.0, our cube contains $19.3/197 \times N$, which is about $0.1 N$ or about 6×10^{22} atoms. From this we can calculate the size of the atoms, treating them as oranges in a cubical crate. A gold atom is thus calculated to be about 2.5×10^{-8} cm in diameter.

Consider a cubical crate of oranges. If you have 10 oranges on a side, how many oranges in a layer? How many layers? How many oranges in the crate? If you have 4000 oranges in another crate, how many do you have on the side? If the crate is 160 cm on the edge, what is the distance between the centers of the oranges? What is the diameter of the oranges? Does it make much difference if the layers are slightly staggered?

If you have 6×10^{22} oranges (atoms) in a crate 1 cm on the side, how many atoms do you have in a row along the edge? What is the distance between the atoms? What is the diameter of the gold atoms? What assumptions do you make in these calculations? What do you mean in saying that atoms "touch?"

26. Rutherford's experiments indicating the extreme concentration of the mass of the atom in a nucleus explained a long-standing puzzle in astronomy. The companion of the star Sirius was found to have a density of 60,000 grams per cc. A teaspoon of this material would weigh nearly 1 ton. The densest material known on the earth is osmium, weighing 24 grams per cc.

However, the densities of nuclei are enormously greater. If the radius of the nucleus is 1/10,000 the radius of the atom, what is its volume? If the mass of the nucleus is essentially the same as the mass of the atom, what is the density of the nucleus? Calculate the density of the proton, if the mass is 1.6×10^{-24} grams and the radius is 3×10^{-13} cm.

27. It is difficult to define precisely the "radius" of a nucleus. In Figure 11-20, b is taken as the radius of the gold nucleus. What precisely is b? If the alpha particle had a greater kinetic energy, would b have the same value?

28. What reasoning first led Rutherford to assume that heavy nuclei contain alpha particles? Why was the idea abandoned? What suggested that they contain protons? What suggested that they contain neutrons?

29. What does the neutron become, if it emits an electron? If a nucleus emits an electron how does the resulting nucleus compare with the original, in the number of protons? In the number of neutrons? In the number of nucleons?

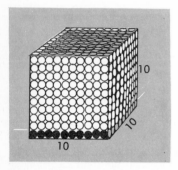

Fig. 11-27. Calculating the size of a gold atom. For 1000 atoms, a row of 10 on edge. That is, 10 in a row; 10 rows in a layer; 10 layers in the cube.

30. What is atomic number? How is it determined experimentally? What is atomic weight? How is it determined experimentally?

31. By what experimental methods do we determine the number of protons in the nucleus? The number of neutrons in the nucleus? The total number of nucleons in the nucleus? The charge on the nucleus? The number of planetary electrons?

32. The atomic number of sodium is 11. The atomic weight is 23. Draw a schematic structure of the sodium atom, showing the number of protons and neutrons in the nucleus, the nuclear charge, and the number of planetary electrons.

33. The atomic weights of two uranium isotopes are 235 and 238 respectively. What is the atomic number of each? Draw the structure of each isotope.

34. Uranium-238 emits an alpha particle to give an element called uranium-X_1. How many protons is the uranium-238? How many neutrons? How many protons in the uranium-X_1 nucleus? How many neutrons? The uranium-X_1 is an isotope of what known element?

35. Uranium-239 emits a beta particle giving a new element. Write the structure of the uranium-239 atom, showing the number of protons and neutrons. If a beta particle is emited, what happens to one of the neutrons? How many protons and neutrons in the resulting atom? What is the atomic weight and the atomic number of the new element? What is the name of the new element? If the new element emits, in turn, another beta particle, what element would it become?

36. Three isotopes of hydrogen are known, with atomic weights 1, 2, and 3 (or protium, deuterium, and tritium, respectively). Draw the structures of each. Even with the large differences in mass, the chemical properties are still practically the same. Thus deuterium burns in oxygen to form water. It is somewhat denser than ordinary water, and is called "heavy" water, but all the properties are those of water. Write an equation for the burning of heavy hydrogen to form heavy water. What is the molecular weight of heavy water? Would you expect it to react with lime, CaO? What will it form?

37. *Operational Definition of an Element.* The discovery that each element in all its various isotopes gives but one characteristic x-ray spectrum (one characteristic pair of lines) serves to define an element independently of any theory. Using only directly observable phenomena, define an element. Similarly define a chemical compound and distinguish between the two.

38. The wavelengths of the characteristic pair of x-ray lines increase for the lighter elements until they become ultraviolet light; for helium and hydrogen the wavelengths are in the ultraviolet region. However, there is no difficulty in following the series of lines to hydrogen or in the opposite direction to uranium and the transuranium elements. On what experimental basis do we say that all the elements up to nobelium are now known? What does this mean in terms of theory?

12

PLANETARY ELECTRONS AND CHEMISTRY

1. INTRODUCTION

According to the Rutherford theory, the outer part of the atom is a tenuous envelope of negative electrons. We have already referred to this as the "cloud" of electrons. In terms of mass, this outer envelope is negligible; here the total weight of electrons is less than a thousandth part of the total weight of the atom. In terms of volume, on the other hand, this region of the atom is most important. It is practically the whole atom, since the tiny nucleus occupies but a millionth of a millionth of the total volume. It is this outer envelope that determines practically all the physical and chemical properties of the atom.

Evidence for this important conclusion will be presented in considerable detail in the following discussion, but a simplified reasoning can be given at this point. Since each element has a distinct set of physical and chemical properties, it appears likely that the properties of the elements are determined by the nature of the electron cloud; for in each element, the atoms have the same number of electrons and presumably the same cloud structure. Further support on this point is derived from the behavior of isotopes. The isotopic atoms of a given element have the same number of electrons and presumably the same arrangement. Since they also have the same chemical properties, the evidence is strong that the properties depend on the number and the arrangement of the electrons in the cloud.

The reader has already seen how the number of electrons is determined from the atomic number. The total number of electrons is the same as the atomic number. But how is their arrangement determined? It is not difficult to see where to look for the answer. If the physical and chemical properties of the atoms depend on the arrangement of the electrons, then it should be possible to map out the arrangement by studying the properties. Conversely, having succeeded in mapping out the arrangement, we should be able to explain the physical and chemical properties of the atoms.

Of the many physical and chemical properties of the elements, the study of light and the characteristic spectra that the elements emit contributed most directly to an understanding of the structure of the atom. This is not surprising, since light is emitted by electrons oscillating and accelerating in the electric fields within the atoms. It is understandable, therefore, that the study of the spectra has revealed the nature and strength of these fields and the energies of the electrons imbedded in them. We will discuss more systematically the essential parts of the story.

While the main features of the Rutherford picture of the atom were well established by experiments, a great deal of difficulty was encountered in the attempts to work out in detail the structure of the electron cloud. The picture of a massive and positively charged nucleus at the center, surrounded by negatively charged electrons, appeared satisfactory at first sight. It is analogous to the solar system, with a central sun attracting the planets. In both cases, the central body attracts the planetary bodies with a force that decreases as the square of the distance. Therefore, by applying the laws of motion it should be possible to describe the atom just as logically and precisely as the solar system. If the attempt is successful, then the atom will be understood to the same extent as the solar system.

The simplest atom is that of hydrogen, having one proton as the nucleus and one planetary electron. Applying the laws of motion we see at once that the electron in the atom cannot stand still. It is attracted by the nucleus and would fall into it, for the same reason a planet would fall into the sun if it stood still. In the case of the planet, its inertial tendency to go in a straight line keeps it from falling into the sun. This tendency is balanced by the attraction of the sun, so that the planet is bent or accelerated into a curved path and is compelled to go around the sun. If the electron obeys the laws of motion—and since it is a material body we must assume that it does—then the electron, too, is bent or accelerated, and is compelled to move in circles or ellipses around the nucleus.

At this point a basic difficulty arises in the attempt to understand the atom. Unlike a planet, the electron is a charged body. Therefore, the electron should obey not only the laws of motion, but also the laws

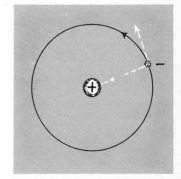

Fig. 12-1. Like a planet, the electron must be in motion to keep from falling into the nucleus.

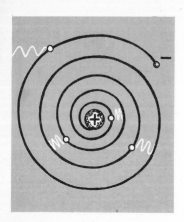

Fig. 12-2. An accelerating electron should radiate and spiral into the nucleus.

of electric charges, as formulated by Maxwell in his electromagnetic theory. If the electron goes around the nucleus, it is accelerated. But if it is accelerated, it should radiate light. For according to Maxwell's theory, an accelerating electric charge emits radiation. Since the energy of the emitted radiation comes from the energy of the emitting charge, the electron should lose energy at every turn and move closer and closer to the nucleus. The ultimate result is obvious. In each revolution the electron would be drawn closer and closer to the nucleus, emitting more and more of its energy, until it is swallowed by the nucleus. Thus, in much less than a millionth of a second, the atom would disappear as an atom.

Moreover, the electromagnetic theory predicts precisely the type of light to be expected. As discussed in Chapter 5, the wavelength of the emitted light depends on the rate of loss of energy—that is, on the amount of acceleration; the greater the loss of energy, the shorter the wavelength. As the electron spirals into the nucleus, the electric forces become stronger and stronger, and the electron should radiate light of shorter and shorter wavelength. The light should be continuous, the wavelengths moving progressively into the ultraviolet, until the electron disappears into the nucleus. This was called the "ultraviolet catastrophe" by the physicists who carried out the above reasoning.

Thus, it appears impossible to understand the atom according to the Rutherford plan. The electron cannot stand still, because it would fall into the nucleus; nor can it revolve, for then it would radiate its energy and spiral into the nucleus. The difficulty is fundamental. There is no way of conceiving of a stable atom that obeys the laws of motion and is also in accord with the electromagnetic theory. Yet there is no question that the hydrogen atoms are stable. They are found in the laboratory and everywhere in nature. They have been in existence for billions of years, and there is no indication that they are about to collapse or that they will ever collapse. Moreover, the light emitted by hot hydrogen gas does not give a continuous spectrum as predicted by the theory. The spectrum consists of discrete and characteristic wavelengths. Something obviously is radically wrong.

If we are to understand the atom, something has to alter. Either the laws of motion do not apply to the atom or the electromagnetic theory has some serious flaw. The laws of motion have been the basis of all exact science up to this time (that is, 1913). They are the basis for the understanding of the motions of ordinary bodies on the earth, the motion of planets in the solar system, the motion of stars in the remote regions of space, and the motions of molecules in a gas. To give them up means to destroy the foundations of the superstructure of science. The case for the electromagnetic theory is almost as strong. With the help of the electromagnetic theory we can understand light and all radiation, radio broadcasting, radar sets, and x-rays. Yet the basic laws of nature as understood so far are not in accord with the phenomena inside the atom. The only thing to do is to reexamine the basic laws and theories and to attempt to reformulate them from a fresh viewpoint.

2. BOHR'S THEORY OF THE STRUCTURE OF THE ATOM

The courageous step of breaking with the past was taken in 1913 by Niels Bohr (1885-   ), a student of Rutherford. He reasoned that the clues for reformulating the laws of nature might be found in the spectrum of hydrogen. The spectrum is a record of the changes in energy that the electron suffers within the atom. Each line in the spectrum—each wavelength—represents and, indeed, is a direct measure of the energy emitted by the electron. It represents the difference in energy the electron has before and after emission. Since a single photograph is produced by the light coming from millions of atoms in the hot gas, it is reasonable to expect that all possible energy changes in the atom are recorded in the photograph. Therefore, by studying the spectrum it should be possible to measure the differences in energy that the electron has within the atom. By working backward from this information, it might be possible to determine the conditions within the atom and to reformulate the new laws that describe them.

Fig. 12-3. Niels Bohr introduced quantum concepts and new laws of mechanics governing the behavior of the atom. *(The Bettmann Archive.)*

Assumptions

Reasoning in this manner and examining the spectrum of hydrogen, Bohr formulated his new theory of the structure of the hydrogen atom. Taking the liberty of rewording it somewhat, we shall present its main points, properly called *assumptions,* explaining their meaning and some of their implications in the process.

1. *Discrete orbits.* According to Bohr, the electron within the atom can revolve only in certain orbits, which are at definite distances from the nucleus. The electron can only be in one of these orbits. It cannot be in any position outside an orbit, at least not for any measurable or *finite* length of time. In each of these orbits the electron has a definite amount of energy, a part of which is kinetic and a part potential. The farther the electron from the nucleus, the greater its total energy. The electron has the lowest energy when it is in the innermost or first orbit (just as water on the earth has the lowest energy at sea level). The

Fig. 12-4. Discrete orbits in the atom. The electron can revolve in definite orbits only, but it can "jump" from one orbit to another.

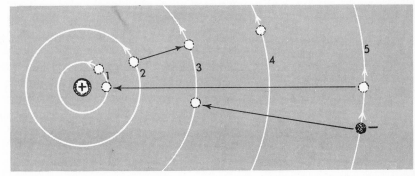

electron, of course, cannot get nearer to the nucleus than the first orbit.

This assumption of discrete orbits is rather startling. Nowhere in Newtonian mechanics does such a restriction exist. For example, a planet can have an orbit anywhere around the sun, provided it has the right amount of energy for that distance. However, for the atom this restriction is necessary in order to explain why the electron does not fall into the nucleus. The electron cannot get nearer the nucleus than the innermost orbit for it has to be in one of the orbits. This and other points become more clear in the second assumption.

2. *Nonradiation in an orbit.* Second, Bohr assumed that *so long as the electron revolves and remains in a given orbit it does not radiate.*

This assumption is clearly in flat contradiction to Maxwell's electromagnetic theory. According to that theory, as the electron revolves, it is accelerated, and hence it should radiate. Yet Bohr boldly stated that this part of Maxwell's theory does not hold for the atom. He found it necessary to make this assumption in order to explain the stability of the hydrogen atom and the absence of a continuous spectrum in hydrogen. This becomes more clear in the third assumption.

3. *Transitions between orbits or energy states.* In his third assumption, Bohr considered how radiation is produced. The electron *does radiate,* but *only when it "jumps" from an outer orbit to an inner orbit.* Normally, the electron is in the innermost orbit, where it has the lowest possible energy. If, however, the electron happens to be in an orbit further out, where it has more energy (see below), sooner or later it will fall or "jump" into an inner orbit where it has less energy. *It is at this instant* (in *this kind of acceleration*) *that the electron radiates,* and the amount of energy it radiates is the difference in energy it has between the two orbits; that is, the electron radiates the amount of energy it loses in going from an outer orbit to an inner orbit. If the electron happens to be in an orbit far out, it may either land at intermediate orbits and cascade down to the innermost orbit or it may go clear down to the innermost orbit in a single jump.

The converse process takes place when energy is added to the atom. A simple way of raising electrons to higher energy levels is by heating the gas, thus speeding up the atoms. If two fast-moving atoms collide, the electrons of one or both atoms will be raised to higher levels, provided the energy of impact is sufficiently high. However, the electron will absorb only that amount of energy necessary to raise it to one of the higher energy levels and disregard any fractions thereof. In other words, *absorption* of energy also occurs in "jumps."

4. *Emission of light in packages.* In the fourth assumption, Bohr specified the nature of the emitted radiation. When the electron jumps from an outer to an inner orbit, it emits the difference in energy as a "package" of light, called a "photon" or sometimes a "quantum" of light. The energy carried by the photon is, of course, the energy lost by the electron. The greater the difference in energy between the two levels ("the bigger the jump"), the greater the energy of the emitted photon.

The energy carried away by the photon can be expressed and

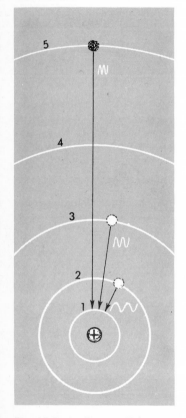

Fig. 12-5. In "jumping" from an outer to an inner orbit the electron emits radiation. The bigger the "jump," the shorter the wavelength of the radiated light.

measured in several meaningful ways. As explained in Chapter 5, the energy of the photon is proportional to the frequency associated with the photon.

$$E = h \cdot f$$

where h is known as Planck's constant and has the value of 6.6×10^{-27} erg-seconds. A more meaningful way to describe the energy of the photon is the following: Since for any kind of wave, the higher the frequency the shorter the wavelength, then the greater the energy of the photon the shorter the wavelength. In other words, the *longer the wavelengths observed* in the *spectrum,* the *smaller the energy jumps of the electron that produced them.* Thus, by observing the wavelengths of the emitted light, it is possible to work back and calculate the energy levels in the atom.

With a little arithmetic, we can indicate the calculations. Since for light the wavelength times the frequency is equal to velocity, that is,

$$\lambda \cdot f = c$$

then

$$f = \frac{c}{\lambda}$$

and

$$E = h \cdot \frac{c}{\lambda}$$

In this equation, h has the value 6.6×10^{-27} erg-seconds and c is the velocity of light—that is, 3×10^{10} cm per sec. Therefore, by measuring the wavelength we can calculate the energy—that is, the number or ergs the electron lost in making the particular jump in which it emitted this particular wavelength.

Thus, there are four essential points, or assumptions, in the Bohr theory. The first three were original with him. The fourth he borrowed from Planck, but gave to the idea of "quantum" a more precise and useful meaning. He accepted all the other laws of mechanics and of the electromagnetic theory. Taken together, they constitute a new set of laws and principles by which we hope to understand the microworld of the atom.

It would carry us too far afield to follow all the deeper implications of these revolutionary ideas. They sound quite outlandish not only to the layman but even to the physicist. These ideas mark the introduction of a series of strange concepts, in terms of which a description of the microworld within the atom is attempted. To be sure, for each assumption, there is some experiment that suggests it; nevertheless, this does not make it less strange. There is only one justification for accepting Bohr's postulates, but that justification overrides all possible objections. With these assumptions and ideas it is possible to predict and to understand the spectra of the elements, and with additional developments to explain a wide range of the physical and chemical properties of the elements. Without them, it is impossible to go further.

Using this theory, Bohr and his followers were able to explain the spectrum of hydrogen and to calculate the wavelengths observed in it, with an accuracy which is indeed uncanny. Having deduced the energy levels in the hydrogen atom from measurements of a few wavelengths, they could calculate all the other wavelengths in the spectrum with an accuracy of a few parts per million. The physicist can now do even better than that. From independent measurements of the mass and charge of the electron and the proton, the speed of light, and Planck's constant, *h,* they can calculate all the wavelengths of the hydrogen spectrum, and these agree remarkably well with the wavelengths measured on a photographic plate. Another interesting achievement is the calculation of the size of the innermost orbit of the hydrogen atom. The size of this orbit is the size of the hydrogen atom under normal conditions. The calculated value agrees very well with the diameter of the hydrogen atom as estimated from the density of solid hydrogen and other independent methods (Ex. 4).

At the risk of becoming somewhat involved, we shall relate still another achievement of general interest. It is possible to pick each wavelength in the spectrum and to decide which particular transition (or jump) of the electron in the atom is responsible for it. This incidentally will illustrate the type of "detective" work that permits us to "see" inside the atom.

On examining the complete spectrum of hydrogen, we find that it consists of three or four distinct groups of lines, each in a different region of the spectrum. One group or "series" is in the ultraviolet region. This group had been known for a long time as the Lyman series, after its discoverer. Another one, the Balmer series, is in the visible region and is the one often photographed in color and shown in textbooks (Fig. 12-6). The others are spread out in the infrared region of the spectrum.

Each series, as well as the lines in them, can be identified by simple

Fig. 12-6. Identification of the spectral lines of hydrogen (bottom) with electron jumps (top). The line with the shortest wavelength in the Lyman series (extreme left) corresponds to a fall of the electron from infinity to the innermost first orbit.

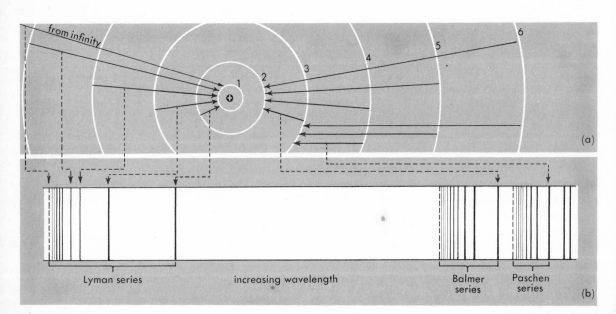

Lyman series   increasing wavelength   Balmer series   Paschen series

reasoning from the Bohr model. Since the Lyman series is the farthest in the ultraviolet and the wavelengths in this series are shortest, the wavelengths must be emitted by electrons losing the greatest amount of energy. The lines in this series, therefore, must be emitted by electrons falling from higher levels down to the lowest energy level—that is, down to the innermost orbit. Similarly, the Balmer series in the visible region must be due to electrons falling from higher levels only to the second orbit. The other series must be due to electrons falling to the third, fourth, or fifth levels, respectively. These falls represent relatively small losses in energy; hence the emitted light has long wavelengths and is observed in the infrared region of the spectrum.

Using the same reasoning it is possible to identify the individual lines within each series. In the Lyman series, which is due to electron falls to the innermost orbit, the first line at the extreme right (Fig. 12-5) has the longest wavelength. This wavelength has the least energy in this series, and must be due to the smallest possible fall to the innermost orbit. This can only be a fall from the second orbit to the first. The next line has a shorter wavelength and must be due to the greater fall from the *third* orbit to the first. Similarly the other lines in the series can be identified.

Beyond a point, however, a minor difficulty is encountered. The lines come closer and closer together, and cannot be resolved even by the best spectroscopes. We can understand this, of course, from the Bohr theory. As the electron falls from higher and higher orbits, the *added* energy becomes less and less. This is so because at great distances from the nucleus the attraction for the electron becomes weak. Consequently, it does not make much difference whether the electron in falling to the first orbit starts from orbit 63 or from orbit 62, for example. In this example, the difference in energy drop—the difference in the wavelength—would hardly be measureable. As a result, the lines, having nearly the same energy, merge into one another.

Ionization Energy

Pursuing this point to its ultimate conclusion leads to one of the most interesting and useful concepts. What is the shortest wavelength to be found in the hydrogen spectrum? The answer is quite obvious. It is the wavelength that is emitted by the electron falling from *infinity* down to the innermost orbit. That amount of energy is the maximum energy the electron can give up. The word "infinity" should not cause uneasiness. To the electron in the hydrogen atom, "infinity" is less than 1/100,000 inch. Long before the electron is removed this far out from the atom, the attraction of the nucleus is so weak that the electron is, in fact, lost to the atom. In other words, the atom has *ionized* (Ex. 5).

This reasoning leads directly to the concept of *ionization energy*. It is the energy required to remove an electron from the lowest orbit in the atom to *infinity* and thus result in ionization of the atom. On a little reflection, it is obvious that this energy is equal to the energy given off by an electron falling from infinity to the lowest level. This jump would be recorded in the spectrum as the shortest line in the Lyman series. By simply measuring the limit of the Lyman series, we can calculate the ionization energy, using the equation $E = hc/\lambda$, given above.

On carrying out the calculations, we obtain a value of 13.55 electron volts. (An electron volt is a unit of energy acquired by an electron falling through a potential difference of 1 volt: an electron volt is equal to 1.60×10^{-12} ergs; see Ex. 6.) Parenthetically, the ionization energy of hydrogen has been measured by a direct experiment and found to be 13.59 volts, almost exactly as predicted (Ex. 7).

3. THE ARRANGEMENT OF ELECTRONS IN SHELLS

The Helium Atom

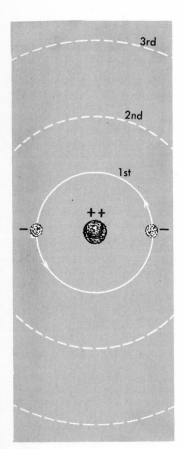

Fig. 12-7. The helium atom. Both electrons are in the first orbit.

After these successes of the theory, Bohr and others proceeded to map out the structure of the atoms of the other elements, using the hydrogen atom as the model. The helium atom is the next in complexity. The helium nucleus has a charge twice that of hydrogen and, of course, is surrounded by two electrons. Each of these electrons is attracted by a positive charge twice that of hydrogen and is repelled by the other electron. Although each electron repels the other, the repulsion is smaller than the attraction, because the electrons are on the average further from each other than from the positive nucleus. The net result is a greater attraction for each electron by the helium nucleus, compared to the hydrogen nucleus.

The same reasoning leads to the expectation that all the orbits in the helium atom hold electrons more firmly than the corresponding orbits in the hydrogen atom. The greater charge on the nucleus causes the orbits to "tighten" so to speak. Therefore, the electron gives up more energy in falling between corresponding orbits of the helium atom than of the hydrogen atom. This increased energy of fall—increased loss of energy in the transition—should be reflected in the spectrum as a shortening of the wavelength. On comparing the helium spectrum with the hydrogen spectrum, and identifying the corresponding lines, we find them all much shorter. To be sure, the helium spectrum is more complicated than that of hydrogen, due to the presence of two electrons. However, it is not too difficult to detect and identify each line in the spectrum with a particular transition in the atom, just as in the case of the hydrogen atom. From this a calculation of the amount of shortening of each wavelength will show them to be almost exactly as predicted.

Without going into the complicated calculations we can illustrate the method and the type of reasoning by carrying out a "rough" mathematical estimate. We will attempt to predict the ionization energy of helium. This is the energy required to remove just one electron from the helium atom sufficiently far to ionize it, leaving a helium ion with a single positive charge, He^+. For the hydrogen atom the ionization energy is 13.5 electron volts. If in the neutral helium atom both electrons are in the first orbit, each is attracted by double the positive charge. If this were the only difference, we would expect *double* the ionization energy. However, each electron repels the other, thus counteracting in part the attraction of the nucleus. Because of their mutual repulsion, the electrons will be somewhere opposite each other most of the time, their combined motions describing a "shell" around the nucleus. Therefore the repulsion of each electron on the other is roughly *one eighth* as great as the attraction by the nucleus. This is so because the charge on the other electron is only one unit (making the repulsive force one half as great as the attractive) and the electron is roughly twice as far from the other electron (reducing the repulsive force further by a factor of 4).

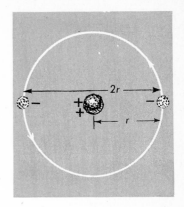

Fig. 12-8. Estimating the energy required to remove the first electron from the helium atom.

Thus, by this rough analysis, the ionization energy of helium should be a little less than twice that of hydrogen, or about $1\frac{7}{8}$ times 13.5 electron volts. A good estimate is about 25 electron volts. More accurate calculations will give better estimates, but we are not interested in high accuracy at the moment. Instead, we examine the helium spectrum, locate the proper series, and measure the shortest wavelength in that series. It corresponds to 24.6 electron volts—a remarkable confirmation of our reasoning. But there is a further check. We can measure directly the energy required to ionize helium in a highly evacuated tube, and find it to be about 24.6 volts (Ex. 7). Thus the evidence indicates that both of the electrons in helium are in the first orbit—the first shell. More significantly we have gained confidence in the essential correctness of the Bohr theory and a strong indication that the theory also applies to the helium atom.

Before leaving helium we will estimate the energy required to remove the *second* electron from the helium atom, *after the first one has already been removed*. This is the *second* ionization energy of helium. It is the energy required to remove the remaining electron from a singly charged helium ion, He^+, to form He^{++}. Although the He^+ particle is not neutral, the situation is actually simpler than in the neutral helium atom. The He^+ ion is just like the hydrogen atom, except that the central nucleus has double the charge. The fact that it is also heavier has no appreciable effect. But the greater charge attracts the electron more strongly and since there now is no other electron to provide repulsion, the shells "shrink" considerably. By taking the proper account of the forces and distances, we conclude that the electron is held *four* times more firmly in the He^+ ion than in the hydrogen atom; that is, the energy increases as the *square* of the charge. We examine the helium spectrum, locate the shortest series in the extreme ultraviolet, and measure the shortest line in that series. It corresponds to 54 volts, almost exactly 4 times 13.595.

Fig. 12-9. The He^+ ion is like the hydrogen atom, but all orbits are smaller, due to the greater charge on the nucleus.

It is important to emphasize one point to avoid confusion. This analysis shows that in the *undisturbed* helium atom both electrons are in the first orbit. Each electron is held with the same amount of energy *while both are in the atom*. The difference between the first and second ionization energies is only what is to be expected if the electrons are removed *in succession.*

We are now ready to discuss the atoms of the heavier elements. As the atoms become more complex and the nuclear charge as well as the number of electrons increase, the complexities increase enormously. It becomes more and more difficult and eventually impossible to carry out exact calculations. At the same time the spectra show more and more lines and eventually become so hopelessly complex as to be impossible to untangle. It is possible, however, to carry out less exact calculations, or even rough estimates and still get an approximation of the energy states in the atom. The ionization energy alone, which can be measured by several experimental methods, can provide a good deal of information. Further, after correlating the chemical properties with atomic structure, chemical methods can be developed to yield supporting information.

A good understanding of the hydrogen atom will serve as a model and a guide. The study of the helium atom has already shown that it contains the same pattern of orbits as the hydrogen atom, except that the orbits are correspondingly smaller due to the shrinking effect of the larger positive charge on the nucleus. With the atoms of greater nuclear charge, more shrinking is expected, but we can calculate the amount. Before proceeding, let us restate the conclusions reached so far.

In the helium atom both electrons occupy the *first orbit* under normal conditions. We arrived at this conclusion by comparing the ionization energies. This in turn gives a good picture of the helium atom. The two electrons, revolving very rapidly at the same distance from the nucleus and covering all points in quick succession many times per second, effectively form a sphere or "shell" around the nucleus. With this picture and these sound principles as guides we can now examine the more complex atoms.

The Lithium Atom

The next atom is that of lithium, with a nuclear charge of +3. In analogy to helium, the first suggestion is to *assume* that all three electrons are in the first shell, at equal distances from the nucleus. On this assumption, the first ionization energy is estimated as follows: Each electron is attracted by three positive charges, but is repelled to some extent by two negative charges from greater distances. Thus the ionization energy would be somewhat less than three times that of hydrogen. A good estimate might be about 34 electrons.

On examining the spectrum of lithium, which fortunately is not too complex, we locate the proper series and measure the shortest line in that series. The ionization energy is only about 5.4 electron volts. We measure the ionization energy in evacuated tubes, and again find it to be about 5 electron volts. Moreover, we know from chemistry that lithium is a metal and forms positive ions easily, which means that it loses an electron easily. It could not require much energy to remove the electron from the lithium atom. There is no question that the ionization energy of lithium is about 5 electron volts. But this is not in agreement with the calculations.

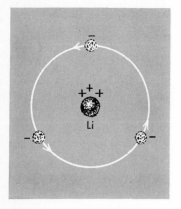

Fig. 12-10. If all three electrons of lithium, Li, were in the first orbit, the ionization energy would be about 34 electron volts.

A reexamination of the reasoning above shows that the ionization energy of lithium should be about 34 electron volts, on the assumption that all three electrons are in the first shell. Obviously, that is not the case. One of the electrons of lithium is held much more weakly than expected. Therefore, this electron must be in a shell further out. On repeating the calculation for the electron in the second orbit, we get an estimate of about 5.4 electron volts, in agreement with experiments.

These experimental facts and reasoning lead to the idea that the electrons are arranged in the atom in "shells." Let us dwell on this point a little longer, because the idea of "shells" first arises here, and its meaning, and the evidence for it are clearest here. Lithium has three ionization energies, each being a measure of the energy required to remove *successively,* the first (or outermost) electron, the second, and then the last. The first electron comes out very easily—a mere 5.4 volts, which can be measured directly. The second electron is much more difficult to remove. It requires 75 volts. This is much greater than would be expected from the fact that the electron is removed from an already positive ion, Li^+. This electron must, therefore, be in the deeper interior, where the forces are much greater. The third electron requires still greater energy than the second, but the *added amount* is precisely what is expected from the fact that it is removed from Li^{++} ion which has just twice the charge of Li^+. Therefore the last electron to be removed is held in the atom no more firmly than the second.

On reconstructing the interior of the atom from our measurements of the ionization potentials, we find the following. In the *undisturbed* lithium atom, one electron is very weakly held, and two electrons are held much more firmly, but *equally* firmly. We pictorialize this information by saying that two electrons are in the interior forming a shell and one electron is farther out in the second shell. Even if the Bohr theory were to be abandoned, these statements could still be made. The Bohr theory has served us well, but this knowledge is based on firm experimental evidence quite independent of the theory. Independent confirmation that the lithium has one shell more than the helium atom comes from the fact that the lithium atom is *larger* than the helium atom (Ex. 4).

The idea of shells is dramatically substantiated by the examination of the more complex elements. For the present we consider only the first (or lowest) ionization energy of the succeeding heavier elements. After lithium, the next element is beryllium, with four electrons. Its first ionization energy is 9.32 electron volts. This is a little less than twice that of lithium, as expected. Therefore, this electron is also in the second shell, so that beryllium has two electrons in the second shell and two in the innermost. The fifth element is boron, and its first ionization energy is 8.3 electron volts. This is a little less than expected, but the discrepancy is small and is most probably due to minor factors, which may be disregarded in the rough estimates. Therefore, the boron atom has *three* electrons in the second shell—three electrons rather weakly held—and two electrons in the innermost shell, firmly held.

Continuing, the first ionization energy of the next element, carbon,

The Concept of Shells

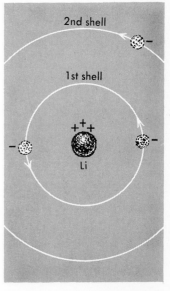

Fig. 12-11. In the lithium atom, one electron is weakly held (in second shell) and two electrons are very firmly held (in first shell).

is 11.2 electron volts, and of nitrogen, 14.5—about as expected, if the additional electrons go into the second shell. For the next element, oxygen, it drops slightly to 13.6 electron volts (again probably due to another minor factor), but then it rises to 17.4 for fluorine, and to 21.6 for neon. Thus, for the eight elements from lithium to neon, there is a small and gradual rise in the energy with which electrons are held in the atoms, and these eight electrons must be in the second shell.

In sodium, the next element after neon, there is a sudden and dramatic drop. The first ionization energy of sodium is only 5.12 electron volts. This is even less than that of lithium. Such an abrupt change in the trend implies that the eleventh electron of sodium is further out from the nucleus than the second shell. This conclusion is confirmed by the examination of the succeeding elements. The first ionization energy rises gradually until the inert gas argon is reached, for which the ionization energy is 15.8 electron volts. Then it again drops abruptly to 4.3 electron volts for potassium. Table 12:1, giving the lowest ionization energy of the first twenty elements, clarifies these relations.

The pattern, which is already evident, continues after calcium. The ionization energy rises gradually (though somewhat irregularly) to 13.9

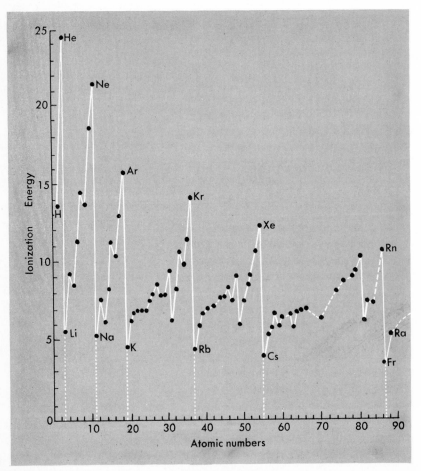

Fig. 12-12. Periodicity in the first ionization energy. The number of electron volts required to remove the first electron from atoms of successive elements. Note the dramatic drop after each inert gas, indicating the beginning of a new shell.

TABLE 12:1

H	He						
13.59	24.58						
Li	Be	B	C	N	O	F	Ne
5.39	9.32	8.3	11.2	14.5	13.6	17.4	21.6
Na	Mg	Al	Si	P	S	Cl	A
5.1	7.6	6.0	8.1	11.0	10.3	13.0	15.8
K	Ca						
4.3	6.1						

electron volts for krypton, which is the next inert gas; then drops abruptly to 4.2 for rubidium, the immediately following alkali metal. This regularity continues to the end of the periodic system as shown in Figure 12-12.

4. ELECTRON CONFIGURATION AND THE PERIODIC SYSTEM

The correlation of ionization energy with the periodic system discussed in the last section is both unexpected and significant. At the beginning of each period the ionization energy starts with a small value, increases gradually, though somewhat irregularly, and attains the highest value in the inert gas at the end of the period. Then it drops abruptly to begin the next period with the next alkali metal. Thus, the ionization energy of the elements rises and falls periodically as do so many other properties of the elements.

The ionization energy is not, however, merely another property. According to the Bohr theory, it is a direct measure of the firmness with which electrons are held in the atom. Therefore, the regularities observed in the periodic system can now be used as a further aid in uncovering the structure of the atom. This aid is most welcome, especially when the calculations become hopelessly complex and the observed spectra too complicated to decipher. Having mapped out the main features of the structure from the periodic system, we can return for more accurate calculation and more precise analysis of the spectra. To facilitate its location in the periodic system (Fig. 12-13) the atomic number of the element is given above the symbol. Thus, iodine (53) means that iodine is the fifty-third element.

Using the periodic system we can readily determine the number of shells in a given atom and the number of electrons in each shell. Appar-

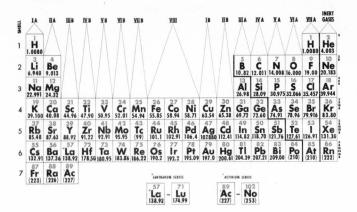

Fig. 12-13. Periodic table (reduced).

ently a new shell begins with a new period since the ionization energy drops with the alkali metal that begins the new period. Thus, with lithium (3) the second shell begins, and with sodium (11), the third. Similarly, iodine (53) is in the fifth period, and hence has five shells; and uranium (92) is in the seventh period and has seven shells.

The next step is to determine the number of electrons in each shell. This is rather easy for the first twenty elements. The elements of the first period have only one shell, and since there are only two elements, the shell can contain up to two electrons. Therefore, hydrogen has one electron in the first shell and helium has two. The elements of the second period have two shells, and since there are eight elements, the second shell can have up to eight electrons. Thus lithium, with its three electrons, has two electrons in the first shell and one in the second. This conclusion is further confirmed by a more exhaustive study of the ionization energies, as shown earlier. We can draw a diagram of the atom, showing the full structure, or we can condense the notation by writing the symbol with the number of electrons in each shell in parentheses, thus: Li(2,1).

For the remaining elements of this period, the structures follow without difficulty. Each successive element has one more electron than its predecessor and this electron goes to the second shell. The structure of these elements, in full and in condensed notation, is shown in Figure 12-14. Thus, neon has 8 electrons in the second shell, and presumably the shell is complete with 8 electrons.

Fig. 12-14. Electron configuration of the elements of the second period.

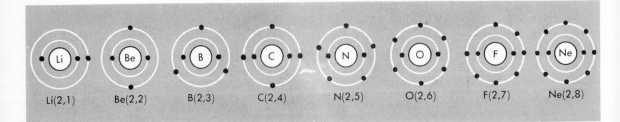

Li(2,1)   Be(2,2)   B(2,3)   C(2,4)   N(2,5)   O(2,6)   F(2,7)   Ne(2,8)

The conclusion that the second shell can contain only 8 electrons is further justified by the following facts: The next element, sodium, is in the third period, and hence it has three shells. Therefore, sodium with its 11 electrons must have the structure Na(2,8,1). Similarly, the structure of chlorine (17) must be Cl(2,8,7), and that of argon (18) must be Ar(2,8,8). Since argon is an inert gas and the last member of this period, we might be led to suppose that the third shell is also complete with 8 electrons.

However, this is not the case, and the *real* maximum of the third shell is 18 electrons. Beyond this point, complications occur, and although we wish to avoid these, we shall give the reasoning so that the interested reader will at least get the sense of the argument.

The next element after argon (18) is the alkali metal potassium (19), and this element is in the fourth period. Therefore, its nineteenth electron must be in the fourth shell, and its full structure must be K(2,8,8,1). Similarly, the next element, calcium (20), has the structure, Ca(2,8,8,2). So far, this seems to confirm the impression that the third shell can contain only 8 electrons. But the next element destroys this impression. The structure of scandium, with its 21 electrons, is Sc(2,8,9,2). The last electron added went into the *third* shell. This can be further confirmed by a more detailed study of the ionization energies, but for our purposes this is not necessary (Exs. 13, 14). This trend continues for the next eight or nine elements. Thus copper (29) has the structure Cu(2,8,18,1), with 18 electrons in the third shell. From here on, the simple regularity observed in the earlier periods returns. Thus the next element, zinc (30), has the structure Zn (2,8,18,2); gallium (31) has the structure Ga(2,8,18,3); and so on until the inert gas, krypton (36), is reached at the end of the period, with the structure Kr(2,8,18,8). Thus, the real maximum of the third shell is 18 electrons.

Similar, but more complicated reasoning, leads to the conclusion that the real maximum of the fourth shell is 32 electrons. The fourth shell seems to be complete with 8 electrons as found in the inert gas, krypton (36), given above. The next element is the alkali metal, rubidium (37), with the structure Rb(2,8,18,8,1), and the next is strontium (38), with the structure Sr(2,8,18,8,2). But the next 10 electrons go to the fourth shell and the period ends with the inert gas, xenon (54), with the structure Xe(2,8,18,18,8). In the next element, the alkali metal, cesium (55), the one electron goes into the sixth shell, but after the second electron is added, the next electrons go into the fifth and fourth shells. On approaching the end of the period, the fourth shell receives its full share of 32 electrons. The structure of the inert gas, radon (86), at the end of the sixth period is Rn(2,8,18,32,18,8).

The rewarding result of this more complicated analysis is the emergence of certain regularities which make it possible to write the electron arrangement of any element with almost complete certainty. The first regularity is that the maximum number of electrons in successive shells is 2,8,18,32. At first sight these numbers do not mean much, but rewriting them, as in the third, fourth, or fifth columns, of Table 12:2 immediately shows a pattern.

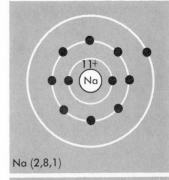

Na (2,8,1)

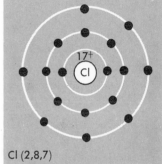

Cl (2,8,7)

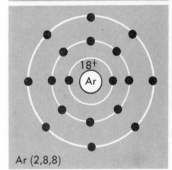

Ar (2,8,8)

Fig. 12-15. Electron structure of three common atoms: Na(2,8,1); Cl(2,8,7); Ar(2,8,8)

Maximum Number of Electrons in a Shell

TABLE 12:2

Shell 1	2	2×1	2×1^2	$2(1)$
Shell 2	8	2×4	2×2^2	$2(1+3)$
Shell 3	18	2×9	2×3^2	$2(1+3+5)$
Shell 4	32	2×16	2×4^2	$2(1+3+5+7)$

Thus, in the fourth column the maximum number of electrons in a shell increases as the *square* of the serial number of the shell.

What this pattern means may not be evident, but it must have some deep significance, for it governs the structure of the atoms. A related regularity is that the higher shells become complete or "temporarily" complete with 18 electrons, or with 8 electrons. A further significant point to note is that (except for helium) all the inert gases have 8 electrons in their outermost shells. The number 8 represents a complete outer shell for neon (2,8) and a "temporarily" complete shell for the heavier inert gases.

Another significant finding is that the regularities are simple at the beginning and at the end of each period. The reader will remember that these elements form the full columns, or *main groups* in the periodic system. The first element in each period has 1 electron in its outermost shell. These are the alkali metals, forming the first main group. Similarly, all the elements of group II have 2 electrons in their outermost shells, and those of group III have 3 electrons. The same regularity appears in the right-hand side of the periodic system, at the end of the periods. The elements of group V have 5 electrons in their outermost shells; those of group VI have 6; those of group VII have 7; and as we have already seen, the inert gases have 8. A regularity is at once apparent. In the main groups, *the number of electrons in the outermost shell is the same as the group number*. The intermediate groups—the subgroups of the periodic system—also exhibit regularities, but these are quite complicated and will not be discussed further.

With these rules, it is a simple task to write the electron configuration of any element. For example, calcium, element number 20 with 20 electrons is in the fourth period and hence has four shells. The first shell has 2 electrons, and the second 8, without question. Since it is in group II, the outmost shell has 2 electrons. Therefore, the third shell must have 8, to account for all the electrons. Hence, its complete structure is Ca(2,8,8,2). As another example, iodine with its 53 electrons is in the fifth period and hence it has five shells. The first three shells must be 2,8,18. Since iodine is in the seventh period, the fifth shell must have 7 electrons. This leaves 18 electrons for the fourth shell, and the complete structure is I(2,8,18,18,7). Similarly, the structure of the other elements may be written (Ex. 16).

By returning to make a finer analysis of the same type, we can explain the minor discrepancies found within each period. The reader will recall that in the second period, the first ionization energy does not rise steadily, with successive elements, but shows slight drops. A finer analysis shows that, while all the 8 electrons in the second shell are

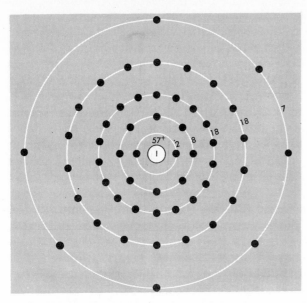

Fig. 12-16. The iodine atom, I(2,8,18,18,7).

held with about equal firmness, the first 2 electrons are held a little more firmly than the remaining 6. This means that the second shell really consists of two closely lying "subshells," one combining 2 and the other 6 electrons. By the same analysis, the third main shell is found to consist of three subshells, containing 2, 6, and 10 electrons, respectively. These facts can be shown pictorially as follows:

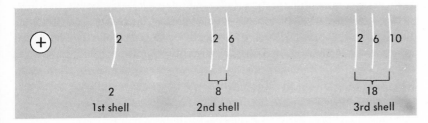

Fig. 12-17. The resolution of main shells into subshells.

It is not necessary to pursue this analysis further, for no new principle is involved. The reader, however, may find interest in this pattern of numbers, and may already see why the outer shell begins to fill before all the subshells of the previous shell are filled, and why there is a great tendency to have a "temporarily" complete shell with 8 electrons, as found in the inert gases (Exs. 18, 19).

Conclusion

The tremendous success of the Bohr theory, even when applied with approximations from the spectra and with the aid of the periodic system, would normally lead us to conclude this section with the glowing assurance that our knowledge of the interior of the atom is now precise and complete. Some sobering facts, however, prevent such a satisfaction. When exact calculations are carried out, even for the simpler atoms, the results are found to disagree in some respects with the observed spectra. Apparently the theory is not quite right and further examination raises even more fundamental difficulties. The theory does not specify what happens during the "jump" of the electron from one orbit to the other. Nor does it explain why a given orbit can contain so many electrons and no more. And what of the sizes of the orbits? They cannot be measured directly. We measure the energy differences in the spectra and from these calculate the distances at which the electrons are expected to be from the nucleus. But these distances are not measured directly. We do not even know whether "distance" has the same meaning in the atom as in ordinary experience. We do, however, know that the "distances" are roughly correct, since the sizes of the atoms determined from the density of the elements agree in a general way with the sizes calculated by the Bohr theory (Refs. 12.2, 12.3, and 12.4).

To obtain a better agreement between theory and experiment, other more complicated theories have been proposed. These are called "quantum mechanics" or "wave mechanics." These theories are highly mathematical and we do not propose to discuss them here, except to mention that they conceive of the electron *as a wave as well as a particle*. These theories do predict the wavelengths in the spectra with exact precision.

However, these theories are "nonvisual." The difficulty of conceiving of something as both a wave *and* a particle *at the same time* (mentioned in the chapter on light) reappears here, and additional difficulties arise. As a consequence, these mathematical *quantum* theories do not permit us to build a model of the atom or to imagine it in terms of ordinary experience. Exhaustive discussion of these theories for the past thirty years has led to the conclusion that the conditions within the atom cannot be visualized in terms of the mechanical concepts of ordinary experience. The concepts, distance, time, particle, wave, and the like, lose their meaning when applied inside the atom. Yet these theories predict the phenomena accurately and with certainty. (It is possible, of course, to conceive of an electron as a *wave alone,* and this conception has certain merits, as suggested in Ex. 21.)

The reassuring thing about the Bohr theory is that it does predict the phenomena almost as well as the newer mathematical theories. We know that the Bohr theory is not quite correct, but it has the advantage of permitting us to visualize a model and to reason from it. We use the Bohr theory, not because it is the "correct" model, but because it is the only model possible. Knowing this limitation, we can always correct our conclusions using the mathematical theories if the model leads us astray. But the model will generally lead to the correct conclusions (Ex. 20).

Thus, using the Bohr theory, and with information from the spectra and from the chemical properties of the elements, we have been able to determine and visualize the structure of the atoms. But if we can determine structure from the properties, then we should be able to do the converse. From the structure of the atoms it should be possible to explain and understand the chemical and physical properties of the elements. We shall embark on this project in the next section.

5. ATOMIC STRUCTURE AND THE CHEMICAL BEHAVIOR OF THE ELEMENTS

One of the most far-reaching outcomes of the theory of electron configuration is the understanding and explanation of the physical and chemical properties of the elements. On several occasions we have remarked that the chemical and physical properties of the elements depend upon the structure of their atoms. This is one of the most fundamental principles in all the study of matter. It is the explanatory principle of Democritus that differences in the various forms of matter are to be understood as due to differences in the sizes, shapes, motions, and arrangements of their particles. Having elucidated the structures of the atoms, we proceed to explain why each element is different from all the other elements, and why some elements are so similar to one another and yet so markedly different from other elements. We look for the specific part of the structure, whose similarity explains the similarity of properties in similar elements. We seek to pinpoint the part of the structure that is responsible for each specific chemical property, and to identify the precise changes in structure which are responsible for the drastic changes observed in a given chemical reaction.

In interpreting properties in terms of structure we make use of the periodic system, taking advantage of the tremendous integration of knowledge that it represents. As discussed at length in Chapter 10, the periodic table is a comprehensive organization of all the elements, their properties and reactions. The metals are on the left-hand side of the table, the nonmetals on the right, and that unique group of elements, the inert gases, in a single column just after the nonmetals (or just before the metals). Throughout the periodic system, the metallic and the nonmetallic properties vary. The most important metallic properties are electrical conductivity, reducing power, base-forming power, and positive valence. Similarly, the most important properties of the nonmetals are the opposite properties—namely, insulating power, oxidizing power, acid-forming power, and negative valence. The places in which these properties appear in the periodic system and the regularity with which they vary from row to row or from column to column provide a ready pattern in which to identify the structure that is responsible for the properties and to explain the properties in terms of the structure.

On examining the structures of the elements in the periodic system, and especially those in the main groups, we are impressed by a most obvious fact already noted earlier. The elements in a given group have the same number of electrons in their outermost shells. Thus, all the alkali metals have one electron, the alkaline earth metals of group II have two electrons, and the halogens in group VII have seven electrons in their outermost shells. This simplicity is shown by a comparison of their full structures.

Structure and Properties

Similarity of Structure in the Same Chemical Family

Li 2,1	Be 2,2	F 2,7
Na 2,8,1	Mg 2,8,2	Cl 2,8,7
K 2,8,8,1	Ca 2,8,8,2	Br 2,8,18,7
Rb 2,8,18,8,1	Ba 2,8,18,8,2	I 2,8,18,18,7
Cs 2,8,18,18,8,1	Sr 2,8,18,18,8,2	At 2,8,18,32,18,7
Fr 2,8,18,32,18,8,1	Ra 2,8,18,32,18,8,2	

A major principle emerges from the examination of these structures. Since the elements of each group are so markedly similar to one another, the chemical properties must be determined predominantly by the number of electrons in the outermost shell. Thus, in the alkali metals, the only feature common in their structures is the one electron in the outermost shell. This one electron, therefore, must be the chief factor in determining the properties of these elements. The fact that these atoms differ so widely in the number of shells and in the total number of electrons does not seem to make much difference. The presence of the other electrons and the other shells, with consequent differences in size, apparently have only a minor effect. It may make a difference in the *degree* of these properties (as we shall presently see), but the essential character of the element is determined by the one electron in the outermost shell.

Similar consideration of the other groups confirms this idea. The chemical properties of the alkaline earth metals in group II are determined predominantly by the two electrons in the outermost shells of their atoms. Likewise, the similarity of the chemical properties of the halogens in group VII are determined almost entirely by the seven electrons in the outer shells of their respective atoms. Similar statements can be made about the other main groups of the periodic system.

Since the number of electrons in the outermost shells is the predominant factor in determining the chemical properties of the atoms, we can condense further the notation of their structure and write the symbol of the element surrounded by as many dots as there are electrons in the outermost shell. Thus, all the elements of the second and third periods can be written as follows:

Second period   Li·   Be: B·   ·C·   ·N·   O: ·F: :Ne:

Third period   Na·   Mg: Al·   ·Si·   ·P·   S: ·Cl: :Ar:

For most of our discussion this notation contains all the information needed. We should keep in mind, of course, that in the second period the electrons are in the second shell and in the third period they are in the third shell, and to recall the whole structure, if necessary, in a given discussion.

Let us now see more precisely how the electrons in the outermost shell determine the properties, and consider first, the electrical conductivity. The alkali metals have one electron in the outermost shells of their atoms, and this electron is held rather loosely. In sodium, Na·, for example, the electron can be removed with only about 5 volts. A wire made of sodium consists of many atoms, each with a loosely held electron (See Fig. 12-18).

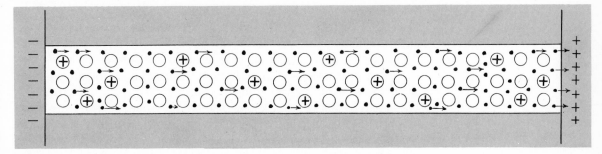

Fig. 12-18. Conduction of electricity in a metal due to surging of electrons from negative terminal to positive terminal.

If the wire is now placed in an electric field, across a potential of whatever origin, the electrons surge toward the positive terminal sliding from atom to atom without much resistance. The motion of these electrons *is* the electric current. Low resistance, of course, means high conductivity, and thus the high conductivity of sodium is explained.

The same reasoning explains the high conductivity of all the alkali metals. In fact, we may continue the reasoning and explain the small differences in the conductivity of the elements in this group. On going down the table, we find the lone electron in successive shells farther and farther out, and since the electron gets farther from the attracting nucleus, it is held less and less firmly. Therefore, the conductivity should *increase* down the table, and experiments show that it does. Taking into account all the factors involved (such as the packing of the atoms in the wire and the number of atoms in the cross section of the wire), it is possible to calculate, quite accurately, the conductivity of all the alkali metals, and thus explain the observed values. By similar reasoning we can explain in detail other electrical properties of the alkali metals, such as the photoelectric effect responsible for their use in the "electric eye" (Ex. 23).

The same reasoning will explain the decrease in conductivity on going from element to element toward the right, across a row in the table. The next element after sodium (11) is magnesium (12), and has two electrons in the outermost shell, Mg: Each of these electrons is more firmly held than the one in sodium. This is so because there are +12 charges on the nucleus of the magnesium atom and only +11 on the sodium nucleus. Perhaps a better way of seeing the contrast is to consider *as a single unit* that part of the atom inside the outermost shell. This is called the *kernel,* and for sodium as well as magnesium it consists of the nucleus and the first two shells that are completely filled. The net charge on the sodium kernel is +1, since there are +11 charges on the nucleus and 10 negative electrons in the first two shells. In magnesium the kernel has a net charge of +2.

$$\overset{+}{\text{Na}} \;\cdot \qquad\qquad\qquad \overset{++}{\text{Mg}} \;\;:$$

Since the electrons are held more firmly by the magnesium atom, they experience a greater resistance in sliding from atom to atom when the potential is applied to the wire. Hence the conductivity of magnesium should be smaller than that of sodium and experimentally this is found to be true.

On going across the table, the number of electrons increases, but so does the nuclear charge and the kernel charge. As a result, the electrons are held more and more firmly. Disregarding minor irregularities (due to the existence of subshells, and to differences in the packing of the atoms in the conductor), a general rise should occur in the resistance, or a drop in conductivity. This is exactly what is found. Silicon (14) is hardly a conductor—it is a "semiconductor"—and phosphorus is a nonconductor, by any ordinary standards. The next element, sulfur (16), is so poor a conductor that it is used as an insulator. The electrons are held so firmly they do not slide from atom to atom when a potential is applied to a bar of sulfur. It takes extremely high voltages to break down an insulator made of sulfur and to cause the motion of electrons through it. Thus there is a general and marked decrease in electrical conductivity, on going toward the right in any row in the periodic table.

This analysis brings out more clearly the distinction between metals and nonmetals. Ignoring for a moment the inert gases and hydrogen (which is a unique element), we can make the following statements. Metals are elements whose atoms contain one or a few electrons in their outermost shells, and hold these electrons rather weakly. In these elements, the outermost shells are just beginning to be filled. In the nonmetals, on the other hands, the atoms have several electrons in the outermost shells. The shells are nearly filled, and the electrons are *held quite firmly*. The fewer the electrons in the outermost shells and the more loosely they are held, the more pronounced the metallic character. The more nearly complete the shell, the more firmly the electrons are held and the more pronounced the nonmetallic character. Thus metallic character increases toward the *left* of the periodic table and *down* the columns. Francium (87) is the most metallic of the elements, because it has only one electron, and it has it on the seventh shell, the farthest out from the nucleus. Similarly, nonmetallic character decreases toward the *right* and *up* the columns. Fluorine (9) is, therefore, the most nonmetallic of the elements. It needs but one electron to complete its shell of eight, and this shell is nearest the nucleus, where the electrons are attracted the most strongly. Between these two extremes, the metallic character becomes less and less pronounced on moving toward the middle of the table, and the nonmetallic character decreases approaching the middle of the table from the opposite direction. Somewhere near the middle, actually nearer to the nonmetallic side, are the elements of intermediate character. Those intermediate elements show either both weak metallic and weak nonmetallic properties, or some of the metallic and some of the nonmetallic properties.

This conception of metallic and nonmetallic character and the other principles of the theory can now be applied to explain quite precisely the chemical properties and reactions of the elements. Perhaps the most fundamental of all questions regarding chemical properties is why do any chemical reactions take place. Chemical reaction means combinations and recombinations of atoms, and these imply attraction between atoms. When the atoms are neutral, the positive and negative charges exactly balance. Why is it then that the atoms do not remain neutral and not combine at all?

To explain this apparent paradox, we will examine those atoms that never combine with other atoms and hence do not have any chemical properties. These are the atoms of the inert gases. The molecules of these gases consist of but one atom, and the fact that they are gases down to very low temperatures means that the atoms have very little attraction for one another. Examination of their complete structures,

He 2
Ne 2,8
Ar 2,8,8
Kr 2,8,18,8
Xe 2,8,18,18,8
Rn 2,8,18,32,18,8

suggests a clue for their antisocial behavior. The outermost shells of the inert gases are either complete or "temporarily" complete. The first two elements have their outermost shells entirely complete, and the remaining have as their outer part two complete subshells of the higher shells. More elaborate mathematical analysis shows that the positive and negative electric forces are satisfied and that there are no stray forces of any consequence, outside these shells.

Let us now examine two typical atoms that do react. Sodium and chlorine are good examples. Sodium is one of the most active metals and chlorine is one of the most active nonmetals. When chlorine gas is passed over metallic sodium, a violent reaction takes place, a great deal of heat is given off, and sodium chloride—ordinary table salt—is formed.

Why Atoms React

$$Na + Cl \rightarrow NaCl$$

The electron theory provides an insight into what happens during this reaction. The sodium atom has one electron in the third shell, and this is held rather weakly. Only 5.1 electron volts will remove it. The chlorine atom, on the other hand, has seven electrons in the third shell, and these are held very firmly. It takes 13.0 electron volts to remove any one of them.

This does not give the answer but further reasoning will. *If there were* an *eighth* electron in the outermost shell of chlorine, this electron would also be held quite firmly. The energy can be calculated with the Bohr theory, but it can also be estimated roughly, by reasoning as follows: The seven positive charges on the chlorine kernel hold seven electrons with sufficient force to correspond to 13 electron volts of energy for each. If an eighth electron enters the shell—and there *is*

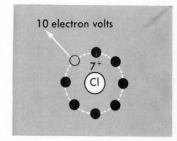

Fig. 12-19. About 10 electron volts are required to remove the first electron from the chloride ion $\left[:\ddot{C}l: \right]^{-}$. The kernel charge of +7 holds eight electrons.

room for just one more electron in the shell—then the seven positive charges of the kernel, that is, the same field, would hold all eight electrons, but with somewhat less energy for each. To be sure, the entering eighth electron would alter the field somewhat. It would repel the other seven electrons, and in turn be repelled by them, thus causing the shell to expand somewhat. But this would not alter the fact that each of the electrons would still be held very firmly. A fair estimate is that about 10 electron volts will be necessary to remove any one of them. This reasoning is confirmed by measuring the *first* ionization energy of the

chloride ion $\left[:\ddot{C}l: \right]^{-}$. The energy required to remove the eighth electron is found to be 10.2 volts (Ex. 25).

Electron Transfer   Let us now return to the reaction between sodium and chlorine. If a sodium atom holding its electron with about 5 electron volts of energy happens to come near a chlorine atom, which can hold an *eighth* electron with about 10 electron volts, then the chlorine atom will pull the electron away from the sodium atom.

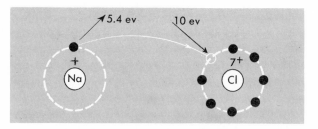

Fig. 12-20. The sodium electron is attracted by the chlorine atom more strongly than by the sodium atom.

In a real sense, the electron from the sodium atom *falls into* the shell of the chlorine atom where the attraction is greater (or the energy lower). It gives up the difference in energy in the form of heat or light. It acts no differently from a stone falling from a high mountain into a valley where the attraction of the earth is greater and changing its potential energy into heat as it lands.

The transfer of the electron from the sodium atom to the chlorine atom has other consequences. The sodium atom, having lost one electron, is no longer neutral; it is a positive ion, Na^{+}. Similarly, the chlorine atom, having acquired an additional electron, is a negative ion

$\left[:\ddot{C}l: \right]^{-}$. If there were only one sodium ion and one chloride ion, isolated from other ions, the two would attract one another and form a molecule of sodium chloride, $Na^{+}Cl^{-}$. However, in proximity to other ions, other interactions will occur. If they happen to be in the molten state, each sodium ion will be attracted by chloride ions from all directions, and each chloride ion will be attracted by sodium ions from all directions. Each ion would then move more or less independently, as a separate particle. If, on the other hand, the temperature is low enough to form a solid, the Na^{+} ions and the Cl^{-} ions will arrange themselves in the pattern of a crystal, each surrounded by six atoms of the opposite sign. In any case, the product of the reaction consists of separate positive and negative ions. There is ample experimental evidence for these conclusions. Molten sodium chloride, as well as solutions of it in water, conduct the electric current. Moreover the charge on the ions can be measured by measuring the amount of charge required to discharge 1 gram-atom of each (Ex. 27).

On reexamining the reaction between sodium and chlorine we get a further insight into what happens. The sodium atom, in losing one electron, remains with only two shells; but now its outermost shell is the second shell *and it is complete*. Its full electron structure is $Na^+(2,8)$, which is identical with the structure of the inert gas neon, $Ne(2,8)$. It differs from the neon atom, to be sure, in that it is a positively charged particle, but that does not seem to interfere with its stability. Similarly, the chlorine atom, $Cl(2,8,7)$, on gaining one electron completes its third shell, and attains the structure $Cl^-(2,8,8)$, which is identical with the structure of the inert gas argon, $Ar(2,8,8)$, except that it is a negative particle. The full change is summarized in the equation:

$$Na\cdot + \cdot\ddot{\underset{..}{Cl}}: \;\rightarrow\; Na^+ + \left[:\ddot{\underset{..}{Cl}}:\right]^-$$
$$(2,8,1)\quad(2,8,7)\quad\quad(2,8)\quad\quad(2,8,8)$$

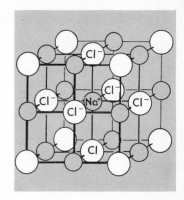

Fig. 12-21. In a crystal of sodium chloride each sodium ion (Na^+) is attracted by six surrounding chloride ions (Cl^-).

The cause of the reaction is the low attraction of the metallic atoms for their electrons, coupled with the high attraction of the nonmetallic atoms for extra electrons. From this analysis we derive the guiding principle that explains why this chemical reaction takes place. The inert gas structures are extraordinarily stable. The configurations of sodium and chlorine are unstable if the atoms are next to one another. The attractive forces of the sodium atom for its own electron are too weak, and the attractive forces of the chlorine atom for this electron are too strong by comparison. Therefore the electron leaves the sodium atom and falls into the shell of the chlorine atom. In both cases the atoms either lose or gain electrons and in the process assume the stable configuration of the inert gases. They do so even at the expense of electrical neutrality. The sodium atom (the metal atoms) lose electrons, thus becoming positive ions; the chlorine atoms (the nonmetal atoms) gain electrons, and become negative ions.

The principle is general and is applicable to other elements. The same analysis can be carried out with all the alkali metals in their reactions with chlorine to form the chlorides. In each case the alkali metal atom gives up electrons to assume the structure of the inert gas atom that just precedes it. Similarly, the atoms of all the halogens react like chlorine, and form negatively charged ions with the structures of the inert gas atoms that immediately follow them. The principle is applicable to the alkaline-earth metals of group II. In this case, the atoms have two electrons, held somewhat more firmly than the one electron in group I, but still quite weakly in comparison to the halogens. Consequently, these atoms lose their electrons to the halogen atoms. The magnesium atom, for example, loses two electrons, which are attracted by two separate chlorine atoms. It becomes a doubly positively charged magnesium ion with the structure of neon, $Mg^{++}(2,8)$, and attracts the two negative chloride ions that have been formed in the process.

$$\text{Mg:} \; + \; 2 \cdot \overset{..}{\underset{..}{\text{Cl}}}\text{:} \; \longrightarrow \; \overline{}\text{:}\overset{..}{\underset{..}{\text{Cl}}}\text{:} \diagdown \overset{++}{\text{Mg}} \diagup \text{:}\overset{..}{\underset{..}{\text{Cl}}}\text{:}\overline{}$$

Incidentally, this also explains why the formula for magnesium chloride is $MgCl_2$ (see valence, below).

Extension of the same ideas to the elements of group III shows that these atoms lose three electrons and form ions with a triple positive charge. For example, aluminum (13), Al: loses three electrons to become $Al^{+++}(2,8)$ ion and the formula for aluminum chloride is $AlCl_3$. On the nonmetallic side of the table, the atoms in group VI have six electrons on their outermost shells, and hence lack two electrons to complete them. Thus, the oxygen atom $\overset{..}{\text{O}}\text{:}$, gains two electrons to form the oxide ion $\left[\text{:}\overset{..}{\underset{..}{\text{O}}}\text{:} \right]^{=}$. Thus, at least for reactions between the active metals and the active nonmetals, the principle can be stated as follows: *The atoms tend to lose or to gain electrons, and assume the configurations of the atoms of the nearest inert gas.* We trust that the reader will not interpret this statement as meaning that the atoms "desire" to assume complete shells, for esthetic reasons. The above analysis shows that the inert-gas structures represent the balance of forces, in which the energy of the system is lowest.

Electrovalence   Without realizing it, we have already explained *valence,* at least in those compounds in which the atoms exist as positive or negative ions. This type of valence has been known for a long time and is called *electrovalence.* It is numerically equal to the charge on the ion and is determined experimentally by measuring the number of faradays (96,500 coulombs) that are required to discharge 1 gram-atom during electrolysis. Thus, since 2 faradays ($2 \times 6 \times 10^{23}$ electrons) are required to liberate 1 gram-atom (6×10^{23} atoms) of magnesium, at the negative pole, each magnesium ion requires two electrons to be discharged, and hence has a charge of $+2$. The electron theory explains *why* the magnesium atom should have a valence of $+2$. It has two electrons on the outermost shell which it loses in forming compounds. Electrovalence, therefore, is the number of electrons lost (positive) or gained (negative) by the atoms in forming their compounds.

It is also quite clear why elements in the same main group of the periodic system exhibit the same valence. They have the same number of electrons in their outermost shells. The atoms of group I have one electron that they give up and hence acquire a valence of $+1$; those of group II can give up two electrons, and exhibit a valence of $+2$. Thus, on the metal side, the electrovalence is the same as the group number and it is positive. It is equal to the number of electrons in the outermost shell, which can be easily lost. On the nonmetal side, the electrovalence is the number of electrons needed to complete the shell of eight. It is numerically equal to the group number subtracted from eight, and it is negative.

Returning to the guiding principle we can now explain the general phenomenon of chemical activity and the various types and degrees of chemical activity that the elements exhibit. Chemical activity is the tendency of the atoms to assume inert gas configurations—to assume structures with the lowest energy. The most active metals are the alkali metals, because their atoms have only one electron to lose, and of these elements, francium (87) is the most active, since its atom has the electron on a shell farthest out. As the attraction for electrons increases, either because the electrons are on shells nearer the nucleus or because there are more electrons on the outer shell, or for both reasons, the chemical activity of the metals decreases. In the activity series of the metals, the alkali metals are at the top; the elements of the next few groups are in the middle; and at the bottom, are the inactive elements of the transition subgroups, or those near the nonmetal side. Thus, while the exact position of a metal in the activity series is a measure of the relative attraction for electrons (taking all the factors involved under the condition under which they are measured), the general trend found in the series confirms and, in turn, is explained by the electron theory (Ex. 29).

By similar reasoning, the most active nonmetals are the elements that have the strongest attraction for electrons. Consequently, the halogens are the most active nonmetals because their atoms lack but one electron to complete their shells of eight. Of the halogen atoms the fluorine atom is the most active, because the extra electron it attracts enters the shell nearest the nucleus, where the attraction is strongest. As the attraction for the extra electrons required to fill the shell decreases, either because the shells are farther out or because more electrons are needed to fill the shell, or for both reasons, the nonmetallic activity decreases. Thus, chlorine is less active than fluorine, because the electron needed is on the third shell instead of the second. Similarly, oxygen is less active than fluorine, because it needs two electrons to fill the shell, instead of one. In this way we can explain the relative position of the nonmetals in the activity series of the nonmetals (p. 273).

Again without realizing we have almost explained oxidizing and reducing activity, as well as oxidation and reduction. Long before the electron theory was developed, "oxidation" was defined as the "burning" of a substance in oxygen or in other nonmetals. On reexamining the reaction of sodium with chlorine, which is the "burning" of sodium in chlorine, we get a new insight into the process.

$$Na \cdot + : \overset{..}{\underset{..}{Cl}} : \longrightarrow \overset{+}{Na} \: : \overset{..}{\underset{..}{Cl}} : ^{-}$$

In this reaction, the sodium is oxidized. But now, in terms of the electron theory, the sodium atom *loses* an electron in the process. Therefore, *oxidation* of a metal is the *loss* of electrons by its atoms. Similarly, the other terms can be reinterpreted. The chlorine, which is the oxidizing agent, *gains* electrons in the process. Since the oxidizing agent is reduced during the reaction, *reduction is the gain* of electrons. The *reducing agent loses* electrons; and the less attraction it has for its electrons, the more easily it loses them and the greater its reducing power. The *oxidizing agent gains* electrons; and the greater the attraction it has for electrons, the greater its oxidizing power.

The reader will recognize at once that the chemical activity of the metals is reducing activity, and the chemical activity of the nonmetals is oxidizing activity. The more weakly the metal atoms hold the electrons, the more easily they will give up the electrons and the greater the reducing power of the atoms. Hence the reducing power increases toward the *left* and *down* the table. Similarly, the greater the attraction for electrons, the greater the oxidizing power of the nonmetals. Hence the oxidizing power increases toward the *right* and *up* the table.

In a given chemical reaction, the violence of the reaction depends on both the activity of the metal and the activity of the nonmetal. The reaction will release more energy as the *difference* in the attraction between the metal atom and the nonmetal atom increases. The farther apart the elements are in the periodic system, the more violent the reaction. Thus the reaction between francium (87) and fluorine (9) is the most violent. Fluorine has the greatest attraction for electrons and francium the least. Hence francium releases the electron without much expenditure of energy, the greater part of the energy released during the "fall" of the electron into the fluorine atom being given off as heat or light. Reactions between atoms less dissimilar than these two extremes result in less violence. The nearer two atoms are to the middle of the table, the smaller the difference in their attraction for electrons, and the smaller the tendency to react, or to release much energy, if they do react.

These conclusions can be rephrased in terms of the octet picture. If the metal atoms have one or two electrons in their outermost shell, they lose them rather easily; if the nonmetal atoms lack one or two electrons, they gain them easily. Consequently, reactions between these metals and nonmetals will take place readily and be quite energetic. An atom with three or four electrons, however, will not give them up so easily. Nor will an atom lacking three or four electrons have sufficient attraction to hold three or four extra electrons to complete its shell. The mutual repulsion of all these extra electrons makes such structures unstable. As a result, adjacent elements in the middle groups of the periodic system either do not react with one another or react with release of small amounts of energy. For the same reasons ions with +3, +4, or −3 charges are rare and simple ions with charges of −4 are never found.

Let us now summarize the electron theory developed so far. It logically explains in accordance with the principles of physics why chemical reactions take place at all. Atoms react with one another to form the more stable structures of the inert gases. The metal ions lose electrons, and the nonmetal ions gain them, forming positive and negative ions, respectively. The theory explains why the compounds between metals and nonmetals are conductors of electricity in the fluid state. It explains valence as the charge on the ions and predicts the formulas of compounds. It explains chemical activity and specifically oxidation and reduction as loss or gain of electrons. Finally the theory explains why some reactions are violent, and others are mild or do not occur.

The theory in its simplest form does not by any means, however, explain all chemical reactions. A great many chemical reactions take place between adjacent elements in the periodic system. This is especially true among the nonmetals, which form numerous compounds with each other. Rather significantly, the majority of these compounds are nonconductors, either in the molten state or in solution. Obviously these compounds do not consist of ions. Atoms apparently can combine and assume more stable structures, with lower energy, even though they do not become ions. We will attempt to modify the theory in order to explain these cases, but without doing violence to any principle.

The best approach to this problem is with an extreme case. As the reader knows, chlorine gas has the formula Cl_2, and contains two chlorine atoms per molecule. Apparently, two chlorine atoms have a more stable structure (lower energy) when they are combined as a pair in a molecule than when they exist as separate atoms. Each chlorine atom has seven electrons in the outermost shell. When two chlorine atoms come close to one another, it is still possible for the lone electron of one atom to "fall" into the unfilled shell of the other atom, giving the following arrangement:

$$: \overset{..}{\underset{..}{Cl}} \cdot \;\; \overset{\longleftarrow}{\underset{\longrightarrow}{+}} \;\; \cdot \overset{..}{\underset{..}{Cl}} : \;\; \text{------------} \;\; : \overset{..}{\underset{..}{Cl}} : \overset{..}{\underset{..}{Cl}} :$$

Comparison of these structures shows that the two chlorine atoms in the arrangement on the right have *lower* energy than the two separate atoms on the left. Each of the electrons between the two atoms is now attracted quite strongly by *both* atoms instead of one.

Thus, we salvage in a modified form the principle of "complete shells of eight." Each chlorine atom has eight electrons in its third shell, but with the compromise that two of the electrons are simultaneously in the third shell of the other chlorine atom.

This pair of electrons is *shared* between the two chlorine atoms. Since each chlorine atom attracts the shared pair of electrons with equal strength, the electrons cannot be removed from either atom; and thus neither atom can become a negative ion with a full complement of eight electrons. The two atoms stay together, by their mutual strong attraction for the same pair of electrons. The pair of electrons serves as a "cement," keeping the atoms together and is called an *electron-pair bond*. As a consequence, the chlorine molecule does not ionize; this is confirmed from the fact that liquid chlorine is a nonconductor.

Comparison between the chlorine molecule and sodium chloride brings out the similarities and differences between the two extreme modes of combination of atoms to form molecules.

$$\overset{+}{Na} \;\; : \overset{..}{\underset{..}{Cl}} : \overset{-}{} \qquad\qquad\qquad : \overset{..}{\underset{..}{Cl}} : \overset{..}{\underset{..}{Cl}} :$$

In both molecules the chlorine atom is surrounded by eight electrons. In both cases there is an electron pair between the atoms. Beyond this point, however, there are marked differences. In the chlorine molecule on the right, the electron pair between the atoms is held with equal strength by the other chlorine atom, and the molecule does not ionize, as already explained. In sodium chloride, on the other hand, the situation is markedly different. The electron pair between the atoms is attracted strongly by the chlorine but very weakly by the sodium. The slightest thermal agitation at almost any temperature above absolute zero would cause the chlorine to move independently, carrying the elec-

trons with it, thus becoming a negatively charged chloride ion, $\left[\, :\ddot{\underset{..}{Cl}}: \,\right]^{-}$

and leaving behind a positive sodium ion, Na^+. The attraction of other sodium ions for the chloride ion, and of other chloride ions for the sodium ions would contribute further to overcoming whatever little attraction there might be between the chlorine and the sodium atoms under consideration.

Conductors and Insulators

This analysis gives a deeper insight into ionization and ultimately explains why certain substances are ionic and others are not. It all depends on how much difference there is in the attraction of the two atoms for the electron pair between them. We will consider a whole series of molecules formed by chlorine atoms combining with the atoms of the third period elements.

$$\text{Na}\overset{..}{\cdot}\overset{..}{Cl}\!: \quad \text{Mg}\overset{..}{\cdot}\overset{..}{Cl}\!: \quad :\overset{..}{Cl}\overset{\cdot}{\cdot}\text{Al}\overset{..}{\cdot}\overset{..}{Cl}\!: \quad :\overset{..}{Cl}\overset{\cdot}{\cdot}\text{Si}\overset{..}{\cdot}\overset{..}{Cl}\!: \quad :\overset{..}{Cl}\overset{\cdot}{\cdot}\text{P}\overset{..}{\cdot}\overset{..}{Cl}\!: \quad :\overset{..}{Cl}\overset{\cdot}{\cdot}\text{S}\overset{..}{\cdot}\overset{..}{Cl}\!: \quad :\overset{..}{Cl}\overset{..}{\cdot}\overset{..}{Cl}\!:$$

These structures can be written by pairing the lone electron of chlorine with one electron of the other atom. The larger dots distinguish the electrons originally belonging to chlorine. It is interesting that except for the first three cases, the other atom also has eight electrons surrounding it. Each electron pair between the atoms acts as a "bond," holding the atoms together by their mutual attraction for it. These bonds are not equally strong, however, because the atoms do not attract the electron pair between them with equal strength.

Consideration of the *relative* attraction of the joining atoms for the electron pair between them brings out significant differences in these molecules. In this series, the chlorine atom is combined successively with atoms that range from the most metallic sodium to the least metallic, which is chlorine itself. In the first compound, NaCl, the electron pair is attracted strongly by the chlorine but very weakly by the sodium. This compound, therefore, is expected to ionize freely, and experiments show that it is ionized even in the solid state. In the second compound, $MgCl_2$, the magnesium atom attracts the electrons somewhat more strongly than sodium, but still quite weakly compared to the chlorine atom. Consequently this compound will ionize, but not quite 100 percent. In $AlCl_3$, the aluminum atom attracts the electron pair still more strongly, and begins to give to the chlorine atom some serious competition. As a result, molten $AlCl_3$ ionizes only to a small extent.

In the next compound, $SiCl_4$, chlorine encounters real (strong) competition for the electron pair. The silicon atom attracts the electron pairs quite strongly, and although it attracts them less strongly than chlorine, it will not let them go. As a result $SiCl_4$, which is a liquid at ordinary temperatures, is an extremely poor conductor. To the extent that it does conduct, however, the chlorine goes to the positive pole, showing that it is a negative chloride ion and has succeeded in pulling the electron away from silicon. There are other ways of showing that the chlorine in $SiCl_4$ has a greater "hold" on the electrons than silicon, but we shall not go into them here (Ex. 34). In the next compound, PCl_3, the attraction of phosphorus is fairly comparable to that of chlorine, and in SCl_2, the attraction of sulfur is more nearly equal to that of chlorine. These compounds become progressively better insulators, and their related electrical properties decrease progressively. In the last molecule, Cl_2, the attraction of the two atoms for the electron pair becomes, of course, equal and liquid chlorine is the best insulator of this series.

In this discussion, we have uncovered another difference between compounds formed by electron transfer and those formed by electron sharing. In the former, the compounds consist of positive and negative ions, with little attraction between any two particles other than the electrostatic attraction between oppositely charged particles. Consequently, the ions move independently in the liquid state, being attracted by many particles around them. In the solid state, however, these particles assume a regular pattern, alternating between positive and negative ions. As a result each particle is held strongly by the neighbors in the pattern of the crystal (p. 377). The substance, therefore, is saltlike and has a high melting point. It requires high thermal agitation to break these ions loose from the crystal, and hence to melt the solid.

In the compounds formed by electron sharing, on the other hand, the main attraction is between the joining atoms. Each atom strongly attracts the shared pair of electrons and, as a consequence, the atoms stay together. These substances form *true molecules*. The molecule has a stable structure, but has little attraction for neighboring molecules. As a result, these substances are either gases or liquids with low boiling points or solids with low melting points. The molecules of these substances retain their structures on melting or on boiling. They retain most of their structures even during drastic chemical reactions (Ex. 35).

Thus, by comparing the relative attraction of the atoms for the electron pair between them, we can predict whether a given molecule will be formed by electron transfer or by electron sharing, and, in the latter case, estimate the "degree of sharing." Similarly, we can predict which substances will be good conductors and which will be insulators. We can explain why some substances ionize extensively, why others ionize slightly, and why others do not ionize at all. To be sure we cannot tell without numerical data just what degree of ionization a given difference in attraction for the electron pair represents, but we can make *relative* comparisons. For example, knowing that both magnesium chloride and aluminum chloride ionize, we can tell which will ionize the more extensively.

Acids and Bases

The explanation of ionization as due to differences in the attraction for the electron pair has prepared the ground for the explanation of another universal chemical reaction. We refer to the phenomena of acids and bases, which are exhibited by all the elements. Before entering that discussion, however, it is necessary to consider the chemistry of that unique element, hydrogen. The reader will recall that the hydrogen ion, H^+, plays an important role in the properties and reactions of acids and bases. In a real sense all the phenomena of acids and bases are due to the properties of hydrogen ion, which is the most unusual ion.

The hydrogen atom is the simplest of the atoms and has one electron in the first shell, $H\cdot$. At first sight, it appears similar to the alkali metals, but the physical properties belie this similarity. Hydrogen is a gas down to very low temperatures, condenses to a clear liquid, and freezes to a waxy transparent solid. In none of these states does it conduct electric current, nor does it have any of the other physical properties of the metals. Physically, hydrogen is a typical nonmetal. Chemically the similarity to the alkali metals is more formal than real. To be sure it is a reducing agent, and under certain conditions, it loses an electron to form a positive H^+ ion. In these properties, it acts like a metal. But its compounds with the halogens are not saltlike, and it forms numerous compounds with other nonmetals, the vast majority of which are not conductors. To make matters more confusing, it reacts with metals to form saltlike substances such as NaH, in which the hydrogen carries a *negative* charge $[H:]^-$ (Ex. 36). Thus hydrogen shows a curious mixture of metallic and nonmetallic properties.

The mystery is dispelled by a closer examination of its structure. Since the hydrogen atom, $H\cdot$, has one electron in its outermost shell, we would expect a similarity to the alkali metals. But it is equally fair to consider it as *lacking* one electron to fill its outer shell, and assume the structure of the inert gas helium. In this respect it is similar to the halogens. When it *loses* the electron, it acts like an alkali metal, forming H^+ ions; when it reacts with the metals, such as $Na\cdot$, it *absorbs* an electron to form $[H:]^-$ ions. In the vast majority of the reactions, however, the hydrogen atom neither loses nor gains electrons, but shares them with other atoms. This follows readily from its high ionization energy. Whereas 4 or 5 electron volts will remove the electron of the alkali metals, it takes no less than 13.5 electron volts to remove it from hydrogen. This energy is about as high as the first ionization energy of the typical nonmetals. As a consequence, the hydrogen atom shares electrons with other atoms. A hydrogen atom $H\cdot$ shares an electron with another hydrogen atom, forming a hydrogen molecule, $H:H$, which is a gas. This explains why pure hydrogen is neither a conductor nor metallic in any of its physical properties.

The hydrogen atom shares electrons with the atoms of all the nonmetals. With a chlorine atom, for example, it forms a molecule of hydrogen chloride.

$$H\cdot \ + \ \cdot \overset{\cdot\cdot}{\underset{\cdot\cdot}{Cl}}: \ \rightarrow \ H:\overset{\cdot\cdot}{\underset{\cdot\cdot}{Cl}}:$$

This compound is a gas, boiling at $-83.7°$ C. Even in the liquid state, pure hydrogen chloride is an extremely poor conductor of electricity. Hence the electron pair is shared in the molecule, as would be expected from a comparison of the ionization energies (13.5 for hydrogen and 13.0 for chlorine). With oxygen, hydrogen forms water, two hydrogen atoms combining with one oxygen atom to form a molecule.

$$2\text{H}\cdot \ + \ \cdot \overset{..}{\underset{..}{\text{O}}}\cdot \ \rightarrow \ \text{H}\!:\!\overset{..}{\underset{..}{\text{O}}}\!:\!\text{H}$$

Water, too, is an extremely poor conductor; when pure, it is even poorer than hydrogen chloride. Three hydrogen atoms share electrons with a nitrogen atom, forming ammonia, $\text{H}\!:\!\overset{..}{\text{N}}\!:\!\text{H}$, and four hydrogen atoms
$$\text{H}$$
combine with a carbon atom to form methane, $\text{H}\!:\!\overset{..}{\text{C}}\!:\!\text{H}$. Hydrogen
$$\text{H}$$
forms similar compounds with the other nonmetals. All these compounds are either gases or low-boiling liquids, water being somewhat of an exception. The conductivity of these compounds, in the pure liquid state, is either extremely small or absent altogether. There is no question that they are formed by electron sharing.

An unexpected phenomenon, however, occurs when some of these liquids are mixed. If a small quantity of hydrogen chloride is added to water, the resulting solution is an excellent conductor. It is ordinary hydrochloric acid. The solution contains H^+ ions and Cl^- ions, as shown by electrolysis measurements. What has happened, obviously, is that the hydrogen chloride molecules have ionized, and the bond between hydrogen and chlorine has been broken. But why should this happen under these conditions? Why is hydrogen chloride a nonconductor when pure, and an excellent conductor in water solution?

The Hydronium Ion

To understand this phenomenon, two factors must be considered. The nature of the hydrogen ion and the effect of the environment—the effect of the solvent. Of all the ions, the hydrogen ion is unique. *It is but a nucleus.* Whereas all the other ions are approximately as big as ordinary atoms having at least one shell, the proton is extremely small— about 10,000 times smaller in diameter. If the proton leaves an $\text{H}\!:\!\overset{..}{\underset{..}{\text{Cl}}}\!:$ molecule, it is now an independent particle of small size, with a strong positive charge, and seeks the negative electrons wherever it can find them.

The environment now assumes importance. All around the proton are water molecules, $\text{H}\!:\!\overset{..}{\underset{..}{\text{O}}}\!:\!\text{H}$, with two unshared pairs of electrons in the periphery of the oxygen atom. Consequently, the proton attaches itself to one of the electron pairs of a water molecule, thus forming a new ion with a positive charge, $\left[\ \text{H}\!:\!\overset{..}{\underset{..}{\text{O}}}\!:\!\text{H}\ \right]^+$, and leaving behind the
$$\text{H}$$

chlorine with a negative charge, which becomes the *chloride ion.* The change is indicated as follows:

$$\overset{\frown}{H\!:\!\ddot{O}\!:\!H} \ + \ H\!:\!\ddot{C}l\!: \ \rightarrow \ \left[\begin{array}{c} H \\ \ddots \\ H\!:\!\ddot{O}\!:\!H \end{array} \right]^{+} + \left[\ :\!\ddot{\ddot{C}}l\!: \ \right]^{-}$$

The attractions, of course, are reciprocal. A water molecule coming near a hydrogen chloride molecule would attract the proton away from the chlorine, thus forming the same two ions.

This explanation is, of course, based on theory, but it is supported by energy considerations. The electron pairs around the chlorine, $:\!\ddot{\ddot{C}}l\!:$, are held quite strongly, since the charge on the chlorine kernel is +7, and there is only one extra electron. Around the oxygen atom, $:\!\ddot{\ddot{O}}\!:$, on the other hand, the electron pairs are held less strongly, since the charge on the oxygen kernel is only +6 and there are two extra electrons. Without going into secondary factors, it is quite clear that the electrons are held less firmly on the oxygen, and hence the proton is attracted to the electron pair there, rather than remaining with the chlorine. The result is the formation of $\left[\begin{array}{c} H \\ \ddots \\ H\!:\!\ddot{O}\!:\!H \end{array} \right]^{+}$ ions and Cl⁻ ions.

We can now explain the small but finite conductivity of pure water. It is possible for a proton to leave one water molecule and attach itself to the electron pair of another water molecule.

$$\overset{\frown}{H\!:\!\ddot{O}\!:\!H} \ + \ H\!:\!\ddot{O}\!:\!H \ \longrightarrow \ \left[\begin{array}{c} H \\ \ddots \\ H\!:\!\ddot{O}\!:\!H \end{array} \right]^{+} + \left[\ :\!\ddot{O}\!:\!H \ \right]^{-}$$

When this happens 2 ions are formed: the positive $\left[\begin{array}{c} H \\ \ddots \\ H\!:\!\ddot{O}\!:\!H \end{array} \right]^{+}$ ion and the negative $\left[\ :\!\ddot{O}\!:\!H \ \right]^{-}$ ion. However, there is no good reason for a proton to leave an oxygen atom that has only *one other* hydrogen atom attached to it, leaving a negative ion behind it, and go to a neutral molecule where the oxygen atom has *two* hydrogen atoms already attached to it. Those few ions that venture to do so, due to accidental high thermal agitation, quickly return to the $\left[\ :\!\ddot{O}\!:\!H \ \right]^{-}$ ion, and neutralize it. Consequently, water is essentially a nonconductor. However, at any given moment a *few* protons are temporarily attached to water molecules —about two molecules per billion—and this explains the small ionization of water. Similar reasoning explains the small ionization of other pure liquids (Ex. 37).

Thus the electron theory explains why hydrogen chloride is an acid, **Acids** and in fact what an acid really is. An acid is a hydrogen compound which, when dissolved in water, forms conducting solutions by reacting with

the water forming positive $\left[\begin{array}{c} \text{H} \\ \text{H:O:H} \end{array} \right]^+$ ions and negative ions char-

acteristic of the acid. The $\left[\begin{array}{c} \text{H} \\ \text{H:O:H} \end{array} \right]^+$ ion is called the hydronium ion.

Since it is really a proton attached to a water molecule the hydronium ion can be written as $H^+(H_2O)$. It is a *hydrated* hydrogen ion. In talking about water solutions, we may write it simply as H^+ provided we remember that it is hydrated. All the common properties of the acids are due to the hydrogen ion which is the ion they have in common.

A great many hydrogen compounds behave like hydrogen chloride. They are nonconductors in the pure state but conduct in water solution. These are acids, and form hydrogen ions. Among the common acids are the following: HCl, HBr, HI, and the more complex HNO_3, $HClO_4$, H_2SO_4, H_3PO_4, and CH_3CO_2H. Sulfuric acid, for example, though hardly a conductor when pure, ionizes in water as follows:

$$2H:O:H + H:O:S:O:H \rightarrow 2\left[\begin{array}{c} \text{H} \\ \text{H:O:H} \end{array} \right]^+ + \left[\begin{array}{c} :O: \\ :O:S:O: \\ :O: \end{array} \right]^=$$

Note that the proton leaves the oxygen of sulfuric acid, in preference to the oxygen in water.

The reader should not get the impression, however, that all the hydrogen compounds are acids or that all acids are equally strong. The vast majority of the hydrogen compounds do not dissolve in water, and of those that do dissolve, only a relatively small number act as conductors. Moreover, of those that conduct, only a few are excellent conductors, the majority ranging from moderate to extremely poor. Since ionization is responsible for conductivity, it must depend on very special conditions and on a delicate balance of attractions. The relative strength of these attractions determines whether a hydrogen compound will ionize and how extensive that ionization will be.

The theory permits us to estimate the relative strength of the attractions, for the proton. The general formula for an acid can be written as $H:\ddot{X}:$, where X is either a single atom or an atom in a larger molecule. The reaction between the water and the acid will

$$H:O:H + \left[H:\ddot{X}: \text{——} \right] \rightarrow \left[\begin{array}{c} \text{H} \\ \text{H:O:H} \end{array} \right]^+ + \left[:\ddot{X}: \text{——} \right]^-$$

take place only if the proton is attracted more strongly by the electron pair in the water molecule than by the electron pair in $:\overset{..}{X}:$. This in turn will depend on how strongly X attracts the electron pair. If X has a strong attraction, which means that the positive electric field is strong at the distance of the shell, then this hydrogen will leave X and prefer the electron pair of the water molecule, resulting in extensive ionization. If, on the other hand, X has a weak attraction for the electron pair (relative to the water molecule), the proton will stay with X, and the substance will not ionize. It will not be an acid. The intermediate cases are obvious. If X attracts the electrons about as strongly as the oxygen of the water molecule, then some protons will leave and some will stay, and the substance will ionize to some extent, depending on the relative attractions. Therefore, whether a hydrogen compound is an acid and whether it is a strong or a weak acid depend on the nature of X.

This analysis explains why acids are characteristically compounds of nonmetals. Nonmetal atoms have high attraction for electrons in their periphery. If X is a nonmetal atom it will have a strong attraction for electrons, and the proton will be released readily. The more nonmetallic the atom, the stronger the acid. Thus HCl is a much stronger acid than H_2S,

$$H:\overset{..}{\underset{..}{Cl}}: \qquad\qquad H:\overset{..}{\underset{..}{S}}:H$$

because chlorine has a greater attraction for electrons than sulfur. Similarly, PH_3 is even weaker than H_2S. In fact it is hardly an acid.

The same reasoning holds for the more complex molecules. In the most common acids, X usually contains oxygen—a nonmetal attached to some other nonmetal. Considering perchloric acid and sulfuric acid, whose structures are comparable,

$$\begin{array}{cc}
:\overset{..}{O}: & :\overset{..}{O}: \\
H:\overset{..}{\underset{..}{O}}:\overset{..}{\underset{..}{Cl}}:\overset{..}{\underset{..}{O}}: & H:\overset{..}{\underset{..}{O}}:\overset{..}{\underset{..}{S}}:\overset{..}{\underset{..}{O}}:H: \\
:\overset{..}{\underset{..}{O}}: & :\overset{..}{\underset{..}{O}}:
\end{array}$$

we can readily estimate their relative strengths. In the first molecule the central atom is chlorine with 7^+ charges on the kernel. Consequently all the electrons including those on the oxygen atoms in the periphery are held very firmly—more firmly than the electrons in the water molecule. Perchloric acid, therefore, is a very strong acid. In the second molecule the central atom is sulfur, with a charge of only 6^+ on the kernel. Consequently the electrons are held less strongly than in the perchloric acid, and the sulfuric acid is weaker than perchloric, though still fairly strong. By similar reasoning we can explain why phosphoric acid, H_3PO_4, is weaker than sulfuric, and why it is only a moderately strong acid. In this analysis secondary factors, such as the number of hydrogen atoms per molecule, have been neglected; but when these are considered in full, they do not invalidate but rather confirm the general conclusion that the more nonmetallic the element the stronger the acid (Ex. 38).

The regularities that the acid property exhibits in the periodic system can now be explained. The acid properties are characteristically exhibited by hydrogen compounds of the nonmetals. The more typical the nonmetal, the stronger the acid. On comparing acids with similar structures, we find that the acids become stronger on going toward the *right* of the periodic table and *up* the columns.

While the fact that metals do not form acids has been explained, it is not yet clear why they form bases. Of course, we can say in a nonexplicit manner that since bases are the opposite of acids, the metals, which are the opposite of nonmetals, should form bases. To get an explicit picture, however, it is essential to get first a clear conception of what a base is. This is achieved most directly by defining a base in terms of an acid.

The most characteristic reaction of a base is to destroy an acid by combining with it. This means to destroy an H^+ ion (or more explicitly the $\left[\begin{array}{c} H \\ H{:}\ddot{O}{:}H \end{array} \right]^+$ ion), by combining with it. A typical base is sodium hydroxide, $Na{:}\ddot{O}{:}H$, which in water solution consists of Na^+ ions and $\left[{:}\ddot{O}{:}H \right]^-$ ions. On mixing a solution of sodium hydroxide with hydrochloric acid, both the acid and the basic properties disappear leaving some more water and a solution of ordinary salt.

$$Na^+ + \left[{:}\ddot{O}{:}H \right]^- + \left[\begin{array}{c} H \\ H{:}\ddot{O}{:}H \end{array} \right]^+ + \left[{:}\ddot{C}l{:} \right]^- \quad\text{---}\quad 2H{:}\ddot{O}{:}H + Na^+ + Cl^-$$

The theory makes it clear why this happens. The attraction of the $\left[{:}\ddot{O}{:}H \right]^-$ ion for the proton is stronger than that of the water molecule.

The $\left[{:}\ddot{O}{:}H \right]^-$ has three electron pairs exposed, but more important, it is negatively charged as a whole. Consequently, the proton migrates from the hydrogen ion to the $\left[{:}\ddot{O}{:}H \right]^-$ ion, forming a water molecule and releasing the water molecule on which it was riding. Consequently, both the H^+ (hydronium) ions and the OH^- ions disappear as such, and both the acid and the base properties for which these ions are respectively responsible disappear. Only the Na^+ ions and Cl^- ions remain. These did not really take part in the reaction, but if they are in equal numbers, they are nothing more than a solution of ordinary salt.

Therefore, the real agent responsible for the basic properties of NaOH is the $\left[{:}\ddot{O}{:}H \right]^-$ ion. This ion attracts and neutralizes the H^+ ions, forming water. The essential process of *neutralization* of an acid with a base is the union of hydrogen and hydroxide ions to form water (Ex. 39). It is a matter of language whether we call a "base" the whole compound NaOH or the OH^- ion in it. A base is any substance that contains or gives $\left[{:}\ddot{O}{:}H \right]^-$ ions in water solution, and the more ions this substance releases—that is, the more extensively it is ionized—the stronger the base. So the question "What elements form bases?" shifts to the question, "What elements form compounds which readily release OH⁻ ions?"

We need not look far for the answer. The reason that sodium hydroxide, Na:Ö:H, ionizes readily, releasing OH⁻ ions, is because the sodium atom attracts the electron pair very feebly, compared to the oxygen atom. The same reasoning that explains why Na:Cl: is ionic applies here. Sodium hydroxide is formed by electron transfer and is an excellent conductor of electricity in the molten state and in solution. In the compounds with the general formula

$$M:\overset{..}{O}:H$$

the nature of M determines whether the substance is a base and how strong it is. If M is a metal, it has weak attraction for electrons and the substance is a base. The more metallic M is, the less the attraction for electrons and the more readily the substance ionizes. Thus NaOH is a stronger base than $Mg(OH)_2$ and this in turn is a much stronger base than $Al(OH)_3$. Sodium hydroxide—caustic soda or lye—is one of the strongest bases possible. Its ionization is practically 100 percent. Magnesium hydroxide, $Mg(OH)_2$, is much weaker. It is milk of magnesia, which is mild enough to take internally to neutralize stomach acidity. Aluminum hydroxide ionizes so weakly that it can hardly be called a base. These relations are observed throughout the periodic system. The elements form stronger bases on moving toward the left and down the periodic system (Ex. 40).

Recapitulation   We have elaborated the electron theory of atomic structure to explain the physical and chemical properties of the elements. While the discussion was limited to a few physical and chemical properties, the properties selected are the most important and are universally exhibited by all the elements and their compounds. The reasoning has been carried sufficiently far to show that these properties are inter-related and ultimately depend on the structure of the atoms. Chemists, physicists, and engineers, using the same reasoning, correlate and explain the myriad properties and reactions of all the elements and their compounds, which is to say of all matter.

Practically all the properties and reactions encountered in everyday life depend almost entirely on the structure of the outer part of the atom. This, in turn, depends entirely on the nuclear charge which determines the number of available electrons. A given number of electrons arrange themselves in a definite pattern and that pattern determines the properties. All chemical changes, even the most violent, are due to relatively slight changes in the periphery of the atom. The inner shells are hardly disturbed. In order to carry out more drastic changes, it is necessary to penetrate the shells and disturb the tiny nucleus. If the disturbance is sufficiently violent to change the nuclear charge, a different element will result with the structure and properties appropriate to it.

In recent years, modern science has succeeded in doing precisely that and more. But the energies required to penetrate into the nucleus and the energy required or released during the nuclear changes, make the energy of the most violent chemical reactions pale into insignificance. This long and exciting story will be taken up in the next chapter.

NOTES AND EXERCISES

1. In the model originally proposed by Rutherford, the hydrogen atom is similar to the earth-moon system, with the earth corresponding to the nucleus and the moon to the electron. In what essential respects is the moon different from the electron? Why is the moon-earth system expected to be stable, but the electron-nucleus system unstable?

2. State the four assumptions of the Bohr theory, pointing out in what respects each assumption is different from the laws of motion as applied to heavenly bodies. If these assumptions were applicable to the earth-moon system on a corresponding scale, what consequences would follow? Would it be possible, for instance, to put artificial satellites into *any* orbit? Once in a stable orbit would they ever fall to the earth?

3. How does the Bohr theory explain the stability of the hydrogen atom? The presence of discrete lines in the spectrum? The absence of a continuous spectrum?

4. The diameter of the hydrogen atom can be estimated roughly from the density of solid hydrogen. At $-262°$ the density of solid hydrogen is 0.0808 gram per cc. What is the volume of 1 gram of solid hydrogen? How many atoms are present in 1 gram of hydrogen? What is the "average" volume of a single hydrogen atom? What is the diameter of the "average" hydrogen atom? How does this compare with 1.06×10^{-10} cm, as calculated by the Bohr theory? In a similar manner the radii of the others may be obtained from the atomic volume (see also Ex. 11-25).

5. The energy drop of the electron in the atom is deduced from the spectrum. What quantity is measured in the spectrum. How do we know that the Lyman series represents drops to the lowest orbit? Which line in the series represents a drop from the second orbit to the first? Why do the lines of shorter wavelengths become more closely spaced? Why do they eventually merge? What energy drop does the shortest wavelength represent?

6. Calculate the energy of an electron volt in ergs. The charge on the electron is 1.6×10^{-19} coulombs. Since a volt is a joule per coulomb, how many joules in an electron volt? Since a joule is 10^7 ergs, how many ergs in an electron volt?

7. In a Nobel Prize winning experiment, Franck and Hertz measured directly the ionization energy of hydrogen. In a cathode-ray tube (essentially as in Fig. 11-7, p. 323) containing highly rarefied hydrogen, they shot cathode rays—that is, electrons. Starting with very low voltages, they gradually increased the voltage, and measured the very small current flowing through at each voltage. On plotting the voltage against the current they obtained the diagram in Figure 12-22. There is a sharp increase in the current at 13.59 volts.

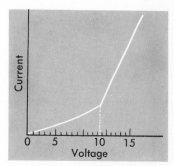

Fig. 12-22. Ionization energy of hydrogen. At 13.5 volts the cathode rays remove the electrons from the hydrogen atoms, causing ionization and an increase in the current.

To what is the current in the tube due? If an electron in the beam hits an electron of a hydrogen atom but does not have enough kinetic energy to remove it, what happens to the moving electron? What happens to the hydrogen electron? Will the atom ionize? If the moving electron in the beam has sufficient kinetic energy to remove the electron from the hydrogen atom, what will happen to the hydrogen atom? How will this affect in the current? If the energy of the electrons in the beam is 13.59 volts or more in order to produce heavy ionization, what is the energy of the electron in the hydrogen atom? Draw a graph showing the curve to be expected with helium in the tube.

8. What evidence in the spectra demonstrates that the electrons are held more firmly in the helium atom than in the hydrogen atom? How is this predicted by theory? What is the evidence that both electrons of helium are held in the atom with equal energy? Does this mean that they are in the same shell?

9. What is the evidence that the lithium atom has two shells? How do we know that the innermost shell contains two electrons? That the outermost contains only one?

10. How do we know that the second shell can contain as many as eight electrons? More generally, how do we find the number of electrons a shell can contain, as a maximum?

11. Consider the element calcium, Ca (20). How many electrons are there in the first shell? In the second? In the third? In the fourth? If you had at your disposal experimental means for removing all the electrons in succession, what pattern would you find in the successive ionization energies?

12. Draw diagrams and also write the condensed electronic structures of the following elements: Li, C, O, F, Ne, Na, Mg, Cl, K.

13. The electron structure of scandium, Sc (21), is 2, 8, 9, 2. How do you suppose this was determined? If the third shell could contain only eight electrons, what would the structure be? The electron structure of iron, Fe (26), is 2, 8, 14, 2. If the third shell contained only eight electrons what would the electron structure of Fe be? What type of element would Fe be?

14. Which element in the fourth period is an inert gas? How many electrons does it have? What is its electron configuration? How many electrons are there in its third shell? In which element of this period is the third shell first completed?

15. What is the maximum number of electrons that the first shell can contain? The second? The third? The fourth? Can you predict the maximum number of electrons the fifth shell could contain? The sixth? What is the rule?

16. The structure of any element in the main group can be written by a judicious application of the rules. The atomic number of bromine, Br, is 35. How many electrons does it have? Since bromine is in the fourth period, how many shells does it have? Sketch the nucleus with the shells and continue. How many electrons in the first shell? How many in the second? Since bromine is in the seventh (main) group, how many electrons in the outermost shell? Therefore, how many electrons in the third shell? Repeat for Sr (38), for Sb (51). Can you continue for Ba (56); for Po (84); for Ra (88)?

17. The simple rules applicable to the main groups are not directly applicable to the subgroups. Examine the electron structure of several elements in Table 10:4 for example, Fe (26), Cu (29), Ag (47). Do you see any pattern? Do you see any pattern in the transition elements of the fourth period? Fifth? In the lanthanide series? In the actinide series?

18. A few simple rules regarding the subshells may be given. In the last column of Table 12-3 the squares (1, 4, 9 . . .) have been expressed as the sums of successive odd integers. By multiplying out by 2, the number of electrons in each completed subshell is obtained. Thus, the second shell has two subshells, one with 2 × 1 electrons and the other with 2 × 3. How many electrons does the third shell have? The fourth? The fifth? In the *fourth main shell*, how many electrons in the first subshell? In the second? In the third? In the fourth? How many transition elements do you expect? How many lanthanide elements? How many elements in the main groups? Can you define an inert gas in terms of completed shells or subshells?

19. The subshells are designated by the letters *s, p, d,* and *f* in that order (and by extension by *g, h,* etc.). Thus if the *s* subshell of any shell contains two electrons as a maximum, the *p* subshell contains six electrons and so on.

The main shells are indicated by the Roman numerals. Thus 3*p* means the second subshell of the third main shell. Thus the structure of carbon (6) may be written C(2)(6) indicating only the number of electrons in the main shells, or C(2) (2, 4) indicating the number of electrons in the subshells as well.

Further it may be designated as follows: C $1s^2$, $2s^2$, $2p^4$, the superscripts indicating the number of electrons in the subshell.

The origin of these letters is interesting. Long before the modern theories, the spectroscopists conceived of the atom as an electric "grand piano," oscillating to give tones and overtones, corresponding to colors or wavelengths observed in the spectra. The low frequencies were thought to be the *fundamentals*—hence *f.* The characteristic lines of many elements were thought to be the *principal* frequencies—hence *p.* The *sharp* lines in the spectrum were called *s,* and the *diffuse* lines were called *d.* The Bohr theory and the modern quantum theories have altered this interpretation radically, but the designations still remain.

Write the structure of chlorine (17) showing the electrons in the main shells. Repeat showing the number of electrons in each subshell. How many 1*s* electrons in the chlorine atom? How many 2*s*? How many 2*p*? How many 3*s*? How many 3*p*? Write the complete structure in terms of letters *s, p, d,* . . . Repeat for the radium atom, Ra (88).

20. A. Sommerfeld extended the Bohr's theory to include elliptical orbits. With further extensions, a "visual" picture of the atom has been developed. The manner in which the electrons "move" within the atoms is specified by four numbers, called quantum numbers. The first quantum number, *n,* specified the "size" of the orbit. Thus, the first orbit is 1; the second, 2; and so on. The second quantum number specified the "ellipticity" of the orbit. Thus 3*d* means a circular orbit, 3*p* designates an elliptical orbit with one unit of ellipticity, 3*s* designates an elliptical orbit with two units of ellipticity. The third quantum number specified the "orientation" of the orbit in space. For example, the *p* orbits are in planes inclined to one another. Finally, the fourth quantum number specified the direction in which the electron "spins" on its axis as it is orbiting around the nucleus. It may spin in the same direction as it revolves (just as the earth spins in the same clockwise direction as it revolves around the sun) or it may spin in the opposite direction. According to a principle formulated by Pauli, there can be no more than one electron in an atom which can be specified by all four quantum numbers (Ref. 12.4). After further reading try these equations.

What is the size of the 2*s* shell? What is the "shape" of the 2*s* shell? How many orientations are possible for orbits in this shell? If the electrons

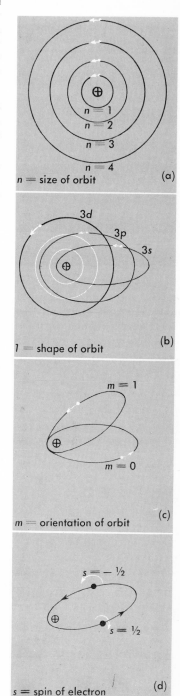

n = size of orbit   (a)

l = shape of orbit   (b)

m = orientation of orbit   (c)

s = spin of electron   (d)

Fig. 12-23. Sommerfeld's pictorial interpretation of quantum numbers.

are revolving in such an orbit, how many ways can they spin relative to the direction they revolve around the nucleus? How many electrons could be in the orbit and still be designated as different?

What is the "size" of the $2p$ shell? How does it compare with the $2s$ shell? What is the "shape" of the $2p$ orbit? How many "orientations" are possible for this type of orbit? How many ways can the electron spin in each of the orientations? How many $2p$ electrons can an atom have as a maximum? How many electrons can an atom have altogether in the second shell?

21. The following reasoning suggests a transition toward the non-mathematical wave-mechanical theories. The electron orbiting around the nucleus may be considered as a disturbance in the positive electric field surrounding the nucleus. In order that the disturbance be stable, it should form standing waves analogous to waves produced by interference in water. For this to happen, the orbit must be of the right length and the shortest length must be one full wavelength. The electron cannot be nearer the nucleus than that, and hence this is the first orbit. If more energy is available, the electron can move further out to move in an orbit of twice the wavelength. It cannot be in between and still produce a stable wave pattern. Can you explain why the electron cannot be anywhere between the two orbits?

This picture, in three dimensions, can be formulated mathematically. The mathematics describes the "modes" in which the electrons can vibrate to produce stable "standing" waves. It is remarkable that these modes of vibrations are described by the quantum numbers discussed in Exercise 20.

22. From the position in the periodic system write the "dot" structure of the following elements: Mg(12); O(8); C(6); Si(14); Pb(82); the alkali metals; the inert gases; the halogens; the elements of group V.

23. In the "electric eye" (p. 147) a photon of light acting like a bullet ejects an electron from the metal surface. A part of the energy of the photon ($E = hf$) is utilized to remove the electron from the atom in the solid. The remainder, if any, is given to the ejected electron as kinetic energy. Why are only the metal atoms suitable as the active surface of the photoelectric cell? Why are the alkali metals most suitable? Which atoms would be the most suitable?

24. Why are the metals conductors of electricity? Why are the non-metals insulators? Which is the better conductor, sodium (11) or magnesium (12)? Lead (82) or tin (50)? Bismuth (83) or arsenic (33)? Which is the better insulator, sulfur (16) or selenium (34)?

25. The ionization energy of ions can be measured in the same manner as those of neutral atoms. For example, that of the chloride ion $\left[:\overset{\cdot\cdot}{\underset{\cdot\cdot}{Cl}}: \right]^{-}$ can be obtained from the spectrum of sodium chloride, NaCl. Does it require more or less energy to remove an electron from the chloride ion than from the chlorine atom? Why?

26. If an isolated sodium atom were to react with an isolated chlorine atom, and the two stayed far apart, how much energy (in electron volts) would be given off? If they came close enough to form an NaCl molecule, would the energy be more or less? If many such pairs formed a crystal would the energy be more or less? Explain.

27. How do we know that the sodium atom in reacting with a chlorine atom loses an electron and that the chlorine atom gains one? What is the electronic configuration of the sodium atom before the reaction? What is the charge on the sodium ion after the reaction? How is this experimentally

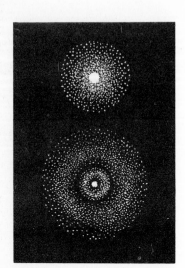

Fig. 12-24. The wave-mechanical concept of a hydrogen atom (top) and an argon atom (bottom). The electron or electrons are represented as a cloud of varying density around the nucleus. (After Pauling)

determined? What is, then, the configuration of the sodium ion? What is the configuration of the chlorine atom? Of the chloride ion? What is the essential process in this reaction?

28. Why is the valence of sodium $+1$? Why is the valence of all alkali metals $+1$? Why is the valence of magnesium $+2$? Why is the valence of the halogens -1?

29. Why is sodium more active than magnesium? Why is magnesium more active than aluminum? Would you expect magnesium or calcium to be the more active? Why?

30. Why are metals reducing agents? Why are nonmetals oxidizing agents? Which is a better oxidizing agent, chlorine or bromine? Chlorine or sulfur? Why?

31. Which metals form ions most easily? Which nonmetals form ions most easily? Why are ions with a charge of $+4$ so rare? Why are ions with a charge of -4 never found?

32. Develop the argument that the atoms are most stable when they have shells of eight. Is more energy given off when two chlorine atoms gain electrons by electron sharing (as in the formation of two chloride ions) or when they form bonds by sharing?

33. Which of the following would you expect to be electric conductors and which insulators in the liquid state? KCl, RaF_2, H_2O, SO_2, $BaCl_2$, SCl_2, SCl_6, ICl_3. How can you tell? Which is the better conductor, $AlCl_3$ or $MgCl_2$?

34. Silicon tetrachloride, $SiCl_4$ is a nonconducting liquid, and hence it contains no chloride ions. Nevertheless, it is easy to demonstrate that the chlorine has a greater "hold" on the electrons. On adding water, $SiCl_4$ forms silicic acid and hydrochloric acid.

$$SiCl_4 + 4HOH \rightarrow H_4SiO_4 + 4HCl$$

If a current is passed through the resulting mixture, the chlorine goes to the positive pole. How does this show that chlorine had effective control on the electrons, even in $SiCl_4$?

35. A typical example of a compound formed entirely by electron

$$\begin{matrix} & H\ H & \\ H{:}C{:}C{:}O{:}H \\ & H\ H & \end{matrix}$$

sharing is ethyl alcohol, H:C:C:O:H. It is a nonconductor. When alcohol

(as a wine) is oxidized it becomes acetic acid (as in vinegar), the formula of which is

$$\begin{matrix} H & \ddot{O}{:} \\ H{:}C{:}C \\ H & {:}\ddot{O}{:}H \end{matrix}$$

In this relatively violent chemical reaction a part of the molecule was oxidized. Was the rest of the molecule disrupted? Are the carbon atoms still joined to one another? Are any other bonds still intact?

36. Lithium hydride, LiH, is a salt-like substance, conducting electric current in the liquid state. To which pole would you expect the lithium to travel? To which the hydrogen? At which pole is the hydrogen liberated? Draw the electron structure of the hydride ion. What happens to this ion at the electrode?

37. How do you explain the very small conductivity of liquid HCl? Which are the positive ions? Which are the negative?

38. Which is the better conductor, HCl or H_2S? H_2SO_4 or H_3PO_4? Which is the stronger acid, H_2SO_4 or H_3PO_4? H_3PO_4 or H_3AsO_4?

39. Write the equation for the neutralization of hydrochloric acid with sodium hydroxide in two ways. Consider the hydrogen ion as H^+ and as H_3O^+.

Is there any essential difference? What part of the NaOH is "really" the base?

40. Which is the stronger base, KOH or $Ca(OH)_2$? $Ma(OH)_2$ or $Al(OH)_3$? $Mg(OH)_2$ or $Ba(OH)_2$?

13

THE ATOMIC AGE

1. INTRODUCTION

On the west end of Stagg Field at the University of Chicago, where the grandstands were located, a bronze plaque reads as follows:

ON DECEMBER 2, 1942 MAN ACHIEVED HERE THE FIRST SELF-SUSTAINING CHAIN REACTION AND THEREBY INITIATED THE CONTROLLED RELEASE OF NUCLEAR ENERGY.

In these simple but dramatic words, Enrico Fermi (1901-1958) and his coworkers recorded for posterity the historic event of the first successful experiment in unlocking the prodigious sources of energy stored within the nucleus of the atom. Two and a half years later, at dawn of July 16, 1945, the first atomic bomb was exploded on the sands of New Mexico, and three weeks after this, on August 6, 1945, the world was to be electrified—and horrified—by the explosion of the first atomic bomb over a populated military target. Hiroshima, a city in Japan of 300,000 people, lay in ruins from the explosion of a single bomb containing a charge of no more than a few pounds. In a single flash—hotter than the center of the sun—70,000 inhabitants perished outright, and a whole section of the city disappeared in vapor.

The immediate result of the explosion of this bomb, and of another bomb over Nagasaki two days later, was the quick ending of World War II. But the unparalleled destructiveness of the bombs left humanity with a frightening problem. A giant had been released—one far more terrible and far more powerful than any mythological monster conceived

Fig. 13-1. Plaque at the site of the first self-sustaining pile at the University of Chicago. (*Argonne National Laboratory photo.*)

by the imaginative Greeks. No story teller throughout history had dared invent such a monster. Yet he was here—a stark reality. Would this giant be a menace threatening to destroy civilization and all human life on this planet, or would it be possible to tame him and use his enormous strength to do the work of the world? How could the giant be controlled? These were the questions that thoughtful men everywhere asked, after they recovered from the shock.

Since that time the menace has increased and the questions have been more urgent. The giant has grown to prodigious proportions. More powerful atomic bombs were devised and these were followed by hydrogen bombs of practically unlimited destructive power. One bomb can now wipe out the metropolitan area of New York or Moscow or London. The radioactivity from the explosions of the bombs already on stockpile can make human life and animal life impossible anywhere on the earth. For the first time in history man has in his hands the power of total self-destruction (Refs. 13.7 and 13.24).

On the other side of the ledger, since that first atomic explosion ways have been found to tame the giant. Devices have been invented which release the energy more slowly than in the bombs and at controllable rates. Engines have been built to power submarines and other vessels of war, but also merchant ships. Reactors have been built to operate steam engines, to generate electricity, to heat cities, and to power factories. The deadly radioactive materials produced in the reactors have been isolated and are used for studies in medicine, in industry, and in pure science. The application of atomic reactions to peaceful purposes is just beginning. Man has in his hands enormous power for further technological developments.

Power of itself is neither good nor evil. Man decides the purpose for which to use it. He can destroy himself or he can make life on the earth more abundant. The decision is up to him. Moreover, the decision does not belong to the scientists alone; it is the responsibility of every citizen, everywhere. Whether he makes the right decision or not depends primarily on the moral strength and enlightenment of the entire society. This much, however, is evident. If the average citizen is to make a wise choice, it is important, if not essential, that he have some understanding of the tremendous power with which he is dealing. This becomes even more evident with the realization that his answers can not be final. The problems will recur and the occasions for decision will increase. Atomic energy is here to stay. On the one hand, the bomb will always be within easy reach as a menacing possibility. On the other hand, the applications of atomic power will multiply and modify the daily lives of all people. Man has entered in the atomic age and cannot retreat from it. Civilization can control the giant it has created only through knowledge and understanding. In the discussion that follows we shall attempt to contribute to this understanding.

It may not be generally realized that the successful release of atomic energy in Fermi's historic experiment was neither an accident nor a lucky discovery. It was the result of the coordinated effort of the leading scientists in this country engaged in the gigantic war project known by the code name of Manhattan District Project. The design and the success of the experiment depended on a long chain of previous discoveries and reasoning, each dependent on preceding developments. The story goes back to the beginning of the century, and proceeds to the present time in an unbroken series of great discoveries and the insights arising from them. The story, of course, can be traced back even further, but that is not necessary for those who have obtained even a general background of the development of the atomic theory and the basic principles of physics, as treated in the previous chapters.

Fig. 13-2. Fermi. The initiator of the nuclear age. (Los Alamos photo.)

Tracing the story of atomic energy from the beginning of the century discloses two main themes—two rather distinct aspects. One is the fact that energy is released during extraordinary types of changes in which nuclei of atoms of one element are transformed into nuclei of atoms of other elements. The basic framework for understanding the nuclear changes is provided by Rutherford's concept—formulated around 1910—of the structure of the nucleus. From the previous discussion of the main features of this theory the reader knows a good deal of this part of the story. The significant points will be mentioned as needed, but the reader is advised to review the discussion in Chapter 11.

The second aspect of the story is the release of the energy itself. The energy is released during the nuclear changes, and for this reason it is more properly called *nuclear* energy. Underlying the understanding of the source of this energy is Einstein's theory of relativity, formulated around 1905. We have only touched upon this complicated theory and we do not intend to go deeply into it now (Ex. 1 and Ref. 13.2). Fortunately, all that is necessary for our purpose is one of its important conclusions. One of the logical deductions of the theory is that *mass* and *energy,* two apparently unrelated entities, are *equivalent.* One entity may change into the other. If, *for any reason,* a certain quantity of mass *disappears,* then a definite quantity of energy *appears* in its place. Conversely, if a certain quantity of energy *disappears,* then a

Fig. 13-3. Einstein. Author of the theory of relativity. (The Bettmann Archive.)

definite quantity of mass—a definite *weight* of material—*appears* in its place.

The theory goes further to give the numerical value of this equivalence. In the famous equation

$$E = c^2 \cdot m$$

the constant of equivalence, the "exchange rate," is the square of the velocity of light. In the metric system the velocity of light, *c,* is equal to 3×10^{10} centimeters per second, and therefore c^2 is equal to 9×10^{20}, which written in full is 900,000,000,000,000,000,000. This means that when 1 gram of material disappears, 9×10^{20} ergs of energy appear.

$$E \text{ (in ergs)} = 9 \times 10^{20} \times m \text{ (in grams)}.$$

It is important to emphasize, however, that the words "material disappears" mean that the matter *literally disappears* in these transformations. The gram of material is not *scattered* over a room or into the atmosphere; it has *gone out of existence, as mass*. It is not to be found anywhere in the universe. In its place, 900 *billion-billion* ergs have appeared somewhere. This energy may appear as heat (as 21.8 trillion calories); or as radiation in the forms of light, x-rays, or gamma rays; or as the energy of moving rockets; or as any of the other conventional forms of energy. The energy from 1 gram of material is equivalent to the explosive energy of 20,000 tons of TNT, as can be readily calculated. Next to the startling conclusion that mass and energy are equivalent entities is the staggering magnitude of the "exchange rate" (Ex. 2).

Einstein's theory does not specify under what conditions mass will change into energy, or under what conditions energy will change into mass. It is not that kind of theory. The theory merely states that it is possible for one to change into the other, and permits the calculation of the amount of energy appearing from the amount of mass disappearing, and vice versa. A consideration of the very large "exchange rate" between mass and energy, however, suggests the conditions under which these transformations might be observed. Energy-matter transformations in detectable amounts could take place only in changes caused by forces of enormous magnitude, acting over short distances in a limited volume of space, and in a short time. Such forces, if they exist, must be millions of times more powerful and more concentrated than ordinary electric forces, and billions upon billions of times more intense than gravitational forces (Ex. 3).

It so happens that such forces exist within the nuclei of atoms. As the story unfolds we shall relate how it became known that strong forces exist there, and how they are measured. Before doing that, however, it will be advantageous to reexamine the structure and constitution of the nuclei of the atoms as described by the Rutherford theory. We shall first examine the changes in structure observed during nuclear transformations and explain them in terms of the nuclear theory. We shall then return to consider the changes in energy associated with changes in structure.

2. MODERN ALCHEMY

The transmutation of one element into another was the dream of the alchemists for over 2000 years. Despite their fervent zeal and unimaginable toil, the alchemists never succeeded, nor ever came near their goal. We now know the reason for their failure. In their most elaborate experiments and most fantastic concoctions, they were carrying out nothing more than ordinary chemical reactions. The most violent reactions in their experiments were merely effecting superficial changes in the outermost shells of the atoms. Yet, ironically enough, nuclear transformations were constantly going on around them. The disintegration of uranium and other minerals had been going on in the rocks since the beginning of time. But the alchemists did not recognize these, and they would not have recognized them as such even if they did happen to observe them. They had no adequate theory to guide them. The superiority of modern scientists in recognizing these changes, and in eventually transmuting elements at will, lies essentially in the fact that a theory of the structure of the atoms has been developed, which permits the recognition of these transmutations and an understanding of them as nuclear changes.

According to the simple Rutherford theory, already discussed in some detail on page 342, the nuclei of the atoms are made up entirely of protons and neutrons. The proton is the nucleus of the hydrogen atom, carries a positive charge of one unit (that is, equal to the charge of the electron but opposite in sign), and weighs a trifle less than the hydrogen atom—about 1/2000 less. The neutron carries no charge and weighs a trifle *more* than a hydrogen atom. Since both particles weigh very nearly one unit—that is, 1/16 of the weight of the oxygen atom, which is taken as the standard for the weights of atoms and molecules—the weight of either particle may be taken as equal to 1, to a very close approximation. In size also these two particles are alike, each being about 1/10,000 of the full hydrogen atom in diameter (one *trillionth* in volume). With these two particles alone, it is possible to account for the sizes, charges, and weights of nuclei to a very high degree of approximation. If there are other particles in the nuclei, they must be very light and would be needed only to account for finer detail and to provide greater depth of understanding (Ex. 4 and Refs. 13.15, 13.21, and 13.31). The proton is symbolized as p^+ or simply p, and the neutron as n. In diagrams the proton is often represented by a crossed circle, $\oplus$, indicating the positive charge, and the neutron by an open circle, $\bigcirc$, indicating no charge. The two particles are known collectively as *nucleons*.

The constitution of any nucleus can be specified by merely giving the number of protons and neutrons in it. The total number of protons and neutrons accounts for the total weight of the nucleus—and of the whole atom—to a high degree of approximation. This total is, of course, the atomic weight of the atom, symbolized by the letter A, and obtained by several experimental methods of physics or chemistry. The number of protons alone accounts for the charge of the nucleus. It is equal to the atomic number and determines the chemical properties of the atom. This number, usually symbolized by the letter Z, can be obtained either from the order of the element in the periodic system or from the wavelength of its characteristic x-ray spectrum. The number of neutrons is merely the difference between the atomic weight and the atomic number. Thus helium, with the atomic weight of 4, has in its nucleus four nucleons, and since it is the second element in the periodic system (atomic number 2), two of these are protons. The remaining two nucleons must be neutrons. The structure of the helium nucleus, therefore, is

Similarly, the nucleus of uranium, the ninety-second element, with an atomic weight 238, contains 238 nucleons, of which 92 are protons and the remaining 146 (238-92) are neutrons.

The nuclei are represented more conveniently in a condensed rotation by using the chemical symbol of the element and writing the atomic weight on the upper right of the symbol and the atomic number on the lower left. Thus, the helium nucleus is written as $_2\text{He}^4$, and the uranium nucleus as $_{92}\text{U}^{238}$. Although it is not necessary to write the atomic number since the symbol of each element specifies its own unique number, it is better to write it, as a reminder. It is essential, however, to write the atomic weight to specify the particular isotope under discussion. Thus, the less abundant uranium isotope with the atomic weight 235, is written as $_{92}\text{U}^{235}$. The number of neutrons can then be ascertained at a glance as the difference between the atomic weight and the atomic number (Ex. 5).

Spontaneous Transmutation of the Elements

In natural radioactivity we encounter for the first time changes in which the nuclei alter. As already discussed on page 331, uranium, radium, thorium, and several other elements give off alpha, beta, or gamma rays. Since in these processes the radioactive elements are transformed into other elements, these radioactive changes are not ordinary chemical reactions. In chemical reactions only the periphery of the atom is altered (Chap. 12); the inner shells and the nuclei in the deep interior are not disturbed. In radioactive changes, however, the elements themselves are altered and this means that the nuclei themselves are transformed. In emitting the rays, the nuclei lose a part of their mass or a part of their charge, or both, as well as a great deal of their energy. In so doing they break down into simpler and more stable nuclei.

The emission of the alpha particle from a radioactive nucleus is the simplest to explain by the Rutherford theory. Since the alpha particle is a helium nucleus, $_2He^4$, the emitting nucleus loses four units of mass and, specifically, two protons and two neutrons. Consequently, the remaining nucleus has two protons and two neutrons fewer than the emitting nucleus. For example, uranium-238 gives off an alpha particle and becomes a new nucleus.

$$\left(\begin{array}{c} 92p^+ \\ 146n \end{array}\right) \rightarrow \left(\begin{array}{c} 90p^+ \\ 144 \end{array}\right) + \left(\begin{array}{c} 2p^+ \\ 2n \end{array}\right)$$

$$_{92}U^{238} \rightarrow {}_{90}Th^{234} + {}_2He^4$$

The remaining nucleus has the atomic weight of 234. More significantly, however, it is no longer the nucleus of an uranium atom. Since two protons are lost in the emission, the remaining nucleus has a charge of $+90$; therefore it is the nucleus of the ninetieth element which is thorium. It is an isotope of ordinary thorium and has all the chemical properties of thorium. Thus the emission of an alpha particle decreases the atomic weight by four units and the atomic number by $+2$ units. Since the resulting lighter element has an atomic number smaller by two units, it is found in the periodic system two places to the left of the emitting nucleus.

The emission of a beta particle presents quite a puzzle, at first sight. The beta particles are negatively charged electrons, emitted at high speeds. Deflection in strong magnetic fields and measurements of the m/e ratio leave no doubt that they are the same particles found in cathode rays. Nor is there much question that the electrons are emitted from the nucleus. The tremendous speeds (approaching that of light) can only be imparted to these particles by the powerful electric fields found only within the nucleus. We have assumed that the nucleus contains only protons and neutrons. How then explain the emission of electrons from the nucleus?

An obvious and apparently simple answer is to take the emission of the beta rays at its face value and assume that there are electrons inside the nucleus neutralizing some of the protons. In fact, this explanation was accepted before the discovery of the free neutron and for some years afterwards (Ex. 6). This explanation, however, raises other difficulties not yet mentioned. The size of the free electron has been roughly estimated and found to be as large or larger than some of the nuclei. How, then, can electrons be "contained" in a nucleus that is smaller than the electron? If there are any electrons in the nuclei, they must be present in some unusual form. They cannot be the ordinary free electrons observed outside the nuclei.

The puzzle was solved by reexamining the structure and the behavior of the neutron after the latter was "discovered" as a free particle outside the nuclei. The neutron has no charge, to be sure, and in size it is about as large as the proton. Up to this time it was regarded as a tiny blob of neutral matter—uncharged, uniform, simple, and stable.

But in later experiments it was found that the neutron is unstable and apparently not so simple. It decays with a half-life (page 336) of about 13 minutes, emitting an electron and becoming a proton. Starting with a pound of neutrons, half of them will disintegrate within approximately 13 minutes, each giving an electron and a proton. In another 13 minutes, half of the remaining neutrons will disintegrate, and so on. An electron and a proton are precisely the two parts of a hydrogen atom, and if the experiment is carried out in a closed vessel (an incredibly difficult task, as will be explained later), the resulting protons and electrons will form ordinary hydrogen.

Thus, a neutron contains precisely the two parts that make up a hydrogen atom and can become a hydrogen atom under the proper conditions. The neutron, however, is *not* a hydrogen atom. It is much smaller than a hydrogen atom—one trillionth in volume. We must think of it as a single small package, a "close association" of a proton and an electron. The neutron and its decay may be represented as follows:

$$\left(p^+e^- \right) \;\rightarrow\; p^+ \;+\; e^- \;+\; \text{energy}$$

The neutron also has more energy than a hydrogen atom, and this fact will explain other characteristics of the neutron, to be taken up presently.

Returning to the radioactivity of heavy atoms, we can now explain the emission of beta rays. All the nuclei (except that of ordinary hydrogen) contain neutrons. The neutrons, which are unstable outside the nucleus, are apparently stable when present within the nuclei of most of the ordinary atoms. If this were not the case, all nuclei would be unstable and all elements found in nature would be radioactive. However, in a few instances, a neutron is unstable even inside a nucleus. In these relatively rare nuclei, a neutron emits an electron, as a beta ray, and becomes a proton that remains in the nucleus. The resulting nucleus has one *more* proton but one *less* neutron than the original nucleus. For example, the nucleus of Th-234, just considered, emits an electron and becomes a new nucleus.

$$\left(\begin{array}{c} 90p^+ \\ 144n \end{array} \right) \rightarrow \left(\begin{array}{c} 91p^+ \\ 143n \end{array} \right) + e^-$$

$$_{90}\mathrm{Th}^{234} \;\rightarrow\; _{91}\mathrm{Pa}^{234} \;+\; _{-1}e^0$$

The resulting nucleus is that of a new element, with a nuclear charge of +91. It is the element, protoactinium, the next element in the periodic system. The atomic weight is still 234, since the mass of the emitted electron is negligible and the sum of the protons and neutrons is still the same (Ex. 8).

The emission of gamma rays does not change the emitting nucleus into a nucleus of another element. Gamma rays are like x-rays and consist of packages of light or *photons* of very high frequency. The photons have no charge, and they have no mass when at rest. (Photons at rest— that is, a beam of light, *at rest*—makes no sense. Ex. 9.) The gamma ray photons, however, have a great deal of energy, which they carry away from the emitting nucleus. Consequently the emitting nucleus loses considerable energy in the process. It is still the same isotope of the same element, but having lost energy, it is presumably more stable. Thus, we are inevitably led to consider the energy changes which accompany the radioactive transformations.

The radioactive elements release large amounts of energy not only during the emission of gamma rays, but in the emission of alpha and beta rays as well. The alpha particles are ejected with speeds up to one tenth that of the speed of light and since their mass is considerable, their kinetic energy ($\frac{1}{2}mv^2$) is very high. The beta particles are much lighter, but their speeds approach that of light, and hence their kinetic energy is high also. The kinetic energy lost by an emitting nucleus can readily be calculated from the speed and the mass of the emitted particle. The energy lost can also be observed experimentally. A sample of radium, for example, is always warmer than the surroundings, due to the fact that the rays are stopped within the container and the kinetic energy of the rays appears as increased speed of the molecules in the container. A gram of radium in 1,590 years will release heat equivalent to the burning of 515 pounds of coal. This is such a staggering amount of energy, we feel impelled to ask what the *source* of this energy is, but we shall postpone discussing this point. But whatever the source of this energy, there is no question that the radioactive nuclei have excess energy, which makes them unstable.

Thus, the theory explains the transmutations of radioactive elements found in nature. The radioactive elements are unstable and disintegrate, releasing energy in the process to become more stable structures. They may or may not emit material particles in the process but they always release a part of their excess energy. In any given instance, however, the resulting nucleus may still be unstable. In that case it will emit, in turn, one or more of the rays to become still more stable. This process will continue until a permanently stable element is formed.

Among the heavy elements three series of radioactive elements have been recognized. One series begins with uranium-238, which by successive emissions of rays changes into other elements and finally becomes lead-206. The full series is given on page 335, but may be summarized in one equation as follows:

$$_{92}U^{238} \rightarrow {}_{82}Pb^{206} + 8 \, _2He^4 + 6 \, _{-1}e^0$$

Another series begins with thorium-232 and ends with lead-208. A third series begins with uranium-235 (or protoactinium-231) and ends with lead-207. There is evidence for a fourth series beginning with neptunium-237 and ending with bismuth-209. In all four series the end-products are stable. It appears that all the elements above bismuth (element 83) are unstable, while bismuth and lead (element 82) and the lighter elements found in nature are stable. (A few unstable elements lighter than lead are also found in nature).

It is rather significant that the rates of decay of the radioactive elements are remarkably constant and are not affected by any external conditions, however drastic. Each radioactive nucleus has its own characteristic rate of decay. Neither high temperatures nor high pressures, neither strong electric fields nor strong magnetic fields, and not even violent chemical reactions have any detectable effect on the rate of decay of a given element. This, of course, is expected from the theory of atomic structure. The rate of decay depends on the structure and the instability of the nucleus. The stresses mentioned above, although severe by ordinary standards, are far too mild to affect the nucleus in the deep interior of the atom.

In natural radioactivity the transmutations that can be observed are limited to those elements that are naturally unstable and decay at their own rate. Moreover, nothing can be done to alter or to control these nuclear changes. To transform the stable elements some way will have to be found to probe directly into the nucleus.

Artificial Transmutations of the Elements

The first artificial transmutation of one element into another was definitely accomplished by Rutherford in 1919 in a very simple experiment. He bombarded nitrogen gas in a chamber with alpha particles from a radioactive source and obtained a few atoms of oxygen and hydrogen, thus transmuting two elements (nitrogen and helium) into two other elements (oxygen and hydrogen). Before we discuss the reaction in detail, and relate how he knew that the transmutation took place, it will be helpful to examine the reasoning that led him to try the experiment in the first place.

In order to transmute an element it is necessary to alter the nucleus itself; for a stable element, it is necessary to reach the nucleus and disturb it with sufficient energy to cause it to change into a different nucleus. To do this a projectile is needed with sufficient energy to penetrate the protective shield of the electron shells and to hit the nucleus. Moreover, when the projectile reaches the nucleus, it should have enough energy left to cause a violent disturbance.

Natural radioactivity provides just such a projectile. The alpha particles are emitted with speeds of several thousand miles per second and they go through several centimeters of air, or through thin metallic foils, before their energy is spent. In penetrating matter, the alpha particles go right *through the interior* of several thousand atoms, as we have already seen in the scattering experiments. On tearing through the atoms in gases, the alpha particles attract and drag electrons behind them, leaving positive and negative ions along their path. These ions become the centers of condensation of droplets of water under the proper conditions of the Wilson cloud chamber. The water droplets appear as white streaks, marking the paths of the rays. Thus, not only are there projectiles available, but they are easily observed, especially in gases.

But it is one thing to have the projectiles and quite another to hit a nucleus. The nucleus is so small that the chances of hitting it are extremely remote. The alpha particle, which is itself a nucleus (the nucleus of the helium atom), can travel great distances through the interior of an atom without ever coming near the nucleus. Even though the alpha particle may travel through several thousand atoms, the chances are still very small that it will strike a nucleus.

The possibility of hitting the nucleus is still further reduced for another reason. Both the helium nuclei used as the projectiles and the target nuclei are positively charged. Even if the alpha particle came near a nucleus by chance, the positive charge of the nucleus would repel it and deflect it away. The reader has already seen this effect in the scattering experiments with the gold leaf (p. 337). In that experiment, the gold nuclei, having a charge of +79 units, sharply deflect the few alpha particles that happen to come near them, and turn back completely those very few that happen to be aiming directly at them. However, by choosing as targets the lighter elements, whose nuclei have relatively small positive charges, the chances for successful hits are increased. The alpha particles *may* have enough kinetic energy to overcome the repulsion and enter the nucleus.

Reasoning somewhat in this manner, Rutherford decided to try the experiment. He chose nitrogen as the target element because it has a nuclear charge of only +7 units and it is a gas. He shot thousands of alpha particles into the gas contained in a chamber (Fig. 13-4). Admittedly, this was a "shot gun" technique, like trying to kill rabbits by shooting indiscriminately into a forest on a dark night. Nevertheless, Rutherford thought it was worth the try. In his very first experiments he obtained results. Using an old-fashioned spinthariscope he observed sparks far out of the range of the alpha particles. He correctly interpreted the sparks as due to protons, the only atomic particles that are lighter than helium nuclei and could have such a range. Apparently, a few direct hits had been scored, and the protons were the fragments of the exploding atoms in the first successful atom-smashing experiment.

The experiment was soon repeated in a Wilson cloud chamber, in which the event could be directly observed and photographed. One of the early photographs is shown in Figure 13-5. It is interesting to mention in passing, that out of 500,000 photographs, only 8 showed direct hits. The history-making hit is recorded in the track of the alpha particle that forks into two tracks. The long thin track is due to the proton, and the thick bent track is due to a heavy nucleus of mass 17, further identified as oxygen-17. The identifications were confirmed, subsequently, by carrying out the experiment in strong magnetic fields. The "bending" of the tracks provided m/e measurements, which definitely identified the various particles.

Interpreting the event in terms of the nuclear theory, the alpha particle, $_2He^4$, penetrates the nucleus of a nitrogen atom, $_7N^{14}$. Momentarily, the two nuclei fuse and form a *compound* nucleus, which contains 9 protons and 18 neutrons—that is, all the particles of the target and the projectile. This is a nucleus of a fluorine atom, since the atomic number is 9, and may be written as $_9F^{18}$. This nucleus, however, contains excess energy (including all the kinetic energy of the alpha particle) and is, therefore, unstable. In a very short time (about 10^{-11} seconds), the compound nucleus breaks up into a proton and an oxygen atom, the latter containing 8 protons and 9 neutrons. In the explosion, these fragments recoil with speeds inversely proportional to their masses. The event may be shown as follows:

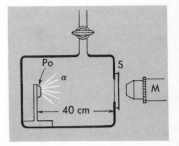

Fig. 13-4. The first artificial transmutation. Rutherford observed flashes with the spinthariscope on the screen, S, well beyond the range of the alpha particles (α) from polonium (Po).

Fig. 13-5. An early photographic record of the transmutation of nitrogen and helium into oxygen and hydrogen. *(Photo by W. D. Harkins, University of Chicago.)*

$$_2He^4 \quad + \quad _7N^{14} \quad \rightarrow \quad [_9F^{18}] \quad \rightarrow \quad _8O^{17} \quad + \quad _1H^1$$

It is instructive to consider this nuclear reaction in more detail, for it is typical of all nuclear reactions. It is not an ordinary chemical reaction, since different elements appear on the left and different elements on the right side of the equation. In ordinary chemical reactions, the atoms do not alter and hence the same number of atoms of each element appear on the left as on the right side of the equation; but in nuclear reactions, the atoms of the reacting elements change into atoms of other elements. Several quantities, nevertheless, are still conserved. For one, the total electric charge remains the same. Thus, the sum of the positive charges, implied in the atomic numbers, is 2 + 7 on the left, and 8 + 1 on the right. Likewise, the sum of the atomic weights on the left (4 + 14) is equal to the sum of the atomic weights on the right (17 + 1). This is almost, although not quite, the law of conservation of mass—it is a good approximation of it. The nuclei do not weigh *exactly* whole numbers, and the sum of the weights is not *exactly* the same before and after the change (see p. 425).

Following the announcement of the first successful experiment in atom smashing, Rutherford and the other physicists throughout the world at that time went all out on a "rabbit-hunting" spree. They bombarded one element after another with alpha particles and succeeded in smashing a great number of the lighter elements (Ex. 10). Of course, in these reactions only a few atoms were smashed at a time. As the data were gathering, however, they yielded a great deal of information about the structure and the stability of the nuclei, the forces that hold them together, and the fragments into which they break up. With this knowledge more satisfactory theories have been developed which, in turn, led to new discoveries and to new techniques to smash the atoms.

Atom-smashing Machines

Atom smashing soon developed into a big enterprise; machines were invented to produce artificially and in abundant quantities projectiles with energies as high and eventually far higher than those of the alpha particles from natural radioactivity. These machines speed up positive ions of light nuclei by means of electric or magnetic fields, or by combinations of the two. Perhaps the best known of these machines is the cyclotron, invented by E. O. Lawrence in 1931. Its construction and operation is typical of these machines, and is based upon well-known and simple principles.

The essential part of the cyclotron consists of a hollow metal cylinder, a few feet in diameter and a few inches between the top and bottom (Fig. 13.6). It is a double disk, cut through the center into two hollow pieces, each resembling the letter D—in fact, they are called the "dees." The dees are separated from one another by a small gap.

At the center a wire filament is mounted with provisions to heat it electrically. The assembly is enclosed in another cylinder, which is nonmetallic (and hence nonconducting) and air tight so that it can be evacuated. The whole assembly is then placed between the poles of a powerful electromagnet whose poles have an area somewhat larger than the dees. Finally, the dees are connected to a source of alternating current of high voltage and high frequency, so that the dees can be given charges opposite to one another and which alternate several million times per second.

The production of high-speed projectiles by the cyclotron may be illustrated by taking protons as an example. Hydrogen gas at low pressure is introduced into the chamber and the filament is heated. As the hydrogen molecules hit the hot filament they dissociate into hydrogen atoms, some of which ionize forming positive hydrogen ions or protons. No sooner are the protons released, however, than they are strongly accelerated toward the dee that happens to be charged negatively at that moment (left "D," Fig. 13-6), being repelled at the same time by the other dee (right "D"), which is positive. Inside the dee a proton, under the influence of the uniform magnetic field, travels a circular path. Having traveled a semicircle, it emerges from the dee into the gap.

If at this instant the charge on the dee is changed to positive—as can be done by delicately adjusting the strength of the magnetic field and the voltage and frequency of the alternating current—the proton will be given an additional acceleration across the gap into the right dee, which is now negative. Inside the second dee the proton again travels in a semicircle, but of larger radius because the proton has now acquired a higher speed. Since the length of the semicircular path is proportional to the speed, the proton reaches the other side just as the

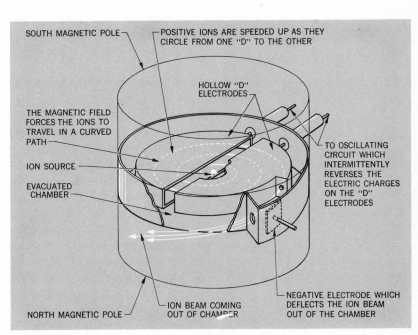

Fig. 13-6. The cyclotron produces atomic projectiles at very high energy. (From Selwood, *General Chemistry*, 3d ed. New York: Henry Holt and Co., 1959.)

SOUTH MAGNETIC POLE

POSITIVE IONS ARE SPEEDED UP AS THEY CIRCLE FROM ONE "D" TO THE OTHER

HOLLOW "D" ELECTRODES

THE MAGNETIC FIELD FORCES THE IONS TO TRAVEL IN A CURVED PATH

ION SOURCE

EVACUATED CHAMBER

TO OSCILLATING CIRCUIT WHICH INTERMITTENTLY REVERSES THE ELECTRIC CHARGES ON THE "D" ELECTRODES

NEGATIVE ELECTRODE WHICH DEFLECTS THE ION BEAM OUT OF THE CHAMBER

NORTH MAGNETIC POLE

ION BEAM COMING OUT OF CHAMBER

Fig. 13-7. The University of California bevatron speeds up particles to energies of 6 billion electron volts. *(University of California photo.)*

charge on the dee becomes positive (Ex. 12). It is then accelerated for the third time. Thus, the proton is accelerated at each crossing of the gap and travels in larger and larger semicircles. By the time it reaches the periphery of the dees, it has circled thousands of times and has acquired speeds of several thousand miles per second. The proton is deflected out of the chamber by a negative electrode. It flies straight out, like a sling shot, and hits the target placed in its path.

The cyclotron produces a continuous stream of protons of very high energies. By using different gases in the chamber, projectiles consisting of the nuclei of the lighter elements are obtained. Thus, with heavy hydrogen the beam consists of deuterons, which are the nuclei of heavy hydrogen; with helium, the projectiles are helium nuclei, He^{++}. The newer cyclotrons and other similar machines—such as the synchrotron, the betatron, the cosmotron, and the linear accelerators, operating on similar principles—produce intense beams of these and heavier nuclei up to calcium and even heavier. Some of the machines produce beams of high-speed electrons. The speeds of these projectiles approach that of light and their kinetic energies are truly stupendous. The energy, usually expressed in electron volts (p. 360), goes up to billions of electron volts. The reader will appreciate the magnitude of these energies by recalling (p. 209) that the kinetic energy of a gas molecule at room temperature is a fraction of an electron volt, and that the energy of the most violent chemical reaction (such as the union of a sodium atom with a chlorine atom) is but a few electron volts (See Chap. 12, Ex. 26).

Cosmic Rays   Meanwhile another source of powerful projectiles was recognized in nature. Cosmic rays that constantly bombard the earth from outer space have been found to consist, in part at least, of high-speed charged particles of prodigious energies. The energies of some cosmic-ray particles run up to many billions of electron volts. It is not yet known how they are produced and accelerated, nor whether they originate within the stars or in interstellar space, but it is definitely known that they come from outer space (Ex. 13). On hitting the targets in detection instruments, either at sea level or high up in balloons, the cosmic-ray particles also produce nuclear changes revealing further the structure of the nuclei.

New Discoveries

With this ever-increasing arsenal of atomic artillery, from both natural and artificial sources, the physicists went after the tiny nucleus. A series of great discoveries followed one another in rapid succession. Among the fragments of the disintegrating atoms new and hitherto unobserved particles were found. In 1932, first the neutron, then the positron were discovered (Refs. 13.16 and 13.23). In 1934, artificially induced radioactivity was discovered. As a result it is now possible to produce isotopes of ordinary elements which are radioactive and hence not found in nature. In 1939 the phenomenon of nuclear fission was observed, and this discovery led directly to the atomic bomb and nuclear reactors. In 1950, nuclear fusion was accomplished, which led to the development of the hydrogen bomb. Meanwhile, in many reactions new elements more complex than uranium were synthesized, until now the periodic system has been extended to element 102 (and may well be extended beyond). These discoveries are interrelated and new ones may be expected. We shall discuss these discoveries one by one, although not in strict chronological order.

The Discovery of the Neutron

The neutron was discovered in one of the early experiments before the advent of the high-power projectiles. When beryllium-9 is bombarded with alpha particles from polonium, the first step is the formation of a compound nucleus of carbon-13, just as expected from the temporary fusion of the two nuclei,

$$_2He^4 + {_4}Be^9 \rightarrow \left[{_6}C^{13} \right] \rightarrow \ ? \ + \ ?$$

The subsequent break up of this compound nucleus, however, created quite a puzzle when first studied. One of the fragments is a very penetrating type of radiation. It travels great distances without being absorbed and yet it can be detected far from the target. It produces very little ionization in traveling through gases and, hence, leaves no tracks in the Wilson cloud chamber. Obviously it is not a charged particle and can be only one of two things. It is either a gamma ray of tremendous energy or a neutral particle of small weight. At first the physicists were of the opinion that it is a gamma ray, but in 1932 Chadwick of the Cavendish Laboratory proved that it is a neutral particle of matter, about as heavy as the proton. It was subsequently named the neutron.

We can follow Chadwick's argument by repeating his experiments in a cloud chamber. (Fig. 13-7). The chamber is filled with nitrogen

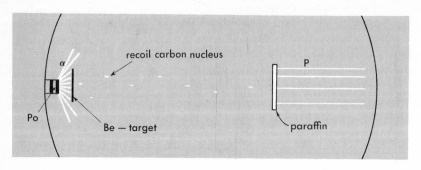

Fig. 13-8. The detection of neutrons. Invisible between the beryllium (Be) target and the paraffin plate, the neutrons eject protons from the latter, as shown by the proton tracks, p.

gas, in which the tracks of ionizing particles are easily visible. Alpha rays from polonium (visible as heavy tracks) are directed against a beryllium target, with which they react to form the compound nuclei of carbon-13, $_6C^{13}$. For long distances beyond the beryllium target (that is, beyond the point at which the carbon-13 is formed) hardly any tracks are visible. Only a few short and very heavy tracks appear, and these can be easily identified as due to the recoil of nitrogen nuclei, after being hit by the invisible radiation. However, on placing a thin sheet of paraffin wax at some distance beyond the beryllium target, as Chadwick did, a large number of tracks appear *beyond* the paraffin screen. These tracks are very long and thin, and can be readily identified as protons moving at high speeds. Apparently, something has hit the hydrogen atoms in the paraffin and has given a high momentum to the protons.

Chadwick calculated the speed of the protons by measuring their range in the nitrogen gas, and reasoned that only material particles of mass comparable to that of the proton could eject from paraffin such a large number of protons and give them such high speeds. Gamma rays or x-rays do not eject protons from paraffin in this way. Chadwick then measured the recoil of the nitrogen nuclei and compared it with the speeds of the protons. On the assumption that the same kind of particles hit both the nitrogen nuclei and the protons, he obtained a fairly good estimate of the mass of the invisible neutral particles. He confirmed his reasoning by taking into account the masses *and* the energies of all the particles involved. He found that the invisible particles are a trifle heavier than the protons; he named them "neutrons." According to the most recent measurements, the mass of the neutron is 1.00893 and that of the proton is 1.00813 atomic-mass units.

The discovery of the neutron made possible an explanation of the breakup of the compound nucleus of carbon-13. This nucleus emits a neutron of mass 1 and becomes the nucleus of the ordinary carbon-12 atom.

$$_6C^{13} \rightarrow {}_6C^{12} + {}_0n^1$$

Further direct evidence for this interpretation comes from experiments carried out in a cloud chamber containing gaseous compounds of beryllium (Fig. 13-9). The alpha particles from polonium hit a beryllium-9 nucleus in a gas molecule and form the compound nucleus, carbon-13. When the compound nucleus breaks up, it forms a heavy atom of mass 12 which recoils and appears as a heavy track. This track can be identified by the bending in a magnetic field as carbon-12. Therefore, an invisible particle of mass 1 must have been thrown in the opposite direction. The invisible particle can be identified only in the sense that if a paraffin screen is placed in the position shown, a proton is ejected. It is a happy coincidence that the proton has a mass about equal to that of the neutron, for in the collision the neutron transfers its momentum to the proton. It is like a billiard-ball collision. In a head-on collision, the moving ball stops and the stationary ball picks up all the momentum.

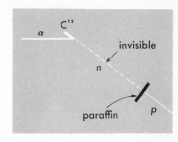

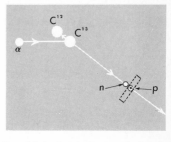

Fig. 13-9. Production and detection of a single neutron. *(Top)* events as observed in cloud chamber. *(Bottom)* interpretation of the tracks.

The critical reader might question the sufficiency of the evidence for the existence of a particle that cannot be "seen" even in the sense of leaving tracks in a cloud chamber. However, the properties of the neutron are such that the conclusion for its existence must be based on this kind of indirect evidence. Since the neutron is so small in size and has no electric charge, it goes through ordinary matter without interacting with it. As it travels through the atom it neither attracts nor repels the planetary electrons, and affects them only if it happens to hit them directly. The neutron also ignores the nuclei, unless it happens to score a direct hit. In fact to ordinary atoms the neutron is like a ghost, passing through thousands upon thousands of them without any effect, and only now and then hitting an electron or a nucleus without forewarning. For this reason, too, a sample of neutrons has never been displayed; for no container, however "solid," would hold them. They go through the walls of the container, as though the latter were an extremely coarse sieve. Yet the evidence from the measurements is so clear that we are not only confident of their existence, but have learned a great deal about their properties. We can make large quantities of free neutrons, measure their speeds by the momentum they impart to stationary protons in paraffin, and carry out many reactions with them.

The discovery of the neutron was of fundamental importance for several reasons. For one thing it confirmed the earlier speculations that a neutral particle of about the mass of the proton exists within the nucleus and justified the Rutherford theory of the structure of the nuclei. The decay of the neutron into a proton and an electron explained the emission of beta rays in radioactivity, as already discussed. This decay, and especially the mass and energy of the neutron compared with its fragments, gave a further insight into the stability of the nuclei and the interconvertibility of mass and energy. Moreover, the neutron turned out to be a unique projectile with which to carry out new nuclear reactions and, in turn, led to a clearer understanding of the new discoveries that were soon to follow—for example, the discovery of the positron and of artificial radioactivity. It led directly to the discovery of nuclear fission and to the synthesis of transuranic elements.

The very fact that neutrons have no charge makes them excellent projectiles. They can approach a nucleus without experiencing any repulsion and if they have sufficient energy, they may enter the nucleus and cause it to explode. A great many reactions of this type have been observed. For example, when oxygen is bombarded with fast neutrons, the neutron enters the oxygen-16 nucleus forming a compound nucleus of oxygen-17, which then explodes into a carbon-13 nucleus and a helium nucleus.

$$_8O^{16} + _0n^1 \rightarrow \left[_8O^{17}\right] \rightarrow _6C^{13} + _2He^4 + \text{energy}$$

How easily a neutron will enter a nucleus depends not only on the speed of the neutron but also on the particular target nucleus. Some nuclei can be penetrated with great ease, even by slow neutrons. For example, slow neutrons moving no faster than hydrogen molecules at room temperature—1 or 2 miles per second, with energies of a fraction of an electron volt—can penetrate readily a beryllium-10 nucleus causing it to break up into a lithium nucleus and an alpha particle.

$$_5Be^{10} + _0n^1 \rightarrow \left[_5Be^{11}\right] \rightarrow _3Li^7 + _2He^4 + \text{energy}$$

Incidentally, this reaction, accompanied by heavy ionization in a Geiger counter by the emitted fragments, is a very delicate method for detecting slow neutrons.

Before continuing with other reactions of the neutrons, we shall describe two other discoveries made at about the same time and related to the reactions and properties of the neutrons.

Discovery of the Positron

A few months after the discovery of the neutron, Carl D. Anderson of the University of California observed a strange new particle in photographs of cloud tracks produced by cosmic rays. His apparatus consisted of a cloud chamber in a powerful magnetic field. Over the chamber he placed a thick lead plate. Two types of rays entered the chamber from above: cosmic rays that had sufficient energy to go through the lead plate, and rays that were produced by the occasional

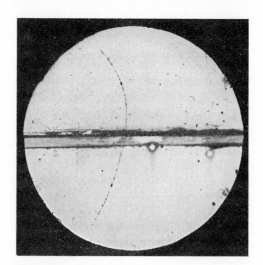

Fig. 13-10. Discovery of the positron. The pair of thin tracks, sharply bent in opposite directions by the magnetic field are due to positive and negative electrons, respectively. (Photo by C. D. Anderson.)

smashing of an atom in the lead plate. If any of these rays were charged particles, they would form cloud tracks that would be curved by the magnetic field. From the thickness of the tracks and from their direction and amount of bending, Anderson could identify the particles and estimate their energies.

Most of the particles were positively charged nuclei, although many were negative electrons. Occasionally, however, a most unusual track appeared in the photographs. It was thin, long, and strongly bent, and in every way similar to the electron tracks except that it was bent in the opposite direction. There was no question that it was a *positive* particle. The mass of this particle was that of the electron, but its charge was positive. It was the twin or rather the mirror image of the electron. It was named the positive electron or the *positron*. It is symbolized as e^+ or $_{+1}e^0$ or β^+.

As might be expected, the discovery made quite a sensation. Here was a positive particle, much smaller than the proton. In one respect the discovery simplified matters by reintroducing symmetry in the microworld. Electronic particles of equal mass and equal charge exist, and the charge may be either positive or negative. But it also complicated matters—what of the relation between proton and positron, neutron and positron, proton and neutron? And why are the positive electrons so rare? Many of these questions began to be resolved a year or so later after the positrons became plentiful. Positrons were observed to be emitted by unstable nuclei in another new phenomenon—artificial radioactivity.

It is rather interesting that artificial radioactivity was also discovered in a simple type of experiment. In 1934, M. and Mme. (Irene) Joliot-Curie were bombarding light nuclei with alpha particles, and they noticed that the targets were emitting radiations even after the source of alpha particles was withdrawn. For example, on bombarding aluminum with alpha particles, an unstable nucleus of phosphorus-31 is formed which immediately breaks up into a phosphorus-30 nucleus and a neutron,

Discovery of Artificial Radioactivity

$$_{13}Al^{27} + {}_2He^4 \rightarrow \left[{}_{15}P^{31} \right] \rightarrow {}_{15}P^{30} + {}_0n^1$$

In so far as this reaction goes, it is of the usual type and was fairly well understood by 1934. The Joliot-Curies, however, observed that the target, containing the phosphorus-30, continued to emit rays long after the bombardment had ceased. These rays decreased in intensity with time, in a manner similar to the naturally radioactive elements. They dissolved the aluminum target in acid and separated the phosphorus-30 from the aluminum by ordinary methods of chemical analysis. They found that the phosphorus-30 decayed with a half-life of about 2.5 minutes forming a nucleus of silicon-30, and a *positron*.

$$_{15}P^{30} \rightarrow {}_{14}Si^{30} + {}_1e^0$$

The emission of the positron by the nucleus raises a problem. Where did the positron come from? Its positive charge could come only from the proton. Apparently a proton within this unstable nucleus of phosphorus-30 emits a positron and becomes a neutron

$$p^+ \rightarrow n + e^+$$

With this assumption, the radioactivity of phosphorus-30 can be explained. A phosphorus-30 nucleus, $_{15}P^{30}$, with 15 protons and 15 neutrons, becomes a silicon-30 nucleus, $_{14}Si^{30}$, with 14 protons and 16 neutrons. However, whether the explanation of the origin of the positron tells the full story or not, the facts are beyond dispute. The Joliot-Curies proved the emission of the positrons by bending them in magnetic fields and proved the formation of the silicon atoms by similar bendings as well as by chemical analysis.

The reader might wonder how it is possible to carry out chemical separations and identifications with quantities of materials so small as to be unweighable and invisible. However, the principles upon which these separations are made are remarkably simple. The basic idea is that an isotope of an element, whether radioactive or not, has all the chemical properties of that element. For example, phosphorus-30 has all the chemical properties of phosphorus. The fact that its nucleus is unstable does not alter its chemical behavior. The atom does not know that its nucleus might blow up in the next ten minutes or in the next ten days; as long as it is a phosphorus atom it behaves like a normal phosphorus atom. Therefore, if to the aluminum target, a weighable quantity —say a few milligrams—of ordinary phosphorus is added and the aluminum is separated from phosphorus by the standard chemical methods (usually by precipitation as the phosphate), all the phosphorus

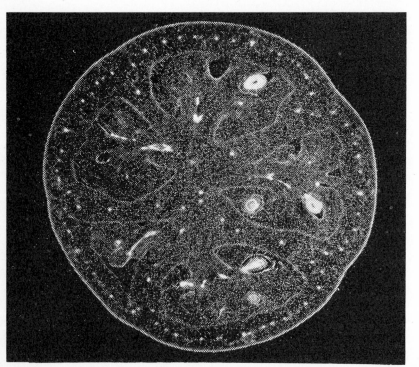

Fig. 13-11. Section of tomato fruit showing accumulation of radioactive phosphorus. The radioactive isotope has all the chemical properties of ordinary phosphorus. (Photo by American Smelting and Refining Co.)

atoms including the radioactive atoms that mixed with them precipitate as the phosphate. The precipitate is now radioactive since the phosphorus-30 atoms continue to decay at their characteristic rate after the separation. In this way hopelessly unweighable quantities of radioactive elements can be identified.

The procedure in this example, of course, is based on the assumption that radioactive phosphorus was known to be present. However, if the radioactive phosphorus were only suspected of being present, the same procedure would either confirm its presence in the phosphate precipitate, or if the precipitate was not radioactive, prove that the radioactive element was not phosphorus. If the latter were true, repeating the procedure with other elements in the vicinity of aluminum would, after a few trials, pin down the element responsible for the radioactivity (Ex. 17).

Radioactive isotopes of many common elements were soon produced by similar reactions. In fact, at least one, and in most cases several, isotopes of every element have been synthesized artificially since that time. It is significant to note that the radioactive isotopes are not present in the elements found in nature. The artificially radioactive isotopes are short lived, almost without exception. If radioactive isotopes were ever constituents of the elements in the original material that formed the earth, they must have decayed long ago. The reader can perhaps sense the bearing of this fact on the minimum age of the earth (Chap. 15).

The reader has no doubt noticed a shift in our language. So far, the expression "atom smashing," has been used in describing nuclear reactions. But the discussion makes it clear that in many nuclear reactions, atoms are synthesized as well as "smashed." In fact, in the very first experiment of Rutherford, the isotope, oxygen-17 was synthesized from nitrogen-14 and helium-4. In these reactions, not only have unstable isotopes of the ordinary elements been synthesized, but, isotopes have been made artificially of those elements for which no stable isotopes exist. For example, isotopes of element-85, the halogen beyond iodine, have been synthesized. This element was named astatine, meaning "unstable," because none of its isotopes are stable, and hence it is not found in nature. Similarly, elements 43, 61, and 87 have been synthesized, and the gaps in the periodic system have been filled. Of particular interest is the synthesis of elements beyond uranium, which resulted in the extension of the periodic system (see p. 418).

The neutron plays a very important role in the production of radioactive isotopes, although the latter have also been produced by other means. As already mentioned, neutrons are excellent projectiles. They have no charge and penetrate the nuclei readily. Whereas the alpha particles, the protons, and other heavy projectiles, having positive charges, are strongly repelled by the positive nucleus; the neutrons experience no such repulsion. To be sure the neutrons must still find the tiny nucleus, but when they do come upon it, more or less by chance, they need not overcome any force. Once a neutron enters the nucleus it forms an isotope of the same element, but one unit heavier. It so happens that, quite frequently, the new isotope is not one of those found in nature. The phosphorus-30 isotope, for example, is not found in ordinary phosphorus. This means that it is unstable and hence radioactive.

In the case of the light elements the radioactive isotopes usually decay by the emission of either a positive electron or a negative electron. If a positron is emitted, the new element is an isotope of the element that is one atomic unit smaller. The decay of phosphorus-30 given above is an example of this type. It forms silicon-30, and silicon is one column to the left of phosphorus in the periodic system. Another example is sodium-22. It decays into a positron and neon-22.

$$_{11}\text{Na}^{22} \rightarrow {}_{10}\text{Ne}^{22} + {}_{1}e^{0}$$

On the other hand if a negative electron is emitted, an element with one atomic unit greater is formed, and is found in the next column of the periodic system, just as in the case of the beta emission of the naturally radioactive elements. For example, sodium-24 emits a negative electron forming magnesium-24.

$$_{11}\text{Na}^{24} \rightarrow {}_{12}\text{Mg}^{24} + {}_{-1}e^{0}$$

Which way a radioactive isotope will decay depends primarily on the stability of the element into which it decays. The reader will note that neon-22 is a stable isotope, and therefore sodium-22 decays into it; similarly, magnesium-24 is a stable isotope, and therefore sodium-24 decays into it (Ex. 18).

The versatility of neutrons for use as projectiles and for producing radioactive isotopes is almost unlimited. Whereas the charged projectiles —even those accelerated to enormous energies by the modern machines —are effectively repelled by the high charge of the heavier nuclei, the neutrons enter the heavy nuclei just as easily as the light ones. For example, neutrons enter a copper-65 nucleus with relative ease.

$$_{29}\text{Cu}^{65} + {}_{0}n^{1} \rightarrow {}_{29}\text{Cu}^{66}$$

The resulting copper-66 decays into zinc-66 with the emission of a negative electron

$$_{29}\text{Cu}^{66} \rightarrow {}_{30}\text{Zn}^{66} + {}_{-1}e^{0}$$

Similarly, gold-197 becomes gold-198, which in turn decays into mercury-198. In some cases the neutrons enter the heavy nuclei with extreme ease. A good example is cadmium-106, forming cadmium-107, which then decays into silver-107. This, incidentally, is the basis for using cadmium rods to absorb unwanted neutrons and thus control the reactions in nuclear reactors (Ex. 17).

Synthesis of Transuranium Elements

Extremely interesting results are obtained by the reaction of neutrons with the very heavy elements at the end of the periodic system. These elements are naturally radioactive, but that is not relevant at the moment. The relevant point is that these elements contain the heaviest atoms found in nature. If a neutron enters the nuclei of these atoms, then atoms still heavier than those found in nature may result. This is precisely what happens.

On bombardment with neutrons, uranium-238 forms uranium-239 in the usual way.

$$_{92}U^{238} + {_0}n^1 \rightarrow {_{92}}U^{239}$$

Subsequent to this reaction, however, a significant although not entirely unexpected event occurs. The $_{92}U^{239}$ decays with the emission of a negative electron, forming an atom of element-93.

$$_{92}U^{239} \rightarrow {_{93}}X^{239} + {_{-1}}e^0$$

This is a *new element* beyond uranium, which was hitherto the last element in the periodic system. The new element was named neptunium, Np, in analogy to the planet Neptune, beyond Uranus. (Uranium itself was named after the planet Uranus, which had been discovered a short time before the element in 1846.)

The interest in this reaction does not stop here. Neptunium itself is radioactive, emitting also a negative electron to become element 94. This element was named *plutonium,* after Pluto, the planet beyond Neptune.

$$_{93}Np^{239} \rightarrow {_{94}}Pu^{239} + {_{-1}}e^0$$

It is regrettable that the astronomers did not discover new planets beyond Pluto (if there be any) to provide additional names; for the physicists and the chemists went on to synthesize still heavier elements. Some of these elements were synthesized by repeating the same treatment to the already heavier elements. For example, plutonium-239 absorbs a neutron to become plutonium-240, which then decays to americium-240, $_{95}Am^{240}$, and this in turn to curium-240, $_{96}Cm^{240}$. Other elements were synthesized by bombarding the already heavy nuclei with high-speed nuclei of the lighter elements. For example, when uranium-238 is bombarded with carbon-12 nuclei, the element 98, californium, is produced.

$$_{92}U^{238} + {_6}C^{12} \rightarrow {_{98}}Cf^{248} + 2\,{_0}n^1$$

Thus, by one method or another, and usually by a combination of several methods, new elements have been synthesized and the periodic system has been extended. As we go to press, element-103 has been reported. We confidently expect that even heavier elements will have been synthesized before this account is read.

One of the most far-reaching discoveries of modern science is the reaction of nuclear fission. The neutron plays a unique role in this reaction. When natural uranium is bombarded with neutrons of various

The Discovery of Nuclear Fission

energies, in addition to the absorption of neutron by the uranium-238 isotope, another and more significant reaction takes place. This other reaction is masked by the main reaction, and went undetected (or misinterpreted, Ex. 19) for some time. The other reaction is the absorption of a neutron by the uranium-235 isotope present in the natural uranium to the extent of only 0.7 of 1 percent.

The normal expectation is for the uranium-235 to absorb a neutron to become uranium-236

$$_{92}U^{235} + {}_0n^1 \rightarrow {}_{92}U^{236}$$

and this indeed does happen. But the U^{236} behaves in a wholly unexpected manner. Instead of emitting some small particle, it is so unstable that it breaks up into two large fragments and emits two or three neutrons at the same time. One of the ways it breaks up is as follows:

$$_{92}U^{236} \rightarrow {}_{56}Ba^{141} + {}_{36}Kr^{92} + 3\,{}_0n^1 + \text{energy}$$

The first indication that uranium-236 undergoes *fission*—that is, breaks up into two large fragments—was obtained by Hahn and Strassmann in Germany in 1939 just before the beginning of World War II. In a long series of experiments these chemists finally identified the element barium among the fragments. Obviously the other fragment must be krypton, if the smaller fragments are uncharged neutrons. This follows from the fact that the nuclear charge of barium (56) added to the nuclear charge of krypton (36) gives the nuclear charge of uranium (92). As soon as the presence of barium was announced, physicists throughout the world confirmed the results by repeating the experiment and by carrying out other experiments. The presence of heavy particles of intermediate atomic weight was further confirmed by the very heavy ionization they produce in an ionization chamber, and the heavy tracks in cloud chambers. Not all the fragments were barium and krypton; other combinations of fragments were obtained, with atomic weights neighboring barium (around 140) and krypton (around 90). In every case the sum of the atomic numbers was 92, the atomic weight of uranium. Likewise, in every case, neutrons were observed (Ex. 20).

The confirmation of the fission reaction created unprecedented excitement among the physicists and soon among the responsible government officials in this country and elsewhere. It may not be obvious why an obscure reaction observed by starry eyed scientists should cause such alarm, but a couple of simple facts about this reaction will point out the significance. In the first place, the amount of energy released during fission is extraordinarily large, even when compared with the large amounts of energy involved in radioactivity and other nuclear reactions so far observed. The reader will be able to calculate it for himself, after the systematic discussion in the next section of the energy relations.

The other fact lies in the release of neutrons during fission. Neutrons are the primary agents that initiate the reaction by combining with U-235 to form the unstable U-236. If neutrons are regenerated, and especially if more than one is formed per fission, then they can attack other U-235 atoms and repeat the fission, which again regenerates them. The process can be repeated and will snowball until the whole mass of U-235 has fissioned, releasing enormous amounts of energy. It becomes what is called a "chain reaction," much like a chain letter which if unbroken would paralyze the postal service. Of further significance in the nuclear chain reaction is the fact that each absorption of a neutron and the subsequent explosion of the U-236 is extraordinarily fast. It is over in about a millionth of a billionth (10^{-15}) of a second. The possibilities of a weapon of enormous destructive power should now be as apparent to the reader as it was to the physicists in 1939, at the beginning of World War II.

The development of the atomic bomb, the military uses of nuclear energy, as well as the development of nuclear reactors for peaceful purposes will be discussed in Section 4. At this point it will be more instructive to consider some of the implications of this great discovery.

The discovery of nuclear fission opened the possibility of large-scale nuclear reactions and large-scale release of nuclear energy. The nuclear reactions observed up to this time involved a few atoms or a few billion atoms—quantities altogether negligible. Several reactions had been observed in which more energy was released than fed into the reaction, but the total amount of energy released was again too small to be of practical consequence. With the possibility of a chain reaction, however, the total amounts of materials reacting, the total amounts of radioactive materials produced, and the total amount of energy released have hardly any limit. It was soon found that other heavy elements besides uranium-235 can undergo fission. For example, other isotopes of uranium, several isotopes of thorium, and, in fact, all the heavy elements can undergo fission, under the proper conditions. Thus the total mineral reservoir of the heavy elements on the earth becomes a potential source of industrial power and of radioactive isotopes for use in medicine, in industrial research, and in further research in basic science.

Nuclear Fusion

This survey of nuclear transformations would be conspicuously incomplete without the mention of nuclear *fusion,* which is a process opposite to that of fission. When light nuclei come together, under the proper conditions, they fuse into heavier nuclei with the release of large amounts of energy. The most important of these reactions is the fusion of hydrogen nuclei to form helium nuclei. Since the beginning of the century this process was thought to be going on in the interior of the sun and the stars and to be the source of the energy of these bodies. Nuclear fusion was finally accomplished in the development of the hydrogen bomb. Research is currently going on with the purpose of finding ways to carry out such reactions under controlled conditions. The fusion reactions will be discussed in Section 4.

Recapitulation

The story of the transmutation of one element into another, the disintegration of the elements, and the synthesis of new elements are developments of the twentieth century. Early in the century the spontaneous disintegration of naturally radioactive elements was understood. In 1919 the first artificial transmutation was carried out by Rutherford.

Then in quick succession the neutron, the positron, and artificial radio-activity were discovered. With more powerful projectiles, artificially accelerated, and with neutrons, countless transformations have been observed, and can be carried out at will. The discovery of nuclear fission and later that of nuclear fusion permitted transmutations on a large scale. It is now possible to carry out nuclear transformation almost as easily as ordinary chemical reactions.

There is, however, one aspect of these transformations of matter which has been deliberately suppressed in this account so far. It is the aspect of the energy relations of these transformations. This story will be taken up in the next section.

3. THE ENERGY WITHIN THE NUCLEUS

Introduction   One of the great insights of modern science has been the recognition of the principle that no process in nature occurs without either the expenditure or the release of energy. While this principle is true of all natural processes, it is of special significance in nuclear changes. In these reactions the amounts of energy involved are extraordinarily large. This in itself would be significant. But it becomes more significant, in view of the fact that large changes in energy imply corresponding changes in mass, which may be large enough to be detectable. For according to the theory of relativity (p. 399) 1 gram of mass is equivalent to 900-billion-billion ergs.

$$E \text{ (in ergs)} = 9 \times 10^{20} \cdot m \text{ (in grams)}$$

Even though the "exchange rate" between mass and energy is so large, the enormous amounts of energy involved in nuclear changes may be sufficient to result in measurable changes in weight.

A number of implications immediately follow. Nuclear changes suggest themselves as the candidates for processes in which the theoretically predicted mass-energy transformations can be observed experimentally. This has been found to be the case, as will be shown presently. This fact in turn implies that for every large change in energy, the corresponding change in weight is no longer negligible. Therefore, we cannot hope to explain fully the nuclear changes as mere combinations, separations, and rearrangements of "unchanging" ultimate particles. It is necessary to take into account the energy changes and the corresponding changes in mass.

This consideration might appear as a disturbing complication. Actually, however, it is a welcome opportunity. It permits a more accurate description and understanding of the nuclear changes. It makes possible a deeper insight into the forces that hold the nuclei together; the identification of the causes for their stability or instability; the prediction of what nuclear reactions might take place; and the calculation of the energy to be expected from them. It provides a deeper insight into the structure, behavior, and fundamental nature of matter.

The first indication that the nuclei contain extraordinary amounts of energy came from empirical observations in natural radioactivity. It was discovered early that radioactive materials in closed containers become warmer of their own accord. A sample of radium, for example, is always warmer than its surroundings. Careful measurements show that when 1 gram of radium decays completely, it releases no less than 3.68 million calories. This is equivalent to the burning of 1030 pounds of coal. Radium, therefore, represented a much more concentrated source of energy than anything that had been previously observed. Similar concentrations of energy are found in the other naturally radioactive elements.

The immediate source of the heat of radium can easily be identified. Radium emits alpha particles with a speed of about 10,000 miles per second. Knowing the speed and the mass of the alpha particle we can readily calculate its kinetic energy. It is this kinetic energy which the trapped alpha particles impart to the other molecules in the container that causes a rise in temperature. Similar measurements can be made on the beta particles and the gamma rays emitted by the several radioactive elements.

The source of the energy can be traced one step further back, at least in the case of the emission of alpha particles. When a radium nucleus breaks up, it forms the nuclei of two rare gases—radon and helium.

$$_{88}\text{Ra}^{226} \rightarrow {}_{86}\text{Rn}^{222} + {}_{2}\text{He}^{4}$$

Both of these nuclei are positively charged—the radon nucleus having a charge of +86 units and the alpha particle +2 units. Therefore, there is a strong repulsion between these particles. The heavier radon nucleus imparts to the alpha particle the tremendous speed of 10,000 miles per second, while it recoils with a much smaller speed. The sum total of the kinetic energies of the fragments is observed as heat in the sample.

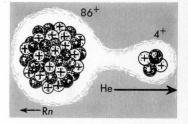

Fig. 13-12. Disintegration of a radium nucleus into a radon nucleus (+90) and a helium nucleus (+2), which strongly repel each other.

While this analysis provides a further insight into the disintegration process, it merely pushes the question one step further back. More basic questions arise. Where did the radium atom get the energy in the first place? If the disintegration energy is due to the repulsion of the positive charges, how was the radium nucleus ever assembled, and how does it stay together? The puzzle is now greater than ever. Rather than ask, "Why does a radium atom disintegrate" the question now is "Why is the radium atom so stable?" Why does it wait 1590 years, on the average, before it disintegrates? Further reflection raises a still more basic question, "Since all nuclei contain positive charges, why are any of them stable?" About 300 stable isotopes are found in nature. Why are they stable, and what forces hold them together?

Evidence for Nuclear Forces

The evidence for the existence of nuclear forces can be obtained quite directly by a more detailed examination of one of the simplest nuclei, the helium nucleus. According to the Rutherford theory, this nucleus consists of two protons and two neutrons.

This picture looks both simple and reasonable. It accounts for the experimental facts that the helium nucleus weighs four atomic units and has a charge of +2 units. It also accounts for the fact that in size it is only a little larger than the proton—about 10^{-13} centimeters. As long as no questions are raised about the forces *implied* in this model, we can rest in innocent complacency.

The presence of two protons so close together, however, implies tremendous repulsive forces. The repulsive force can be estimated by Coulomb's Law of electrostatic repulsion, knowing the charge on each proton and the approximate distance between them. Since the charge on each proton is 4.8×10^{-10} esu and the distance between them is about 10^{-13} cm, the force, f, is,

$$f = \frac{Q_1 Q_2}{r^2} = \frac{(4.8 \times 10^{-10})\,(4.8 \times 10^{-10})}{(1 \times 10^{-13})^2} = 23 \times 10^6 \text{ dynes}$$

This force, 23-million dynes, is about 23 kilograms or more than 50 pounds. It is tremendous for such small particles. It is sufficient to accelerate the protons to several thousand miles per second.

Yet the protons in the helium nucleus do not fly apart. On the contrary, the alpha particle is very stable. It remains intact in high-speed collisions with other nuclei; and there is other evidence for its very high stability. The only conclusion we can draw is that there must be *powerful attractive forces* of some type in the nucleus. These forces must be sufficiently strong to counterbalance the repulsive forces between the protons and to confer a high stability upon the nucleus.

The first impulse is to suggest that the attractive forces are gravitational attractions between the material particles, identical with the attraction between the sun and the earth. A simple calculation, however, dispels this idea. We know the mass of each proton (1.6×10^{-24} grams) and the distance between them. We find the attraction to be about 10^{-29} dynes (Ex. 3). This force is billions upon billions of times weaker than the repulsive forces between the protons and too hopelessly weak to account for the stability. There is no escaping the conclusion that these attractive forces are of some new and hitherto unknown type— perhaps attractions at close range between protons and neutrons, or between neutrons and neutrons, or perhaps even between protons and protons. But whatever the nature or origin of these forces there can be no question of their existence or of the fact that they are much stronger than electric forces. Calling them *nuclear* forces we proceed to investigate their magnitude and possible origin.

One of the most fruitful ways to investigate the nuclear forces is to consider the energy changes that they imply. Strong forces imply large amounts of energy whenever motion takes place either against these forces or by these forces. For instance, in the process of taking a helium nucleus and separating it into its four component particles—two protons and two neutrons—a great deal of energy must be supplied, in order to overcome the strong attractive forces. Or in the opposite process—that is, forming a helium nucleus by bringing together two protons and two neutrons—the strong attractive forces will pull the particles together and release a great deal of energy. In either case the amount of energy must be very large, in view of the fact that the forces are very strong.

Mass-energy Equivalence

It is precisely at this point that the mass-energy equivalence comes into prominence. The amount of energy released or absorbed may be large enough to result in detectable differences in mass. In the first process, since energy has to be supplied to separate the particles, the four particles have more total energy when separate than when they are together forming a single nucleus. If mass and energy are equivalent, as the relativity theory predicts, the four particles should weigh *more* when separate than when they are combined into a compact alpha particle.

The experimental verification of this conclusion is one of the triumphs of modern science. It is possible to weigh separately the proton, the neutron, and the alpha particle, with an accuracy of one part per million or better. Comparing these weights we find that the alpha particle weighs *less* than two free protons and two free neutrons. The calculations are as follows: The proton weighs 1.007595 and the neutron 1.008987 atomic-mass units, respectively. Therefore, two protons and two neutrons weigh

$$2 \times 1.007595 = 2.015190$$
$$2 \times 1.008987 = 2.017974$$
$$\overline{}$$
$$4.033164 \text{ atomic-mass units}$$

On the other hand, an alpha particle determined independently weighs only 4.002779 atomic-mass units. This weight is smaller by 0.030385 atomic-mass units. This means that if we start with 2.015190 *grams* of protons and 2.0017974 *grams* of neutrons, and somehow succeed in fusing them into alpha particles, we shall lose 0.030385 *gram* of mass. Similarly, if we start with about 2 pounds of protons and 2 pounds of neutrons, we would lose about 0.030385 *pound* of mass. This amount of mass is easily weighable.

If now the *assumption* is made that mass and energy are equivalent, it is possible to calculate the amount of energy that must be released in such a process. Since 1 gram is equivalent to 900 billion-billion ergs, then 0.030385 gram of mass is equal to $0.030385 \times 9 \times 10^{20}$ or 2.75×10^{19} ergs. This is 27.5 billion-billion ergs, or 660 billion calories. It is a staggering amount of energy, equivalent to the explosive energy of 20,000 tons of TNT, or equivalent to 26.6 million kilowatt hours (Ex. 2).

There are several other meaningful ways of expressing this energy. Depending on how the reaction takes place, the energy may be released either as gamma radiation or as radiation of other types, including heat and light, or it may well appear as kinetic energy of the alpha particles. If all the energy becomes kinetic, each alpha particle will receive 45.8 millionths of an erg. This may appear small, but it is equivalent to a temperature of 333-million degrees centigrade.

Still another way of expressing this energy is in terms of the voltage drop necessary to speed the alpha particle to this energy. An electron volt is the energy imparted to an ion of one negative (or positive) unit of charge, by a voltage drop of 1 volt. Now, since a unit electronic charge is 1.6×10^{-19} coulombs, an electron volt is 1.6×15^{-19} joules or 1.6×10^{-12} ergs. Therefore, to give to the alpha particle 45.8×10^{-6} ergs of kinetic energy requires $45.6 \times 10^{-6}/1.6 \times 10^{-12}$ or 28.3 million electron volts of electric energy. The reader can make these calculations for himself using simple arithmetic (Ex. 21).

Whether the reader carries out the calculations or not, there is one relation worth understanding and remembering for the following discussion. Since 1 gram of mass is equal to 9×10^{20} ergs, one atomic-weight unit is equal to this number divided by Avogadro's number. That is, the mass of a hypothetical particle of exactly one atomic-weight unit (a trifle smaller than the proton) is equivalent to 9×10^{20} divided by 6×10^{23} or 1.5×10^{-3} ergs. Now since one electron volt is equal to 1.6×10^{-12} ergs, then one atomic-weight unit = 931.2-million electron volts.

This is a convenient and meaningful way of expressing the mass-energy equivalent. The mass is expressed in atomic-mass units (amu) and the energy is. million electron volts (Mev) or sometimes in thousandths (kilo) electron volts abbreviated as kev. Therefore,

$$1 \text{ amu} = 931.2 \text{ Mev}$$

So far we have carried the argument by merely *assuming* that mass and energy are equivalent and that the "exchange rate" is correctly given by the relativity theory. Both of these assumptions were verified in one of the most significant experiments of this century. In 1932, Cockroft and Walton bombarded lithium atoms with high-speed protons and obtained alpha particles. Later Dee and Walton repeated the experiment in a cloud chamber (Fig. 13-13). The proton, with energy of about ½-million electron volts enters the nucleus of the lithium-7 atom, and forms a compound nucleus of beryllium-8. The latter instantly breaks up into two alpha particles, which fly in opposite directions with equal speeds.

$$_3\text{Li}^7 + {_1}p^1 \rightarrow [{_4}\text{Be}^8] \rightarrow {_2}\text{He}^4 + {_2}\text{He}^4 + \text{energy}$$

It is possible to find the energy released in this reaction in two different ways. Experimentally measuring the range of the alpha particles in air (8.31 cm) indicates the energy of each particle as 8.67-million electron volts, or a total of 17.34 Mev for both alpha particles.

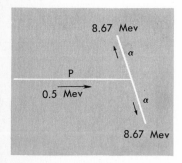

8.67 Mev

α

P

0.5 Mev

α

8.67 Mev

Fig. 13-13. Experimental proof of mass-energy equivalence. Tracks of proton hitting a lithium nucleus, which then explodes into two alpha particles, moving in opposite directions.

Since the proton entered the nucleus with the initial energy of 0.5-million electron volts, the net energy released in this reaction is 16.84-million electron volts.

The other way to find the released energy is to calculate it from the loss of mass. The two alpha particles weigh *less* than the lithium nucleus and the proton, as shown by adding the weights before and after the reaction.

before		after	
Li^{+++}	= 7.01657	He^{++}	= 4.00278
p^{+}	= 1.00760	He^{++}	= 4.00278
	8.02417		8.00556

The loss in mass is 8.02417 − 8.00556 or 0.01861 atomic-mass units. Since each atomic-mass unit is 931.2-million electron volts, the loss in mass corresponds to $0.01861 \times 931.2 = 16.80$-million electron volts. This is in very close agreement with the measured value 16.84 Mev. It confirms the mass-energy equivalence and the correctness of the exchange rate. Since that time, other measurements have confirmed the relativity theory, not the least important being the dramatic release of energy in atomic bombs, nuclear reactors, and hydrogen bombs.

Stability of Nuclei

The experimental observation of the energy-mass equivalence in nuclear processes not only confirms the existence of powerful nuclear forces, but also explains the stability of the nuclei in terms of the well-established principles of physics concerning energy changes. It does more than that. It provides a powerful and relatively simple method for calculating the stability of any given nucleus. All that is necessary is to weigh the nucleus and compare its weight with the weights of the particles that make it up, or with the weight of the possible fragments into which it may decay. The difference in weight is a measure of its stability or instability (Ex. 24).

To make this procedure clear, let us consider once again the helium nucleus. As already calculated, this nucleus weighs less than two protons and two neutrons by 0.030385 atomic-mass units. This mass is equivalent to 0.030385 × 931.2 or 28.3-million electron volts of energy. In order to break up a helium nucleus into the four component particles, it is necessary to add to it the equivalent of 0.00138 atomic units of mass in the form of 28.3-million electron volts of energy. Any amount of energy less than that is not sufficient to break up a helium nucleus. This means, of course, that the helium nucleus is an exceedingly stable particle.

In the same way we can examine other nuclei. One of the simplest is the nucleus of heavy hydrogen, called the deuteron, $_1H^2$. It consists of a proton and a neutron.

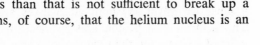

The deuteron weighs 2.014191 atomic-mass units, whereas a proton and a neutron taken separately weigh 2.016582 mass units (1.007595 + 1.008987). Thus, the deuteron is lighter than the two constituent particles by 0.002391 atomic-mass units, which is equivalent to 2.23-million electron volts. Therefore, the deuteron is also a very stable particle.

The high stability of deuteron is of interest because of the simplicity of the particle. The deuteron consists of only one proton and one neutron. There are no electric repulsive forces between them. Any stability must be due to *attraction* between the proton and the neutron. Thus, in this nucleus at least, we can pin point the cause of the stability as due to high attractive nuclear forces between neutrons and protons. This might explain the function of the neutrons in making the nuclei of the heavier elements stable, as we shall show presently.

Another interesting particle is the neutron itself. It weighs more than the proton and indeed more than the entire hydrogen atom. It decays into a proton and an electron,

$$n \rightarrow p^+ + e^-$$

the fragments taken together being nothing more than a full hydrogen atom.

Can we explain the stability or rather the instability of the neutron? It weighs 1.008987 atomic-mass units, whereas a proton weighs 1.007595 and an electron 0.000550 atomic-mass units, respectively. Taken together they weigh 1.008145 atomic-mass units. Therefore, the neutron weighs *more* than the full hydrogen atom by 0.000842 mass units which is equivalent to 782-thousand electron volts. Thus, the free neutron is unstable. It emits an electron with kinetic energy of 782-thousand electron volts and becomes a proton in the process.

We are now in a position to examine another puzzle. In the discussion of artificial radioactivity (p. 415) the emission of positrons was explained as due to the change of a proton into a neutron and a positron. On comparing this reaction

$$p^+ \rightarrow n + e^+_.$$

with the previous reaction, the puzzle becomes evident. Is the neutron a proton and an electron; or is the proton a neutron and a positron? That is, does

$$n = \left(p^+ e^- \right) \text{ or does } p^+ = \left(n e^+ \right)$$

To this puzzle only a qualified answer can be given. Although in a sense we might say both alternatives are true, in reality, neither is. The neutron is a proton and an electron *plus* 782-thousand electron volts of energy. On the other hand, a proton is a neutron and a positron *minus* a certain amount of energy. This energy can be calculated from the mass difference. A neutron weighs 1.008987 and a positron weighs 0.000550 atomic-mass units, respectively. The total mass, 1.009537, is considerably more than the mass of the proton, 1.007515. Consequently, the proton cannot break up unless the equivalent amount of energy is added. When a proton changes into a neutron in the artificially radioactive nuclei, the energy must come from the arrangement of the particles in the unstable nuclei. Outside these nuclei the protons are exceedingly stable particles.

These principles are general and can be applied to the understanding of the stability or instability of all the nuclei. All the stable nuclei found in nature weigh less than the separate protons and neutrons of which they are composed. The stability of a given nucleus can be measured by the amount of mass by which it is lighter than the separate particles. This deficiency in mass can be variously expressed as "mass defect," "packing fraction," or "binding energy." It is called "binding energy" if it is calculated as the difference between the actual weight of a given nucleus and the total weight of the protons and neutrons of which it consists. It can be expressed in mass units or in electron volts of energy. For certain purposes it is expressed in electron volts of energy released per nucleon, on the average. Thus the binding energy of the alpha particle is 28.3 for the whole particle, or 7.1-million electron volts per each of the four nucleons.

The binding energy per nucleon has been calculated for the stable isotopes found in nature and is given in Figure 13-14. A number of interesting relations emerge from the examination of this diagram. As expected, all the stable isotopes have a positive binding energy. That is, all weigh less than the separate nucleons, and all are stable with respect to them. The proton and the neutron have, of course, zero binding energy, for they are the standards of comparison. But for the other light particles (the deuterons, tritons, alpha particles, etc.), the binding energy per nucleon increases very rapidly up to nuclei of atomic weight around 20. Then the binding energy per nucleon increases more slowly to nuclei of mass around 55 or 60. For a small range beyond atomic weight 60, there is little change in the binding energy per nucleon. But from atomic weight around 70 and on, the binding energy per nucleon decreases, slowly at first and then more rapidly, toward the very heavy elements. Thus the binding energy per nucleon is highest for the intermediate elements of atomic weight around 60.

The binding energy per nucleon can be read directly in Figure

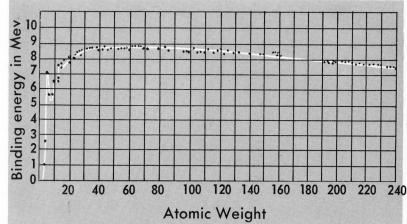

Fig. 13-14. Binding energy in millions of electron volts per nucleon. It is a maximum for elements of atomic weight of about 60.

13-14. For an element of atomic weight 60, say nickel-60, $_{28}Ni^{60}$, the binding energy is about 8.8-million electron volts per nucleon. This means that if 28 protons and 32 neutrons were to be assembled to form a nickel nucleus, 8.8-million electron volts would be released *per average nucleon,* or 8.8 × 60 Mev altogether. On the other hand the binding energy of helium-4, $_2He^4$, is only 7.1-million electron volts per nucleon. Similarly, the binding energy of uranium-238 near the end of the graph is only about 7.5-million electron volts per nucleon. The maximum amount of energy per nucleon is released for elements of atomic weight around 60. These intermediate elements, therefore, are the most stable.

Another way of interpreting the graph is as follows: If a supply of protons and neutrons is used to build nuclei and if helium nuclei are built using two protons and two neutrons each time, then 7.1-million electron volts will be released for each nucleon. But if nuclei of, say, neon-20 are built, 8.0 Mev per nucleon will be released. The maximum energy is released in building elements in the neighborhood of iron-56 or nickel-60. Thereafter, additional energy is released every time a proton or a neutron is added, but *not as much per nucleon.* By the time the naturally radioactive elements are reached, the additional amount of energy per nucleon has dropped to about 5.5-million electron volts. This might explain, in part at least, the instability of the naturally radioactive elements (Exs. 22-25).

A Simple Theory of Nuclear Structure

The conclusions drawn from the binding-energy graph are perfectly sound. The binding energies have been determined by experimental methods, and so long as the law of conservation of mass energy holds—and it has been found experimentally to hold in all cases—the stability or instability of any given nucleus can be calculated. However, this line of reasoning does not "explain" either the nature of the forces nor "why" a particular assemblage of particles is stable. For that, we need a *theory* that presents a "mental picture." We need a theory that will start with the forces (or energies) between the ultimate particles and will explain the stability in terms of some arrangement of these particles.

Unfortunately a completely satisfactory theory of the nucleus has not yet been developed. However, some progress has been made in this direction. The reader will recall that the stability of the deuterium nucleus implies the existence of strong attractive forces between the proton and the neutron, at close range. In the deuterium nucleus, the binding energy is 0.002391 atomic-mass units or 2.23-million electron volts, per nucleon. Similar examination of other simple nuclei gives a fair idea of the strength of the forces between a neutron and a neutron and between a proton and a proton at close range. They are quite large in all cases.

A considerable insight into the stability of the nuclei is obtained by taking into account both the repulsive and the attractive forces. The *repulsive* forces are those between the charged protons. These forces are electrostatic in character and vary inversely as the square of the distance. They weaken rapidly with increasing distance, but not too rapidly. On the other hand, the *attractive* forces are the mysterious nuclear forces between the nucleons. It is not known how they weaken with distance, but the evidence indicates that they weaken much more rapidly than the electrostatic forces. Perhaps they weaken as the fifth or sixth power of the distance. This means that they are extremely strong at very short distances and become very rapidly weak at greater distances.

On reexamining the helium nucleus, we can venture a rather simple but not too unreasonable explanation for its stability. All four nucleons are close together, and probably "touch" one another.

Each of the neutrons strongly attracts each of the protons; and since the nuclear forces are very strong, they more than counterbalance the strong repulsive forces between the protons. In addition, there are strong attractions between protons and protons, and between neutrons and neutrons. As a result, the helium nucleus has a high stability.

On comparing the proton with the neutron, it is evident that the neutron is preferable in adding to the stability. The protons do add to the stability by their attractive nuclear forces, but they also add to the instability by their electric repulsive forces. On the other hand the neutrons add to the stability, but not to the instability; the neutrons only attract, they do not repel. Consequently, the neutrons may be considered as "nuclear cement" in contributing only attractive forces. Although the true state of affairs is doubtless more complicated, this explanation is reasonable as a rough approximation.

The role of neutrons as "nuclear cement" is borne out by the examination of the other stable nuclei. In Figure 13-15 the number of neutrons is plotted against the number of protons for the nuclei found in nature. It is most remarkable that all the stable isotopes lie in a rather narrow belt. For a given element—that is, for a given number of protons—the number of neutrons does not vary very much. For a few elements only one combination of nucleons is stable. Such examples are fluorine, $_9F^{19}$, with 9 protons and 10 neutrons; and sodium, $_{11}Na^{23}$, with 11 protons and 12 neutrons. These elements consist of only one stable isotope. There are many elements that consist of only two or three isotopes. Only in the middle of the periodic system are there elements consisting of several isotopes. Tin, element-50, contains the maximum number of stable isotopes—ten in all. However, past the middle of the periodic system, the number of stable isotopes again decreases. Rather significantly beyond bismuth (element 83) no isotopes are stable.

Further examination of the neutron-to-proton ratio throws additional light on the cause of stability of the nuclei. In the first 20 or so elements, there are many elements with a number of neutrons *equal* to the number of protons. In addition to helium, $_2He^4$, with two protons and two neutrons, are carbon, $_6C^{12}$; nitrogen, $_7N^{14}$; oxygen $_8O^{16}$; magnesium $_{12}Mg^{24}$; silicon $_{14}Si^{28}$; sulfur $_{16}S^{32}$; and calcium $_{20}Ca^{40}$. Also significant is the fact that these isotopes are the most abundant found in nature. Evidently, starting from helium and adding one more proton

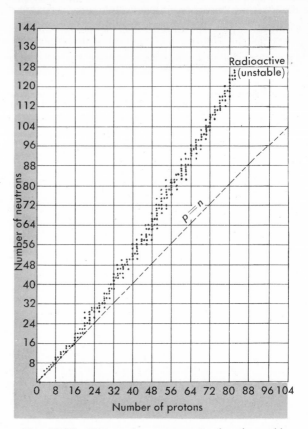

Fig. 13-15. Neutron-to-proton ratio for the stable nuclei. The ratio is 1:1 for light elements (dotted line) but gradually increases to about 1.5:1.

to form the next element, one more neutron is needed to counterbalance the repulsive force of the added proton.

To be sure there are some minor departures from this rule. The most important exception is the nucleus of ordinary hydrogen, which is just a proton. Other exceptions are fluorine $_9F^{19}$, sodium $_{11}Na^{23}$, and aluminum $_{13}Al^{27}$. But these depart only by one unit from the one-to-one ratio, and there are only a few instances of departure by two or more units. Apparently, for the lighter elements, as many neutrons are needed to counterbalance the repulsive forces of the protons. Under these conditions maximum stability is obtained. If for a given number of protons there are too few or too many neutrons, the nucleus is unstable and is not found in nature.

This conclusion is confirmed by the examination of the radioactive isotopes of the lighter elements. These isotopes have been synthesized artificially and have a neutron-to-proton ratio different from that of the stable isotopes found in nature. According to our hypothesis, this is the reason for their instability. They contain either too many or too few neutrons for the number of protons. Hence they decay by emitting either a negative electron or a positron. If the number of neutrons are too many, a neutron emits a negative electron thus becoming a proton.

A good example is carbon-14, $_6C^{14}$, with 8 neutrons and 6 protons. It emits an electron to give nitrogen-14, with seven neutrons and seven protons.

$$_7C^{14} \rightarrow {}_7N^{14} + e^-$$

If, on the other hand, the number of neutrons are too few, a proton emits a positron thus becoming a neutron. A good example is magnesium-23, which emits a positron to give sodium-23.

$$_{12}Mg^{23} \rightarrow {}_{11}Na^{23} + e^+$$

Thus the neutron-to-proton ratio not only explains the stability of the natural nuclei, but also predicts the decay process of the artificially radioactive isotopes of the lighter elements.

Beyond about element 20 (calcium-40) the neutron-to-proton ratio of the stable nuclei increases gradually. Thus, iron, $_{26}Fe^{56}$, has 30 neutrons to 26 protons; silver, $_{47}Ag^{108}$, has 60 neutrons to 47 protons; and gold, $_{79}Au^{197}$, has 118 neutrons to 79 protons. The heaviest stable isotope, bismuth-209, $_{83}Bi^{209}$, contains 126 neutrons to 83 protons. The ratio continues to increase in the naturally radioactive elements. Thus in uranium-238 the ratio is 146 neutrons to 92, which is more than $1\frac{1}{2}$ to 1.

The simple hypothesis that neutrons act as "nuclear cement" by attracting the protons at close range explains, in a qualitative way, the increase of the neutron-to-proton ratio in the heavier elements. In the lighter nuclei, the particles are close together. The protons strongly repel the other protons, but the neutrons attract even more strongly the protons they touch, and fairly strongly the protons not too far away. However, in going to heavier elements the number of particles increases and also the nuclei become larger in size. As a result the balance of forces gradually shifts. The repulsive forces between the protons are still strong since they decrease only as the square of the distance. Consequently, even distant atoms in the same nucleus are repelled fairly strongly. On the other hand, the attractive forces between protons and neutrons (and between the other nucleon) decrease very rapidly with distance (Fig. 13.16). A two-fold increase in distance decreases the electrostatic force to one fourth $\left(\frac{1}{2^2}\right)$, but the nuclear force to perhaps one sixty-fourth $\left(\frac{1}{2^6}\right)$.

Continuing the argument, we can understand the instability of the naturally radioactive elements. Apparently, beyond bismuth-209, the nucleus has grown so large that the repulsive forces between the protons cannot be counterbalanced by any number of neutrons. Consequently all nuclei beyond this isotope are unstable and hence naturally radioactive. They emit alpha or beta particles or gamma rays to achieve stability. Under certain conditions they even break up into two large fragments and undergo the fission reaction.

Thus, while this hypothesis is not good enough to permit the calculation of the binding energies, or even a confident estimate of them, it does give a general idea of the stability or instability of the nuclei.

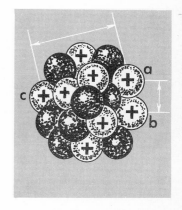

Fig. 13-16. Neutrons as nuclear cement. Neutrons attract only. Protons attract and repel. Proton (a) both attracts and repels neighboring (b), but only repels distant (c).

Moreover, regardless of the precise explanation, the conclusions drawn from the binding energies are correct, since the binding energies are experimental values. Hence, a comparison of the weight of a given nucleus and the weights of the possible fragments immediately indicates if a given nucleus is stable. Also, from the binding energies it is possible to calculate the amount of energy released in a given change. The hypothesis will not indicate whether the change *will take place* or how rapidly, but it will show whether the change is possible, and provide a means for calculating the amount of energy released, *if the change does take place* (Ex. 24).

A reexamination of the binding-energy curve indicates two general ways in which large amounts of energy can be released. Since the elements in the middle of the periodic system are the most stable, *large* amounts of energy will be released either by breaking up the heavier nuclei into intermediate elements, or by fusing light nuclei into intermediate elements. The first reaction is the *fission* reaction, which has been carried out in atomic bombs and in nuclear reactors on a large scale. The second is the *fusion* reaction, carried out, again on a large scale, in the hydrogen bomb. These two important reactions will be considered in the next section.

4. NUCLEAR BOMBS AND NUCLEAR REACTORS

Prior to the discovery of nuclear fission in 1939, the possibility of carrying out nuclear reactions on a large scale appeared extremely remote. While thousands of nuclear reactions had been observed and could be carried out at will, the total amount of matter reacting was extremely small. In most of these reactions, only a few atoms reacted at a time. Even in the strong beams of the powerful accelerators, only a few billion atoms reacted, and these quantities are far too small to be weighable. To be sure, several reactions had been observed in which more energy was released than was necessary to speed up the projectiles. However, in these experiments the majority of the projectiles were wasted. The nuclei were so small that only a few projectiles scored hits. Therefore, the total energy necessary to produce the beam was many times greater than the energy released from the few atoms reacting. The possibility of starting a reaction that would release enough energy to run continuously by itself seemed hopelessly out of reach.

The Atomic Bomb   The situation changed overnight with the discovery of nuclear fission. In 1939 Otto Hahn and F. Strassmann in Germany reported that they identified the element barium among the fragments produced by the bombardment of uranium-235 with neutrons. The possibility of a large-scale reaction became immediately obvious to the physicists in the United States and elsewhere. Such a reaction would release enormous amounts of energy and could be used in a weapon of unprecedented destructive power. Excitement ran high and a wave of voluntary censorship descended on all public discussion and publications in this field. When President Roosevelt, the military, and Congress were advised of this possibility, they acted with dispatch to provide the funds and to secure the best scientific talent available for further investigation of this reaction.

Why all this excitement? Why was the identification of barium among the fragments so highly significant? Half of the answer lies in the binding energy of the' nuclei involved. The other half lies in the neutron-to-proton ratios. Let us proceed to explain.

When uranium-235 is bombarded with neutrons, the first step is the formation of the unstable uranium-236,

$$_{92}U^{235} + n \rightarrow {_{92}}U^{236}$$

which immediately breaks up. Since barium is one of the fragments, there must be at least one other large fragment. If the uranium nucleus splits into only two major fragments—as was proved soon afterwards—the other fragment must be krypton. This follows from the fact that the atomic number of barium is 56 and that of krypton is 36, the two adding up to 92, which is the atomic number of uranium.

$$_{92}U^{236} \rightarrow {_{56}}Ba + {_{36}}Kr + ??$$

Both of these product elements are of intermediate atomic weight and therefore have very high binding energies (p. 429); that is, the fragments weigh considerably less than the orginal nucleus. The difference in mass must be released in the form of energy, initially as kinetic energy of the moving fragments. A simple comparison of the atomic weights shows that the loss of mass is about 0.240 atomic-mass units. This corresponds to more than 200-million electron volts per fission, which is far more energy than had hitherto been observed in *any* nuclear reaction.

The magnitude of the energy, however, is only half of the story. By itself it would not be too significant. The other half of the story is to be found in the neutron-to-proton ratio and in the emission of neutrons during the fission. In the reaction,

$$_{92}U^{236} \rightarrow {_{56}}Ba + {_{36}}Kr + ??$$

the atomic weights of barium and krypton are not indicated because it is not yet clear which isotopes of these elements are formed, nor what other fragments, if any, are produced.

At this point, the neutron-to-proton ratio comes into prominence. The heaviest stable isotope of barium is Ba-138, and the heaviest stable isotope of krypton is Kr-86. The atomic weights add up to only 224 at the most, and this sum is 12 neutrons less than the splitting uranium-236. There are too many neutrons in the fragments to form stable nuclei. Consequently, the isotopes of the fragments must have several neutrons more than the heaviest stable isotope, and they would be highly radioactive. They would emit several electrons in rapid succession to become stable nuclei. They may even emit neutrons.

Indeed, the most exciting possibility is that free neutrons are emitted during the fission. This possibility appears reasonable at once. The uranium-236 has so many neutrons over and above the stable nuclei of the fragments, that one or more neutrons might be expected to be released in the process. If more than one neutron per fission is released, it becomes possible to have a *self-sustaining* reaction.

The reasoning to this conclusion is straightforward. The neutron in this reaction is not just another fragment. It is the particle that initiates the fission. If it is released as the *result* of the fission, it can attack another uranium-235 nucleus and cause another fission, which again regenerates it. The process can be repeated and if the conditions are proper, the entire mass of uranium-235 can split into the fragments releasing enormous amounts of energy. In the event that more than one neutron is released per fission, the neutrons will multiply at each generation and the reaction will snowball to explosive violence. It is this possibility of a *chain* reaction that makes the emission of free neutrons so exciting.

With these possibilities immediately apparent, further research was undertaken. It was soon established that the uranium-236 invariably splits into two major fragments, although not always into barium and krypton. It may split into other pairs of nuclei, but in every case the atomic numbers add up to 92. One of the fragments has the atomic weight somewhere around 140, and the other somewhere around 90. More than 20 pairs of fragments have been identified. It was also established that in all cases two or three neutrons are released per fission, the average being about 2.5 (Ex. 20).

Thus, in fission the basic requirements for a chain reaction are met. Energy is released and the initial reagent, the neutron, is regenerated and actually increases in amount as the reaction proceeds. There remain, however, a number of secondary problems to be solved. The conditions must be found under which the generated neutrons will find and attack the fissionable atoms in succession.

The first problem is the preparation of pure uranium-235. This isotope is found only in natural uranium, but it occurs there to the extent of about 0.7 percent, which is barely one part in 140. It had already been established that the more abundant uranium-238 does not undergo fission with neutrons. On the contrary, the uranium-238 absorbs neutrons to undergo different types of reactions. It forms uranium-239 which does *not* fission. Therefore, the presence of uranium-238 interferes with the chain reaction in two ways. It dilutes the uranium-235, decreasing the chances of the neutron to hit the latter—just as it is more difficult to hit a duck by chance, if the flock is spread out. In addition, the U-238 removes the neutrons by absorbing them. In order to have a chain reaction it is necessary to separate the uranium-235 from the uranium-238.

The separation of the two isotopes is an extremely difficult job. Both isotopes of uranium have, of course, the same electronic structures and, therefore, the same chemical properties. Hence, the isotopes cannot be separated by chemical methods. They do, however, differ slightly in mass—235 as against 238. As a consequence, the two isotopes behave slightly differently in any process that depends on the mass. For example, at the same temperature, the lighter U-235 moves on the average slightly faster than the heavier U-238. By taking advantage of this slight difference in speed, it is possible to separate them.

In one such process, the gaseous compound UF_6 is prepared from natural uranium. This compound so prepared consists of a mixture of $U^{235}F_6$ and $U^{238}F_6$, with molecular weights 349 and 352, respectively. When this gas is allowed to diffuse upward in a long column (see p. 176) against another gas, the lighter $U^{235}F_6$ reaches the top faster, and the mixture is richer in the $U^{235}F_6$ molecules. After long and repeated diffusions, the $U^{235}F_6$ is finally obtained pure and the metal is recovered from this compound. There are several variations of this method, all based on the difference in the rate of diffusion, due to the slight difference in speed.

Another method is to separate the isotopes in a mass spectograph, which is essentially a positive-ray tube described on page 345. Natural uranium or one of its gaseous compounds is placed in the tube, and the uranium isotopes emerge as positively charged ions, say $(U^{235})^+$ and $(U^{238})^+$. A magnetic field bends the lighter U-235 ions more than the heavier U-238 ions. The beams are allowed to enter separate compartments. By long and continued operation of the tubes, small but weighable quantities are finally collected. Other methods, all laborious and costly, have been developed based on similar principles. The reader probably appreciates the enormous engineering problems involved in isotopic separations on a large scale.

After obtaining pure uranium-235, another problem remains to be solved. As already stated, in order to have a chain reaction, the neutrons generated from the first fission must attack other uranium-235 atoms and be regenerated. Since the generated neutrons have very high speeds (10,000-30,000 miles per second) and the U-235 nuclei are very small, many of the neutrons will go through the sample of U-235 without hitting a nucleus and be lost to the surroundings. If the sample is too small, not enough hits will be scored in the sample and, consequently, not enough neutrons will be regenerated to maintain the chain reaction.

The solution of this problem is obvious. Increasing the size of the sample, increases the chances of the neutrons hitting a nucleus before they leave the sample. The continuing increase in the size of the sample, must ultimately result in its reaching a size (depending somewhat on the shape) in which the number of hits is just sufficient to regenerate enough neutrons to assure one additional hit after each explosion of an atom. If the sample is smaller than that, the chain reaction will die down. If it is larger than that, even slightly, the reaction will snowball

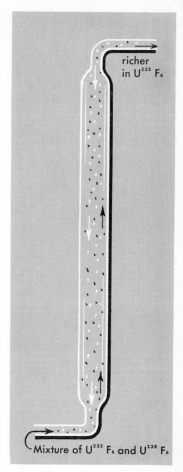

richer in $U^{235} F_6$

Mixture of $U^{235} F_6$ and $U^{238} F_6$

Fig. 13-17. Separation of U^{235} from U^{238} by thermal diffusion. The gaseous mixture of UF_6 following path of black arrows is richer in the lighter $U^{235}F_6$ on reaching the top.

Fig. 13-18. An early phase of a nuclear detonation at Eniwetok during the 1951 atomic bomb tests. (*Joint Task Force Three.*)

to explosive violence. We say explosive, because the time it takes a neutron to meet another U-235 nucleus is extremely short (Ex. 30). This exact size of the sample is called the *critical size* or *critical mass.* For uranium-235 the critical mass has been a closely guarded military secret, but from published data, it is estimated to be from 2 to 4 pounds for a spherical shape.

We are now in a position to describe the atomic bomb and how it detonates. The charge consists of two pieces of pure uranium-235, each smaller than the critical mass, and separated by some distance from one another. Each of the two pieces is perfectly safe, for an indefinite length of time, provided the two are a few feet from one another. For detonation, these two pieces are brought together by some mechanism. A simple mechanism to imagine is to use one piece of uranium-235 as the target, and the other as a projectile, in a small, short-range gun with an ordinary explosive (see Fig. 13.24). When the two pieces are brought together, the combined mass becomes *greater than the critical mass,* and the chain reaction can proceed. A single neutron is sufficient to start the reaction, and there are always some stray neutrons present from cosmic rays and from spontaneous fissions. Once started the chain reaction proceeds with explosive violence. It is over in a small fraction of a second, develops a temperature of about 70-million degrees, and releases energy equivalent to more than 20,000 tons of TNT. The bombs exploded on the test ground of New Mexico and over Hiroshima, in 1945, were of this type.

From these principles of the operation of the atomic bomb, two things are obvious. It is not possible to produce a "small" or an "experimental" atomic bomb with pure uranium-235. In order to have any chain reaction at all, it is necessary to have a sample at least equal to the critical mass. It is equally obvious that it is not possible to make a very large atomic bomb. If the bomb is assembled from two pieces, each must be smaller than the critical mass and, therefore, the two pieces combined must be less than *twice* the critical mass. Of course, a larger bomb may be assembled by bringing together three or more pieces, but these pieces must come together at exactly (or almost exactly) the same instant and this is exceedingly difficult. It is reported that bombs have been assembled which are equivalent to about 25 atomic bombs of the Hiroshima type.

Since 1939 several other nuclei besides uranium-235 were found to undergo fission on bombardment with neutrons. One of these is the still rarer isotope uranium-233. Another fissionable atom is thorium-233. The most important fissionable atom is plutonium-239. The atomic bomb exploded over Nagasaki was a plutonium bomb. This isotope does not occur in nature, but must be manufactured synthetically from uranium-238. The synthesis of plutonium-239 was accomplished by Fermi in the now famous atomic "pile," on December 2, 1942, two and a half years earlier than the explosion of the first atomic bomb near Los Alamos. It is the prototype of all nuclear reactors on a large scale.

Nuclear Reactors

The same basic principles that apply to the atomic bomb also apply to the nuclear reactors and to the prototype, the atomic pile. However, the conditions and the arrangements are somewhat different. In the atomic pile it is necessary to control the explosive violence of the fission reaction, and this implies that an arrangement must be designed in which the snowballing can be slowed down.

The direction of the search for this design is obvious. If uranium-235 is diluted by mixing it with uranium-238, some of the neutrons will escape and some will be absorbed by the uranium-238. By using the right proportions of U-235 to U-238, the right size of the sample and the right shape, it should be possible to allow the reaction to snowball as slowly as desired and attain any designated rate of fission of the U-235. Once a given level of activity is attained it can be kept at that level by absorbing any excess neutrons generated. This can be done by using certain elements, such as cadmium, indium, or boron, which absorb neutrons (Ex. 32).

The Uranium Pile

Reasoning somewhat in this manner Fermi and his collaborators conceived the idea of using natural uranium as the starting material. Natural uranium contains uranium-235, already diluted 1 part to 140. This is a high dilution, but if it is not too high, it would be of tremendous advantage. It is much easier to obtain pure natural uranium even in large amounts than to concentrate the U-235 by the laborious methods of isotopic separation.

The first investigation into this possibility looked very discouraging. The dilution of U-235 in pure natural uranium is indeed too high, and a chain reaction cannot be maintained in it. It must be remembered that in order to have a chain reaction, at least *one* neutron from each explosion of an atom must attack another U-235 atom in natural uranium. Two distinct difficulties appeared. In the first place, the high dilution meant that the critical size of the sample must be increased considerably in order to reduce the loss of neutrons from the sample. Estimates indicated that the size may have to be increased to prohibitive proportions. The second difficulty was even more serious. The dilution of 1 to 140 is so high that most of the neutrons are absorbed by the more plentiful U-238 and result in a nonfission reaction. In fact, at this dilution the U-238 absorbs so many neutrons that it leaves *less than one* neutron per fission to react with the U-235. Consequently, a chain reaction cannot be maintained in natural uranium, no matter how large the sample (Ex. 34).

These difficulties, however, did not discourage Fermi and the other atomic scientists, but merely challenged their ingenuity. The reader has probably already thought of a way of solving this problem. Why not use *partially* enriched uranium in which the dilution of U-235 is not so high? This would increase the chances of the neutrons hitting U-235 atoms. It means, of course, partial enrichment by the laborious isotope separation methods. As a matter of fact this was the direction of further development after the war, as will be discussed later. But Fermi and his collaborators overcame these difficulties even in natural uranium, by a very ingenious arrangement.

It was known to Fermi at that time that the chance of reaction of neutrons with U-235 depends among other things on the speed of the neutrons. *Slow neutrons react much more readily with U-235 than with U-238,* whereas fast neutrons react much more readily with U-238 than with U-235. The reason for this difference in behavior need not concern us here but it is sufficient to know that *there is* this difference. Unfortunately for the chain reaction, the neutrons released in the fission of U-235 are fast neutrons. Therefore, the main difficulty narrowed down to the fact that the neutrons released by previous fissions are too fast. If a way could be found to slow down the neutrons *before* they are absorbed by the U-238, their chances of attacking a U-235 nucleus first will be increased.

Once the difficulty was reduced to the problem of slowing down some of the neutrons, the solution became rather obvious, at least in principle. Neutrons can be slowed down by collisions with other nuclei, provided they do not react with them. The lighter the nuclei with which they collide the more rapidly the neutrons are slowed down. The neutrons behave like moving billiard balls, which are most effectively slowed down by colliding with other billiard balls of comparable size. Consequently, if instead of using pure natural uranium some light element is incorporated with it, then some of the fast neutrons will be slowed down sufficiently and thus increase their chances of reacting with the U-235 rather than the U-238.

The incorporated light material is called the "moderator." Ideally, hydrogen is the most effective moderator, since the protons have about the same mass as the neutrons. However, after considering the various materials available at that time, Fermi decided on carbon. Carbon atoms are relatively light, with an atomic weight of only 12. They do

Fig. 13-19. Fermi's atomic pile in which the first self-sustaining chain reaction was carried out. (U. S. Army photo.)

not absorb neutrons appreciably and the material could be obtained pure in the form of graphite. Fermi built the pile using graphite bricks in which lumps of natural uranium were embedded at various intervals. Incidentally, it is this feature that gave the name "pile" to this reactor. For the particular arrangement of graphite bricks and metallic uranium, the critical size turned out to be a huge block, somewhat spherical in shape and about 8 feet in diameter (Fig. 13-19). It required several tons of very pure natural uranium in the form of the free metal.

The principles may be summarized by describing the operation of the pile. The pile is first built to almost critical size by piling graphite bricks containing lumps of uranium. To make sure that the reaction will not run away, one or more cadmium rods are inserted part way through holes in the pile. The cadmium absorbs some of the neutrons and prevents the pile from becoming critical. On adding the last graphite brick the pile becomes a trifle greater than critical. By this time some stray neutrons from cosmic rays or from spontaneous fission have already started the reaction by attacking a few U-235 nuclei, and these explode releasing energy and two or three fast neutrons. The generated neutrons divide into two major fractions. A certain fraction of the fast neutrons are slowed down by colliding with carbon nuclei, and some of these attack other uranium-235 atoms and regenerate fast neutrons. The reaction snowballs fairly rapidly, but not explosively, and the pile gets hotter and hotter. The remaining neutrons—the greater portion—react with uranium-238 nuclei to form U-239, which ultimately becomes Pu-239.

The ratio of the neutrons attacking U-235 to those absorbed by U-238 depends on the ratio of graphite to uranium, on the ratio of U-235 to U-238 in the uranium, and to some extent on the geometrical design. The pile is accurately designed so that one fast neutron per fission attacks the U-235, while the remainder attack the U-238. (A few neutrons are lost by escaping from the pile and for other reasons.

Ex. 32.) The pile can further be controlled by the cadmium rods. If the controls are pushed in, the cadmium rods absorb some of the neutrons and particularly the fraction attacking the U-235, and the chain reaction slows down or even dies down. If the controls are pulled out, the number of neutrons attacking the U-235 increases to slightly more than one per fission, and the reaction snowballs slowly. After the reaction has attained a given level, it can be maintained at the level by careful manipulation of the controls. In the first experiment, the pile was successfully operated at a steady output of ½ watt. On subsequent experiments the level was raised to 200 watts. As the pile operates, energy is released continuously, and the pile must be cooled, by circulating water or other coolant. All the while, of course, plutonium is accumulating in the pile.

Production of Plutonium   Fermi's original purpose in designing the atomic pile was not so much to generate energy for external purposes as to use the energy released as well as some of the generated neutrons in order to manufacture plutonium. As already seen, the neutrons react with uranium-238 to form uranium-239.

$$_{92}U^{238} + {_0}n^1 \rightarrow {_{92}}U^{239}$$

This isotope does not fission. It is, however, radioactive with a half life of 23.5 minutes, emitting an electron to become element 93, which was named neptunium, Np.

$$_{92}U^{239} \rightarrow {_{93}}Np^{239} + e^-$$

The neptunium-239 is in turn radioactive, with a half life of 2.3 days. It emits an electron to become element 94 which was named plutonium, Pu.

$$_{93}Np^{239} \rightarrow {_{94}}Pu^{239} + e^-$$

Plutonium-239 is a relatively stable element. It decays by emitting alpha particles, with a half life of about 24,000 years. More significant, however, is the fact that it is fissionable, just as is uranium-235. It absorbs neutrons to form Pu-240, which then explodes into two fragments and releases two or three neutrons. Moreover, since plutonium is an element different from uranium, it can be separated from the uranium in the pile by ordinary chemical methods. Consequently, the pile provides a process for making pure fissionable material far more easily than by separating the U-235 from natural uranium.

Although the separation of plutonium from natural uranium is quite simple in principle, it is, in practice, quite a task. During the operation of the pile not only plutonium but also large quantities of radioactive fission products are formed. The radioactivity becomes so intense that the materials in the pile (the control rods, the pipes circulating the coolant, etc.) begin to fall apart physically. Consequently, the pile has to be shut down after only a few grams of plutonium have been pro-

Fig. 13-20. One of the three main plutonium production areas in Hanford, Washington. (Photo by Johnson, Richland, Washington.)

duced. The uranium lumps are removed from the graphite blocks dissolved in an acid and subjected to a series of chemical operations in order to separate the plutonium from the tons of unreacted uranium, and from the score or more of radioactive fission products. It becomes a tremendous engineering task because these chemical operations must be done by remote control to protect the personnel against the deadly radioactivity.

Following the successful operation of the atomic pile, large-scale plants were constructed to manufacture plutonium. The first plant was in Clinton, Tennessee; the second plant was built on the banks of the Columbia River, in the State of Washington, where Hanford, a city of 75,000 people, sprang up overnight. The Hanford plant consists of many piles and underground chemical-reaction tanks, operated by remote control. It produces a few grams of plutonium per day, a large amount of radioactive fission products, and heats the Columbia River perceptibly. The main object, of course, is the preparation of the precious fissionable plutonium-239.

Since World War II, a wide variety of nuclear reactors have been designed for the purpose of generating power. These reactors are based on the same principles that have already been discussed. The essential idea is to carry out a fission chain reaction and to use the heat generated in the pile to drive a conventional engine. A simple, though not efficient design, is to circulate water through pipes in the pile. The water draws heat from the pile and becomes steam which can be used to drive a conventional steam engine. Starting with this simple idea, more sophisticated and more efficient designs have been invented.

The designs of the nuclear reactors followed a natural evolution.

Nuclear Reactors for Power

The reactors have been getting less and less ponderous, simpler to operate, easier to control, as well as more efficient. One way of reducing the size should be obvious. If instead of natural uranium, an enriched mixture containing say up to 2 or 3 percent of U-235 is used, the critical size can be reduced considerably. With the availability of plutonium-239, the mixture can be enriched with this fissionable material as well.

Other improvements are almost equally obvious. The graphite moderator has been replaced by hydrogen-containing compounds, such as ordinary water or heavy water. The uranium lumps have been replaced by solutions of uranium compounds dissolved in the moderator. This development gave rise to the so-called "homogeneous" reactor. This reactor is much easier to build and to operate. It is essentially a vessel of the right size and shape containing the solution of the right composition. Moreover, it is easier to draw off the liquid after the reaction has proceeded for some time and to separate the plutonium from the unreacted uranium and the fission products. In some modern reactors, the separation can be carried out in a continuous process.

The first practical reactor to power a vessel was that for the submarine Nautilus in 1954. Since that time reactors have been built for other vessels, as well as for the generation of electric power. It is a new field and is changing very rapidly. Further developments may be expected in the immediate future. The reactors are becoming smaller, although it is unlikely that they can ever become small enough and convenient enough to operate automobiles, or ordinary house furnaces. The chief difficulty is the necessity of thick shields to protect against

Fig. 13-21. The "Nautilus," the U. S. Navy's first atomic-powered submarine, on its initial sea trials. (U. S. Navy photo.)

Fig. 13-22. The "Savannah," the first (projected) atomic-powered commercial vessel. *(Moss Photo Service.)*

the deadly radioactivity. However, for larger vessels, including large airplanes and medium-sized industrial plants, the possibilities are already within sight. The most exciting possibility is the design of a reactor to power a space ship for interplanetary or even interstellar travel. All these possibilities require nothing more than normal development in technique.

The development of practical nuclear reactors as a source of power has a two-fold significance. In the first place, the energy in nuclear fuel is much more concentrated than in ordinary fuels. An airplane powered with nuclear fuel can circle the earth many times before refueling. The fuel can also be transported with little expense. Therefore, under-developed countries far from sources of conventional power may look to this source for industrial development. Equally significant is the fact that the supply of energy to mankind has been increased manyfold. Uranium and thorium have been found to be fairly abundant on the earth. Therefore, the dwindling sources of oil and coal can be replaced by nuclear fuel, thus postponing the shortage of power anticipated from the exhaustion of these ordinary fuels.

Radioactive Waste Products

One of the problems ushered in by the atomic age is the disposal of radioactive waste products. In the explosions of the atomic bombs the products are scattered into the atmosphere. The circulation of the atmosphere brings them over virtually every part of the globe, and the products are carried to the surface by rain or snow or by simple settling after some time. They increase the amount of radioactivity above the level that is always present from cosmic rays and from naturally radio-active materials. These waste materials then become a part of the air or are incorporated into the water and food of plants and animals.

Fortunately, most of the radioactive products are short-lived, decay-ing into products that are harmless or relatively harmless. A few products, however, are unusually detrimental, notably cesium-137 and strontium-90. The latter element is chemically similar to calcium and concentrates in milk and similar products containing calcium. When taken internally it concentrates in the bones. Since it has a half life of 25 years, it continues to emit radioactivity for the life span of the individual. The radioactive rays destroy the material of the bone marrow and the red cells produced in the bone marrow.

Even more sinister is the long-range danger from the effect of the rays on the inheritance genes. The rays, from within the body and from outside, cause mutations and result in stillbirths or in malformed or monstrous children. It is debatable whether the radioactivity already added to the atmosphere from the atomic bombs that have been exploded so far has attained serious levels. There is no question, however, that dangerous levels will be reached if the explosion of the atomic bombs continue.

The same potential danger from radioactivity also exists from the use of fission power on a large industrial scale. The large quantities of radioactive products formed cannot be disposed of by simply dumping them into a river or into the sea. In not too long a time the entire ocean could attain a level of radioactivity detrimental to all life. Various methods have been proposed to meet this problem, one being to bury the radioactive materials in abandoned and dry salt mines, and to keep them for hundreds of years until the radioactivity dies down. Other methods of disposal are being investigated.

The production of abundant radioactive fission products is not an unmixed evil. The various elements can be separated from the reactors and be used in industry, medicine, and pure science. Since they have the same chemical properties as the natural isotopes and undergo the same chemical reactions, they can be used as tracers in complex chemical operations. They can be identified readily in minute quantities by their radioactivity, and can be followed in their complex chemical reactions in the body, in the laboratory, or in industrial chemical operations. The abundant supply of tracers is a tremendous boon to research.

Nuclear Fusion   If the reader reflects on the "binding-energy" curve of the elements given on page 429, he will immediately see another possibility for obtaining nuclear energy on a large scale. The binding energy is greatest for the elements of intermediate atomic weight. Just as it is possible to obtain large amounts of energy by breaking down heavy nuclei into intermediate elements, it should be possible to obtain even greater amounts of energy by fusing very light nuclei into the heavier nuclei of the intermediate range.

The most obvious reaction is the fusion of four atoms of ordinary hydrogen to form a helium atom,

$$4H \cdot \rightarrow He: + \text{energy}$$

or, what amounts to the same thing, the fusion of four protons and two electrons to form a helium nucleus. From the binding energy of the respective particles or from the difference in mass, the total energy produced is 25.7 Mev for every alpha particle produced. This corresponds to 660 billion calories for every 4 grams of hydrogen reacting. It may be of interest that as early as 1917 this reaction was suspected to be responsible for the prodigious sources of energy that the sun and the stars squander by radiating it into space (see Chap. 14).

For this reaction to take place, however, the protons must collide at very high speeds in order to overcome their mutual repulsions. Calculations show that the speeds necessary for reaction are tens of thousands of miles per second. Such speeds are easily attained with accelerators, but as we have already seen, reactions by means of accelerator beams are hopelessly inefficient. On the other hand, to attain such speeds by thermal motion, temperatures of several hundred-million degrees are necessary. Such temperatures were unattainable on the earth until recently—and still are! Even in the interior of the sun, the temperature is not that high. It is estimated to be only about 20-million degrees. Consequently other mechanisms had to be postulated to explain the source of energy of the sun and the stars (pp. 484 and 497). For this problem—the release of nuclear energy by fusion on the earth—other reactions must be investigated, that may proceed at much lower temperatures.

We may investigate the reactions of other light particles, getting the information from experiments with accelerators and from accurate measurements of the weights of the particles involved. Of particular interests are the reactions of the nuclei of the two heavier isotopes of hydrogen, deuterium and tritium. The lighter of the two is the deuteron, $_1H^2$, containing a proton and a neutron. The heavier is the triton, $_1H^3$, containing one proton and two neutrons. Related to these two is another light particle, the nucleus of helium-3, $_2He^3$, containing two protons and one neutron.

When a deuteron at high speed collides with another deuteron, at first the two combine to form a nucleus of helium-4. Under these conditions this nucleus is unstable and immediately breaks up. It may break up in either of two ways: either into a helium-3 nucleus and a neutron releasing 3.25 Mev of energy:

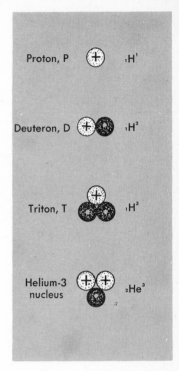

Fig. 13-23. Particles important in nuclear fusion.

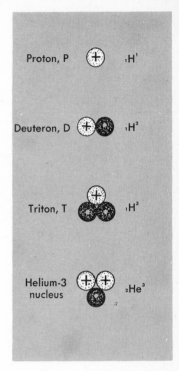

or it may break up into a tritium nucleus, and a proton, releasing 4 Mev of energy:

The net result of this encounter is that one deuteron grabs either a proton or a neutron from the other. In either case the amount of energy is roughly the same, and it is very large.

One of the encouraging aspects of this reaction is that the deuterons react with one another at much lower speeds than do the protons. Calculations as well as experiments show that a certain fraction of the deuterons react even at 1500 miles per second. To put it in a more meaningful way, at 100-million degrees enough deuterons move sufficiently fast to make the reaction quite appreciable. The temperatures necessary are still high, but not quite so high. Our search is proceeding in the right direction. Apparently the presence of the neutron makes the deuteron more reactive than the proton.

As might be suspected the reaction of a deuteron with a triton takes place at still lower temperatures. In this reaction, the two nuclei fuse to form the unstable, helium-5 nucleus, which immediately breaks up into a helium-4 (stable under these conditions) and a neutron releasing 17.6 Mev.

This reaction not only takes place at much lower temperatures but releases about five times the amount of energy.

Equally promising is the reaction between a deuteron and a helium-3 nucleus. In this reaction an unstable lithium-5 nucleus is first formed, which then breaks up into a stable helium-4 nucleus and a proton releasing 18.3 Mev.

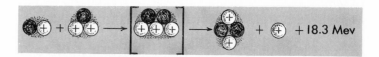

This reaction releases an even greater amount of energy and, as expected, takes place at lower temperatures.

The reader no doubt suspects by this time that the reaction between two tritons should take place at still lower temperatures and, in fact, it does. The tritons, containing two neutrons each, fuse at relatively lower speeds, to form an unstable helium-6 nucleus, which then explodes to form a helium-4 nucleus and two neutrons (Ex. 36). This reaction not only takes place at the lowest temperature of the previous reactions so far considered, but releases the greatest amount of energy per encounter. Several other reactions have been investigated but will not be discussed here.

Thus there are several fusion reactions that release enormous amounts of energy. By judicious search reactions have been found that take place at temperatures far lower than those required for the fusion of protons. However, we are far short of our goal. Of the materials available on the earth, only deuterium is relatively abundant. It exists in all the natural waters to the extent of about 1 part in 6000. Tritium is far too rare (1 part in a million) to be of practical consequence.

Helium-3 is even less abundant on the earth. If these materials are to be used for fusion energy, they must be manufactured artificially as in the case of plutonium.

Moreover, we are far from our goal in attaining high temperatures. Even though the required temperatures are relatively low for some of these reactions, they are still of the order of many millions of degrees.

Up to 1945 the fusion reactions were of theoretical interest only. The highest temperature attained by man for a sustained length of time was the temperature of the electric arc, about 5000° centigrade. This is cooler than the surface of the sun which is about 6000°. In a few experiments, to be sure, temperatures of perhaps 25,000° had been attained for fleeting moments. These temperatures are far below the millions of degrees necessary for fusion reactions. Consequently, no one could take seriously the possibility that a self-sustaining fusion reaction could be carried out on the earth.

The first successful detonation of the uranium atomic bomb near Los Alamos, however, changed this picture suddenly and dramatically. The temperature inside the exploding bomb was estimated at 70 to 100-million degrees in the initial stages. This temperature is four or five times higher than the temperature at the very center of the sun. Even though the temperature drops rapidly as the fireball expands, it remains at many million degrees for some time. Moreover, before the fireball begins to cool, it has attained a volume of several cubic feet. Here we have a good-sized furnace of unbelievable hotness in which fusion reactions may take place.

It occurred to Enrico Fermi, J. R. Oppenheimer, Edward Teller, and others that fusion reactions may be initiated and sustained in the interior of the fireball. If any of the heavy isotopes of hydrogen are present in the fireball, they would fuse, giving off their own energy. The energy given off would, in turn, tend to raise the temperature of the fireball or at least delay its cooling until more hydrogen materials are ignited. Ultimately, of course, the cooling by expansion will take the upper hand, but by that time the energy released would be many times that of the atomic bomb alone. The reader no doubt recognizes in this description the essential idea of the hydrogen bomb.

The exact design of the hydrogen bomb is a military secret, but its essential features are not hard to figure out. To begin with, an ordinary atomic bomb is assembled, consisting of, say, two subcritical pieces of U-235 or Pu-239. Surrounding the two subcritical pieces and filling all free space around, there are packed the light isotopes which can fuse at the temperatures about to develop. In all probability, the fusible material is deuterium, which is readily available in quantity. It is extremely unlikely to be tritium or helium-3. These substances are far too rare on the earth. Most probably, too, the deuterium is in liquid or solid form, for it is desirable to have it as compact as possible. It may very well be in the form of heavy water but it is more likely to be lithium deuteride, LiD_2, which is a solid. There is an additional reason for this. The lithium itself can react with neutrons to form the easily fusible tritium and thus generate additional reagent (Fig. 13.24).

The Hydrogen Bomb

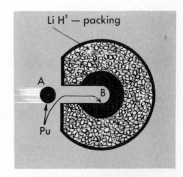

Fig. 13-24. The hydrogen bomb (diagrammatic). A subcritical mass of plutonium (B) is surrounded by a packing of lithium deuteride (LiD_2). For detonation an additional mass of plutonium (A) is shot into (B).

Precisely what reactions take place during the detonation of the hydrogen bomb is likewise a military secret. In all probability the precise reactions are not known too well, even to the scientists working with the bomb. However, again it is not difficult to figure out what happens.

First, the atomic bomb inside the assembly is set off in the usual way. The fireball forms practically instantly, developing temperatures of perhaps 70-million degrees. As the fireball expands, it engulfs the deuterium, and raises its temperature. The deuterons flying at high speeds collide with other deuterons and react to form tritium and helium-3, releasing 3.25 and 4 Mev, respectively. The plentiful deuterons attack these products, too, forming helium-4, and releasing 17 or 18 Mev. All the while, of course, protons are abundantly released as well as neutrons. If lithium is present in the packing, the lithium-6 will react with deuterons to form helium-4, and tritium, so that further quantities of tritium are available for fusion. After some time, the cooling due to expansion predominates. The reactions slow down and stop, and the unreacted material is scattered in the much cooler fireball, but not until amounts of energy have been released thousands of times that in ordinary atomic bombs.

The first hydrogen bomb was successfully detonated in 1954. Its destructive power is unbelievable. It is of the order of thousands of atomic bombs. An island has been blown off the map during a test explosion in the Eniwetok atoll in the Pacific. It is possible to wipe out the entire metropolitan area of New York with a single hydrogen bomb.

From the description of the bomb and its operation it is obvious that it is not possible to have a "baby" hydrogen bomb. The thermonuclear bomb cannot be smaller than one atomic bomb. In a real sense the atomic bomb is the *fuse* that sets off the fusion reaction. On the other hand, there seems to be no upper limit to the size of the hydrogen bomb. With very compact fusible materials, and of the right type, hydrogen bombs may be made of almost any size.

Fig. 13-25. Hydrogen bomb explosion at a distance of 50 miles. (U. S. Air Force and the U. S. Atomic Energy Commission.)

The successful detonation of the hydrogen bomb very naturally raised the hopes of carrying out fusion reactions under controlled conditions. The enormous quantity of energy released, coupled with the plentifulness of deuterium, makes the problem an exceedingly important one. But the difficulties encountered are equally great and appear insurmountable. It is quite unthinkable to attempt to control the reaction inside the fireball. To have a fireball at all, it is necessary to have the energy of at least one atomic bomb. What is required is a furnace that has the *temperature* of the fireball, but not the *total energy*.

This is a return to the problem of developing temperatures of millions of degrees, but without the help of the atomic bomb. Again we turn to the accelerators for the high speeds corresponding to high temperatures, and again we dismiss the suggestion because of their hopeless inefficiency. A faint hope appears in the phenomena of the electric discharge, as exemplified in the electric arc. Sustained temperatures of 5000° can be readily obtained, and for fleeting moments temperatures several times that can be reached. It may be possible to study the phenomena in the electric arc and related phenomena and learn how to increase the temperature of the discharge.

In the electric arc, high temperatures are obtained by a sequence of events somewhat as follows: At first the current flows as the electrodes are touching, but as they are slowly separated, a small discharge takes place in the gap by ionization due to the high difference in potential. The gas in the spark is then further ionized due to the high temperature. As the electrodes are separated further the gas material becomes essentially a mixture of positive ions and electrons, which under the influence of the potential move toward the opposite poles. The collisions at high speed produce further heat and cause further ionization and hence more current, and still higher temperatures. Quite rapidly, the temperature rises to about 5000° C. The conducting material in the spark, the grand mixture of positive ions and electrons, is called *plasma*.

There are two difficulties, somewhat related, that limit the temperature of the electric arc. As the plasma is heated, it expands and therefore cools, on the same principle as any expanding gas, or the expanding fireball, for that matter. In addition, the spark cools, because it radiates intensely. If the spark could be contained and kept from expanding and from radiating, the temperature would continue to rise indefinitely.

But what kind of container could be used to hold the hot plasma? The container must remain solid at these temperatures and be extraordinarily strong to withstand the tremendous pressures that develop, due to the rise in temperature. No such material exists or can exist. All known materials melt and vaporize below 4000° C. It appears altogether hopeless.

It occurred to several physicists independently that since plasma is a mixture of charged particles, it may be possible to contain it in a magnetic field. A magnetic field is nonmaterial and can exist at any temperature, yet it can exert powerful magnetic forces on charged particles in motion. The problem now becomes to devise a magnetic field, of the right shape and sufficiently strong to contain the plasma. If a material container is not possible, perhaps a magnetic container is. Such a container would be in effect a "magnetic bottle."

Controlled Fusion Reactions

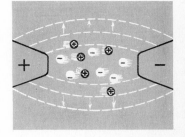

Fig. 13-26. Plasma in an electric arc. The heat developed expands the plasma (dotted curves) and lowers the temperature.

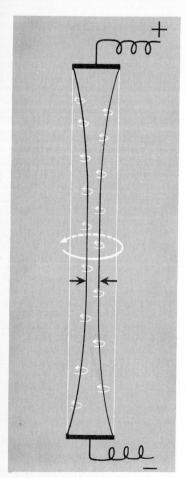

Fig. 13-27. The pinch effect. The magnetic lines of force of each wire add to a single magnetic field (large white circular arrow) surrounding both wires.

An obscure phenomenon in electricity, known for a long time, suggested the answer. It was discovered by Ampere early in the last century and came to be known as the "pinch" effect. As already discussed (p. 103) a wire carrying a current is surrounded by a circular magnetic field, at right angles to the direction of the current. If two rather limber wires are strung parallel and fairly close to one another, and a current in the same direction is sent through both, the two wires surge toward each other and may actually touch. What happens is rather simple to explain. Each of the wires is surrounded by a magnetic field in the same circular direction, and since the wires are close together to begin with, the magnetic field of one wire surrounds the other wire as well. The result is that an essentially single magnet field surrounds both wires and since the magnetic lines of force act as elastic bands, they react on the wires carrying the current and cause them to come together. The reader may have seen this phenomenon demonstrated in science fairs, science museums, or in popular lectures (Fig. 13.27).

Out of this phenomenon came the idea of the "magnetic bottle." In a plasma moving at high speed, the motion of the positive charges in the same direction and of the negative charges in the opposite direction constitute a current. Each moving charge is surrounded along its path by its own magnetic field and the field of all the other moving charges. All these fields are in the same circular direction. As in the case of the two wires, these magnetic fields merge into one single strong magnetic field, surrounding the moving charges of the plasma. The field in turn exerts a force on the moving charges, and causes them to come together. This force "pinches" the plasma. The greater the current—that is, the greater the number of moving charges in the plasma and the greater their speed—the greater the pinching effect.

The reader may wonder why the pinching effect does not prevent the electric arc itself from expanding. The answer is that it does to some extent, but that the force is rather weak. In the case of the electric arc, the speeds and the number of charges are relatively small, and the pinching effect is negligible. To produce strong magnetic fields and hence high magnetic pressures, currents of hundreds of thousands of amperes are needed. A fortunate circumstance helps even further. It turns out that the pinching pressure of the magnetic field increases as the *square* of the current. Doubling the current increases the pressure fourfold, (2^2); increasing the current a thousand-fold increases the pinching pressure a million fold (1000^2). Therefore, by increasing the current to very high values, magnetic fields of enormous pinching pressure can be obtained.

Since about 1950 very active research has been going on, both in this country and abroad to find the conditions and to invent devices for producing very high currents in the plasma and hence very high magnetic pressures. In one of the most promising devices, the plasma is produced and contained in a metallic tube of the shape of a doughnut. The entire device is essentially a transformer and operates on the well-known principle of electromagnetic induction. It consists of a square soft iron core which serves as the core of the electromagnet. The primary coil consists of thousands of turns of heavy wire capable of carrying high

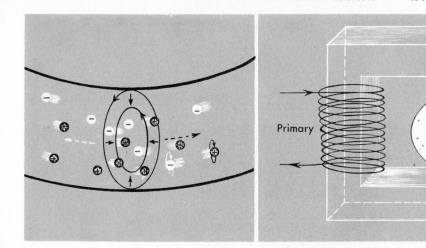

Fig. 13-28. Plasma in a "magnetic bottle." The individual magnetic fields of the moving charged particles add into a single powerful magnetic field (black circular arrows) pinching the plasma.

Fig. 13-29. Apparatus for producing plasma at very high speeds (temperatures). The plasma in the doughnut-shaped container is in effect the secondary coil of a transformer consisting of a single turn.

currents. The secondary coil contains the plasma and is in reality the secondary coil of *one single* turn.

The operation of the device is essentially as follows: A high current is sent through the primary, building up a strong magnetic field in the iron core, and this magnetic field, of course, surrounds the doughnut-shaped tube as well. When the current in the primary is suddenly cut off, the magnetic field collapses very rapidly, and can induce a very high current in the secondary. Currents as high as 200,000 amperes have already been reported.

Now the secondary coil, the doughnut-shaped tube, contains deuterium, at very low pressure. By an auxiliary device, the deuterium is heated until a part of it ionizes to positively charged deuterons and negatively charged electrons.

In other words, the material in the tube is plasma. When the magnetic field collapses, the high voltage speeds up the positive deuterons in one circular direction (say clockwise) and the electrons in the opposite direction (counterclockwise). Very high speeds are rapidly attained, and the mutual collisions between deuterons, electrons, and neutral deuterium atoms, very soon result in practically complete ionization. Since there is very little resistance in the tube, the speeds of the particles quite rapidly attain very high values, which is the same as saying that very high currents are induced.

It is at the moment that high speeds are attained that the pinching effect becomes prominent. Each moving charge is surrounded by a magnetic field at right angles to its motion, and as the charge goes in a

Fig. 13-30. A demonstration model showing the magnetic-field pattern of a "figure-eight" shaped Stellarator. (Project Matterhorn, Princeton University.)

circle along the axis of the doughnut, it is accompanied by a magnetic field. The magnetic fields of all the moving charges add up to a single powerful magnetic field that has the shape of the doughnut container. In fact since the lines of force do not cross metallic surfaces, the magnetic field crowds within the doughnut-shaped container, and by the pinching effect, they force all the moving charges toward the center of the axis. In this way, deuterons can be speeded up to many thousands of miles per second. They cannot escape from their magnetic prison.

In the last reported experiments, speeds equivalent to 6-million degrees have been attained, for short periods of time (about 0.004 second). At these speeds a small fraction of the deuterons collide, and a small fraction of the collision result in fusion. So far the amount of fusion is not sufficient to maintain itself as a self-sustaining reaction. However, the prospects are very good that still higher speeds will be attained and for longer periods of time. It is entirely possible that before this account is read, this feat may have been accomplished.

Should these experiments succeed, the problem of energy on the earth will be solved forever. The supply of deuterium, the "ideal" nuclear fuel, is practically inexhaustible. It is present in the ocean to the extent of about one part in six thousand. One gallon of ordinary water contains enough deuterium to have the energy equivalence of 350 gallons of gasoline. All countries can have unlimited supplies of energy. In time, perhaps, engines will be developed to power space ships for the manned exploration of the solar system and eventually the stars.

At present, these may be mere speculations. However, knowledge of the atom and of the nucleus has provided a very powerful means of studying the structure, past history, and probable origin of the earth, of the solar system and of the stars. It may appear paradoxical that the understanding of the microworld is precisely the key that unlocks the mysteries of the macroworld. But such is indeed the case, as we shall see in the next two chapters.

NOTES AND EXERCISES

1. It is beyond the scope of this book to discuss the theory of relativity. An excellent account is found in Ref. 13-2. A few relations, however, are of interest.

The theory of relativity predicts that the mass of a moving body increases with speed according to the equation

$$M_v = \frac{M_0}{\sqrt{1 - \dfrac{v^2}{c^2}}}$$

where M_0 is the mass at rest, M_v the mass at velocity v, and c is the velocity of light equal to 3×10^{10} cm per sec. If a bullet, weighing 1 gram at rest, is speeded to $1/10$ the speed of light what will it weigh? What will it weigh if accelerated to $1/2$ the speed of light? To 0.9 the speed of light? What speed must it attain to double in mass? What will it weigh if it could be accelerated to the speed of light?

A force of 1 dyne will accelerate 1 gram of mass 1 cm per sec for every second it acts on it. What force is needed to accelerate a bullet weighing 1 gram, from 0 to 1 cm per sec in 1 second? If the mass increases with speed, is the force necessary to speed in 1 second the bullet from 10,000 to 10,001 cm per sec more, less, or equal to 1 dyne? What force is necessary to accelerate it from 29,970,000,000 to 20,970,000,001 cm per sec? What force is necessary to accelerate it to the speed of light? Why is the force increasing indefinitely? What happens to the mass at these high speeds?

According to relativity the increase in mass is due to the kinetic energy. The kinetic energy acts as mass (in fact, *is* mass) and is added to the mass at rest. This analysis, perhaps, helps us understand the meaning of mass-energy equivalence.

2. The explosion of TNT is essentially a reaction of ordinary combustion, and gives off energy comparable to the burning of coal. Coal (considered as pure carbon) burns according to the equation

$$C + O_2 \rightarrow CO_2$$

A pound of coal on burning gives off 3,600,000 calories. How many calories will be given off in the burning of a ton of coal? Since a calorie is 41,800,000 ergs, how many ergs are given off in the burning of a ton of coal? How many tons of coal must be burned to give off 9×10^{20} ergs? How much mass will be lost in burning this quantity of coal? How much less would the carbon dioxide weigh than the original coal plus the oxygen?

3. The relative strength of gravitational, electric, and nuclear forces can be estimated by considering the two protons in the helium nucleus. The mass of each proton is 1.6×10^{-24} g; the charge is 4.8×10^{-10} esu and the distance between them about 10^{-13} cm. The gravitational attraction between the protons is given by Newton's law of gravitation (p. 45).

$$f = G \cdot \frac{m_1 m_2}{r^2}$$

where $G = 6.67 \times 10^{-8}$; m_1 and m_2 are the masses in grams; r is the distance in centimeters; and f is the force in dynes. Calculate the gravitational force in dynes. The electric repulsion is given by Coulomb's law (p. 97).

$$f = \frac{Q_1 Q_2}{r^2}$$

Calculate the repulsive force in dynes. How do the two forces compare? If the protons do not fly apart, what can you say about the magnitude of the attractive nuclear forces?

4. In the past two decades, a host of other subatomic particles have been discovered. First the mesons, or "heavy electrons" of which there are at least three types: the pions (π electrons) having 273 times the mass of the electrons; then the mesons (μ electrons) having 535 the mass of the electron and the kayons (K) 930 times the mass of the electrons. Each of these types exists as positive, negative, and neutral. In addition, particles as heavy as the proton (including the antiproton), and heavier, have been observed. It is not yet known how these particles enter into the ultimate structure of the nuclei. For further discussion of these strange particles see Refs. 13.12, 13.16, and 13.28.

5. Write the structure of the nucleus of $_{92}U^{335}$. How does it compare with $_{92}U^{238}$ in the number of protons? In the number of neutrons? In total number of nucleons?

6. According to the early theory of Rutherford (before the discovery of the neutron) the nucleus contained protons and electrons, with the former in excess. Consider the nucleus of the sodium atom, $_{11}Na^{23}$. Since only protons have appreciable weight, how many protons should it contain? How many electrons? Why? How many "free" protons? How different is this theory from the later theory?

7. Write the structure of the full hydrogen atom and of the neutron? In what respects are they the same? In what respects are they different? Write the reaction for the disintegration of the neutron.

8. Protoactinium-234, $_{91}Pa^{234}$, emits a beta particle. Write the reaction diagrammatically. Indicate the number of protons and neutrons in the disintegrating and in the resulting nuclei. How do the nuclei compare in the number of protons? Neutrons? Total number of nucleons? What element is the resulting nucleus?

9. A moving electron has mass for two reasons. It has a rest mass and it has additional mass because it has kinetic energy. If you stop a moving electron which part of its mass is lost? Which part is left? If you stop a photon, which part of its mass is lost? Is there any mass left? Does a "wave at rest" make sense?

10. When aluminum-27 is bombarded with alpha particles, silicon-30 and a proton result. Write the equation, both symbolically and diagrammatically, showing the intermediate compound nucleus and the final products.

11. In bombarding a gas with alpha particles, why is it so difficult to hit the nuclei. What happens to the energy of most of the alpha particles? Is it more likely to hit nuclei of a solid than a gas? Why or why not? Is it more likely to score a hit on an oxygen nucleus than on a chlorine nucleus? Why or why not?

12. In the cyclotron, consider the path of an accelerated proton in the dees at various speeds. If the speed is twice as great, what is the length of the arc? What is the length of time required to travel the larger arc? Will it travel through the dee in the same time as if it had a lower speed? Would there be any difference as the proton approaches the speed of light? Explain.

13. How do we know that cosmic rays come from outer space? Would you expect the intensity to increase, decrease or remain the same at higher altitudes? If the cosmic rays originated from the rocks, what should happen to their intensity at higher altitudes? If the cosmic rays are charged particles from outer space, what sort of deflections would one expect from the earth's magnetic field?

14. Why is the neutron so difficult to detect? Why does it show no cloud-chamber tracks? Why is it so penetrating? How does paraffin help to detect it? If you had a beam of neutrons, how would you prove it?

15. Why are neutrons "excellent projectiles" for nuclear reactions? Write the equation for the reaction between a neutron on a nitrogen atom.

$$_7N^{14} + _0n^1 \rightarrow$$

16. Examine the Anderson photograph (Fig. 13-10) and identify first the electron and then the positron tracks. What is the evidence that the positron track is due to a light particle? That its mass is equal to that of the electron? That it is positively charged?

17. When a cadmium rod is bombarded with neutrons, the $_{48}Cd^{106}$ absorbs a neutron forming cadmium-107, which decays with a half life of 6.7 hours into silver-107 and a positive electron. The silver-107 in turn decays with a half life of 44.3 seconds to give cadmium-107 and a negative electron. Write the equations for these reactions. Knowing that silver chloride is insoluble, but cadmium chloride is soluble, how would you prove that the 44.3 second radioactivity is due to silver?

18. Chlorine with an average atomic weight 35.457 consists of two stable isotopes, Cl^{35} and Cl^{37}. It is interesting that Cl^{36} is unstable. It decays with the emission of either a positive electron or a negative electron. Write the equation for each of these modes of decay. What element is formed in each case?

19. The misinterpretation of the effect of neutrons on uranium is one of the classic examples of the influence of preconceived notions resulting in failure to recognize new discoveries. In the decade between 1930 and 1940 Fermi and others bombarded uranium and isolated several elements, which were precipitated with the rare earths, suggesting they were transuranic elements. Some of the work was cited in Nobel prizes. Hahn and Strassmann spent many months attempting to separate a supposedly transuranic element from barium. All attempts had met with failure. At long last it dawned upon them that they could not separate it from barium because *it was barium*. Thus, fission was discovered. It could have been discovered 10 years earlier. See page 434 and Ref. 13.17.

20. Uranium-236 fissions in many ways giving a pair of products. If one of the products is $_{38}Sr^{92}$, what is the other product? Write the equation for the reaction, assuming three neutrons to be given off.

21. A volt is defined as a joule per coulomb. Therefore a coulomb volt is 1 joule of energy. Moreover, a joule is defined as 10^7 ergs. Since an electron is 1.6×10^{-19} coulombs, how many joules in an electron volt? How many ergs? A watt second is also a joule. How many joules in a watt-minute? In a watt-hour? In a kilowatt-hour? How many ergs in a kilowatt-hour? How many kilowatt-hours in an electron volt? One atomic weight unit is 1.5×10^{-3} ergs. How many electron volts in an atomic weight unit?

22. From Figure 13-14, which are the most stable atoms? Is energy given off or absorbed in the formation of iron $_{26}Fe^{56}$ by fusion of the lighter elements? By fission of the heavier elements? Starting with hydrogen, which element would you attempt to form to obtain the maximum amount of energy?

23. From Figure 13-14, what is the binding energy of the oxygen atom $_8O^{16}$ in million electron volts per nucleon? What is the binding energy for the whole atom?

24. If two oxygen atoms, $_8O^{16}$, were to fuse to form one sulfur, $_{16}S^{32}$ atom, would energy be given off or absorbed? How much energy per nucleon? How much energy for the entire reaction?

25. Suppose you had 88 protons and 138 neutrons. How much total energy would you get if you made a radium atom, $_{88}Ra^{226}$. How much energy would you get if you made a radon atom, $_{86}Rn^{222}$, and a helium atom, $_2He^4$? Which is greater? Does this explain why radium decays into radon and helium? (At. Wts: Ra = 226.10309; Rn = 222.09397.)

26. Explain qualitatively why the neutron is considered as "nuclear cement"? Why does the neutron-to-proton ratio increase in the heavier elements? Why are all the elements beyond bismuth radioactive? What implication does this have about chances of synthesis of the heavier transuranic elements?

27. Suppose that in an atomic-bomb detonation, 236 grams of U-236 actually fissions according to the equation

$$U^{236} \rightarrow Ba^{141} + Kr^{92} + 3n^1$$

The exact atomic weights are U = 236.125; Ba = 140.952; Kr = 91.934; n = 1.0089. Calculate the amount of mass disappearing. Calculate the energy released, in ergs; in calories; in equivalent tons of coal burning; in Mev.

28. What are the requirements for a chain reaction? How are these requirements met in the fission reaction of U-235?

29. Why is it difficult or impossible to separate U-235 from U-238 by chemical methods? Upon what difference does the method of separation depend? How is it accomplished? Describe the diffusion method and the magnetic method? Can you suggest another method?

30. In solid uranium the atoms are about 2×10^{-8} cm apart. The neutrons released by an exploding U-236 (that is, U-235 plus n) atom move with speeds of the order of 5×10^9 cm per sec. In how much time will they reach a neighboring U-235 atom. Even if a neutron travels through 10,000 atoms before scoring a hit, in how much time will the second atom fission?

31. What is "critical" size? Which would have a larger critical size, pure U-235 or 50 percent U-235 and 50 percent U-238. Why does the "size" depend on the shape?

32. In a mass containing U-235 and U-238, what is the possible fate of the neutrons released by the first exploding U-236 atom? In what ways may the neutrons be prevented from reaching the next U-235 nucleus? If cadmium is present in the sample, how does it affect the chances of the generated neutrons to hit the next U-235 nucleus? How does it affect the critical size? What materials may "poison" a bomb? How many of these neutrons must hit another U-235 atom in order that the reaction be self-sustaining?

33. What is a moderator? What is its function? What elements are best for moderators? Why did Fermi choose graphite in the first pile?

34. A chain reaction is not possible in natural uranium containing 1 part U-235 to 140 parts of U-238. The critical size for this dilution is infinite. Does this explain that no atomic explosions occur in uranium mines? In the geologic past (Chap. 15) natural uranium was richer in U-235 than at present. Would you expect atomic explosions to have occurred in the past?

35. Why is strontium-90 so detrimental to health? Why are other elements, although equally radioactive, not so dangerous?

36. Two tritium nuclei, $_1H^3$, react at relatively low speeds to give a He-6 nucleus, which then explodes into a He-4 nucleus and two neutrons. Write the equation for this reaction, both in symbols and diagrammatically. The atomic weight of $_1H^3$ is 3.016997. From the masses of the other particles given in the text calculate (in Mev) the energy released.

37. Describe the combustion and detonation of the hydrogen bomb. Why is an atomic bomb called the "fuse" of the hydrogen bomb? What is the function of the other components? Is a "baby" hydrogen bomb possible? Is there an upper limit to the size of the hydrogen bomb?

38. What is a "magnetic bottle"? Why is no material container possible for plasma at temperature at which thermonuclear reactions may take place? What is the "pinch" effect?

14

THE STELLAR UNIVERSE

I. EXPANDING HORIZONS

Throughout man's history, his conception of the universe has been an uninterrupted story of expanding horizons. From the earliest times, when man first became conscious of himself and distinguished between himself and the external world, the heavens have been constantly receding and the universe has been getting ever larger. In the unfolding of this story we recognize five more or less distinct stages or periods. These we call, respectively, the anthropocentric, the geocentric, the heliocentric, the galactocentric, and the acentric.

Anthropocentric   The *anthropocentric* period begins in the dim and distant past when man first distinguished between earth and sky. As primitive man recognized the sun, the moon, and the stars, he endowed them with consciousness—like his own. In all primitive religions the sun is a major god, while the moon, the planets, and the brighter stars are lesser gods, demigods, heroes, and animals, as the names of the constellations, still surviving in our language, reveal. Even as he measured the courses of the heavenly bodies and correlated them with day and night and with the seasons, he continued to regard them as intelligences, whose major attention was directed toward him, for good or for evil. In this primitive universe, a mixture of fact and fancy, man was the center.

Anthropocentric views appeared in all early civilizations and con-

Fig. 14.1. *(left)* The Egyptian concept of the Universe. *(right)* The Greek sun god, Helios, carrying the sun on a chariot across the sky. *(The Bettmann Archive.)*

tinued down to historic times. These views existed in Babylon, in Egypt, and elsewhere; they are found in Greek mythology, as well as in Roman and Nordic. Homer's heaven was a dome canopying a flat earth, and was populated by the Olympian gods. These gods, as well as lesser gods, were responsible for the care and movement of the heavenly bodies. In the mind of Homer and his audience, the heavens did not extend much above Mount Olympus. This conception continued down to classical times in Greece, but lingered on to a much later date in the general mind, and still lingers on in some parts of the world even to the present.

The *geocentric* period begins rather abruptly with the "physical" philosophers of Ionia, in the sixth century B.C. By temperament and in accord with their spirit of rational inquiry, these philosophers regarded the heavenly bodies as physical objects. Anaximander, early in the sixth century B.C., was the first to teach that the sun, the moon, and the planets are "stones" like the earth, and revolve around a spherical earth. He ventured the first estimate of heavenly distances on record, teaching that "the moon's circle is 19 times the earth's circle (circumference) and the sun's is 28." (Ref. 1). A century later Anaxagoras (488-428 B.C.) astonished and scandalized his contemporaries by maintaining that the moon is a stone much like the earth and received its light from the sun; and that the sun is a "stone on fire," larger than the Peloponnese. How much larger he did not say, or at least there is no record of such, but the Peloponnese is 150 miles across. The world was getting larger, and the center had definitely shifted from man to the center of the earth.

By the fourth century B.C. the geocentric concept was fairly well developed. Eudoxus (408-355 B.C.), a pupil of Plato, conceived of the universe as a closed system of concentric spheres. At the center of the world was the spherical earth, surrounded by a series of enveloping crystalline spheres, which held in succession the moon, the sun, the planets, and the stars. The largest of these was the sphere of the fixed stars, which also enclosed and limited the *universe*—everything physical that exists. This view came to be generally held. For some philosophers

Geocentric

Fig. 14-2. "The sun is a stone on fire larger than the Peloponnese" according to Anaxagoras (488-428 B.C.).

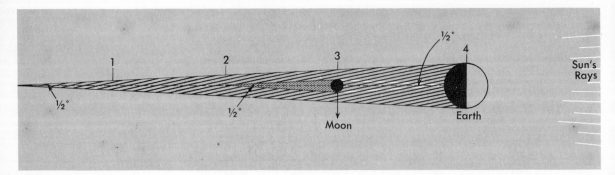

Fig. 14-3. Hipparchus' method of the measurement of the size of the moon and its distance from the earth in terms of earth diameters. The diameter of the earth's shadow at the distance of the moon is nearly three times the moon's diameter; hence the earth's diameter is nearly four times the moon's diameter.

the spheres were physically real, firm enough to hold the heavenly bodies and yet transparent enough to permit the passage of light; for others, the spheres were immaterial or mathematical schemes for purposes of calculation. There was a succession of estimates of the sizes of the spheres, and of the whole universe. These estimates varied considerably, but all agreed that the universe is very large—certainly much larger than was imagined but two centuries earlier.

In the succeeding centuries, as knowledge accumulated from observation and reflection, the geocentric view became more elaborate and more clearly defined. At the same time the estimates of sizes and distances of heavenly bodies became more than bold guesses. In the second century B.C. Eratosthenes (276-195 B.C.) measured the size of the earth as 8000 miles in diameter, as already related in Chapter 2, page 37. A little later Hipparchus (190-220 B.C.) estimated the distance to the moon as 28 earth diameters, which is remarkably close to the true average value of 30 diameters. He obtained this result by comparing the angular size of the moon with the angular size of the earth's shadow, through which the moon passes during a lunar eclipse (Ex. 1). He also estimated the distance to the sun, concluding that the sun is "more than 18 but less than 20" times further than the moon. He obtained the result by observing the moon at exactly first quarter. When the terminator (the line separating the dark from the lighted area) is exactly a straight line, the direction of the moon is less than 90 degrees from the sun. By measuring the angle as 87 degrees (Ex. 2) and by simple geometry he estimated how far the sun must be to account for this. Although he underestimated the distance by a factor of 20 (the true value is 400 times) due to the great difficulty in measuring small differences in angles, his method is perfectly sound.

The geocentric concept did not change significantly from the time of Hipparchus to the time of Copernicus in the sixteenth century. It received a definitive form in Ptolemy (around 150 A.D.), whose "Almagest" has already been quoted on page 35. To be sure, advances resulted—chiefly in predicting more accurately the observations. The pattern, however, remained the same and was the generally accepted view among the learned men throughout the centuries. There were, of course, some dissenting voices. Pythagoras (around 530 B.C.) and his followers taught that the earth is spherical, rotates on its axis, and revolves around "a central fire," Heraclides of Pontus (388-315 B.C.)

INSTITVTIO
ASTRONOMICA

Iuxta Hypotheseis tam Veterum quàm

COPERNICI ET TYCHONIS BRAHEI,
CAPVT PROOEMIALE.

QVAM Plato Astronomiam , alij plærique Veterum etiam Astrologiam dixere. Ex quo autem Chaldæi suas nugas in Doctrinam hanc invexerunt , est ferè Astrologiæ nomen tributum Genethliacæ (quæ & Iudiciaria ferè appellatur.) Astronomia verò nuncupata est, quæ in contemplandis, dimetiendisque Astrorum motu, distantia, ordine, magnitudine, luce , adjunctisque cæteris consimilibus occuparur.

Originem ipsi fecit admiratio ; tum nimirùm, cùm homines præter splendorem, varietatem, multitudinem, amplitudinem Siderum, obseruârunt in ipsis motum tam constantem, tam regularem , tam incessanter diei , ac noctis, æstatisque, & hyemis vicissitudines inducentem.

Commendat illam summoperè dignitas subiectæ materiæ, quæ non alia est, quam amplissima, nobilissimáque totius Mundi regio ; Cælestis nempe , quam homines vt contemplentur, tum obtinere oculos, tum erectos habere vultus à Sapientioribus dicuntur.

Certant de eius inuentione , & antiquitate Babylonij, ob authorem Belum ; Ægyptij , ob Mercurium ; Mauri , ob Atlantem , & Herculem; Græci,ob Iouem, Orpheum, & Atreum; Scythæ, ob Prometheum, &c.

Quorum supersunt Obseruationes , antiquissimi Babylonij sunt; nimirùm habet Ptolomæus aliquot Eclipseis ab iis obseruatas annis paullò plus ante Christum septingentis. Quod de vlterioribus memorant , aut nullo probatur monumento, aut fabulam sapit.

Fig. 14-4. The Ptolemaic Universe as shown by Gassendi, 1658. (Yerkes Observatory.)

Sunt verò Obseruationes eorum , quæ in Astris apparent (ac Phænomena idcirco vocantur) germana totius Astronomiæ fundamenta : quatenus factis comparatisque Obseruationt

Gassendi Obseruationes.

A

held that the earth rotates and that Mercury and Venus revolve around the sun. Aristarchus of Samos (310-230 B.C.) taught that the earth revolves around the sun as a planet. However, these views had not impressed the majority of the ancients, and the Ptolemaic view continued down to modern times.

In size, too, the universe increased but slightly since the time of Hipparchus. Later measurements placed the sun 38 times further than the moon, and Posidonius (135-51 B.C.) increased the distance to about 50 times. This was the largest estimate of the universe by the ancients. The extent of the entire universe was estimated from the relative periods of the sun and the planets. Since it takes the sun one year to return to the same constellation, Mars 2 years, Jupiter 12, and Saturn 30, it was thought that their distances are in the same proportions. Thus, the sphere of Saturn was estimated as about 30 times larger than the sphere of the sun. Accordingly, the sphere of the fixed stars was thought to be just a little beyond the sphere of Saturn (Ex. 3).

Heliocentric   The third period, the *heliocentric,* begins effectively with Copernicus, in the sixteenth century. Although, as already mentioned, some of the ancients had heliocentric views, these never became a part of the stream of thought. Copernicus, however, made an immediate and lasting impression. Starting with the Ptolemaic system, he interchanged the sun and the earth, making the sun the center of the universe and setting the earth reeling in a great circle around the sun.

At first this change did not significantly alter the pattern of the universe or its size. To be sure, the dethronement of the earth from the center of creation drew a profound and violent reaction from philosophers and theologians, as well as from the common man. But the conception of Copernicus did not differ much from that of Ptolemy. In his "Commentariolus," Copernicus writes:

"The celestial spheres are arranged in the following order. The highest is the immovable sphere of the fixed stars, which contains and gives position to all things. Beneath it is Saturn, which Jupiter follows, then Mars. Below Mars is the sphere on which we revolve; then Venus; last Mercury. The lunar sphere revolves about the center of the earth as an epicycle."

However, the implications of removing the earth from the center and setting it in motion had far-reaching consequences on the size and nature of the "immovable sphere of the fixed stars." The celestial sphere had to be very large. Copernicus had to assume that "the ratio of the earth's distance from the sun to the height of the firmament is so much smaller than the ratio of the earth's radius to its distance from the sun that the distance from the earth to the sun is imperceptible in comparison to the height of the firmament."

The reasoning to this conclusion is quite straightforward. If the celestial sphere is relatively small, then the motion of the earth about the center of that sphere should produce certain observable effects. Just what effects would result, would depend on the nature of the celestial sphere. There are two alternatives for the nature of the celestial sphere

NICOLAI COPERNICI

net,in quo terram cum orbe lunari tanquam epicyclo continері
diximus. Quinto loco Venus nono menſe reducitur. Sextum
deniᶜ locum Mercurius tenet, octuaginta dierum ſpacio circū
currens. In medio uero omnium reſidet Sol. Quis enim in hoc

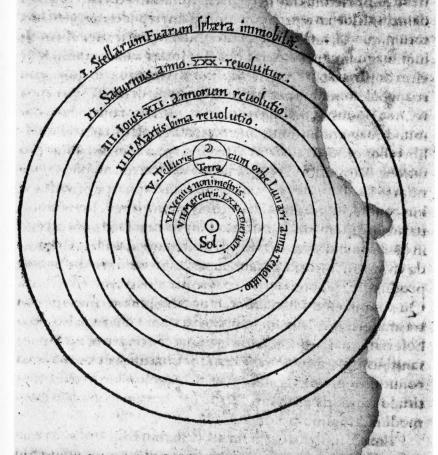

pulcherrimo templo lampadem hanc in alio uel meliori loco po-
neret, quàm unde totum ſimul poſsit illuminare? Siquidem non
inepte quidam lucernam mundi, alij mentem, alij rectorem uo-
cant. Trimegiſtus uiſibilem Deum, Sophoclis Electra intuentē
omnia. Ita profecto tanquam in ſolio regali Sol reſidens circum
agentem gubernat Aſtrorum familiam. Tellus quoque minime
fraudatur lunari miniſterio, ſed ut Ariſtoteles de animalibus ait,
maximam Luna cum terra cognatiōē habet. Cōcipit interea à
Sole terra, & impregnatur annno partu. Inuenimus igitur ſub
hac

Fig. 14-5. The Copernican system as shown in *De revolutionibus orbium coelestium*, 1556. (*Yerkes Observatory.*)

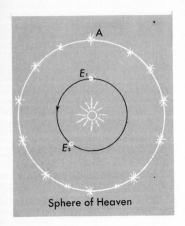

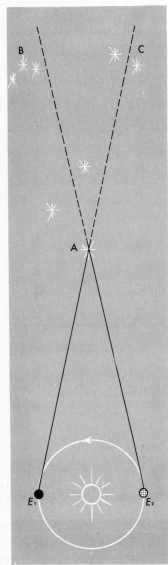

and the stars, either of which implies that the celestial sphere is very large, as seen from the following reasoning.

One alternative is that the celestial sphere is a single surface with the stars on it and, therefore, all the stars are at the same distance from the central sun (Fig. 14-6). In that event the stars (in region A) should appear brighter when the earth is beneath them (E_1) and dimmer when the earth is on the other side of the sun (E_2). Since no variation in brightness during the course of the year had been observed, it could only mean that the celestial sphere is so far away that any difference in brightness is not perceptible.

The other alternative is that the firmament is not a single surface, and that some stars are nearer to the solar system than others. In that event, the nearer stars should appear to shift their position with respect to the more distant stars during the year, because they would be observed from different positions, as the earth revolved around the sun. This phenomenon is called *parallax*. It is the familiar phenomenon of nearby objects appearing to move with respect to more distant objects as we move our heads back and forth (see further below). The ancients as well as the contemporaries of Copernicus looked for parallax and did not find it. To the ancients who had not ventured to conceive of so vast a space, this meant that the earth is not off center, nor does it move off the center. To Copernicus and his followers, on the other hand, this meant that the stars must be very, very, far away. Thus, whatever the nature of the firmament, the heliocentric view implies that the stars must be very distant.

A direct consequence of the acceptance of the heliocentric view is that better estimates of the distances within the solar system were obtained. We have already discussed in Chapter 2, page 44, how Kepler discovered the laws of planetary motion. Most relevant is his harmonic law, which may be stated as follows:

"The square of the periods of the planets are proportional to the cube of their average distances from the sun."

Since the periods had been known fairly accurately since ancient times, their average distances could be readily calculated. Using the earth as one of the planets, the distances of the other planets could be calculated in terms of the earth-to-sun distance. Newton's law of gravitation confirmed Kepler's laws and explained the motions of the planets as due to the attraction of the sun, which weakens precisely as the square of the distance. Thus, it became possible for the first time to make a diagram of the solar system to the correct scale, using the earth-to-sun distance as the unit. The latter is now called the astronomical unit. If one distance were known in miles, all other distances could be calculated in miles.

As already mentioned, the largest estimate of the ancients for the earth-to-sun distance is that of Posidonius, who placed the sun about 50 times further than the moon—roughly about 13 million miles. In 1672 one of the earliest estimates of the moderns was made. Cassini of Paris and Richer of Caynne collaborated to measure the distance of Mars by the method of parallax, which is essentially the method used by surveyors to find distances of high buildings or mountains. Each observed the exact position of Mars against the background of the stars as seen from his respective city and then they compared the apparent shift of the planet as observed from the two positions. Using simple geometry (see below), they could readily calculate the distance of the planet in miles, knowing the distance between Paris and Caynne. From their measurements, and from the plan of the solar system as determined from Kepler's laws, the astronomical unit (that is, the distance of the earth from the sun) was estimated as 87 million miles—fairly close to the most recent value of 93,000,000 miles.

Thus, within 150 years after Copernicus not only the exact shape but also the size of the solar system became fairly accurately known. The earth is 93,000,000 miles from the sun, and Saturn, the furthest planet, about 10 times further. The celestial sphere had receded to great and unknown distances. All efforts to measure parallaxes of stars had failed, indicating only that the stars are very far away. The solar system appeared as an insignificant island in a vast expanse of space.

The great distances of the celestial sphere were further confirmed by another line of reasoning, which also gave a strong indication of the nature of the stars. If the stars do not revolve around the sun like planets, they must be far away. If they are far away, they must have light of their own, since sunlight would be far too feeble to be reflected by them. Could they be suns, too, but at distances so great that they appear dim from the earth? This was certainly a most reasonable conclusion.

That the stars are suns was further supported by evidence brought by the newly invented telescope. Galileo, the first man to turn the telescope skywards, found that the stars appear in the telescope as mere points of light. It will be remembered that the planets appear as measurable disks and although they are cold bodies they reflect a considerable amount of sunlight, due to the large area of the image. In order for the stars to appear as points they must be *very far away* and to appear as bright as they do, they must be *very hot*. Hence they may be suns.

Moreover, Galileo found that the stars are much more numerous than had been hitherto supposed. The reader may be surprised to learn that despite the common expression, "as numerous as the stars," the number of stars actually visible with the naked eye is not over five thousand. However, when in 1610 Galileo turned his telescope toward the sky, he saw for the first time numerous stars never before seen by a human eye.

"To the three stars of Orion's Belt and the six of his Sword," Galileo writes, "I have added eighty other stars recently discovered in their vicinity . . . Near the six stars of the Pleiades there lie more than

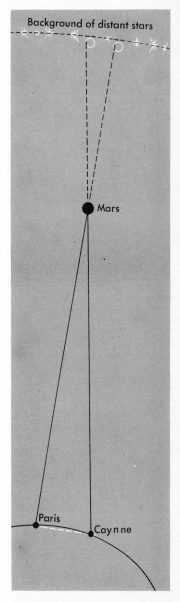

Fig. 14-8. Measurement of the distance of Mars, from the difference in its position in the background of stars when observed from Paris and Caynne.

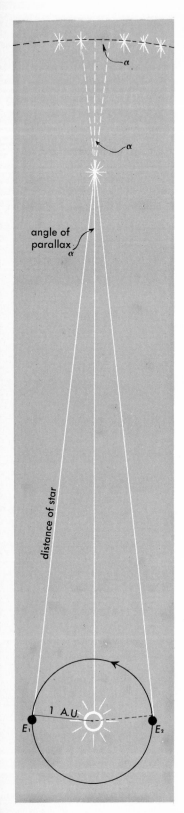

angle of
parallax
α

distance of star

1 A.U.

E_1 E_2

forty others invisible to the naked eye." Galileo also solved the age-old riddle of the Milky Way. As he focused his telescope on any part of the Milky Way, he saw "innumerable stars planted together in clusters" and explained the milky appearance of the Galaxy as due to the combined light of many stars, too faint to be seen individually with the unaided eye.

Thus, on the wake of the Copernican revolution, the universe began to expand to prodigious size. With each increase in the power of the telescopes, more and more stars came within view. Some of these stars may be intrinsically dim stars, no farther than the other stars previously visible. However, it would be difficult to believe that some of these stars are not comparable to others in true brightness, and appear dim even in the most powerful telescopes only because of their great distance from the earth. There could be no question that the universe extends to incredible depths.

Although for three centuries after Copernicus all efforts to measure the parallax of even a single star had met with failure, several lines of reasoning gave some notion of the distances of stars. Newton's reasoning in the seventeenth century is rather instructive, for in principle it underlies one of the methods used today. If we knew the actual brightness of a star, he reasoned, we could easily calculate its distance from earth by comparing the actual brightness with the apparent brightness. Brightness decreases as the square of the distance. At 10 times the present distance the sun would appear 1/100 as bright. If the sun were to appear as bright as Sirius, the brightest star in the sky, it would have to be removed to over 100,000 times its present distance. To appear as faint as the faintest star visible to the naked eye it would have to be removed to more than 10 million astronomical units and to appear as faint as the faintest stars visible through powerful telescopes, it would have to be removed much further still (Exs. 4 and 5).

Suppose, said Newton, we consider the stars as *"standard beacons"* equally as bright as the sun. Then we can calculate their distances, from their apparent brightness. Newton, of course, had no right to assume that all stars are equally as bright as the sun. In fact it is now known that stars range in true brightness from 1/300,000 to 300,000 times the brightness of the sun. Nevertheless, *some* stars might be as bright as the sun, and for these stars Newton's calculations apply strictly. We may not know which stars they are but we can hardly escape the conclusion that some of the stars seen with the naked eye are that far away, and that some of the stars visible only through powerful telescopes are even more distant. The universe is expanding to unbelievable size.

At long last, on December of 1838, the first reliable parallax of a star was measured by Bessel at Köhigsberg. He had noticed that in the course of the year, the star No. 61 in the constellation of the Swan (Cygnus) was shifting its position by a very small amount with respect to the background of stars (Fig. 14-9). At one time of the year Bessel's

Fig. 14-9. The angle of parallax, α, in one half of the apparent shift of a star with respect to the background distant stars, when viewed six months apart. It is the angle formed at the star by two light beams, one to the sun and the other to the earth at position E_1.

Star appeared nearer to one group of faint and presumably very distant stars (Group A), but gradually shifted so that six months later it appeared nearer to a second group of faint stars (Group B). In the following six months the star retraced its shift so that a year after the initial observation it was again in star Group A. Bessel correctly interpreted the shift as being due to the motion of the earth on which he, the observer, was carried in a great circle around the sun. The maximum shift represented the apparent displacement of the star when viewed from opposite points of the earth's orbit (E_1 and E_2), two astronomical units apart. The shift from the *average* position represented the displacement when viewed from two points *one* astronomical unit apart—that is, from the sun and the earth, respectively. By convention this shift is called the *angle of parallax*.

Bessel made a delicate measurement of the small angle by which the star shifted from the average position—it was barely 0.32 second of arc. By simple geometry he calculated the distance to 61 Cygni as 640,000 times the distance between the sun and the earth. More recent measurements give the distance as 680,000 astronomical units.

Let us examine the geometry involved in parallax (Fig. 14-10). The distance between our eyes is about 10 centimeters. If we hold a sharp point, say the point of a pencil, about a foot from our eyes, and look at the point first with one eye and then with the other eye, the point appears to shift with respect to more distant objects. The reader is advised to do this simple experiment. This shift is called parallax and obviously results from the fact that we look at the point from two directions, 10 centimeters apart. When the pencil is not far from the eye, the difference in direction—that is, the angle between the two lines of sight—is several degrees. However, as we remove the pencil to arm's length, the shift becomes smaller and the farther out we remove the pencil, the smaller the angle becomes.

It is easy to calculate how far the pencil must be removed in order to reduce the angle to one degree. In Figure 14.11 the pencil point is at the center of a giant circle, and the eyes are at the circumference subtending an angle of 1 degree. The total circumference of this imaginary circle is 360 times the distance between the eyes. Therefore, the distance to the point (that is, the radius of the imaginary circle) is $360/2\pi$ times the distance between the eyes. This radius is $\frac{360}{2\pi} \times 10$ or 573 cm; it is 5.73 meters, or about 20 ft. In order to subtend an angle of 1 *minute* of arc (which is 1/60 of a degree) the pencil must

Fig. 14-10. *(below)* Parallax. Seen alternately from each eye, the pencil point appears to shift with respect to more distant objects. The shift decreases with distance of the pencil point from the eyes.

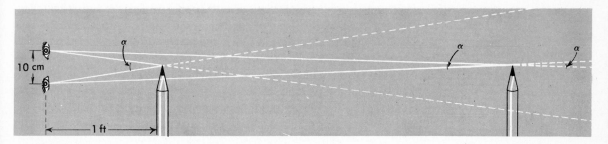

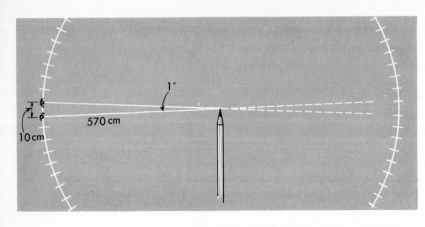

Fig. 14-11. To subtend an angle of 1 degree the pencil point must be 57.3 times the distance between the eyes.

be removed 60 times further, and for an angle of 1 *second* of arc, it must be removed 60 times further still. Thus, for an angle of 1 second of arc the pencil must be removed to $(360/2\pi) \times 60 \times 60$ times the distance between the eyes. This distance is about 205,000 times the distance between the eyes. It is a little over 2 million centimeters, which is about 20 kilometers or about 12 miles.

We can now appreciate Bessel's accomplishment as well as the vast distances of the stars. Bessel's star shifted by about 0.64″ when viewed six months apart, or half of this angle (0.32 second) when observed from two points one astronomical unit apart. This angle is a trifle less than a 1/3 of a second and hence the star must be a little more than 3 times 205,000 as far as the earth-to-sun distance. This is how Bessel obtained the distance of 640,000 astronomical units to 61 Cygni. It is as though he was looking at our pencil point about 40 miles away, first with one eye and then with the other, and measured the angle of shift!

Since Bessel's time the parallax of several thousand stars have been measured. In the very next year, 1839, the parallax of alpha Centauri was measured. It is one of the nearest stars, less than half as far as Bessel's star. The nearest star now known is Proxima Centauri, having a parallax of 0.78″. With the construction of larger telescopes and the development of technique smaller parallaxes have been measured. A great advance was made by the application of photography, around 1880. In this method two photographs of a star are taken six months apart and the apparent shift against the background of stars is measured on the photograph with a micrometer. In this way parallaxes down to about 0.01 second can be measured with confidence. The angle is indeed small. It is as though we stand in Chicago, and placing our pencil point 1200 miles away (somewhere near Boston) we look at it first with one eye and then with the other, and measure the angle between the two lines of sight. With the 200-inch telescope, somewhat smaller angles can be measured with accuracy.

The great distances of stars from the earth already determined make the ordinary units of measurement very inconvenient. The mile is, of course, hopelessly small, but even the astronomical unit (93,000,-000 miles) becomes too cumbersome. One convenient unit is the *parsec*.

It is the distance that a star must be from the earth in order to show a parallax of 1 second (hence, *parsec* from *par*-allax · *sec*-ond). It is equal to 205,000 astronomical units, or about 19-trillion miles. A star having a parallax of 0.01 second is 100 parsecs away. Another convenient unit of distance, in some respects more meaningful, is the *light year*. It is the distance light travels in one year, equal to nearly 6-trillion miles ($186,000 \times 60 \times 60 \times 24 \times 365$). In this unit, the distance to the moon is 1.2 light seconds, to the sun 8.3 light minutes, to the end of the solar system $5\frac{1}{2}$ light hours, and to the nearest star $4\frac{1}{2}$ light years. Since the parsec is 19-trillion miles and the light year nearly 6-trillion miles, a parsec is about $3\frac{1}{4}$ light years. Thus distances of stars up to about 100 parsecs or 300 light years can be measured directly.

Bessel's measurement of parallax introduced the second phase of the heliocentric period. First, it provided direct evidence for the motion of the earth around the central sun. However, no one was excited about this. By this time Newtonian mechanics had so developed and explained all the phenomena within experimental error that no other alternative to the heliocentric view was even remotely reasonable. Second it confirmed the idea that stars are suns; for since their distances could now be measured, their actual brightnesses could be calculated. Though there is wide range in their brightnesses, many of the stars are about as bright as the sun, which makes the sun a rather average star.

More important than either of these consequences, however, is that it made accessible to direct observation a region of space some 300 light years in radius. This huge sphere of space, more than 100-million cubic light years in volume, contains thousands of stars of every description. By measuring their distances, we can find their distribution in space. The stars are on the average 5 light years apart, and are fairly uniformly distributed throughout this volume. Thus, the sun is the center of this directly observable region, and in this sense it is still the center of the universe. Huge as this volume is, however, we are aware that it represents but a small fraction of the total stellar system; for the vast majority of stars do not show any measurable parallax, and hence are beyond 300 light years.

From 1838 to the beginning of this century and even to the present, this accessible region of stellar space in the solar neighborhood has been in a very real sense the astronomer's laboratory. Knowing the distances of the stars, he can calculate their true brightness and their actual distribution in space. From this information, with the development of technique, and with the rise of the basic sciences of physics and chemistry, the astronomer can measure their motions, their masses, their chemical composition, their temperatures, their sizes, and a host of other things about them. In turn, from the information obtained in this stellar laboratory, he has derived new principles that enable him to penetrate deeper and deeper into space. We shall discuss all this in greater detail in the next section.

Pending the fuller discussion of the stars and the modern knowledge of them, we can only sketch here the rest of the story of expanding horizons. Direct measurement of parallax extends to about 300 light years, and the sun is, of course, the center of this accessible region. However, in the solar neighborhood there are certain stars, notably B-type stars and cepheid variables (see Section 3), whose absolute brightness can be determined from their color, their spectrum, and other properties. These stars serve as Newton's "standard beacons," whose distance can be calculated from their true and their apparent brightness. By the use of these stars, as well as by other methods to be described in Section 3, it has been possible to gradually extend measurements to stars further and further out.

At first the stars appeared to extend for many thousands of light years uniformly in all directions. The sun therefore continued to occupy the center of the stellar system. However, around the beginning of the century, it became increasingly clear that the solar system is a part of the Milky Way. Beyond a certain distance stars began to thin out in directions at right angles of the Milky Way, but they continued to be found to great distances in the direction of the Milky Way. The Milky Way appeared as a flat disk or a thin wafer, extending indefinitely. The sun was still somewhere in the middle of this system.

Galactocentric

By 1920, however, as more information was gathered about the size and shape of the galaxy, it became increasingly clear that the sun is *not* the center of the stellar system. We passed over into the galacto-centric period. The galaxy is a vast system of stars of the general shape of a wafer or a thin wheel. It is about 7000 light years thick and about 80,000 light years in diameter. The system contains about 100 billion stars, and rotates slowly about a common center. The sun and the stars in the solar neighborhood are about 35,000 light years from the center. At this distance from the center, the solar system rotates with a period of about 250 million years.

Acentric

Simultaneously with the development of these ideas of the galaxy and the measurement of its size and shape, it became possible to look *outside* of the galaxy and recognize other galaxies. In 1913, the distance to the nearest systems of stars, the Magellanic Clouds, was measured. The Clouds are about 80-thousand light years away and about equal to our galaxy in size. Soon afterwards the distance to the great nebula in Andromeda was estimated. It is about 1½-million light years away. Since that time, more and more distant galaxies have been observed. There are millions of galaxies, extending to the limits of modern tele-scopes and no doubt beyond. Galaxies 2-billion light years away, or more are now measured. Since about 1950 the development of radio astronomy has extended measurements to perhaps twice as far again. There seems to be no end to the world of spirals. Nor is there any way of locating a center. We might call the present period the *acentric period*.

We shall return to give a fuller account of the methods and the reasoning that led to the present grand conception of the stellar universe. In order to do that, however, we need a better acquaintance with the stars and some understanding of the methods by which we gain knowl-edge about them. This we shall do in the next section.

2. THE SUN, THE NEAREST STAR

Although the sun is but one of millions of stars and a rather mediocre one at that, we shall begin the study of the stars with it for several reasons. The sun is *our* star. It is the source of illumination and nourishment, and is necessary for the very existence of all life on the earth. Plato in his Republic called the sun "the most noble and most perfect of all bodies" in the sensible world, and likened it to God in the intelligible world (Book V). Together with the other planets the earth is bound to the sun by gravity and accompanies the sun in all its journeys among the other stars. Its fate is inseparably connected to that of the sun.

More immediately compelling than any of these reasons, however, is the fact that the sun is the nearest star. All other stars, however big or bright, appear as mere points of light even in the largest telescopes. No surface features are discernible, and no hope appears that they will ever be. On the other hand, we can observe the surface of the sun directly, and study its structure. We can measure the sun's temperature, and its brightness, its mass, and its size. Its distance from the earth is the basic yardstick by which all other astronomical distances are measured. Its mass, its size, and its brightness likewise serve as the units of comparison of stellar objects. The methods by which the solar quantities are determined are the same methods that are later applied to the study of the stars. In fact the sun is the preliminary stepping stone to the world of stars.

A good deal of the knowledge about this sun has already been discussed in various connections. This and other information is summarized in Table 14:1, for ready reference. However, it will be most

Data on the Sun

TABLE 14:1
Data on the Sun

Distance from the earth (mean)	92,870,000 $\pm$ 11,000 miles
Diameter (mean)	864,000 mi or 1,390,000 km
Mass	5.97 $\times$ 10^{27} g or 1.32 $\times$ 10^{25} lb
Density (mean)	1.41 (water = 1)
Surface gravity	28 times that of the earth
Temperature at surface	5,700° C or 10,800° F
Temperature at center	20,000,000° C
Period of rotation	$\begin{cases} 25 \text{ days at equator} \\ 34 \text{ days at poles} \end{cases}$
Inclination of equator to ecliptic	7°
Energy radiated from surface (total)	9.07 $\times$ 10^{25} calories per sec
Velocity of escape	383 mi per sec or 617 km per sec
Angular diameter, as seen from the earth	30 min or ½ degree

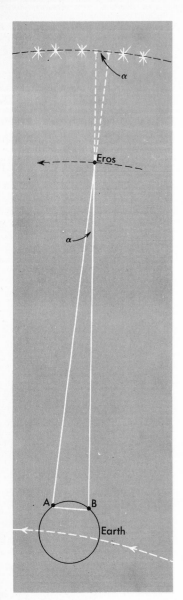

Fig. 14-12. Determination of the distance of Eros from the earth. Photographed at the same instant from two observatories, A and B, and the photographs superimposed.

instructive at this time to describe the methods by which the information is obtained, for the methods give a meaningful understanding to what is known about the sun. Moreover, these are the same methods which, by and large, are used for the study of the stars.

The *distance* to the sun is perhaps the most basic item of information concerning the sun, since most of the other data depend upon it. We have already mentioned the method of parallax, in which the distance to Mars is obtained by measuring the apparent shift of the planet as observed from two places on the earth (p. 467). The same method is used in the most accurate modern measurements. Instead of Mars, however, which is 36 million miles at its closest, the planetoid Eros is used, which comes to within 13 million miles from the earth. The planetoid is photographed at the same instant (Ex. 8) at two observatories A and B as widely separated on earth as possible. Comparing the two photographs against the background of stars, the angle α is measured. Knowing the distance between the observatories, the distance to Eros is calculated, using simple geometry. Now since we know very precisely, from Kepler's laws, the *relative* distances of Eros, earth, and sun, we can calculate accurately the distance to the sun in terms of distances on the earth. The most recent measurement gives $92,870,000 \pm 11,000$ miles as the average distance. Other methods give the same answer, within the limits of accuracy of these methods (Ex. 9).

The *diameter* of the sun is obtained from the distances of the sun and from the apparent size of its disk, as seen from the earth. The angular diameter of the sun is ½ degree, or more accurately 29.4 minutes of arc, on the average. We have already learned by simple geometry that in order to have an angular size of 1 degree, an object must be 57.3 times as far as its actual length (p. 469). Therefore, the sun with an angular diameter of ½ degree, must be twice that far, in terms of its diameter. That is, the distance to the sun must be 2×57.3 sun diameters, d_s,

$$114.6 \, d_s = 93,000,000 \text{ miles}$$

hence $d_s = \dfrac{93,000,000}{114.6}$ miles $= 860,000$ miles (approximately)

Thus, the diameter of the sun is roughly 110 times as large as that of the earth.

The *surface area* and *volume* of the sun can readily be calculated from its diameter. Since the area of a sphere is πd^2, the area of the sun is 23.3 million-million square miles, or 6.0×10^{22} square centimeters. Since the volume of a sphere is $\dfrac{1}{6} \pi d^2$, the volume of the sun is 340 million-billion cubic miles or 1.4×10^{33} cubic centimeters. Perhaps more meaningful is the comparison with the earth. The sun could contain 1,300,000 earths (Ex. 10).

The *mass* of the sun is almost as easy to determine, even though it requires a little more mathematics, and use of the law of gravitation and the laws of motion (Chap. 3). Basically the mass of the sun is determined from the gravitational force with which it compels the earth to go around it at the distance of 93 million miles with a period of one year. The gravitation force, f_g, exerted by the sun on the earth is

$$f_g = G \cdot \frac{M_e M_s}{D_s^2}$$

where M_e is the mass of the earth, M_s is the mass of the sun, and D_s is the distance between them. The constant G is the so-called gravitational constant and is determined in the laboratory. It has the value of 6.67×10^{-8}, which means that two little spheres 1 gram each and at a distance of 1 centimeter between their centers attract each other with a force of 6.67 one-hundred millionths (10^{-8}) of a dyne.

The earth is compelled to go in a circle around the sun, even though it has the inertial tendency to go in a straight line. It resists the bending with an inertial force equal to its mass times the acceleration. For a circle the acceleration is $\frac{v_e^2}{2}$ where v_e is the velocity of the earth in its orbit. Therefore, the inertial force, f_i, with which the earth resists the bending in a circle is

$$f_i = M_e \cdot \frac{v_e^2}{d_s}$$

The two forces, the attractive force, f_g, and the resisting force, f_i, are, of course, equal. By equating the two expressions,

$$G \cdot \frac{M_e M_s}{d_s^2} = M_e \cdot \frac{v_e^2}{D_s}$$

The mass of the earth conveniently cancels, and solving for M_s,

$$M_s = \frac{v_e^2 \cdot D_s}{G}$$

This gives the mass of the sun, M_s, in terms of the velocity of the earth v_e, the distance to the sun, D_s, and the gravitational constant G, all of which can be measured.

We can calculate the velocity of the earth, v_e, from the fact that it takes one year (31.5 million seconds) to travel the total circumference of its orbit, ($2\pi \cdot 93,000,000$ miles), and knowing D_s and G, we can calculate the mass. It turns out to be 2×10^{33} grams or 2×10^{27} tons. More meaningfully, the sun is 330,000 times as heavy as the earth.

Having obtained the mass of the sun and knowing its volume, we can calculate its density. Density is mass per unit volume, and for the sun it turns out to be 1.42 grams per cubic centimeter. It is nearly one and a half times as dense as water. This, however, is the average density. As will be explained presently, the sun is gaseous throughout. Near the surface, the sun is much less dense than the atmosphere of the earth. The sun's density, however, rises to very high values in the deep interior. The pressure increases rapidly with depth due to the weight of the

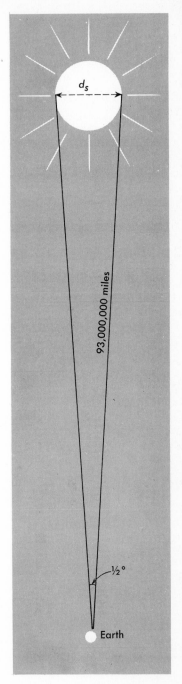

Fig. 14-13. Diameter of the sun, d_s, from its angular size (½°) and its distance from the earth.

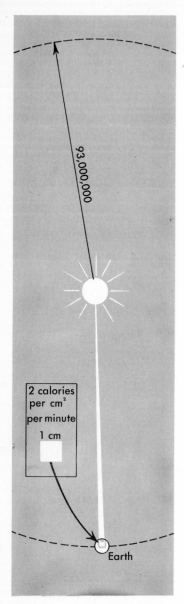

overlying layers of matter, and due to the fact that the force of gravity is very high on the sun. Since the sun is gaseous throughout and, hence, compressible, these pressures result in very high densities (see p. 483).

The *force of gravity* at the surface can be obtained most easily by direct comparison with the earth. The sun is 330,000 times heavier than the earth, and from this factor alone the force of gravity would be 330,000 times *stronger* than on the earth. However, the surface of the sun is 110 times farther from the sun's center, as compared to the surface of the earth from the earth's center. From this factor, the force would be 110^2 times *weaker*. Combining the two factors,

$$\text{gravity on the sun} = \frac{330,000}{110^2} = 28 \text{ times the gravity on the earth}$$

A 200-pound man on the earth would weigh 5600 pounds on the surface of the sun.

The *surface temperature* of the sun can be obtained in two rather distinct ways. One method is to calculate the temperature from the amount of radiation each square centimeter of the sun emits per second. This can be found by measuring the amount of heat received by the earth. Each square centimeter of the earth receives 2 calories per minute or $\frac{1}{30}$ of a calorie per second. The energy received per square centimeter per second multiplied by the total number of square centimeters in a giant imaginary sphere at the distance of the earth would total the amount of radiation received by this giant sphere per second. It is a staggering quantity equal to 3.6×10^{33} ergs or about 9×10^{25} calories per second. Of course, this is the total radiation emitted by the sun. Finally, the total radiation emitted by the sun, divided by the total surface area of the sun gives the amount of energy radiated by each square centimeter of the sun, per second. The value is 1500 calories per square centimeter per second.

It is known from laboratory measurements how the amount of radiation emitted by a hot body depends upon the temperature. For solid black bodies, the amount of radiation increases as the *fourth power* of the absolute temperature; that is, on doubling the temperature of a piece of coal from 600° A to 1200° A, the amount of radiation will be $2 \times 2 \times 2 \times 2$ or 16 times as much (Ex. 11). Having measured the total amount of radiation per second at one temperature, say 600° A, it can be calculated for any other temperature. Conversely, knowing the amount of radiation emitted by a body per square centimeter per second, it is possible to calculate the absolute temperature of the radiating body. To be sure, ordinary solids, liquids, and gases at very high pressures deviate somewhat from this relation, but the necessary small corrections can be readily made. Applying these calculations to the sun shows its surface temperature to be 6000 degrees absolute, which is about 5700° C or about 11,000° F.

The other method of taking the sun's temperature is even more interesting, for it is applicable to the stars as well. Basically, the temperature is determined from the *color* of the sun, or more precisely from its spectrum, as discussed in Chapter 5. From qualitative observa-

Fig. 14-14. Total energy radiated by the sun is the energy that would be received by a giant sphere with a radius of 93,000,000 miles.

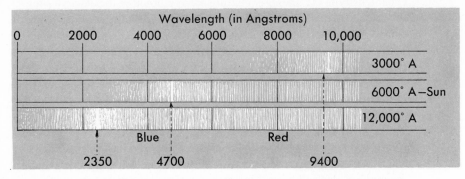

Fig. 14-15. The "brightest spot" in the spectrum shifts to shorter wavelengths with rise in temperature. In the solar spectrum the brightest spot is in the yellow-green, corresponding to about 6000° C.

tions in ordinary experience we know that a black body, on being heated, first emits invisible heat rays in the infrared, then a cherry red in the visible, which changes to orange, then to yellow, then to white, and finally to blue, as its temperature continues to rise. Thus, an estimate of the temperature can be made from the color. Quantitatively, on taking the spectrum during the heating, two relations are discovered. At a given temperature the radiation is distributed over a range of wavelengths, but at some wavelength the radiation is a *maximum*. At this wavelength the spectrum is brightest. Precise measurement shows that the wavelength of maximum radiation—that is, the "brightest spot" in the spectrum—shifts toward shorter wavelength as the temperature increases. By establishing the curves, the temperature of a hot body can be found by merely taking its spectrum and locating the brightest spot in it. In the case of the sun, the brightest spot is in the yellow, at a wavelength of about 4700 A. Calculations from this give a temperature of 6100 degrees absolute (5800° C) for the sun, in close agreement with the previous method (Ex. 12).

The *chemical composition* of the sun is obtained from the examination of its spectrum. The sun is analyzed in essentially the same way as any sample in the laboratory. In the spectroscopic analysis of minerals, the sample is heated to high temperatures and the light emitted from the hot vapor of the sample is passed through a spectroscope. The various elements are identified by their characteristic lines in the spectrum.

Fig. 14-16. Identification of the elements hydrogen (H), calcium (Ca), iron (Fe), carbon (C), and nitrogen (N) in the solar spectrum. (Yerkes Observatory.)

The intensity of the lines is a measure of the amount of the element present. Obviously, it makes no difference whether the light in going from the sample to the spectroscope travels a distance of a few feet in the case of the mineral, or 93,000,000 miles in the case of the sun. In this way the sun is analyzed by the same method as a mineral in the laboratory.

The hydrogen lines in the solar spectrum, and other considerations, indicate that hydrogen is by far the most abundant element in the sun, constituting about 80 percent of its mass. Next comes helium, accounting for another 17 percent. Interestingly enough, helium was discovered in the solar spectrum from the presence of its characteristic lines, in 1965—thirty years before it was found on the earth. (In fact the name "helium" is derived from "helios," the Greek word for the sun.) The most prominent lines in the solar spectrum are the lines of calcium, iron, sodium, carbon, nitrogen, oxygen, and many other common elements, but these elements constitute a relatively small proportion of the mass of the sun. Altogether about 65 elements have been identified in the sun, and probably all are present. The absence of the remaining elements from the solar spectrum is probably due to low abundance or to the fact that these elements give no spectral lines under the conditions prevailing in the solar atmosphere. The abundance of the elements is about the same in the sun as on the earth. The outstanding difference is the very high abundance of hydrogen and helium in the sun. This difference is as expected. The atoms of these elements are very light and cannot be held by the much weaker gravitational field of the earth.

The Structure of the Sun

The *structure* of the outer skin of the sun is obtained by photography. A good deal of information is obtained by photographing the sun directly during the normal day, using all the light as it comes from the sun. Additional information is obtained by photographing it during lunar eclipses. Very revealing information is obtained by using a spectroscope in conjunction with the telescope. Three layers are recognized —the *photosphere,* the *chromosphere,* and the *corona,* respectively.

The *photosphere,* meaning the "sphere of light," is the white-hot luminous disk of the sun. It appears razor sharp in photographs of the edge of the sun and gives the impression that it is a solid surface. However, it is entirely gaseous. The photosphere is a thin layer of gases, probably no thicker than 200 miles. The gases are at high temperatures, but relatively low densities, despite the high pressures caused by the strong gravitational field. Under these conditions the surface is rather smooth with a fairly sharp upper boundary.

The photosphere is the direct source of the light seen on the earth. It emits a continuous spectrum. The gases under these conditions absorb all the light that comes from the interior, and re-emit it. Since the atoms are fairly close to one another and at high thermal agitation, they interfere with each other during the light emission. The atoms, consequently, behave much the same as in a solid and emit light containing all wavelengths and giving a continuous spectrum. When speaking of the surface temperature of the sun, as determined by the brightest spot in the spectrum, we mean the temperature of the photosphere. Probably no light comes directly from depths greater than 200 miles, so that the photosphere effectively cuts out the sun's interior from direct observa-

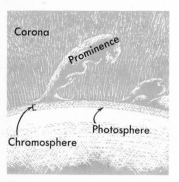

Fig. 14-17. The structure of the visible outer portion of the sun. The chromosphere is barely 200 miles in height.

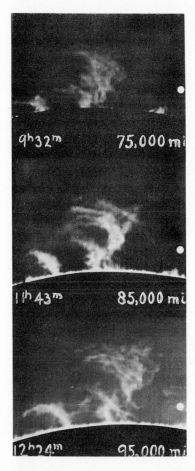
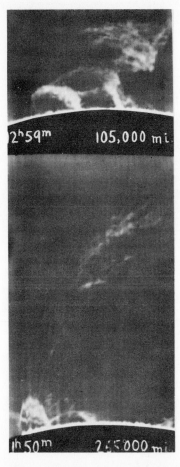
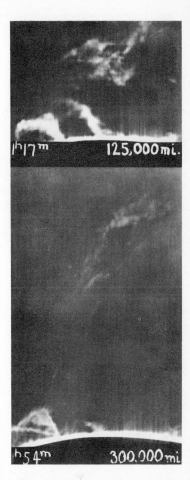

tion. This depth may be considered as the "bottom" of the photosphere, although there is no physical boundary at this level. At the upper boundary, the densities and pressure drop quite sharply, so that the outer surface of the photosphere is a true physical surface.

Fig. 14-18. Extraordinary prominence of October 8, 1920, showing rapid increase in height to 286,000 miles. Forty minutes later it reached 517,000 miles. The dot shows the relative size of the earth. *(Yerkes Observatory.)*

Surrounding the photosphere is a turbulent layer of cooler gases at much lower densities. This layer normally extends to about 5000 miles and is loosely called the "atmosphere" of the sun. It is more properly called the *chromosphere* meaning the "sphere of color," because in this layer the atoms of the elements emit (or absorb) their characteristic wavelengths. The *lines* in the spectrum originate here. The lines are sharp because the emitting atoms are separated widely from one another, and hence do not interfere with each other during radiation. The beautiful scarlet colors photographed during eclipses are due to hydrogen atoms emitting their characteristic light in the chromosphere.

Sometimes another layer, called the *reversing* layer, is recognized in this region, although it is probably not a physically distinct layer. It is called "reversing" because in this region the dark absorption lines of the solar spectrum are produced. The gases in the chromosphere and perhaps at the very top of the photosphere are cooler than the photosphere below. Since the pressures are also low, the atoms absorb the characteristic wavelengths, by resonance, much as a piano absorbs from a mixture of sounds the frequencies characteristic of its strings.

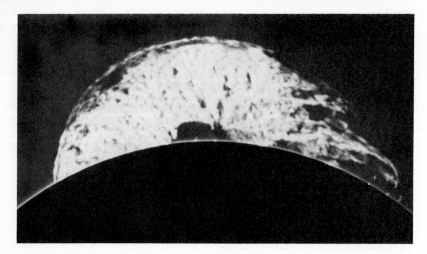

Fig. 14-19. (left) Large eruptive prominence photographed with the 5-inch coronagraph at Climax, June 4, 1946. (High Altitude Observatory, University of Colorado.)

Fig. 14-20. (right) Varying aspects of the great sun-spot group of March and April, 1947, as it was carried across the disk of the sun by the solar rotation. (Mount Wilson and Palomar Observatories.)

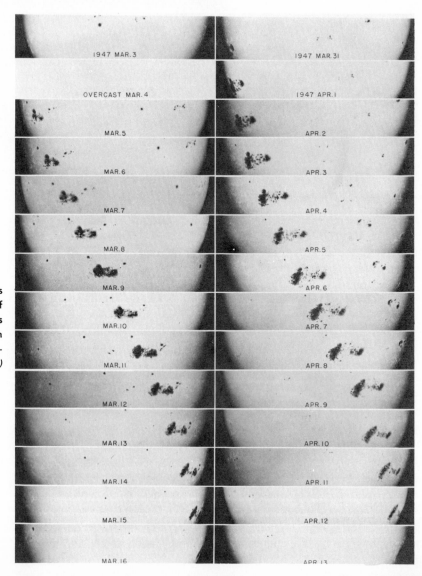

1947 MAR. 3

OVERCAST MAR. 4

MAR. 5

MAR. 6

MAR. 7

MAR. 8

MAR. 9

MAR. 10

MAR. 11

MAR. 12

MAR. 13

MAR. 14

MAR. 15

MAR. 16

1947 MAR. 31

1947 APR. 1

APR. 2

APR. 3

APR. 4

APR. 5

APR. 6

APR. 7

APR. 8

APR. 9

APR. 10

APR. 11

APR. 12

APR. 13

The result is that the photospheric light, which has a continuous spectrum, on passing through this layer is robbed of the wavelengths characteristic of the absorbing atoms. The missing wavelengths appear as dark lines in the solar spectrum. For example, very prominent in the solar spectrum is the dark D line, characteristic of sodium. Most of the elements in the sun are identified by their absorption lines produced in this region.

Two large-scale features of the surface of the sun are the *prominences* and the *sun spots*. These two features are associated mainly with the chromosphere, and are most probably related to each other. They appear to be due to violent storms in the chromosphere. The prominences are observed as tongues of fire at the edge of the sun during solar eclipses, when the moon's disk cuts out the much more intense light of the photosphere. They assume a variety of forms, but most often are curtain-shaped thin filaments arching over great distances—200,000 miles or more. Some prominences remain essentially unchanged for days, but others exhibit violent tornadolike motion. Speeds up to 100 miles per second are not uncommon, and material is often ejected up to 100,000 miles or more, in a matter of minutes. In other prominences, material is observed streaming rapidly into the sun.

The sun spots are dark surface features and are observed on the disk itself. They range from barely observable specks 500 miles across, to giant whirlpools more than 50,000 miles across—1/15 of the sun's diameter. The larger of these are readily visible with the naked eye (using a smoked glass, of course). They appear as dark holes on the photosphere, but in reality are large bodies of gas in whirling motion appearing dark only by contrast, being some 1000 to 1500 degrees cooler than the photosphere. Strong magnetic fields are associated with this motion, and these fields affect the magnetic field of the earth, as well as the weather (Ex. 13).

The sun spots persist from a few days to several weeks. They often appear in groups on both sides of the sun's equator. They move from west to east parallel to the sun's equator. In fact, the motion of the sun spots provides the most direct evidence of the sun's rotation, so that we can speak of the sun's equator. The sun spots travel across the disk in about 13 days, and some of the long-lived ones reappear on the western edge, indicating that the sun rotates with a period of about 25 days. When a large spot reaches the edge, there is usually a marked display of prominences; this, however, is not always the case. The relation between sun spots and prominences is not well understood. Prominences may appear anywhere in the sun's edge, but sun spots are only observed within 45 degrees of the solar equator. They are never seen near the solar poles.

The third layer surrounding the sun is the *corona,* observed (until recently) only during the total eclipse of the sun. At the moment the moon's disk completely hides the brilliant photosphere and only the scarlet ring of the chromosphere and the flamelike prominences are visible, there appears suddenly a pearly envelope, halolike and surrounding the sun. Hence the name *corona,* meaning a "crown." The corona extends to distances as great or greater than the sun's diameter—a million miles or more in some directions. (In a highly rarified state it

Fig. 14-21. Solar corona photographed in the Anglo-Egyptian Sudan during the eclipse of February 25, 1952, by van Biesbroeck. *(Yerkes Observatory.)*

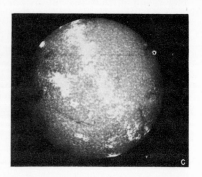

Fig. 14-22. The sun has many faces. A, ordinary light; B, spectroheliogram photo in the hydrogen light (H); C, spectroheliogram in the calcium light; B and C show the distribution of these two elements. *(Mount Wilson and Palomar Observatories.)*

may well extend to the nearest planets, including the earth.) The total light it emits is more than half of that reflected by the full moon. It appears to be photospheric light reflected by an extremely tenuous cloud of electrons. These electrons are at high speed, corresponding to temperatures of half a million degrees. The corona is extremely tenuous, much more tenuous than the best vacuum that can be obtained in the laboratory.

The information presented thus far has been obtained for the most part by using ordinary light during the normal day or during solar eclipses. Two relatively recent developments have greatly increased the available information. One is the invention of the *spectroheliograph.* In this instrument, instead of photographing with all the light coming from the sun, the light is first passed through a spectroscope. One spectral line of an element, say the H_α line of hydrogen, is then selected, and a photograph of the sun is taken using this light alone. The picture thus obtained, called the *spectroheliogram,* gives the distribution of hydrogen over the entire surface of the sun. In the same way the distribution of the other elements is obtained. Photographed in this way, the sun has many faces, each showing the distribution of the various elements at any given time. By successive photographs, or by motion picture photography, the movements of masses of the various elements over the surface of the sun can be traced.

A more recent invention is the *coronagraph.* In this instrument all the light of the photosphere as well as most of the light of the chromosphere is effectively reflected out of the telescope, so that only the much fainter light of the corona can be photographed. In this way the structure of the corona and the changes it undergoes with time can be studied.

Two other methods for observing the sun may be mentioned at this point. One is the study of cosmic rays, x-rays, and short ultraviolet rays emitted by the sun. These rays are effectively absorbed by the atmosphere of the earth and do not reach the telescopes at the earth's surface. However, these radiations can be detected and measured by instruments sent in balloons, rockets, and satellites above the earth's atmosphere. In the last decade, the new field of radio astronomy has been developing, making it possible to observe parts of the long-wavelength end of the solar spectrum. Masses of neutral hydrogen send out radiation in the short-wave radio region and they are observed with radio telescopes (see p. 515).

All the basic knowledge about the sun thus far presented is fairly well established. As the reader can judge from the description of the methods, this knowledge is based quite firmly on direct observations. Each fact is usually determined by several methods that check one another. There are, however, many questions about the sun that cannot be answered with the same degree of confidence. Among these questions the following will occur to the reader. What are the conditions in the interior of the sun? How high are the pressures, the densities, and the temperatures at the center of the sun? What is the source of energy of the sun? How long has the sun been shining and at what rate? How long will it continue to shine? Is it getting hotter or colder? How old is the sun? How did it originate? What is the future and ultimate fate of the sun?

At the present state of our knowledge we cannot answer these questions as definitely as we would like. However, there are some answers that are much more than mere guesses. In some of these we have more confidence than in others. As knowledge accumulates the answers become more definite and are supported by stronger evidence. We shall present some of these and indicate, in general terms at least, the reasoning and the observations upon which they are based, so that the reader will be able to judge for himself the state of present knowledge in these matters.

What are the conditions inside the sun? As already mentioned, it is not possible to observe directly the sun's interior, for the photosphere cuts out effectively all the light coming from a depth greater than 200 miles. However, we know the total mass of the sun, its diameter, its overall density, its gravitational field, its chemical composition, its surface temperature, and the amount of radiation it emits per second. We also know the structure of the atoms, and the behavior of matter up to the highest temperatures and pressures that can be obtained in the laboratory. These are not sufficiently high, to be sure, but can serve as the starting point to the extreme conditions that must exist inside the sun.

Taking all that is known into proper account we can construct a theoretical model (or a limited number of them) for this enormous mass of matter under these conditions. At the surface of the sun two opposing forces must balance. The force of gravity is pulling toward the center, tending to collapse the whole mass into a volume as small as possible. This inward pull must be counterbalanced by expansive forces of which there are two kinds. One is the outward pressure of the intense radiation, which increases with temperature. The other is the outward gas pressure, which also increases with temperature, but in a different way from the radiation pressure. At any point below the surface the opposing forces must likewise balance. With sufficient mathematical skill it is possible to specify how the pressure, the density, and the temperature must increase with depth. According to the best theoretical model, the density of the gas at the center of the sun is about

The Interior of the Sun

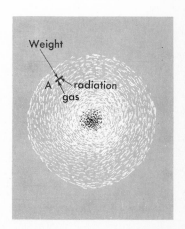

Fig. 14-23. Interior of the sun (diagrammatic). At any level, A, the weight pressure is balanced by the gas pressure and the radiation pressure.

100 times that of water, and the temperature is about 20 million degrees (see p. 497).

We have a fairly good idea of the source of the energy of the sun. By direct measurement it is found that the sun emits 3.6×10^{33} ergs per second. Since we know from geology (see below) that the sun has been shining at essentially the present rate for thousands of millions of years, this amount of energy must come from nuclear reactions in which mass is converted into energy. A simple calculation shows that 3.6×10^{33} ergs of energy is equivalent to 4×10^{12} grams of matter, so that at present the sun is losing 4 million tons of its mass per second.

What nuclear reactions are responsible for this enormous release of energy? There is only a limited number of possibilities, given the composition of the sun and the conditions in its interior. The most likely candidate is the fusion of hydrogen to form helium. It is not a direct union of four hydrogen nuclei to form a helium nucleus. That would require a temperature of several hundred-million degrees. However, at the temperature of the sun's interior, several other reactions are possible and many have been suggested. The most likely is the reaction of two protons to give a deuteron and a positron

$$_1H^1 + {}_1H^1 \rightarrow {}_1H^2 + e^+$$

followed by a series of deuteron fusion reactions to give $_2He^4$, as discussed in Chapter 13, page 446. Now the amount of hydrogen in the sun is known, as well as the temperature and the rates of these reactions under the conditions prevailing in the sun's interior. It is rather significant that the rate of release of energy expected from this reaction is very close to the actual amount of energy radiated by the sun per second. For this reason, modern science is inclined to believe that this is the main reaction, although other nuclear reactions doubtless contribute very small amounts.

The assumption that this reaction is responsible for the sun's energy explains a number of facts, but leaves other questions unanswered. For example, how do we know for how long the sun has been shining? The geologic record provides evidence that the sun has been shining essentially at the present rate for at least 2000 million years. This follows from the fact that sedimentary rocks on the earth have been found that reach to at least this age. Since sedimentary rocks are deposited by *running* water, mostly along ocean shores, the temperature on the earth could not have been very different during all this time. If it were much hotter, all the water would have evaporated. There would have been no ocean and no running water. If the temperature were much colder, the ocean would have frozen—again no running water and no sedimentary rocks. Other lines of evidence indicate (p. 590) that the sun has been shining at essentially this rate for about 5 billion years. (Ex. 15).

We would be running ahead of our story if we were to pursue the other questions at this point. For after all the sun is but one of the stars. More meaningful answers can be given after the study of the other stars, their formation, their age, and their evolution. To this we shall turn in the next section.

3. THE STARS IN THE SOLAR NEIGHBORHOOD

In the exploration of the universe, the first great leap beyond the solar system was to the region of space surrounding the sun. Measurement of parallax made accessible to direct study a volume of space some 300 light years in radius. Whether this region is considered large or small is a relative matter. On the one hand, this accessible region is but a small fraction of the stellar universe. The vast majority of the stars show no measurable parallax and hence are outside this region. On the other hand, this region contains thousands of stars of practically all types. What is known about the stars was first established here. The solar neighborhood became the "proving ground" or the "astronomer's laboratory," where knowledge was gained and principles were tested, which were then later extended to more distant stars. Having studied the sun—the nearest star—in the last section, we will now present the methods and the reasoning that led to our present knowledge of the stars.

It might be well to remark at the outset that all the knowledge of the stars is obtained from the extremely small amount of light received from them. The development of technique has made it possible to record and analyze the light with delicate instruments. The increase in the size of the telescopes makes it possible to gather a greater amount of the feeble light received from them. The application of photography and micrometer methods made it possible to measure small angles and to detect very dim stars. The invention of the spectroscope made it possible to analyze the light into the spectrum, and the development of the basic ideas of physics and chemistry, discussed in the earlier chapters, made it possible to interpret the messages that the light beams carry.

Our study will be further facilitated by remarking at this point that most of the knowledge of the stars is obtained from four basic items of information. These are the *brightnesses* of the stars, their *distances* from the solar system, their *temperatures,* and their *motions.* All four are obtained more or less directly by observation. While additional observations are necessary for some of the properties of the stars, these four items enter again and again into our reasoning, as will become evident in the unfolding of the story.

All the observations made with the naked eye throughout the centuries and later the telescopic observations up to the discovery of parallax in 1838 had yielded but little definite knowledge of the stars. In fact, besides locating a star in a constellation and measuring its angular distance from other stars, almost the only other definite knowledge was its *apparent* brightness. This, however, as already mentioned, is an important and basic item of information.

Brightness of Stars

The apparent brightness of a star is its brightness relative to other stars as it appears from the earth. Stars range in apparent brightness from Sirius, the brightest star in the sky, to those stars that are barely visible with the naked eye. From ancient times the brightness of stars has been measured on a scale called the *magnitude* scale. The twenty brightest stars in the sky are called stars of the "first" magnitude, those next in brightness are stars of the "second" magnitude, and so on to those that are barely visible, which are called stars of the "sixth" magnitude. It turns out that the average star of the first magnitude is about 100 times as bright as stars of the sixth magnitude. On this basis a scale is constructed so that stars of the first magnitude are about 2.5 (that is, $\sqrt[5]{100} = 2.512$) times as bright as those of the second magnitude, 2.5×2.5 times as bright as those of the third magnitude, and so on (Exs. 16 and 17). It may be well to emphasize that *magnitude* is a measure of *brightness* only. It has nothing to do directly with actual size, or apparent size, or mass, or temperature of the star. Indirectly, apparent brightness may be related to these quantities, but that is another matter.

The invention of the telescope brought into view stars of higher than the sixth magnitude—that is, *dimmer* stars—and the magnitude scale has been extended. With the modern telescopes, stars of the twenty-second and twenty-third magnitude can be photographed. Beyond this point, however, it is not possible to go at present. The stray light of the night sky, mostly reflection from the upper atmosphere, is brighter than the stars of the twenty-third or twenty-fourth magnitude, so that longer exposures result in a completely black plate. However, these stars are dim indeed. A star of the twenty-third magnitude is as bright as a candle would appear at 17,000 feet. Every increase in five magnitudes means that the star is 100 times dimmer, so that a star of the twenty-first magnitude is $100 \times 100 \times 100$ or one million times dimmer than a star of the sixth magnitude, which is barely visible to the unaided eye; and a star of the twenty-third magnitude would be about 6 times dimmer still (Exs. 16 and 17). These relations are shown in Table 14:2.

The second basic item of information is the *distance* of a star from the earth. As in the case of the sun, most of the other knowledge depends upon it. It is for this reason that the successful measurement of parallax by Bessel initiated the present era of definite knowledge of the stars. The method has already been discussed on page 468. A star is photographed by the same instrument at two different times, six months apart, and the apparent shift against the background of stars is measured on the photograph with a micrometer. By this method, distances up to 300 light years can be measured with some accuracy. More recently, with the 200-inch telescope, the measurements can be extended to about twice this distance and even rough estimates a little beyond that can be obtained.

Having measured the distance of a star and knowing its apparent brightness from direct observation, we can calculate its *actual brightness*. "Actual" brightness means the total amount of light a star emits. Various terms are used to express the actual brightness such as "real" brightness, "true" brightness, "intrinsic" brightness, "absolute" bright-

TABLE 14:2

Magnitude	Times fainter than 1st magnitude
1	1
2	2.5
3	6.25
4	16
5	40
6	100
7	250
11	10,000
16	1,000,000
21	100,000,000
23	625,000,000

ness, "absolute" magnitude, "absolute" luminosity, and "real" luminosity, among others. It is not necessary to distinguish between these terms for our discussion. Perhaps the most meaningful way to express the true brightness of a star is to compare it with the sun. This is often called simply *luminosity* and can be calculated very easily. Since the observed brightness of any light source decreases as the square of the distance, we can calculate how bright a star would appear if it were at the same distance as the sun, and then compare the two. An alternate procedure that amounts to the same thing is to calculate how bright the sun would appear if it were at the same distance as the star, and then compare the two. Thus, knowing the distance of the star, we can calculate its true brightness from the apparent brightness.

Determination of the true brightness or luminosity of several thousand stars in the solar neighborhood indicates a tremendous range in them. Many stars, to be sure, are of the same order of brightness as the sun. However, there are stars that are hundreds and even thousands of times brighter than the sun. For example, Beta Centauri, which is 300 light years away, is 3000 times brighter than the sun. A more striking example is Canopus. Its parallax is 0.015 second, from which the distance is estimated at 180 light years. This star is no less than 5200 times brighter than the sun. These very bright stars are called *giants*. The term merely means that they are very bright—several thousand times brighter than the sun.

At the other extreme are stars much dimmer than the sun. Many stars are known which are 1/100 as bright as the sun, and there are some which are less than 1/10,000 as bright. These are called *dwarfs*. Again the term merely means that the stars are of low luminosity, relative to the sun. It has nothing to do directly with size as such, though it may be indirectly related to it.

Even the figures given above do not encompass the full range in brightness. On the dwarf side, there must be stars less than 1/10,000 times as bright as the sun that have escaped detection. The reason is obvious. If the star is very dim intrinsically, then it can only be observed if it is relatively near, since brightness decreases as the square of the distance. In fact very dim dwarfs can be seen only in the vicinity of the sun. Moreover, there is reason to suspect that there are stars too small or too cool to give much light. In fact some "dark" stars have been detected from the fact that they eclipse the brighter stars. On the same line of reasoning, since apparent brightness decreases rapidly with distance, there must be stars which are intrinsically still brighter than Canopus. In fact all the stars that are too far to show parallax and yet still appear bright must be intrinsically very bright. As we shall show later, there are some supergiants outside the range of the parallactic method of measuring distances.

The true brightness of a star is, of course, a property of the star itself. It does not depend on the accident of its distance from the earth. It is a measure of the total amount of light the star emits. However, the true brightness of a star depends upon two other factors. First, it depends upon the temperature, which determines the amount of light each square centimeter emits per second. Second, it depends upon the size—that is, upon the total surface area of the star. A star is a giant either because it is very hot, or because it is very large, or for both reasons. Similarly, a star is a dwarf either because it is relatively cool, or because it is very small, or for both reasons. Of these two factors, the temperature can be measured most directly and most easily.

Temperatures of Stars

The temperature of stars can be measured by several methods which are somewhat related. A fair estimate of the temperature can be obtained from the color alone, as was explained in the section on the sun. Red stars are relatively cool stars, having a temperature of 3000 to 4000° C. A good example is Antares in the heart of the Scorpion, with a temperature of 3000° C. Orange stars are somewhat hotter. Yellow stars have a temperature comparable to that of the sun—around 6000° C. White stars are hotter still, and blue stars have temperatures upward of 15,000° C. A good example is the white star, Vega, whose temperature is about 12,000° C (see Table 14:3).

A more accurate estimate of the temperature of a star is obtained from its continuous spectrum. As in the case of the sun, the spectrum of the star is photographed and the "brightest spot" in the spectrum is located. The temperature is then obtained directly from the known relation between the wavelength of maximum radiation and temperature. Thus, the brightest spot in the spectrum of Sirius is 2800 angstroms corresponding to a temperature of 10,000° C. There are, however, two limitations to this method. It is applicable only to stars that have a recognizable continuous spectrum. Moreover, it is applicable only to the brighter stars, since considerable light is necessary to produce a clear enough spectrum to locate the brightest spot. Nevertheless, the temperatures of a large number of stars have been accurately measured by this method.

Spectral Sequence. A much more general method has been derived by which the temperature of a star is estimated from the *type* of its spectrum. From laboratory measurements and from knowledge of atomic structure we know how the *type* of spectrum depends on the temperature. At very high temperatures the material of the star has completely dissociated and exists as single atoms. Consequently the elements in the very hot stars emit their characteristic sharp lines. The particular lines these stars emit and their relative intensities depend upon the temperature. In the cooler stars, other lines appear, characteristic of lower temperatures. As the temperatures decrease further, absorption lines appear, just as in the solar spectrum. At still lower temperatures the elements form chemical compounds; in the spectrum there are bands that are characteristic of these compounds and also are indicative of the temperatures at which these compounds are stable.

In fact long before the more accurate method of locating the "brightest spot" was successfully applied, the stars had been classified according to the type of their spectrum. At the turn of the century the Harvard astronomers found empirically that the spectra of stars fall into a *sequence,* in which the spectra gradually change from one type to another. The sequence was studied extensively by H. N. Russell of Harvard in 1913. The stars were classified into a *spectral sequence,* designating each type by a letter. Originally the sequence was meant

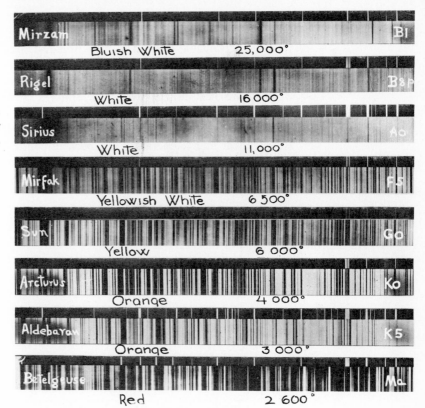

Fig. 14-24. Spectral sequence. The gradual differences are chiefly due to decreasing temperatures. *(Yerkes Observatory.)*

to be alphabetical, but a few changes had to be made in the light of later knowledge. The present classification is O, B, A, F, G, K, M, R, N, S, as shown in Figure 14-24. (A good way of remembering the sequence is the phrase: Oh, Be A Fine Girl, Kiss Me Right Now, Sweet.) Each type is classified further into subtypes.

TABLE 14:3

Type	Typical spectrum	Color	Temperature degrees C	Typical example	Radiation per cm² (sun = 1)
B	Lines of hydrogen, neutral helium, ionized metals	Blue or bluish-white	20,000	Rigel	19
A	Strong hydrogen lines, ionized metals	White	10,000	Sirius	8
F	Lines of neutral metals present	Yellowish-white	8,000	Procyon	2.5
G	Metallic lines, strong	Yellow	6,000	Sun	1
K	Bands of titanium oxide present	Red	4,000	Arcturus	0.2
M	Strong titanium oxide bands	Red	3,000	Antares	0.02

When a sufficient number of stars in the sequence were compared with the temperatures of stars measured by the well-understood and dependable method of "the brightest spot," it became obvious that the sequence was essentially one of temperature. The O-type stars are the hottest with temperatures upward of 30,000 degrees. The B-type stars are next hottest, with temperatures of 20,000 degrees. Our sun is a G-type star, with a temperature of 6000 degrees. The red star Antares is an M-type star. Thus, once the correlation between the type of the star and temperature has been established, it becomes a simple matter to estimate the temperature of a star by merely identifying its type from its spectrum (see Table 14:3).

Sizes of Stars

Having determined the temperature of a star, and knowing its absolute brightness from its distance and apparent brightness, we can proceed to estimate its size. The temperature gives the amount of light each square centimeter of the star emits per second, while the actual brightness gives the total amount of light it emits per second. Consequently, the total area can be calculated and from this, the diameter and the volume. On calculating the sizes of stars astonishing results are obtained. Canopus has a diameter of nearly 100 million miles; and Antares 400 million miles. If Antares were our sun, it would extend to well beyond the orbit of Mars. Thus, this star is a giant, not only in brightness, but also in size.

At first sight, these tremendous volumes appeared unbelievable. Yet in 1920 Albert A. Michelson (1852-1931) succeeded in measuring directly the size of Antares and several other stars. The reader should remember that the size of a star cannot be measured by ordinary photography, because the image of a star is a spurious image of diffraction patterns. A star, no matter how big, is too far away to show a disk. However, by using two mirrors 20 feet apart and reflecting the light into the 100-inch mirror at the Mount Wilson Observatory, Michelson obtained an interference pattern which, when measured and analyzed yielded the size of Antares. The diameter of this star turned out, in fact, to be 428,000,000 miles. These measurements further confirm the method of estimating the size from the total brightness and the temperature.

As an example of the other extreme of size, the dwarf companion of Sirius will be taken. This star is a white-hot dwarf, with a surface temperature of 10,000 degrees. Yet the total brightness is only 1/360 that of the sun. Therefore, the star must be very small in size. On calculation its diameter is found to be only 25,000 miles—smaller than the planet Uranus. There are other white dwarfs still smaller in volume than the companion of Sirius, some having a volume smaller than that of the earth (see p. 495).

Before continuing let us summarize the ideas presented so far. The apparent brightness is measured directly from the amount of darkening on the photographic plate and the distance is determined from the parallax—that is, the apparent shift on photographs taken six months apart. From these two measurements the true brightness is calculated. A comparison of the various stars shows a tremendous range in brightness and two major classifications—the giants and the dwarfs. The temperature of stars is measured directly from their color, or from the brightest spot in their spectrum, or from their spectral type. Their size is calculated from their temperature and their total luminosity. In the case of a few very large stars, their size is measured directly with the interferometer method of Michelson.

Having obtained sufficient information on several thousand stars further correlations are possible. For example, *red giants* must be very large in volume. Red color means a cool star and, therefore, such a star must be *very large* in volume if it is to be a giant—if the total amount of light it emits is very large. Similarly, a white dwarf means a hot star, but small in volume. White color means high temperature and, therefore, such a star must be very small to be a dwarf—to emit a small amount of total radiation.

Another interesting fact that has emerged is the correlation between absolute brightness and spectral type. For example, B-type stars are predominantly giants. The reader will remember that B-type stars are very hot, around 20,000° C. But now from independent methods these have also been shown to be giants; that is, they are both very hot and very big. This will be useful in reaching stars beyond the limits of the parallactic method. Another correlation is that G-type stars (like the sun) are mediocre stars—neither too hot nor too big. They are much smaller than the giants and fall in the upper limits of the dwarfs. Other correlations will be taken up near the end of the section.

Chemical Composition of Stars

Implicit in the discussion of spectra is the fact that the same elements are found in the stars as in the sun—or on the earth. The stars are analyzed in the same way as the sun—or a mineral in the laboratory. The elements in the star are identified from their characteristic lines and from the intensity of the lines. As in the case of the sun, the stars consist mostly of hydrogen with a smaller percentage of helium. The other elements are also present, but in very small quantities. Therefore, the sun is a fair sample of stellar matter, and hydrogen is the predominant element in the stars.

Motions of Stars

The fourth basic item of information, the motion of the stars, can also be measured directly. It must have occurred to the reader that the term "fixed" star is a misnomer. The stars appear "fixed" only because they are so distant that in a generation or even in several generations they still appear sensibly in the same position. However, over the centuries the stars do change their positions. In 1718 Halley pointed out that the star Sirius had moved southward by about $\frac{1}{2}$ degree since the time of Ptolemy, and that Arcturus had moved by a full degree. Measurements by modern instruments reveal that all the stars have motion with respect to the solar system.

The discussion will be clearest by considering the motion of a star to be a combination of two motions. A star *actually* moving in the direction *AB* can be considered as moving *partly* along *AC* and partly along *AD*. The former, is motion across the line of sight and is called *proper motion*. The latter is motion toward the observer and is called *radial*

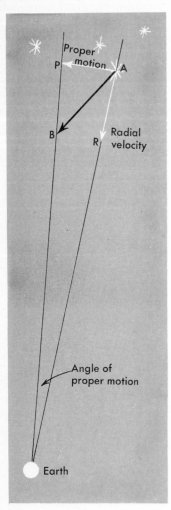

Fig. 14-25. The actual motion of a star, AB, is resolved into proper motion, AP, and radial velocity, AR.

velocity (Fig. 14-25). Each of these components of motion is measured directly but by different methods.

Proper motion across the line of sight results in permanent displacement on the celestial sphere. It is measured in seconds of arc. Consequently, with respect to the background of the very distant stars, the star having proper motion leaves the field of one group of stars and enters the field of another group of stars. This motion is cumulative so that in the course of several years it can be measured from photographs.

A little reflection will reveal that proper motion is more perceptible in the nearer stars than in the more distant. For a given actual velocity of a star across the line of sight, the displacement is inversely proportional to its distance from us; that is, a star twice as far away will be displaced by half the amount, for the same actual velocity. This means, of course, that only stars relatively near will show detectable proper motion. If the star is very far away, it would not show proper motion, unless it has an extraordinary velocity or unless very accurate measurements are carried out over very long periods of time.

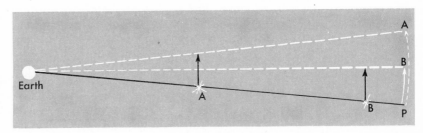

Fig. 14.26. For the same actual velocity, the nearer the star (A) the greater its proper motion (PA).

Knowing the proper motion of a star and its distance we can calculate its motion across the line of sight in miles per second. For example, a star 10 parsecs away with a proper motion of 1 second of arc per year moves 10 astronomical units per year. Since an astronomical unit is 93 million miles and a year is 31.5 million seconds, the component of its motion across the line of sight is $\dfrac{10 \times 93,000,000}{31,500,000}$ or about 30 miles per second.

Proper motion should not be confused with parallax. The latter is periodic. The star returns to the same background of stars exactly a year later if it has no proper motion. On the other hand, if the star does not return to the same exact position a year later, it has a proper motion, and the "permanent" shift is a measure of it. In this way it is possible to untangle parallax and proper motion (Ex. 23).

The *radial velocity* of a star is obtained from the Doppler shift in its spectrum. The principle and its application to light waves is as follows. Each element emits characteristic wavelengths, which can be measured with a high degree of accuracy. If a star contains an element, say hydrogen, the hydrogen atoms in the star emit, or absorb their characteristic wavelength, the same as in the laboratory. If the star, however, is moving toward the earth, the observed wavelength is shortened by a small amount.

This is like a train whistle, which appears to have a higher pitch (shorter wavelength) if the train is moving toward us. Consequently, by measuring the wavelength from the star and comparing it to the wavelength from a laboratory source (which is stationary with respect to the observer), the velocity of the source is calculated. If, for example, the wavelength is shorter by 0.01 percent, the star is moving toward the earth with a speed of 0.01 percent the speed of light, or about 18.6 miles per second. It is quite obvious that if a star is receding from the earth, the wavelength is *lengthened* by an amount depending on its velocity (Ex. 24).

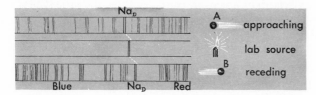

Fig. 14-27. Measurement of radial velocity from Doppler shift. Compared to a laboratory source (middle spectrum) the sodium lines (Na$_D$) shift toward the blue for an approaching star, and toward the red for a receding star.

Having determined both the radial velocity and the proper motion of a star we can calculate its actual motion in space relative to the sun provided we also know its distance. In general this is possible, because stars with large proper motions are also relatively near. Calculations show that stars move with high speeds in all sorts of directions. Speeds of 30 or 40 miles per second are not uncommon.

The measurement of the motion of stars may appear at first sight as only another piece of interesting information. However, together with the other basic information, it opens new fields of investigation. It becomes the key to the measurement of the masses of stars, and ultimately to the distribution of stars in space, and to the structure of the universe.

Let us first be quite clear on the two types of motion and what each type implies. Proper motion is across the line of sight and becomes less perceptible the more distant the star. Conversely, a star with a large proper motion cannot be very distant. Since proper motion is cumulative year after year, it becomes possible to measure proper motions of many stars that are beyond the reach of the parallactic method. To be sure, the exact direction of motion of a given star in space may not be known, or even its actual speed, but a good statistical guess is possible. In this way we get a fair estimate of the distances of very distant stars and thus venture outside the immediate solar neighborhood.

Radial velocity on the other hand is the motion toward, or away from, the earth, and is measured directly in miles per second. This motion does not depend on the distance of a star. Thus, the radial velocity can be measured for stars in the great depths of space.

One of the direct outcomes of the measurement of stellar motions is the discovery of the motion of the solar system itself with respect to the stars in the solar neighborhood. A comparison of the motion of a

Fig. 14-28. Solar motion in local group of stars, toward the constellation, Hercules.

large number of stars shows that, on the average, the stars of the constellation Hercules are approaching the earth with a speed of about 12 miles per second. This is net average of fast and slow stars, some approaching and some receding. In fact, all the stars in half of the sky, around the constellation Hercules, are approaching our solar system on the average. The significant thing is that the stars on the opposite part of the sky are receding from our solar system with an average speed of 12 miles per second. Since motion is relative, the most sensible interpretation is that the solar system is moving toward the constellation Hercules with that speed. This calculation is further confirmed by the fact that stars at right angles to Hercules show the largest proper motion as it should be if the solar system were moving through the local group of stars.

Double Stars   Another important outcome of the measurement of stellar motions is the understanding of double stars, which, in turn, led to the measurement of their masses. It had been noticed long ago that many stars in the sky appear in pairs, or even triplets or quadruplets fairly close together. At first this may not appear significant and we may be inclined to attribute the association as purely accidental. One star may simply happen to be in front of another, although the chances of that happening are extremely remote. In any event, the measurement of parallax shows in nearly every case that the two stars in a double are at the same distance from the earth and hence are physically associated with one another. On the average one out of eight stars is a double star. The ratio may be as high as one out of three. A few are triplets and quad-

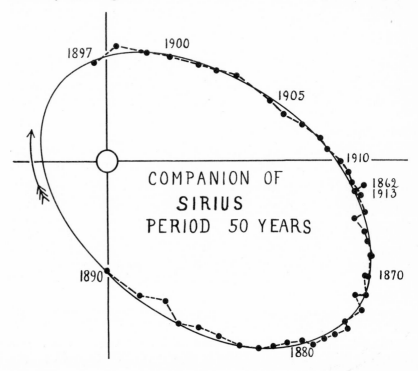

Fig. 14-29. Orbit of companion of Sirius from 1862 to 1913. *(Yerkes Observatory.)*

ruplets, and systems are known with several stars. For example, the second-magnitude star, Castor, is a system of six stars.

The first double star to be investigated extensively was Sirius, which up to about the middle of the last century was thought to be a single star. It is the brightest star in the sky, and relatively near—only 8.8 light years away. It has a large parallax and fortunately also a large proper motion, both of which can be measured accurately. In 1844, Bessel was investigating these two motions trying to untangle them. Unexpectedly, he found that over the years the proper motion of Sirius was not a straight line, as expected, but a wavy path. The only interpretation he could give was that Sirius had a fainter companion, which altered its course periodically. The companion was apparently too dim to be detected next to the brilliant Sirius. In 1862 the companion was actually seen by Alban Clarke. It is a white dwarf, only 1/10,000 times as bright as Sirius, or more meaningfully, 1/360 times as bright as the sun. It is very hot and, therefore, it must be dim only because of its very small size.

Since both stars could now be seen individually and the proper motion and radial velocity of each star could be measured separately, the system could be investigated in full detail. The distance between the two stars could be measured in seconds of arc and since the distance of the pair from the earth was also known, the distance between the two stars could be measured in miles. At the maximum separation the stars are 1700 million miles from one another. At the same time, the period of the wavy path was measured to be 49 years. There was no question that the two stars form a gravitating system, revolving about their common center of gravity (Fig. 14-29).

Since the distance between the stars and the period of revolution about the common center of gravity are known, we can calculate their combined mass, using Newton's law of gravitation, just as for the earth-moon system. The mass of the star system is equal to 3¼ times the mass of the sun. Moreover, since the path and speed of each star can be observed separately, we can calculate the mass of each star. Sirius has a mass 2.4 times that of the sun and its dwarf companion 0.85 times that of the sun.

The astonishing part of this result is the implication about the density of the white dwarf. As already calculated (p. 490) its volume is no larger than that of the planet Uranus; yet its mass is nearly equal to that of the sun. This much mass in such small volume implies enormous density. We calculate a density of 61,000 times that of water. A teaspoonful of this material would weigh nearly a ton on the earth. Since that time other white dwarfs have been investigated. All are very dense, some having densities of the order of half a million times that of water. The conditions inside such a star must be extraordinary indeed (Ex. 27).

Investigations of other double-star systems reveal another fact, in some respects even more significant. From the study of hundreds of double stars it is found that the combined mass of such a system again and again is about twice the mass of the sun. Only a few stars in each system have a mass greater than twice that of the sun, and only a few

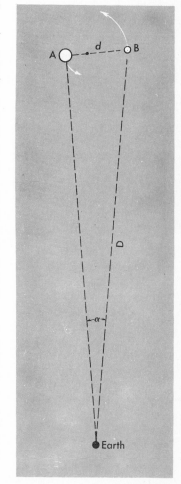

Fig. 14-30. Distance of telescopic binaries. Knowing the distance, d, between the stars, and measuring, α, the distance to the system D, is calculated.

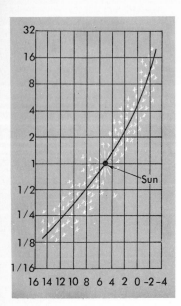

Fig. 14-31. Mass-luminosity relation.

have a mass less than one half the mass of the sun. This is all the more remarkable when we recall that the stars range tremendously in brightness and in densities. For we can now estimate the densities of the red giants. Even if they have several times the mass of the sun, their enormous volumes imply extremely low densities—perhaps lower than the best vacuum obtained in the laboratory. Apparently there are very narrow limits to the mass of material that can form a star, and this has implications about the life history of a star, as we shall presently see.

Having studied a sufficient number of double stars in the solar neighborhood, we can reverse the reasoning and find the distance of a double-star system far beyond the 300 light-year reach of the parallax method, provided the stars can be observed individually. As the stars revolve about one another, each star periodically approaches and recedes from the solar system. Therefore we can measure the period of revolution by merely noting the time between the fastest approach and the next fastest approach. If now we *assume* that the system has about twice the mass of our sun—as most double star systems have—we can calculate the actual distance between them in miles. By measuring the angular separation between the stars, and knowing the separation in miles, we can calculate the distance of the system from the earth.

There is, however, considerable uncertainty in the distances measured by this method. The assumption that the combined mass of the system is twice that of the sun is true only statistically. While the masses of about half of the stars in double-star systems range between half and twice that of the sun, the remaining half deviate from these limits. There are a few stars with masses of 0.1 that of the sun or less and some that are 10 times or more, heavier than the sun. Nevertheless we do not expect to find many stars 100 times heavier than the sun, or many 1/100 as heavy. The greater number, by far, have masses near the average.

Mass-luminosity Relation

Returning to the double stars in the solar neighborhood whose masses can be measured dependably from their distance, periods, and angular separations, we find one of the most important relations discovered in this century. As early as 1905 a definite relation between the mass of a star and its absolute brightness was discovered empirically. On plotting the absolute magnitude against luminosity Figure 14-31 is obtained. The relation between mass and luminosity holds, irrespective of the spectral type of the star, or any other features. The direct application of this relation, called the *mass-luminosity law,* is obvious. The mass of the star can be calculated from its measured absolute brightness. Thus, Betelgeuse, which is about 1300 times brighter than the sun and has a volume 100 million times that of the sun, has a mass of only 15 times that of the sun.

Evolution of Stars

The mass-luminosity law, however, has far-reaching implications about the life history of stars. These implications were theoretically investigated first by Sir Arthur Eddington in the 1920's. Since the mass of a star determines the luminosity, regardless of the spectral type or other conditions, Eddington suggested that the other conditions are so related to the mass as to effectively cancel each other out. Continuing his investigations, Eddington used a reasonable model of a star and derived from it the mass-luminosity relation.

According to Eddington, a star is formed initially by gravitational attraction from a large mass of diffuse interstellar material, mostly hydrogen. As the mass contracts, its size decreases, of course, but its temperature rises from the change of gravitational energy into heat. The total mass available in making the star determines the rate of contraction and, hence, the size. The total mass also determines the temperature and, hence, the spectral type. At any given stage the temperature rises just enough to compensate for the decrease in size, so that the total amount of light emitted remains about the same for long periods of time.

More recent developments in nuclear theory correlate with Eddington's theory, and permit its extension to the later stages of evolution. As the star continues to contract and the temperatures in the interior rise higher and higher, conditions are reached under which thermonuclear reactions begin. The major reaction at first is the conversion of hydrogen into helium, as in the case of the sun (p. 484). But as the hydrogen is used up to form the denser helium, the star contracts still more and the temperatures rise still higher, perhaps to 60 million degrees. The result is the much faster conversion of the hydrogen to helium.

At this point the star begins to increase markedly in brightness (the mass-luminosity law does not hold as well at this stage), because it contracts only slightly while its temperature rises rapidly to very high values. At these temperatures the hydrogen is rapidly transformed into helium, and helium itself begins to be transformed into the heavier elements. The temperatures continue to rise until all the helium and all the lighter elements have been condensed into the elements of intermediate atomic weight. Since these elements have the largest binding energy and are the most stable (p. 429), no further nuclear energy is available. From here on, the star is destined to cool slowly, and to contract. Before final cooling, however, it goes into a flare. The high rate of energy production and the small volume for radiation results in unprecedented temperatures and the star explodes into a nova. An immense amount of radiation, tens of thousands of times that of the sun, is emitted in a few days and a good deal of the material is thrown into interstellar space. Only the core remains, which proceeds to cool to a white dwarf. The white dwarf stage is very long, because the cooling takes place slowly due to the small surface for radiation. Ultimately the star will cool to a cold body.

It would carry us too far afield to go into the details of this theory and its several variants, and to evaluate each idea in it. Suffice it to say that the theoretical considerations are based on sound principles of dynamics and nuclear theory. Nor is it possible to give direct evidence for the course of evolution of stars. It takes billions of years for a star to go through this stage. In the few years during which the stars have been observed no changes can possibly be detected.

There is, however, considerable indirect evidence that is quite convincing, one line of which is relatively easy to follow. A comparison of stars of the same type might find them in the various stages of evolution.

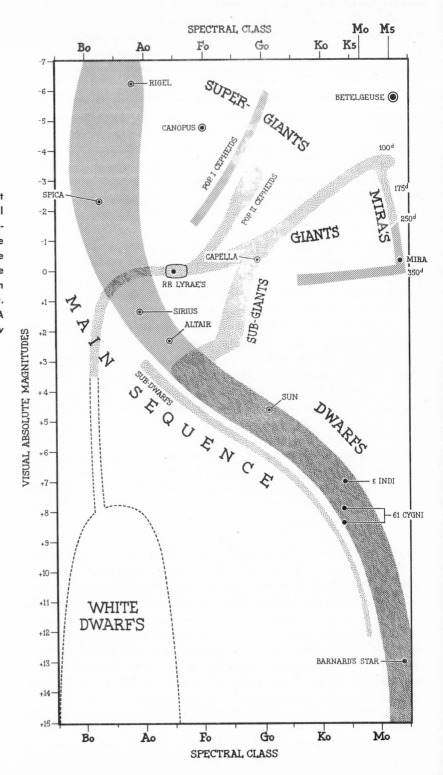

Fig. 14-32. Color-luminosity chart known as the Hertzsprung-Russell diagram, after the early investigators. Stars Bo are blue; Fo are white; Go are yellow and Mo are red. Stars of population I are shown in parallel lines; population II in dotted area (see p. 509). (From Skilling and Richardson, A Brief Text in Astronomy. New York: Henry Holt & Co., 1959.)

The idea can be illustrated by an analogy. A biologist who has not observed oak trees, on going into a forest, may nevertheless be able to work out the life history of the oak tree in a few days. He will observe acorns, little oak trees, big oak trees, old oak trees, and decayed oak tree trunks on the ground. By arranging the various specimens in an order he can figure out the life history of the oak tree, without waiting for an acorn to grow into a giant tree and then decay.

A similar situation is found among the stars. On taking all the stars whose absolute brightness is known from their distances and plotting their absolute brightness against their spectral type (color), the diagram shown in Fig. 14-32 is obtained. The vast majority of stars fall into a curved band known as the *main sequence*. The band forks into the upper left forming the *giant* branch and those toward the lower right the *dwarf* branch. A few stars cluster in other minor patches which may be disregarded.

The interpretation of this band becomes simpler by limiting the discussion to stars with common characteristics. For example, recently Arp and Sandage (Ref. 14-10, p. 143) studied a group of stars in Messier 3. All these stars have similar masses and all probably had initially a mass of 1.2 times the mass of the sun. On plotting their absolute brightness against their spectral type all these stars fall into the lower part of the main sequence and in the giant and the dwarf branches (roughly in the dotted area in Fig. 14-32).

Since the stars in Messier 3 are similar, the band suggests the course of their evolution. A star starts near the bottom of the band and evolves upward along it. At the bottom it is a rather cool red dwarf (Mo), contracting and getting a little hotter. On reaching the fork, it turns into the giant branch and remains of the same magnitude for a long time. At this stage hydrogen begins to be converted into helium. The star expands and cools and becomes first a yellow star (Fo) and then a red giant (Mo). It then retraces its path, contracting and getting hotter. In these stages it evolves very rapidly. On approaching the fork again, it takes the upper path toward the left and follows the dwarf branch. It is still getting hotter and it is still fairly bright but it appears as a white *dwarf*. The light it emits is in the ultraviolet, which is largely absorbed by our atmosphere and hence is unobservable by our telescopes. Moreover, at the distance of Messier 3, a white dwarf is very faint. The star remains in this stage for a very long time.

According to this interpretation, the sun is still at the earlier stages of evolution. It is in the early stages of the horizontal part of the curve leading toward the giant branch. It is a yellow G-type star. In the billions of years to come the sun will evolve into a red giant and ultimately into a white dwarf. Since the sun is a little less massive than these stars, it will evolve more slowly. It is estimated that it will take about 30 billion years for it to become a small white dwarf.

Much more is known concerning the stars and the interested reader is referred to more extensive works on the subject (Ref. 14.4). However, the basic knowledge and the methods by which it is obtained have been presented here. The principles involved are used to extend our knowledge beyond the solar neighborhood, into the much vaster space of the galaxies and the spirals, as will be shown in the next section.

4. THE GALAXY AND BEYOND

Having studied the stars in the solar neighborhood we are prepared to resume the story of "expanding horizons" and take another great leap into the depths of space. We have already indicated in several connections how the growth of knowledge of the stars made it possible to venture beyond the limits of the parallax method. In this section we shall describe the methods that led modern science to locate the solar system within a larger system of stars, the Milky Way, and to reach beyond the Milky Way to other galaxies and to the limits of the universe observable at present.

Star Counts   The early extension of knowledge beyond the limits of observable parallax was made by a method remarkably simple in principle although very laborious in practice. This is the method of "star counts." With increasing power of the telescopes more stars come into view, for two reasons. Relatively near stars, which are intrinsically dim, now become visible, but also more distant stars come within reach of the telescopes. By simply counting the number of stars at each magnification and by taking proper account of these two factors, it is possible to find out how the stars are distributed in the space beyond and how far they extend in any direction. At first, up to moderate magnifications, the stars continued to increase in number at about the same rate in all directions. This would indicate that the stars extend uniformly in all directions from the sun, and that the sun is situated in a "forest" of stars extending indefinitely. In a sense, the sun could still be considered the center of the universe.

Continuation of the method of star counts with higher-power telescopes, however, placed the sun definitely in the plane of the Milky Way. Beyond a certain magnification the stars began to thin out in the directions at right angles to the plane of the galaxy, but continued to increase in number, unabatedly in all directions toward all the parts of the milky band itself. Apparently, the solar system is situated in the *plane* of the Milky Way. At right angles to the plane, we soon run out of additional stars—we have "reached the end of the forest." In the plane of the Milky Way, on the other hand, we continue to see more and more distant stars, with each magnification. That the solar system is situated in the plane of the Milky Way is further indicated by another fact. The Milky

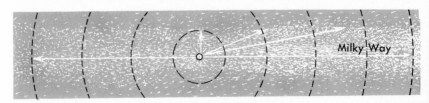

Fig. 14-33. Location of the sun in the plane of the Milky Way. Stars continue to great distances in the plane, but thin out at right angles.

TABLE 14:4
Number of Stars

Magnitude (photographic)	In all the sky (total number)	In plane of galaxy (average per 100 square degrees)	At right angles to galaxy (average per 100 square degrees)	Ratio column 3: column 4
1	10	–	–	–
2	33	–	–	–
3	111	–	–	–
4	343	1.6	0.5	3.2:1
5	1,030	5.2	1.5	3.5:1
6	3,270	15	4.4	3.4:1
7	8,800	43	12	3.6:1
9	64,000	380	83	4.6:1
11	460,000	3,200	430	7.4:1
13	2,900,000	22,000	1,900	11:1
15	16,000,000	140,000	6,300	22:1
17	75,000,000	690,000	19,000	36:1
19	210,000,000	3,200,000	50,000	64:1
21	650,000,000	8,000,000	80,000	100:1

Source: Allen, C. W., *Astrophysical Quantities.* London Univ. Press, 1955.

Way appears from the earth as a *great circle* in the sky, and hence the earth cannot be much off the center of the plane.

This is the last phase of the heliocentric period, to which the science of astronomy had arrived near the end of the nineteenth century. The solar system is a part of a system of stars, the Milky Way, which appears as a flat disk. With respect to the thickness of the disk, the system is somewhere near the middle. Along the flat dimensions of the disk, however, the exact position was not yet known. The disk appeared to extend uniformly in all directions, and also indefinitely, for dimmer stars continued in all directions within the plane. Either the Milky Way extends indefinitely, or it extends very far about equally in all directions. In a sense the sun could still be considered the center of the universe.

In the first two decades of the present century, however, new developments were destined to dethrone the sun from its central position and to give us a better idea of the size and shape of the Milky Way and of the position of the solar system in it. These developments grew out of the understanding of the stars, as discussed in the last section, and was a natural extension of the ideas developed there. The proper motions of stars permit statistical study of the distribution of stars that are several times further removed than those that can be reached by the parallax method. From the study of double stars, which are sufficiently far apart to be seen separately, it is possible to study the distribution of these stars still further out. To be sure both of these methods do not apply with certainty to a given star, but they do hold on the average. Therefore, the results obtained from plotting the distribution of the distant stars in space are statistically valid and dependable.

Early Location in the Milky Way

The most direct and dependable methods for estimating the distances of very distant stars, however, came from the discovery in the solar neighborhood of two kinds of stars, which serve as "standard beacons." One kind are the B-type stars, already discussed on page 489. These stars are characterized by their blue color, by their typical spectrum, and by their high temperature. The spectrum of a typical B-type star contains lines of hydrogen, neutral helium, and ionized metals, and their temperatures are of the order of 20,000° C. In the solar neighborhood, these stars are typically giants, having a luminosity of several thousand times that of the sun. Consequently, if B-type stars appear dim and show no parallax, they must be very far away. But since they are giants, we can estimate their true brightness. Using them as "standard beacons" we can calculate their distances. These stars extend to the remote regions of space (Ex. 30).

The other "standard beacon" is the so-called *cepheid variable*. In the constellation of Cepheus, the star Delta Cephei behaves in a rather unusual manner. It varies in brightness with perfect regularity over a period of about 5.4 days. It begins as a dim star of magnitude 3.4, but in the course of about a day it gradually increases in brightness and becomes a star of magnitude 2.6. Then it wanes in brightness more slowly and reaches again a minimum at the end of 5.4 days. It then repeats the performance. The distance of Delta Cephei is known from its parallax and hence its absolute brightness at any stage can be calculated. At the brightest it is about 700 times and at its dimmest about 400 times as bright as the sun.

In the solar neighborhood quite a few stars of several spectral types behave like Delta Cephei. Therefore, all these stars are called *cepheid variables*. Since their distances are known, their absolute brightness can be calculated. A remarkable relation has been discovered empirically. The periods of these variables are definitely related to their true brightness. These stars fall on a curve as shown in Figure 14-36. This relation is amply confirmed by numerous, although more distant, cepheids (p. 508). Consequently, by measuring their periods, we can calculate their absolute brightness; and, having obtained their absolute brightness, we can use them as "standard beacons" and estimate their distances (Ex. 31).

The relation between period and luminosity could be accepted as a purely observational fact, but we can do better than that by attempting to understand it theoretically. Very early in the study of these stars the assumption appeared reasonable that cepheid variables are pulsating stars. Due to some cause of instability, it appears that at the surface of these stars the gravitational attraction is not neatly balanced by the forces of expansion as in a normal star like the sun (p. 483). When the cepheid star is contracting, apparently the gravitational forces have the upper hand. But as contraction continues, the temperature rises resulting in higher gas pressures and higher radiation pressures within the star. At the same time the total brightness of the star increases because the temperature increases sufficiently to more than compensate for the small decrease in volume. When the star has contracted to a minimum volume, the expansive forces take the upper hand and the star

Fig. 14-34. Observation of distant B-type stars extends the measurement of distance to beyond 300 light years.

begins to expand. But as it expands, it cools, both the gas pressure and the radiation pressure drop, and at the same time the total brightness decreases. At the maximum expansion the gravitational forces again begin to take the upper hand, and contraction resumes. Thus, the star expands and contracts periodically, that is, it pulsates.

Two lines of evidence support the pulsation theory quite directly. In the first place the (measured) temperature is highest near the time when the star is brightest, and lowest at about the time the star is dimmest, just as expected. Moreover, the speed of expansion or contraction can be measured by observing the Doppler shift of the spectral lines. When the star is increasing in brightness, the wavelengths are lengthened; this means that the surface is receding from the earth and the star is contracting. During the dimming period, on the other hand, the wavelengths are shortened, this means that the surface is approaching the earth as the star is expanding. Moreover, we can calculate the distance over which the surface fluctuates since we know the speed and the time. The surface of Delta Cephei, for example, fluctuates by about 800,000 miles, which is a small fraction of the diameter, estimated at 25 million miles. Incidentally, the variation in the Doppler shift provides the best method for the accurate determination of the period.

The causes of the instability of the cepheids are not well understood, but they are probably related to the nuclear reactions taking place in the interior at the various temperatures. Nor is the correlation between luminosity and period clearly derivable from theoretical considerations. However, it is reasonable to expect the two to be related. The rate of pulsation depends upon the gravitational attraction, size, density, and temperature, all of which ultimately depend upon the total mass of the star. But according to Eddington's mass-luminosity law the total brightness also depends upon the total mass. Therefore, there should be a direct relation between the luminosity of a cepheid and its period. Since the beginning of the century, however, long before even this much was understood, the empirically discovered period-luminosity relation has been used to estimate distances of very distant cepheids.

A clearer idea of the shape and size of the Milky Way first came from the study of the distribution of distant B-type stars. Below a certain apparent brightness these stars seem to favor the plane of the Milky Way, and in fact the dimmest of them, and hence the most distant, lie in or very close to the plane. Consequently, it appears reasonable that these giant stars extend at least as far as the Milky Way and that by studying their distribution a fair outline of the shape and size of the galaxy may be derived. Around 1900 it was estimated that the galaxy had the shape of a thin wheel, about 3000 light years in thickness and about 30,000 light years across. Since the B-type stars were distributed fairly uniformly in all directions within the plane, it was naturally concluded that the solar system was somewhere near the center of the system.

However, around 1920 Harlow Shapley of the Harvard observatory analyzed the accumulated evidence and came to the conclusion that the sun is far from the center of the galaxy. At the same time he estimated

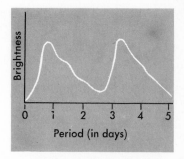

Fig. 14-35. Periodic variation in brightness of Delta Cephei.

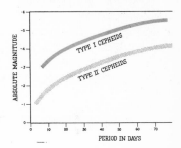

Fig. 14-36. Period-luminosity curves for cepheids of types I and II. The cepheids of Type I are four times brighter (1.5 magnitudes smaller) than cepheids of type II with the same period. Delta Cephei is a red giant of type II (see p. 509). (*From Skilling and Richardson, A Brief Text in Astronomy, Rev. ed. New York: Henry Holt & Co., 1959.*)

The Galactocentric Period

Fig. 14-37. The great cluster in Hercules. *(Mount Wilson Observatory.)*

the dimensions of the galaxy as perhaps tenfold the dimensions previously supposed. This development spelled the end of the heliocentric period and introduced the *galactocentric period*.

Harlow Shapley studied certain groups of stars known as globular clusters. These clusters contain perhaps 100,000 stars, in a single gravitating system. All types of stars are found in a given cluster, including B-type stars and cepheid variables. The clusters themselves are rather numerous. Some are near and some are far from the solar system, for there are bright clusters and dimmer clusters. They are distributed primarily either in the plane of the Milky Way or close to it. It appeared most reasonable that they are a part of the galactic system, so that by determining the distance of the clusters, we have a fair estimate of the dimensions of the galaxy. The problem is similar to estimating the size of a city by surveying its suburbs.

Shapley studied at first a conspicuous cluster, globular in shape, in the constellation of Hercules. He recognized hundreds of B-type stars in it and measured their apparent brightness. All appear rather dim, suggesting a great distance from the earth. On the assumption that these B-type stars are no different on the average from those found in the solar neighborhood, and hence of the same order of true brightness, he obtained their distances. All stars yielded distances of the same order, about 36,000 light years, and this, of course, is the distance of the entire cluster from the earth.

Shapley confirmed his estimate with cepheid variables, which he recognized in the cluster. By measuring their periods he obtained their true brightness, using the curve established in the solar neighborhood. (However, he had to extend the curve somewhat resulting in an overestimate, as will be explained later.) From this he obtained their distance. The cepheid variables gave roughly the same distance as the

B-type stars—namely, about 36,000 light years. Shapley then applied the method to other nearby clusters. An interesting conclusion resulted from these comparisons of the globular clusters. All clusters contain about the same number of stars, and therefore the *clusters themselves* are of about the same absolute brightness.

Shapley had the inspiration to use the clusters themselves as "standard beacons." Since all globular clusters are of the same order of true brightness, the size of their images in the telescope as well as their apparent brightness is an indication of their distance. Shapley found clusters that extend up to seven or eight times further than the Hercules cluster, in the direction of constellation of Sagittarius, the Archer. Significantly enough they are also more numerous in that direction. In the opposite direction they extend only to about twice the distance of the Hercules cluster and become much less numerous. On the idea that the globular clusters extend about as far as the Milky Way with which they are associated, Shapley obtained a fair outline of the Milky Way itself, determined its shape, and estimated its dimensions. Since that time more accurate distances of the clusters have been obtained. (Shapley has overestimated the distances by not taking into account the decrease in brightness due to the absorption of some of the light by interstellar matter.) According to the latest estimates, the center of the Milky Way is in the direction of the constellation of Sagittarius, about 27,000 light years from the solar system. The Milky Way is a giant wheel, about 80,000 light years in diameter and about 10,000 light years in thickness (Ex. 32).

The Size and Shape of the Galaxy

That the sun is off the center of the galaxy was confirmed a few years later by another interesting phenomenon. The stars have a systematic motion relative to the sun. Early in the century it had been observed that all the stars in a large part of the sky around the constellation of Sagittarius have a systematic proper motion at right angles to the line

Rotation of the Galaxy

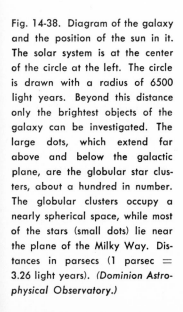

Fig. 14-38. Diagram of the galaxy and the position of the sun in it. The solar system is at the center of the circle at the left. The circle is drawn with a radius of 6500 light years. Beyond this distance only the brightest objects of the galaxy can be investigated. The large dots, which extend far above and below the galactic plane, are the globular star clusters, about a hundred in number. The globular clusters occupy a nearly spherical space, while most of the stars (small dots) lie near the plane of the Milky Way. Distances in parsecs (1 parsec = 3.26 light years). (Dominion Astrophysical Observatory.)

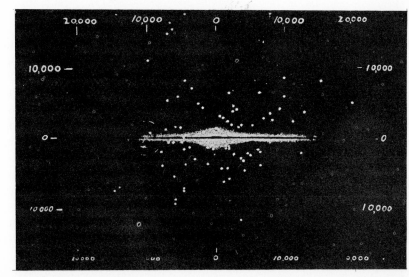

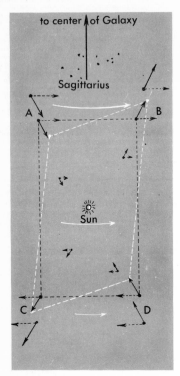

to center of Galaxy

Sagittarius

A

B

Sun

C

D

Fig. 14-39. Rotation of the galaxy and location of the galactic center in Sagittarius. Stars A revolving faster than the sun approach the sun; stars B recede from the sun. The sun leaves behind stars C and approaches stars D.

of sight. All move in the same direction, but rather significantly, the more distant the stars, the faster their motion. Equally significant, all the stars in the opposite part of the sky move in the opposite direction, and again the more distant the stars the faster their backward motion. It appeared as though the sun was "drifting" among the other stars.

Measurement of radial velocities led to the same conclusion. There was a systematic motion of the stars at nearly right angles to the Archer, in the galactic plane. Stars in one part of the sky had a systematic velocity of approach and the further the stars, the greater the velocity. On the opposite part of the sky there was a systematic motion of recession. This phenomenon is called *star streaming*. The net effect of these motions is that a parallelogram drawn between the four positions of maximum speed tended to twist (Fig. 14-39).

The phenomenon of star streaming and the related systematic proper motion are not to be confused with the motion of the solar system toward the constellation of Hercules. The latter is motion of the sun with respect to the local group of stars, at the rate of about 12 miles per second. This systematic motion has to be untangled from the other motions, but it is different and much greater, for the very distant stars.

The phenomenon of star streaming had only one obvious explanation. If the Milky Way was to be a stable gravitating system, then the stars should move around their common center of gravity, which is the galactic center. In accordance to Kepler's laws of planetary motion, the stars nearer the center should revolve faster than those further out, just like the inner planets revolve faster around the sun than the outer planets. As observed from the solar system, the stars nearer the galactic center should stream toward us since they revolve faster around the galactic center. Conversely, the stars further from the galactic center than the solar system should lag behind. (The effect may be visualized by analogy to the solar system. In going around the sun, Mercury and Venus move faster than the earth and the outer planets move slower. Hence Mercury and Venus drift ahead of us and the outer planets lag behind.) From this phenomenon the galactic center was located in the direction of the constellation Sagittarius. By measurement of the amount of streaming we estimate that the sun is about 27,000 light years from the galactic center, and that at this distance the sun revolves around the galactic center with a speed of about 180 miles per second. At this speed it takes the solar system about 200 million years for one revolution (Ex. 33). In other words the sun has made one complete revolution since the beginning of the Age of Dinosaurs (p. 578).

The measurement of the period of rotation of the galaxy has another interesting consequence. It provides an estimate of its mass. For the galaxy is a gravitating system, and the period of rotation at the various distances depends upon the gravitational attraction of the total mass. Using Newton's law of gravitation and some reasonable distribution of mass based on observation, we find that the mass of the galaxy is about 160 billion times the mass of the sun.

Estimates of the total mass of all the stars, however, yield a little over half of that mass. The only reasonable conclusion is that there is interstellar material, mostly hydrogen and smaller quantities of dust particles, almost equal in mass to that contained in the stars. This has further implications. It appears that out of this material stars are still being formed, and that stars will continue to form for a very long time. It also explains the fact that the galactic center is not visible, since large quantities of dark absorbing matter hide from view not only the galactic center, but also most of the stars in the galaxy on the other side of the center.

At the same time that the ideas concerning our galaxy were taking form astronomers were beginning to explore the space outside the Milky Way. In fact many notions about our own galaxy were suggested by observations of other galaxies. For a long time certain objects had been observed outside the plane of the galaxy that also had a milky appearance. The most conspicuous of these objects are the Magellanic Clouds in the Southern sky. They were named after the Spanish navigator Magellan who was the first European to see them, as he crossed south of the equator in 1520 on his historic voyage around the globe. Also conspicuous is the great nebula in the constellation Andromeda. It is an oblong patch of light about 3 degrees in length and easily visible to the naked eye. The telescope had brought thousands of these objects

The Neighboring Galaxies

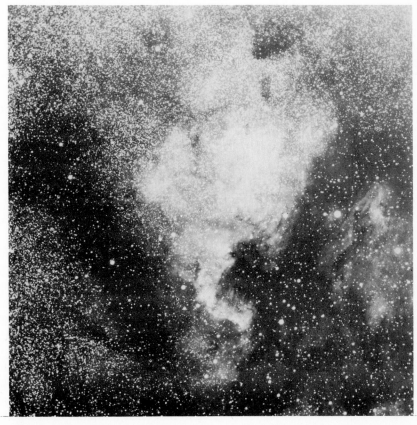

Fig. 14-40. The North American Nebula. *(Yerkes Observatory.)*

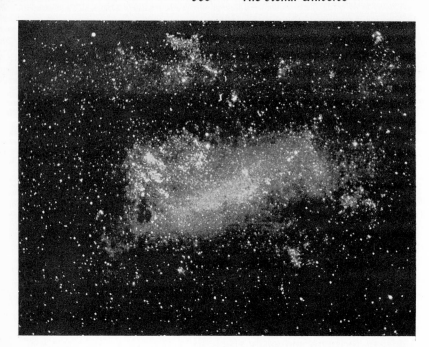

Fig. 14-41. The Greater Magellanic Cloud. Distance about 72,000 light years. *(Lick Observatory.)*

into view. They were called nebulae for they resembled clouds, and sometimes spirals, from the twisted form of many of them.

The milky appearance of these objects and the fact they are observed entirely outside the plane of the galaxy, made it reasonable to suppose that these objects are detached from our galaxy. The suggestion was strong that they are systems of stars but at distances so great they appear through low-power telescopes in the same way as the Milky Way appears to the unaided eye. The more powerful telescopes put into operation at the turn of the century, confirmed this idea. First the Magellanic Clouds and then the great spiral in Andromeda were resolved sufficiently to recognize individual stars in them. There could be no question that these systems are at great distances from our galaxy.

The first estimates of the distance of the Magellanic Clouds were made by Harlow Shapley of Harvard around 1917. Four years earlier Henrietta Leavitt had recognized cepheid variables in photographs of the Clouds, brought from Harvard's station in the Southern hemisphere, then in Peru. She found that the periods of the cepheid variables in the Small Cloud plotted against their apparent brightness followed a course similar to the cepheids in the solar neighborhood. Since the Cloud is so far away, all the cepheids in the Cloud are at practically the same distance from the solar system. Consequently, their absolute brightness is in the same ratio as their apparent brightness, and the periods of the cepheids are related to their absolute brightness in the same way as in the solar neighborhood.

As a matter of historic fact, it was this finding that called attention to the period-luminosity relation of the cepheids and gave the most direct evidence for it. Even if the absolute brightness of the distant cepheids *relative to the sun* is not known, their absolute brightness *relative to one another* is known, since all are at the same distance. If, Shapley argued, we could find in the solar neighborhood a cepheid which had the same period as a cepheid in the Cloud, we could conclude that the two have the same absolute brightness. Having obtained the absolute brightness of the cepheid in the Cloud, we could calculate its distance and hence the distance of the Cloud itself.

Unfortunately, however, Shapley could not make the correlation at that time as directly as he would like. The cepheid variables in the Cloud were all long-period cepheids—ranging from 4 to 127 days. They were all blue giants; of course, they had to be giants to be visible at all at these great distances. On the other hand, the cepheids in the solar neighborhood have shorter periods, and hence are not as bright intrinsically. Shapley could only find 11 cepheids in the solar neighborhood for which dependable distances had been measured, but these ranged in periods only from 1.9 days to 10.2 days. The overlap was not sufficient to insure confidence.

Shapley bridged the gap with an intermediate step. We have already seen that he used the cepheids to confirm the distances of the globular clusters. In each cluster he found many cepheids of periods less than a day and of about the same apparent brightness. Again, since all the cepheids in a given cluster are sensibly at the same distance from the earth, this indicated that they are of the same *absolute* brightness. Thus he was able to confirm the distances of the clusters that he determined from the B-type stars. More relevant to the problem at hand, however, he combined the information from the cluster cepheids with those in the solar neighborhood and obtained a single curve, the cluster cepheids giving him a sort of minimum, or zero point, for the absolute brightness. Using this curve he obtained the absolute brightness of the cepheids in the Cloud and from this the distance of the Cloud. His estimate was about 35,000 light years. This was the first leap into the extragalactic space.

We do not wish to detract in the slightest from Shapley's great accomplishment, for the method is sound in principle. In fact it is the only method available for sounding the depths of space. However, there was a flaw in his particular estimate, and no one suspected it until the middle of the century. No one could imagine anything wrong with it, although indications that something was wrong were creeping in from several sources (Ex. 34).

In the winter of 1941-42 Walter Baade at the Mount Wilson Observatory made some historic studies on star populations in Andromeda (which we shall discuss presently). He found there are two types of star populations in the spiral. In the arms of the spiral, the stars are predominately blue, rich in metallic lines. The cepheids among them are blue giants. The stars in the arms he called Population I. (Incidentally, the stars in the solar neighborhood are also Population I, from which we conclude that we are on the arms of a spiral in our own galaxy.) On the other hand, the stars in the cloudy part of the spiral and also the stars in the globular clusters surrounding the nebula are red stars, poorer in metallic lines. The long-period cepheids among them are, of course, red giants. This second type of stars he called Population II. This in itself would have no bearing on the problem, except for one additional observation. The brightest blue giants are about four times brighter than the brightest red giants. More significantly, *for the same period,* a *blue* cepheid is about *four* times brighter than a *red* cepheid (Ex. 31).

It will be remembered that Shapley used the cluster-type giants to bridge the gap of the periods between the stars in the solar neighborhood (which are Population I) and the stars in the Small Cloud. He used the wrong curve for the long-period cepheids. Since the blue giants in the Cloud are four times as bright as he thought they were, and since light becomes dimmer as the square of the distance, his "yardstick" was too short by a factor of about 2. Shapley recognized this and in 1952 revised his estimate of the distance of the Magellanic Clouds. According to the more recent estimates, using the corrected yardstick, the Clouds are about 80,000 light years from the earth. The diameter of the Large Cloud is 15,000 light years, that of the Small Cloud 10,000 light years and the distance between them 30,000 light years. These are our nearest neighbors.

The correction of the basic "yardstick" has been confirmed by observations from several other sources (Ex. 34). All agree within fairly narrow limits. Further minor corrections and more accurate estimates may be expected, but not a radical revision of the absolute brightness of the cepheids. This is important; for the cepheids are the basic "yardstick" by which all extragalactic distances are measured. These blinking giants are our only means for sounding the depths of space. Even before the correction, they were used to estimate distances to other spirals, following the first estimate of extragalactic distances made in 1917.

The Great Spiral in Andromeda

In the early 1920's, only a few years after Shapley's epoch-making estimate of the distance to the Clouds, Edwin Hubble turned the new 100-inch eye of Mount Wilson Observatory on the Andromeda spiral. This instrument resolved Andromeda into individual stars. In the arms of the spiral Hubble found hundreds of pin points of light, which he could identify as stars and even determine their type. To his great excitement, he identified among them 12 cepheids.

Hubble immediately proceeded to measure their periods (which ranged from 17 to 50 days), to calculate their true brightness, and to estimate their distances. In terms of the corrected yardstick, the distances are about $1\frac{1}{2}$ million light years, and this, of course, is the distance of the spiral. Knowing the distance we can calculate its dimensions. Since the spiral is 3 degrees across, its diameter is about 75,000 light years. In brightness, it is equal to about 100 billion suns. It is quite comparable to our galaxy. It is an "island universe," using the word "universe" to mean "galaxy" (Ex. 35).

The Andromeda nebula has been and continues to be studied most extensively. We are in a very advantageous position for this, being sufficiently distant to get a view of the whole, and yet sufficiently near to study it in considerable detail. Many types of familiar stars have been identified in it, and its general structure has been worked out. Its spiral form suggests rotation, and this has been confirmed by measuring the

Fig. 14-42. The great spiral in Andromeda. *(Mount Wilson and Palomar Observatories).*

Doppler shift of its various parts. One side is approaching our galaxy, while the other is receding.

In fact the study of the Andromeda spiral (and other nearby spirals) has contributed considerably to the understanding of our own galaxy. For we are in the peculiar position of being able to see our neighbors from a favorable perspective while we cannot see our own galaxy since we are enmeshed in it. (We cannot see the forest because of the trees.) The shape of Andromeda, its structure, its size, and its rotation gave us the first ideas of our own galaxy. More recently, suspecting a similarity to Andromeda, we have been able to work out in great detail the structure of our galaxy and to locate the solar system in one of its spiral arms (Ref. 14.13).

After Andromeda, other nearby galaxies have been resolved into individual stars and cepheid variables and other familiar giants have been identified in them. Hence their distances can be measured. With the 200-inch telescope it is possible to resolve spirals up to about 20 million light years away. Cepheid variables cannot be detected further than that with our present instruments.

At first sight it would seem that 20-million light years is the upper limit of our reach into space. We are in the same position with respect to the galaxies as we were with respect to nearby stars, from the discovery of parallax to the beginning of this century. Can the performance be repeated, using the *galactic neighborhood* as a laboratory, just as the solar neighborhood was used earlier? Modern astronomers are doing just that.

In the huge volume of space 20 million light years in radius, there

Spirals as Standard Beacons

are hundreds of spirals, whose distances can be measured by means of cepheids and other familiar giants. On the average the spirals are about a million light years apart—about 10 to 15 times their diameters. They vary in size and brightness, but only within fairly narrow limits. Their diameters range from 1500 to 75,000, but most of them lie between 30,000 and 50,000 light years. In brightness they vary, too, but average about 400 million suns. They vary in shape considerably, partly due to their varying orientation toward us. Some of them are circular with distinct spiral form. Apparently, these are oriented with their plane face up. Others are oval objects like Andromeda, and are apparently tilted. Still others are oblong streaks, and probably seen edge-on. Still others appear globular and seem to be spherical. Their orientation toward us doubtless affects our estimates of their brightness as well as their size (Ex. 37).

Taking into proper account all the available information on spirals in the galactic neighborhood, we can strike a good average of their size and brightness. Then using the spirals themselves as "standard beacons" or "standard yardsticks," studies are continued statistically. On the photographic plates appear smaller and smaller spirals, and also fainter and fainter spirals down to the limits of the sensitivity of the plates. Thus, we can estimate their distances from their sizes on the plate or from the brightness of the image. These results should hold statistically. In this way it is possible to study their average distribution into depths of 2000 million light years. This is the limit of the 200-inch telescope, but the spirals seem to continue beyond. There seems to be no limit to the world of spirals.

Thus, using as "standard beacons" the spirals themselves, we have brought under direct observation a volume of space 100-fold in radius from that accessible with the cepheids alone. There are many uncertainties, but knowledge is growing rapidly. It already appears that galaxies are grouped into larger units and these into larger units in turn, called the *supergalaxies*. Our own galaxy is a part of a local group of 20 galaxies, which in turn is a part of a supergalaxy. The supergalaxy, an oblong assemblage of tens of thousands of galaxies, extends to perhaps 40 million light years in the direction of the constellation of Virgo (Ref. 14.10). Other similar groupings appear, but no overall pattern is

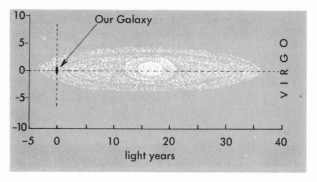

Fig. 14-43. Supergalaxy in the direction of the constellation Virgo. The size of our galaxy is highly exaggerated (after G. de Vancouleurs, courtesy of *Scientific American*).

apparent. In any event present knowledge is too meager as yet to tell if there is a pattern. It is not known whether the spirals are uniformly distributed in space, nor where our own position is with respect to the universe. We are at the center of the known universe, but only in the sense that we are at the center of our own observations. We observe the spirals in all directions and can estimate their distances, brightness, size, and radial velocities.

Red Shift. The measurement of radial velocities of the spirals led to totally unexpected results and to conclusions of the deepest significance. The reader will remember that velocities toward or away from the observer are measured by Doppler shifts of the spectral lines. The radial velocities of a moving body can be measured at any distance provided a photographic image can be obtained that is clear enough to identify and measure the spectral lines. In the case of the spirals, radial velocities can be obtained at present for distances up to nearly 700 million light years.

The Expanding Universe

The radial velocities of the nearby spirals were, of course, measured first. The Doppler shifts indicated that some of our immediate neighbors are approaching us while others are receding from us with moderate speeds. However, examination of the Doppler shifts of the more distant spirals showed an unexpected regularity. All showed shifts toward the red end of the spectrum, indicating that the spirals are receding from us in all directions. Even more remarkable was a relation discovered by Hubble in the 1920's. The further the spiral, the greater the shift toward the red, indicating a higher velocity of recession.

Hubble spent the last 20 years of his life studying this effect. He discovered that the relation is quantitative and is called the velocity-distance law. Double the distance of the spiral, double the red shift, and hence double the velocity of recession. Moreover, these velocities are very high. Thus, a spiral at 6 million light years in *any* direction, recedes from us at a speed of about 350 miles per second; at 18 million light years, the speed is about 1000 miles per second. Hubble continued the studies to the fainter spirals, whose distances could be estimated from the size of their image and their brightness. Over and over again, the smaller the image of the nebulae, the greater the red shift. Regardless of errors in individual spirals, the relation is statistically firm. The further the nebulae, the greater its speed. Thus spirals estimated at 270 million light years recede from our galaxy at 15,000 miles per second. Spirals at 720 million light years, move away from us at 38,000 miles per second—about one fifth the speed of light!

It is interesting to follow the implications of the velocity-distance law. If the relation continues to 2000 million light years (which is the limit at which the 200-inch telescope produces a clear image) the speed would be 105,000 miles per second. This is 60 percent the speed of light. Now the speed of light is the highest speed possible, according to relativity. Consequently, we already have under observation a good fraction of the total universe. In any event, it is impossible *in principle* to observe spirals that recede with speeds near or at the speed of light. The spectral lines would be lengthened to infinity, and could not be

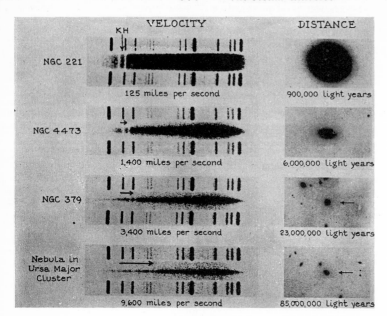

VELOCITY   DISTANCE

KH

NGC 221

125 miles per second   900,000 light years

NGC 4473

1,400 miles per second   6,000,000 light years

NGC 379

3,400 miles per second   23,000,000 light years

Nebula in
Ursa Major
Cluster

9,600 miles per second   85,000,000 light years

Fig. 14-44. The velocity-distance law. The fainter the spiral—and presumably the more distant—the greater the red shift and the greater the velocity of recession. *(Mount Wilson Observatory.)*

recorded. Nor would we get any light, if the source is receding at the same speed at which the disturbance should be coming toward us. Consequently, *if* the red shift continues at the same rate, and *if* red shift means recession, then about 3500 million light years is the largest radius of the universe that can be observed *in principle*.

This conclusion depends, of course, on the assumption that red shift means recession. In the laboratory no one could hesitate to interpret it as so, or in the measurement of speeds in the solar system, or in stars within the galaxy. We have ample confirming evidence from independent measurements of motion. Nor would we hesitate to interpret red shift as recession when it is applied to nearby galaxies. Their rotation as well as their moderate speeds are measured by these means. But in extending the interpretation to the more distant nebulae and obtaining these stupendous speeds, we hesitate. There is no good reason to hesitate, but apparently we are frightened at the implications.

The most far-reaching implication of the red shift is that the universe is expanding. Since all spirals are receding from us uniformly and in all directions, they are receding from one another as well. If we were on another galaxy, say *A,* we would obtain the same result (see Fig. 14-45). From this the conclusion follows that the universe is expanding. At least up to 700 million light years the evidence from Doppler shifts indicates it is expanding and that the more distant the spirals, the faster they move.

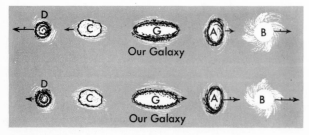

D
C
G
Our Galaxy
A
B

D
C
G
Our Galaxy
A
B

Fig. 14-45. Relativity of expansion of the universe. *(Top),* Observed from our galaxy, G, spiral B recedes twice as fast as A; *(bottom)* Observed from spiral C, spiral B recedes three times as fast.

It is interesting to work backward in time, assuming that the speed has been constant in the past. For we have no reason to assume that the spirals are speeding up or slowing down. No force is known today that would speed them up, and the combined gravitational force of the galaxies is not sufficient to slow them down perceptibly. A spiral, *A*, which is now 700 million light years away was half as far from us some time, *t*, in the past. We can calculate the time, *t*, since we know the distance of the spiral and its speed, but that is not necessary. But a second spiral, *B*, which is now 350 million light years away, was also half as far as it is at present; at the same time, *t*. This follows from the fact that spiral *B* recedes at half the speed of *A*. Since all the spirals follow the velocity-distance law, each spiral was at the time, *t*, half as far as it is at present, and hence the entire universe was half as large. Continuing the argument, there must have been a still earlier time when all the spirals were where we are, *at the same time*. It does not matter whether we say *they* were where *we* now are, or we were where they now are. The point is that all the spirals were together, next to one another. We calculate the time for any and all the spirals and find that they were all together in one great big blob about 5000 million years ago.

Thus we are led to the idea that all the spirals started from the same place some 5 billion years ago. This was the universe then. Father Lemaitre of Belgium conceives that prior to that time the whole universe consisted of a gigantic "atom," containing in it all the matter that exists. It was highly unstable and radioactive. Then, about 5 billion years ago it blew up into gigantic fragments. These fragments, in time, developed into galaxies. The fastest of them are furthest by this time, the slower ones not as far, and that accounts for the velocity-distance law. If this speculation has any truth in it, the universe should continue to expand indefinitely.

We cannot pursue these speculations further, but the reader is referred to a number of articles on the subject (Ref. 14.11). There are many speculations and many conceptions as to the size, shape, and origin of the universe. In these references, questions such as these are discussed: Is the universe finite or infinite? If finite, is it spherical or ellipsoidal or what shape? Is it expanding or pulsating? If it began 5 billion years ago, what was before that time? How did the elements form? The answers are highly tentative but as more knowledge accumulates the answers become more dependable. A good deal of knowledge is already accumulating from the 200-inch telescope.

In the last decade a new source of knowledge was added by the invention of the radio telescope. Neutral cold hydrogen atoms send out a radio frequency of 21 centimeters in wavelength. The reader will remember that a hydrogen atom consists of a proton and an electron. Both of these particles spin on their axis and hence have a magnetic spin. If the proton and the electron have their spins in the opposite direction, the atom is more stable. However, if the spin of the electron is in the same direction as that of the proton, the energy is a little more. The electron will "flip over" and emit the small difference in energy as radiation that is calculated (and measured) to have a wavelength of 21 centimeters. Consequently it can be detected by a short wave radio set. In this way, masses of hydrogen can be detected anywhere in the sky.

The radio telescopes are merely huge direction antennas to detect the masses of hydrogen. Doppler shifts can measure their speeds toward or away from the earth. Survey of the sky has disclosed many masses of hydrogen, otherwise invisible. Many "radio" stars have been located within the galaxy by these means. More significant is the fact that signals are received from "radio spirals" some of which appear to be twice as far as the most distant spirals photographed with the 200-inch telescope. We do not yet know what new knowledge will emerge from these observations or what bearing it will have on the questions raised above.

Thus, human awareness and knowledge of space has been extended from the early beginnings in Ionian Greece to the present universe of spirals. The reader, however, has not failed to realize that this implies an extension of our awareness and knowledge of the extent of time. In looking at a star 40 light years away, we see it as it was 40 years ago. We see Andromeda today as it was 1½ million years ago. The most distant spirals now photographed have sent their light toward the earth at least 2 billion years ago. On looking at the distant spirals we look directly into the past. The universe is very old. It has a long and interesting history. Similar to the story of expanding horizons in space is the story of expanding horizons in time. To this adventure we shall turn in the next chapter.

Fig. 14-46. Radio telescope. Signals from spirals more than 4 billion light years away have been detected. *(Naval Research Laboratory.)*

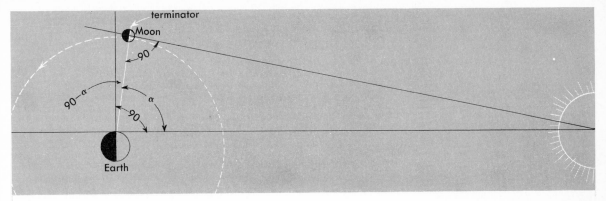

Fig. 14-47. Hipparchus method for estimating the distance of the sun.

NOTES AND EXERCISES

1. Though the method of Hipparchus in estimating the distances of the moon and the sun is mathematically complicated, the sense of his reasoning may be obtained with the aid of Fig. 14-3.

A lunar eclipse takes place as the moon passes through the shadow of the earth. Hipparchus had estimated (Ex. 2) that the sun is much further than the moon and hence larger than the moon. Hence, both the earth and the moon cast conical shadows.

If the earth were the same size as the moon, could there be a total lunar eclipse? If the shadow of the earth, at the distance of the moon, is three moon-diameters, how much larger is the earth than the moon? How can the size of the earth's shadow at the distance of the moon be measured during an eclipse?

The angular diameter of the moon is about ½ degree. From geometry (see p. 469) in order to have an angular diameter of 1 degree, a spherical object must be roughly 60 (57.3) diameters from the point of observation. How many moon-diameters is the distance between the earth and the moon? How many earth-diameters?

2. Consider the moon at first quarter, at the exact instant the terminator is a straight line (Fig. 14-47). What would the angle, α, between the sun and the moon be, if the sun were twice as far as the moon? If the sun were 19 times as far as the moon? If the sun were 400 times as far as the moon (as it actually is)? (Ans. 89°50′) For angle, α, to be exactly 90 degrees how far should the sun be?

3. In an interesting fragment entitled "Psammites" (Sand-reckoner), Archimedes attributes to Aristarchus the following: The diameter of the earth is in the same ratio to the distance of the sun as the distance of the sun is to the diameter of the celestial sphere. The sun is about 20 times further than the moon, and the moon is about 30 earth-diameters from the earth. In terms of earth-diameters, how far is the sun? What is the radius of the celestial sphere? If the diameter of the earth is 8,000 miles (Eratosthenes p. 37) what is the diameter of the "universe" in miles? What is its volume? Interested in expressing very large number by exponents (as powers of 10) Archimedes (making a generous overestimate) then calculates that the "universe" could not contain more sand grains than could be expressed by the number 10^{63} (see Ref. 14.12b).

4. Brightness decreases as the square of the distance. Compared to its present brightness, how bright would the sun appear if it were removed to the distance of Pluto, 40 times further than at present? Sirius is 2,000,000 times further than the sun. How much dimmer would the sun appear at the distance of Sirius? At 10 times that distance? At 100 times that distance?

5. The sun appears 10 billion (10^{10}) times brighter than Sirius. Compared to Sirius how bright would the sun appear at the distance of Sirius? At 10 times the distance of Sirius? How far must the sun be removed to appear as bright as Sirius?

The dimmest star detectable in the largest telescope is about 10 billion (10^{10}) times fainter than Sirius. How much brighter is the sun than the faintest detectable star? To what distance must the sun be removed to appear as faint as the faintest star detectable in the telescope?

6. How far must a foot-rule be removed in order that the angle between one end of the rule, the eye and the other end of the rule is 1 degree? How far must the foot-rule be removed to subtend an angle of 1 minute? One second? 1/100 second?

7. The parallax of Pollux (one of the Twins) is 0.1 second. What is the distance of Pollux in parsecs? In light years? In astronomical units? In miles?

8. In principle, the distance of Eros is determined as follows: Two photographs of Eros are taken simultaneously from observatory A and B (Fig. 14-48). The difference between the position of Eros in the two photographs is angle α in Figure 14-48. If the observatories are 1,000 miles apart, and angle α is 10 seconds of arc, how far is Eros? (See Ex. 6). Now the solar system can be drawn to exact scale, including the orbit of Eros. What observations are necessary for this, and what laws of planetary motion? If the distance to a given position of Eros is known in miles, how can the distance to the sun be calculated?

9. Another method for estimating the distance to the sun comes from the phenomenon of *aberration of light*. In 1659 Horrenow observed that the stars near the zenith and at right angles to the earth's orbit did not cross the meridian at the exact predicted positions, but about 20 seconds of arc *nearer* the zenith. Six months later, the same stars crossed the meridian 20 seconds *further* from the zenith. This periodic shift is different from parallax for this shift is the same for all the stars in a group and is independent of the distance of the stars. In 1755 Bradley (Ref. 2.14, p. 103) interpreted this phenomenon as evidence for the earth's motion around the sun, reasoning as follows:

If light from a star is actually coming vertically (Fig. 14-49) then to an observer on the earth it appears to be coming from a slightly forward direction. Consequently the telescope must be tilted slightly in order to see the star in the field of the telescope. Six months later, the telescope must be tilted in the opposite direction (but again forward).

The angle α, represents the ratio of the speed of the earth to the speed of light. From geometry (see p. 469) for an angle of 20 seconds the ratio is 1/10,000 ($\tan 20'' = 0.0001$). If the speed of light is 186,000 miles per second, what is the speed of the earth? What distance will the earth travel in a minute? In an hour? In a day? In a year? What is the circumference of the earth's orbit? What is the radius? What is the distance to the sun?

10. The diameter of the sun is 110 times the diameter of the earth. What is the ratio of their areas? What is the ratio of their volumes? If the mass of the sun is 330,000 times the mass of the earth, what is the force of gravity on the surface of the sun? What is the ratio of their densities?

11. The surface temperature of the sun is 6000° A and emits 1500 calories per square centimeter per second. The surface temperature of Antares is about 3000° A and that of Vega is 12,000° A. How many calories

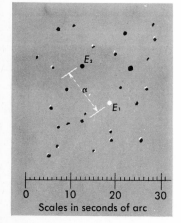

Fig. 14-48. Two photographs of Eros superimposed. Black image of Eros, E_2, is from observatory B, white image, E_1, is from observatory A.

0   10   20   30
Scales in seconds of arc

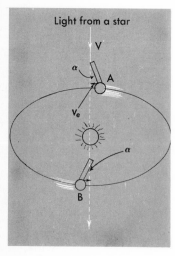

Light from a star

Fig. 14-49. Aberration of light. Angle, α, is 20 sec. Tan α is the ratio of the speed of the earth, V_e, to the speed of light, V.

per square centimeter per second is emitted by Vega? By Antares? Compared to Antares, how much energy (per square centimeter per second) does Vega emit? What color is Antares? The sun? Vega? If Vega and Antares were of the same size and at the same distance, how much brighter would Vega appear?

12. The wavelength of maximum radiation ("the brightest spot") is inversely proportional to the absolute temperature. That is $\lambda_{max} \cdot T =$ constant in the solar spectrum, the brightest spot is 4,700 angstroms ($1 \text{ A} = 10^{-8}$ cm). Calculate the value of this constant. What is the wavelength of the brightest spot in the spectrum of Vega? Of Antares? If the brightest spot in the spectrum of Sirius is about 2800 A, what is its temperature?

13. Sun spot activity has been found empirically to have a maximum every 11½ years. Interestingly enough, the weather on the earth shows the same cycle. At maximum activity, though the sun appears the darkest, the emitted radiation is greatest. A great deal of the emission consists of positive ions and electrons. Would you expect the charged particles to be accelerated by the magnetic fields of the sun spots? Would the charged particles, on reaching the earth, affect the earth's magnetic field? Would you expect aurora displays? Would you expect disturbances in radio and telegraphic communications? Why?

14. Describe the structure of the outer part of the sun. Why is the photosphere sharp? What is the lower limit of the photosphere? Why is the light of the photosphere a continuous spectrum? Why is the chromosphere emitting line spectra? What is the "reversing" layer? Why is it so named? What is the constitution of the corona?

15. The sun radiates into space 4 million tons of its material per second. A long ton is 1,000 kilograms or 1 million grams. Assuming a constant rate, how much mass will the sun lose in a year? In a million years? In 5 billion years? If its present mass is 2×10^{33} grams, what percentage of its mass has the sun lost since its formation?

16. A star of magnitude 1 is how many times as bright as a star of magnitude 2? Of magnitude 3? Magnitude 6? Magnitude 11? 16? 21? 23?

17. The magnitude scale is extended to stars brighter than the first magnitude. Thus a star of magnitude 0 is 2.5 times as bright as a star of magnitude 1. A star of magnitude -1 is 2.5 times as bright as a star of magnitude 0 and so on. The magnitude of Sirius, the brightest star in the sky, is -1.6; Venus reaches a magnitude of -4; the full moon has a magnitude of -11.2; and the sun -26.7. How many times brighter is the sun than the full moon? Than Sirius? Than Venus at its brightest?

18. If a star of magnitude 3 were removed to 4 times its distance by what factor would the brightness decrease? What will be its new magnitude? If the star were removed to 10 times its distance, how would its brightness decrease? What would be its new magnitude? Would its luminosity change?

19. Distinguish between giants and dwarfs. What is a red giant? What is a blue giant? Compare a blue and a red giant of the same absolute luminosity. Which is the hotter star? Which is the larger star? What is a white dwarf? What can you say about its size? Its density?

20. The sun is a G-type star. From this, what can you say about its spectrum? Its surface temperature? Its color? Repeat for Vega, an A-type star. Repeat for an M-type star.

21. The total amount of light emitted by Antares is equal to that of about 3400 suns. Yet the temperature is barely half that of the sun, emitting about 2 percent as much light per square centimeter per second. What does this imply about the size of Antares? How does the surface area of Antares compare with that of the sun? How do the diameters compare?

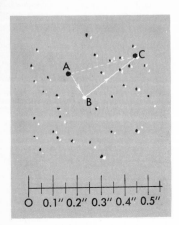

Fig. 14-50. Disentangling proper motion and parallax.

22. The surface temperature of the companion of Sirius is about 10,000 degrees. It emits about 8 times as much light as the sun (per square centimeter per second). Yet its total brightness is 1/3600 that of the sun. Calculate its diameter in miles.

23. Figure 14-50 is a composite drawing of three photographs of the same star in the background of dimmer stars taken six months apart. In the first photograph the star was in position *A*. Six months later it was in position *B*. After another six months it was in position *C*. Using the scale in the drawing, estimate its proper motion, its parallax and its distance from the earth.

24. The wavelength of a line observed in the spectrum of a star is 6001.2 A. The wavelength of the same line from a laboratory source is 6000.0 A. Is the star moving toward or away from the earth? What is the percentage change in the wavelength? Calculate the speed of the star relative to the earth.

25. What is the evidence that the solar system moves toward the constellation of Hercules? With respect to what stars is this motion? How do you suppose the speed (12 miles per second) was determined?

26. What evidence indicated that Sirius is a double star, even before the companion was observed? What is the evidence that the companion is physically associated with Sirius, rather than a star in approximately the same line of sight?

27. Are the extraordinary densities of white dwarfs unbelievable? What is the density of the proton? Of other nuclei? (Also see Exercise 26, Chapter 11.)

28. Assuming the sun to follow a normal course, trace in Figure 14-35 the path of evolution through which it has already gone. Trace the path of evolution in the future. What is the estimated age of the sun? How long before it becomes a white dwarf?

29. How do the star counts permit us to study the stars outside the solar neighborhood, beyond the reach of the parallax method?

30. The star β-Centauri may be taken as an average B-type star with an apparent magnitude of 1. Its distance is 300 light years and its absolute brightness is about 3,000 times that of the sun.

A certain star, *X*, is identified as a B-type, but its apparent magnitude is 6. How many times dimmer than β-Centauri does star *X* appear? Assuming star *X* to be an average B-type star, how does it compare with β-Centauri in true brightness? What is the probable distance of star *X*? Would you accept this result with confidence for this single star? Would you accept it for a group of 50 such stars, if physically associated in a cluster?

31. The period of a certain red cepheid variable is found to be 40 days. Using curve II of Figure 14-36 estimate its true brightness. A red cepheid of this absolute brightness would have an apparent magnitude of −2 at the distance of 32 light years. If the measured apparent magnitude of the star is +17, how far is the star?

If this star were a blue cepheid (with the same period and apparent magnitude) how much brighter would it appear at 32 light years? Why? How much further would it be?

32. How did Shapley estimate the distance of a globular cluster? Having estimated the distances of several nearby globular clusters, how did he estimate the distance of the more distant clusters? What assumption did he make in these estimates? How did he estimate the shape and size of the Milky Way? What assumptions did he make?

33. What line of reasoning suggests that the Milky Way rotates? What observational evidence confirms this conclusion? How is the distance of the sun from the galactic center estimated? How is the period of revolution of the sun about the galactic center estimated?

34. Several lines of evidence suggested that the basic "yardstick" as used prior to 1950 was wrong. For example Hubble noticed that the clusters in Andromeda were about four times fainter in absolute brightness than those in the Milky Way, assuming that Andromeda is 800,000 light years away. If a globular cluster in Andromeda has comparable brightness to those in the Milky Way, what correction should be applied to the distance of Andromeda? To the basic yardstick?

35. The apparent diameter of the Andromeda nebula is 3°. How is this determined? The distance is 1½ million light years. How is this determined? What is the diameter in light years? How does it compare to our Galaxy? How does it compare to the Magellanic Clouds?

36. The diameter of a certain spiral measured on the photographic plate is .03 degree (about 1.8 minutes of arc). How does this compare with the diameter of Andromeda? Assuming (for purposes of calculation) that Andromeda as well as this spiral are "average" spirals, what is the distance of this spiral? Is this estimate reliable for a single spiral? Is it reliable for a group of spirals? (Also see exercise 30.)

37. A certain spiral, *X*, is estimated at 18 million light years from the periods and apparent brightness of cepheid variables in it. Its angular size is about 0.2 degree. Its velocity of recession is about 1000 miles per second.

Another spiral, *Y*, with an angular diameter of 0.01 degree is observed. What is the most probable estimate of its distance? What is the expected speed of recession? How can this be checked? What is the expected brightness compared to spiral *X*? How can this be checked?

The diameter of a third spiral, *Z*, is measured as 0.005 degree on the photographic plate. What is the probable distance and speed of recession? Can these be checked at present?

38. By radio telescope, spirals have been observed about twice as far as those observed in photographs. How is the Doppler shift of the "radio spirals" observed? What happens to the 21 cm radio frequency of hydrogen?

39. If the velocity-distance law holds for the most distant spirals, what is the maximum distance a spiral can be observed? Why? What is the maximum size of the "observable" universe?

40. Summarize the story of "expanding horizons" by making very rough estimates of the diameter of the "universe" as conceived during the five periods designated in the text as anthropocentric, geocentric, heliocentric, galactocentric and the present acentric.

15

UNIVERSAL
HISTORY

Man's conception of his past—of the earth he inhabits and of the larger cosmos in which he finds himself—has been a story of expanding horizons. Just as human awareness has been extended in space to the remote regions of the spirals, so has it been extended back to the remote eons of antiquity, reaching out toward a beginning, if there ever was an ultimate Beginning. This is history in the broadest sense—the history of the Universe. In this chapter we propose to sketch the story of man's increasing understanding of the history of Nature.

The early gropings for an understanding of the past are associated with man's primitive views of his own origin and of creation. In every mythology and primitive religion we find an explanation of the present world in terms of creation by supernatural agencies in the not too distant past. These views appear in Babylonian and Egyptian cosmologies as far back as the record goes, several millenia ago. In Greek mythology also we find an account of supernatural origin, highly poetic and rich in imagination. Uranus, the oldest of the gods, founded the first dynasty, and he, his sons, and grandsons all took part in creating the world and populating it with minor gods and mortal men. It was the main business of the gods to see that the world functions properly. This was the most beautiful cosmogony ever conceived of until modern science gave us an even grander conception of creation, based on observation and reasoning.

As in the case of other primitive beliefs, the Ionian philosophers were the first to challenge the account of Greek mythology. Thales of Miletus, around 600 B.C., thought that the account was too anthropomorphic and could better be left to poets and mystics. He urged that the history of creation be sought in the natural causes to be found in the phenomena. Subsequently, all "physical" philosophers of Ionia and of later classical times looked for the natural causes of earthquakes and volcanoes, of rain and snow, of tides and floods, and of the formation of valleys and mountains.

Despite the naturalistic outlook, however, progress was slow and the explanations were rather crude and, at best, long-shot guesses. Earthquakes and volcanoes, because of their violent character, attracted much of the attention of the ancients. Anaximenes thought that earthquakes are caused by collapsing caverns. Aristotle, after dismissing this view and similar views of other authors, proposed that earthquakes are caused by subterranean winds. He associated earthquakes and volcanoes and thought that the latter are caused by escaping winds meeting deposits of sulfur and setting them afire by friction. The authors of later classical times were hardly nearer the truth, although by this time they had collected some sound observations.

Yet some progress was registered in other directions. Aristotle displayed considerable knowledge of the drainage system of the northern Mediterranean, and of the processes of erosion and deposition by rivers. Fossils had been observed high on mountains and were recognized by many as evidence that the mountains were once below sea level. Herodotus, the historian, impressed by the abundant quantities of sea shells far inland in Egypt, concluded that the sea bottom once extended over most of Egypt. Noting the annual overflow of the Nile and the deposition of layers of soil, he made the pertinent remark that Egypt is the "gift of the River." He went further and asserted that the age of the Nile could be estimated roughly by measuring the total thickness of the sediments. Had this idea been carried out, he might have become the father of historical geology, instead of just the "father of history."

The rather disappointing progress in geologic thought throughout classical antiquity is at once surprising and understandable. It is surprising inasmuch as the phenomena are large scale, are easily accessible to naked eye observation, and require no special techniques or instruments. On the other hand, the geologic processes are slow, and the resulting changes, although easily ascertainable, are not striking. They do not appreciably alter the general appearance of a region in a lifetime or even in several lifetimes.

The more basic reasons, however, are to be found in the complexity of the phenomena and in the complex interplay of the ideas involved. In any historical account there are four distinct elements or ideas. It is instructive to consider them here, for they are pertinent to our study. First, we must distinguish between the *events* that have taken place and the *length of time* during which they took place. The two are intimately interrelated and, indeed, inseparable. We know time because of events, for time without events is meaningless. A great number of events in sequence implies a long time. Conversely, the assumption of a short time predisposes us to look for fewer events in succession. Second, in any historical explanation, it is logically necessary to start with an *initial* situation in the past and show how it has been transformed into the *present*. Since we cannot revisit the past, we must *assume* the initial conditions in order to understand their evolution into the present. But in order to postulate the past, it is necessary to understand the present. This can be a vicious circle. The interplay of these four elements makes it necessary to start by observing the present, making tentative guesses, following the interplay of the ideas and returning for better guesses. The unraveling of the past is a long and tortuous process.

The geologic phenomena available to the Greeks (and available today, for that matter) are extremely complex, and numerous processes go on simultaneously in a given place. Nowhere is there a "model" process uninfluenced or uninterrupted by other processes. The very wealth of the phenomena is embarrassing. To make sense of the welter of flux was more than the ancients were able to do. As a result they did not leave a legacy comparable to the Ptolemaic theory in astronomy. In fact, no significant progress was registered until the eighteenth century.

With the decline of Greece and Rome and the spread of Christianity and allied religions, the account of the Genesis became the dominant principle in the western world. For over a thousand years the central idea was that the Universe was created essentially in the *present state* by the direct action of the Deity, *not so long ago*. The genealogies in the Old Testament, if taken literally, imply a chronology of a few thousand years. The literal interpretation was universally accepted until recently. In 1500, Archbishop Ussher of Ireland, after studying the genealogies in the Bible concluded that the world was created on Sunday, October 26, 4004 B.C., at 9 o'clock in the morning.

Once the account of the Genesis is accepted literally, there is no

Fig. 15-1. The story of Creation from the Genesis. Creation of Eve, by Michelangelo (from the vault of the Sistine Chapel, Vatican). (*The Bettman Archive.*)

reason to look for natural causes. If the universe was created essentially "as is" by Divine Design, there is no reason to explain the shape of things. Moreover the Design is obvious for all to see. Just as day and night alternate so that we can work and sleep, so are the valleys tilted for the waters to run into the sea. Nor is there much room for history. Any changes that might have taken place in the short time since creation must be relatively minor and hardly worth the trouble to investigate.

With the Renaissance, the naturalistic outlook began to spread by degrees. The Copernican revolution upset the Ptolemaic system of the geocentric world. The work of Galileo and Newton replaced Aristotelian mechanics, and their application registered rapid advances in astronomy and physics. The same outlook spread to the biological sciences and to geology. Individuals here and there again began to look for natural causes. Leonardo da Vinci, that universal genius of Venice, noticed the fossils during the digging of the canals of his native city and again gave the correct interpretation that fossils are remains of living things of past eras. The German philosopher, Kant, in the middle of the eighteenth century suggested that the earth might have evolved from a nebula, and in 1796 the French mathematician, Laplace, published a theory elaborating this idea.

However, the return to naturalism did not result in immediate advances in geologic thought comparable to the advances in astronomy and physics. The reasons for this lag are the same as those we discussed in connection with the ancients. The complexity of the phenomena plagued the early students of modern times just as they plagued the ancients. If anything, the naturalists of the sixteenth, seventeenth, and eighteenth century were worse off than the Greeks. Although they had rejected the literal interpretation of the account in the Genesis, the long tradition of the story of Creation and the story of the Flood colored their thinking and subconsciously determined their presuppositions. They looked for "catastrophic" interpretations. The Plutonian theories (named after the god of the Underworld) attempted to explain the origin of all rocks from the solidification of a recently molten earth. The Neptunian theories (named after the god of the Sea) attempted to explain everything in terms of deposition of rocks from a primeval, universal ocean. Advances were made, to be sure, but no general pattern had yet arisen.

The rise of a comprehensive view of geologic processes can be located fairly definitely in the closing years of the eighteenth century. At the time that Lavoisier in Paris was laying the foundations of chemistry, James Hutton in Scotland was formulating the basic principles of geology. From extensive observations of rocks and streams, Hutton came to the conclusion that many of the rocks in his native hills were amazingly similar to the deposits being laid down by streams and waves today. He reasoned that the rocks in the hills represented deposits of previous streams and waves. With a touch of genius, he generalized that the hills of today are the stream beds and ocean beds of yesterday; that the land masses of the earth are in a process of slow and continuous change; and that the processes now going on are sufficient in magnitude to have produced, over a long period of time, all the features of the

Fig. 15-2. James Hutton—"The present is the key to the past."

earth we now see. Being a thorough scholar, he proceeded to marshal evidence to support these far-reaching conclusions.

Hutton's writings made difficult reading, but his ideas had a strong appeal. When elucidated by John Playfair, around 1800, they made an immediate impact on a wide audience of naturalists. Hutton's views struck very deep. They shook to the foundations the belief that the earth is young. The "eternal" hills are but transitory features of a ceaselessly changing landscape. The surface of the earth is a dynamic interconnected system—eroding, sinking, uplifting, eroding again, sinking again. A whole series of detailed investigations were initiated, leading to the present understanding of the geologic past. Underlying these investigations is the principle that the earth has a long and complex history, to be determined by a detailed study of the record now present in the rocks. In Hutton's words, "The present is the key to the past."

The detailed investigations of the record of the rocks led to simultaneous developments in several directions, each influencing the other. However, it will be simpler to follow the story if the knowledge of events is recast into an order, from the immediately known to the more remote. By reconstructing the story, we shall relate how by starting from the present it has been possible to delve into the past, step by step, unraveling events of greater and greater antiquity.

The first part of the story is a discussion of the processes now going on in the present landscape. Everywhere there are powerful agents at work engaged in altering its present features. Rain and rivers, underground water and waves, wind and ice are all relentlessly attacking the landscape and tearing it down. Each of these geologic agents, by cutting a slice of the land, carves into the landscape a form or a feature characteristic of its action. At the same time the material removed is deposited at lower levels in landforms that are characteristic of the agent. The lower levels are attacked in turn. In this gigantic teamwork the ultimate objective of the geologic agents is to reduce the land to sea level or very near sea level.

It is possible to study each of these agents in detail, their mode of action, the magnitude of their forces, and the changes they are now producing. Everywhere a nice correspondence exists between the forces available and the results produced. Furthermore, in any given region we can measure the rate at which erosion is now going on and estimate the time it took to produce the present features, from a previous state that is apparent in the region. We can estimate how long it took *this* brook to carve its deep valley in *this* hill. Estimates vary from region to region and, of course, depend on how clearly we discern previous states and how far back we want to go. But whatever region studied, and however conservative the estimates may be, the repeated conclusion is that geologic agents have been at work for many millions of years.

At this point the first big question arises. If the geologic agents have been actively at work for millions and millions of years, how is it that there is any land left? Is it possible that there are other forces and other agents that work in the opposite direction of the degrading agents. Are there any forces that rejuvenate the land?

With this question we have entered the second part of our story.

Everywhere evidence exists that terra firma is not so firm, but that it is in a process of dynamic movement. Earthquakes and volcanoes provide the most direct and sometimes terrifying evidence. Then there are shores sinking and shores uplifting. However, the most extensive and more convincing evidence is in the rocks themselves. Everywhere on the earth, rocks that must have been deposited under the sea are now found on high land. The tops of mountain ranges contain evidence that they were once sea bottoms. Moreover, in any given region there is evidence of not just one uplift, but of several. Rocks are found deposited in salt water and over them rocks deposited on land, and over these again rocks deposited under sea water. In some regions several such sequences occur. Can we untangle the evidence of previous uplifts, erosions, and depositions from the record of the rocks and reconstruct a continuous story?

For the past century and a half the geologists have been doing precisely that. In any given region where rocks are exposed, it is possible to read the sequence of events. They are usually in the following order: erosion, submergence, deposition, uplift, erosion again, submergence, deposition, and again uplift. In some regions several cycles are recorded. The story begins to be significant when the history of one region is correlated with the history of another region. It thus becomes possible to decipher the combined history of both regions. If the regions are adjacent and continuous rocks are found in both regions, the correlation is simple in principle, although difficult in practice. A better method was found when fossils were recognized to be indicative of their times. Rocks having the same assemblage of fossils must have been deposited at the same time. In this way rocks have been correlated across a continent or from continent to continent across ocean barriers. By this time (1960) nearly all the rocks now exposed on the surface of the earth have been correlated and arranged in sequence from the oldest to the youngest. The net result is a gigantic column more than 100 miles in height containing representatives of the rocks of all ages. It is known as the *geologic column*. In it can be found all the "Record of the Rocks."

This gigantic column gives the history of the earth. Floods and uplifts, deserts and ice ages, and generations of mountains arising only to be leveled to their roots are there. The story of life is in the column —the parade of trilobites, of dinosaurs, of early mammals, and the rise of man. We can now trace life at least as far back as 500 million years with fair certainty.

The record of the rocks contains data for estimating the duration of geologic time. The thickness of the rocks alone provides a rough estimate, but the analysis of radioactive elements with their decay products found in the rocks leads to a much more accurate measure of their age. In this way the age of older and older rocks is measured. Some rocks are more than 3 billion years old.

At the bottom of the column the relations become obscure. So many things have happened since the deposition of these rocks that the record is too fragmentary and indistinct. However, from here on we reinforce our knowledge with astronomical data and nuclear science, and attempt to formulate a theory of the earth's origin and age. We even attempt to correlate the theory of the earth's origin with theories of the possible origin of the entire Universe. However, the further back we go, the less and less certain our knowledge becomes.

This is the story in outline form. In the following sections we propose to elaborate on the various parts of the story and to provide evidence for the conclusions, so significant and far reaching in their implications.

2. THE EVOLUTION OF THE LANDSCAPE

In the more detailed study of the past history of the earth, we shall adopt Hutton's principle and begin with the present landscape, tracing its evolution further and further back. Our study will be facilitated by considering first some general knowledge about the earth and the processes now going on. A good deal of this knowledge has been discussed in several connections, especially in Chapters 2 and 14, and much of it is fairly well known from general information. It is summarized here for ready reference.

General Knowledge about the Earth

The earth is spheroid, about 8000 miles in diameter, somewhat flatter at the poles and bulging at the equator. The polar diameter is about 27 miles shorter than the equatorial, but compared to 8000 miles this difference is hardly perceptible on a 12-inch globe. The major features are, of course, the land masses and the oceans, the latter covering about three quarters of the earth's surface. A single land mass makes up the continents of Asia, Europe, and Africa. The Americas constitute a much smaller land mass, and Australia may be considered an oversized island. The Antarctica is not yet fully explored, but is comparable to Australia in area.

The features next in order are the mountain ranges and the major river valleys, with their enormous and complicated drainage systems. With the conspicuous exception of a chain of mountains stretching across Eurasia, from the Alps through the Caucasus to the Himalayas, nearly all other mountain ranges border the ocean coasts, and are the sites of earthquake and volcanic activity. Relative to the size of the earth, the mountain ranges are minor irregularities. The highest peaks are about 6 miles above sea level, but the average height of the land is about half a mile. Interestingly enough, the deepest ocean troughs are also about 6 miles deep, although the average depth is about $2\frac{1}{2}$ miles. Thus, the total relief is about 12 miles. On a 12-inch globe, these irregularities would be hardly thicker than the coat of paint.

The solid part of the earth is called the *lithosphere,* meaning a "sphere of stone." It has the rigidity of steel, as shown from the speeds of earthquake waves through it. The oceans, the river systems, the occasional lakes, and the ground water form an almost continuous film of water, which is called the *hydrosphere.* The *atmosphere* is the outer gaseous film much smaller in weight than the hydrosphere. If it were to condense to a liquid it would form, on a smooth sphere, a layer less than 30 feet in height. Being gaseous it extends indefinitely, but thins out very rapidly. More than two thirds of the air is below 6 miles. At 50 miles it is thinner than a good laboratory vacuum. Yet there is some air at 200 miles and even higher, as shown from the drag on the artificial satellites.

The chemical composition of the earth has been studied quite extensively. All the stable elements, about 80 in number, occur naturally, and several radioactive elements as well. The atmosphere consists of about 80 percent nitrogen, 20 percent oxygen, and less than 1 percent of the inert gases. It contains on the average about 0.03 percent carbon dioxide, and varying amounts of water vapor. The hydrosphere is, of course, nearly all water, which consists of 89 percent oxygen and 11 percent hydrogen by weight. The ocean contains about 3.5 percent of dissolved minerals, mostly sodium chloride, which is common salt. Several other elements occur in smaller amounts, and many more, including gold and uranium, have been detected in trace quantities.

The composition of the lithosphere is a more complicated problem, for it varies from place to place and also with depth. Moreover, only the outer surface is accessible to direct study, and of this mostly the continental surface. The deepest wells and mines are barely 4 miles deep. There is convincing evidence that some of the rocks now exposed at the surface were once several miles below. All and all, however, we have barely scratched the surface, quite literally.

By extensive sampling and statistical methods we can strike a good average and estimate the composition of the outer portion of the lithosphere to a depth of several miles. In any event this is the portion that concerns us at present. Rather incorrectly it is called the "crust." Eight elements make up more than 98 percent of the matter in the crust. As shown in Table 15-1, oxygen makes up almost half of the weight of the outer lithosphere, and silicon about a quarter. Aluminum and iron constitute another 13 percent; this leaves for calcium, magnesium, sodium, and potassium a couple of percent each. All the other elements make up the remaining 1 percent. Interestingly enough carbon, so prominent and fundamental in living things, is present in less than 0.1 percent, and most of it is in the mineral form as carbonates, limestones, and dolomites. Interesting also is the fact that hydrogen and helium, so abundant in the stars and interstellar space, are quite rare on the earth.

The elements in the lithosphere do not exist in the free state, of course, but in combined form as more or less definite chemical compounds, which are known as *minerals.* Since oxygen is so abundant, we would expect to find the other elements in the oxidized state and indeed

TABLE 15:1

Chemical Composition of the Outer Lithosphere

	Percent
Oxygen	46.5
Silicon	27.6
Aluminum	8.1
Iron	5.0
Calcium	3.6
Sodium	2.8
Potassium	2.6
Magnesium	2.0
Others	1.8

Fig. 15-3. Granite—an example of an igneous rock. The forms of the crystals give evidence that the rock has solidified from a molten condition. *(Wards Natural Science Establishment.)*

we do. A good deal of the silicon is in the form of silicon dioxide, which is quartz or ordinary sand. Quartz is the most abundant mineral found not only on beaches, dunes, and sandstones, but also widely dispersed throughout all the rocks. It is a major constituent of granites. Iron and aluminum also often occur as oxides. However, more frequently, these and the other metals are found as more complex compounds called silicates. In a sense, silicates are more complex compounds of silicon dioxide and the metal oxides. The backbone of the earth are silicate rocks. All the other minerals of the other elements may be thought of as minor impurities imbedded in them.

We must distinguish between minerals and rocks. A *mineral* is a *chemical compound;* a *rock* is a *structure*. Three kinds of rocks are recognized, each kind being indicative of its origin and mode of formation. The *igneous* rocks are crystalline and contain ample evidence that they have solidified from a molten state. Granite is the best example, and basalt is another. The essential difference between them is that basalt contains a greater proportion of iron and magnesium and hence is darker and denser. Igneous rocks are exposed in many places, especially in mountain regions, but underlie all other rocks everywhere in the ocean floor immediately under the water. Since these igneous rocks underlie all other rocks and extend to indefinite depths, they were thought at one time to represent the "original crust" of the earth.

The second group of rocks are the *sedimentary*. These are *layered* rocks. They have all the characteristics of having been deposited as loose material and later consolidated. The vast majority of them have all the earmarks of deposition under water. Good examples are sandstones, limestones, shales, and conglomerates. Technically speaking, coal is a sedimentary rock, and even unconsolidated sediments such as sand beaches, mud deposits, or even soil may be called rocks. Each kind of sedimentary rock contains clear evidence of the conditions under

Fig. 15-4. Sedimentary rocks are layered rocks. Each distinct layer was deposited at one time interval. (From Miller and Haub, *General Zoology*. New York: Henry Holt and Co., 1956.)

Fig. 15-5. Gneis—an example of metamorphic rock. The bonded appearance of mica (black streaks) gives evidence of high pressure and fairly high temperature. (*Wards Natural Science Establishment.*)

which it was deposited and of the agent responsible for its deposition. Conglomerate, for example, resembles coarse concrete and is obviously gravel consolidated and cemented together.

The third class of rocks are the *metamorphic,* the term meaning that they have "changed over." These rocks contain evidence that they have been altered by a combination of heat and pressure, or by heat alone. The original form of the rock is often easily discernible. The majority of them were either igneous or sedimentary. For example, marble is limestone recrystallized under heat and pressure. Similarly, gneiss is metamorphosed granite; and slate is metamorphosed mud or shale. In some instances even metamorphic rocks may be metamorphosed further. Thus mica is slate that has been metamorphosed further; it contains striations and cleavage planes, clearly showing where the pressure was applied. Many gneisses are contorted and have the appearance of "marble" cake. The metamorphic rocks are found in sites of volcanic activity, present or ancient, or in the roots of ancient mountains.

The primary source of *energy* on the earth is the sun. The earth is bathed in an intense stream of solar radiation, receiving a total of 10 billion billion calories per minute. Owing to the curvature of the earth, the intensity at any given place depends on the inclination of the rays. The radiation is most intense directly under the sun, where each square centimeter receives 2 calories per minute. The unequal heating causes expansion and rise of the air directly under the sun, and this is followed by other movements of the air to replace the rising air. The rotation of the earth results in a westward drift of the place of most intense insolation. The net result of these factors is a very complex circulation of the atmosphere. All the phenomena of the weather and

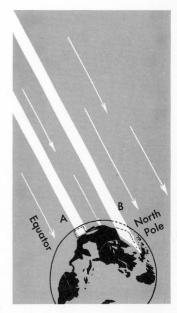

Fig. 15-6. Intensity of sunlight depends on the angle. It is most intense where the sun is overhead (A) and less intense toward the poles (B).

climate are caused ultimately by the unequal heating of the earth by the sun, coupled with the rotation of the earth and the inclination of its axis to the plane of revolution about the sun. In a very real sense the sun is a gigantic heat engine driving the circulation of the atmosphere.

More pertinent to our immediate study, however, is the fact that under the heating by the sun, water evaporates from the oceans and the resultant water vapor is carried by the atmospheric circulation over the continents. There it precipitates as rain or snow, and starts its return to the oceans in the form of rivers, ground water, and sometimes as glacial ice. On this long return it attacks the land by both chemical and physical action, altering the rocks chemically and disintegrating them while at the same time dissolving the soluble material. Physically, water scours and wears down the land, depositing the material at lower levels and eventually at sea level. Thus, the effect of the water returning to the ocean is to tear down the land and ultimately reduce it to sea level.

The circulation of the atmosphere is responsible for wearing down the land in two ways that are even more direct. The high winds that are generated carry great quantities of dust and sand in suspension. With these particles as tools the winds scour the land wherever they blow and carry the material to lower levels and ultimately to the sea. In addition, the winds cause ocean waves, which constantly beat against the coasts reducing them to the level of the sea or below. The five agents mentioned—namely *running water, ground water, glacial ice, wind,* and *waves*—are called gradational agents. These agents, singly and in combination, form a gigantic destructive team with the apparent aim to reduce the land to sea level.

Hutton had this overall picture in mind when he concluded that the forces are sufficiently great to have carved the land into the present form. By studying in detail the forces at work it is possible to explain every feature now present and, step by step, unravel the more and more distant past.

The Grand Canyon of the Colorado

It does not matter much where we begin to decipher the history of our planet. One place is almost as good as another. We have chosen the Grand Canyon for several reasons. It is the most impressive and awe-inspiring spectacle on the North American continent. There the forces and their effects are on a gigantic scale. Moreover, the site is familiar to most, at least from pictures. More important, an examination of the drainage system of the Colorado River over its entire length provides examples of practically all the types of geologic processes. A good deal of the earth's history can be woven around the events recorded on the walls of the Grand Canyon (Fig. 15-7).

From the edge of the canyon on the Arizona plateau a great gorge, 12 miles across and more than a mile deep, winds both upstream and downstream to indefinite distances, finally disappearing behind steep walls. Everywhere massive pillars of rock—the mesas—rise almost perpendicularly. Directly below, the Colorado River appears as a thin silver thread. According to Hutton's principles, the inconspicuous river is the architect of this natural wonder. Is it possible that Hutton was wrong? He never visited the Grand Canyon and is it not easier to

Fig. 15-7. The Grand Canyon of the Colorado River. The river is barely visible. Note the great fault, and the unconformities Pu and Au. *(U. S. Geological Survey.)*

believe that this gap was formed at the time the earth was created, or that it was caused by some gigantic displacement and the river fitted into it later?

The canyon wall, however, provides evidence to substantiate Hutton's principles. Here and there fallen rocks and sloping piles of rock debris precariously hang onto the steep wall. Elsewhere are cracked rocks ready to dislodge and tumble into the abyss below. Trees and shrubs send their roots through the cracks, helping to unloosen the rocks. Everywhere the exposed rock, showing signs of disintegration from the action of the physical and chemical agents of the weather, is altered and visibly different from fresh rock. The amount of activity observed during any one trip down into the canyon is not particularly impressive, but it does prove that the walls of the canyon are wasting away and that the valley is widening, even though very slowly.

A descent to the river level, however, would raise our respect for the Colorado by several magnitudes. What appeared as a thin silver thread from above is now a violent, noisy torrent. Measurements show the stream to be ½ mile wide and at places over 100 feet deep, but its size varies with the time of year. Geologists have measured the river for many years. The current varies from 3000 cubic feet per second in the dry season to 200,000 in flood time; the average is about 20,000 cubic feet per second. The speed and violence of the current also vary according to the volume. In flood time the display of forces is tremendous.

Moreover the river is not silvery. It is dirty and loaded with mud. Samples of the water disclose a good deal of suspended fine clay and silt, but also larger particles of sand and rock, particularly where the current is swift or the agitation high. Heavier particles are dragged along the bottom in large quantities. These range all the way from sand and gravel, to pebbles and stones, to good-sized boulders. Some of the huge boulders that lie everywhere are rounded, apparently having been rolled from upstream; others are angular, obviously having fallen recently from the canyon wall above.

In this violent commotion the rolling rocks pound against each other and against the rocky bed and side of the river. The result of this powerful abrasion is to round off the rolling stones, leaving many of them almost spherical in shape. At the same time the bed and sides wear out under the constant bombardment of the moving stones which act like high-speed missiles. A good deal of the rock is ground to rock powder and joins the suspension load. Much of the load is dropped where the current slackens or the grade decreases, only to be picked up again when the current shifts or quickens in flood time. Certainly some of the huge boulders now lying motionless must have been rolled down from far upstream in high flood, for they are chipped and rounded. No doubt they will be picked up again in future floods.

Estimates of the load carried are impressive. The suspended load is several thousand tons per day. The load dragged along the bottom is even greater. Filtering and evaporating some of the water and then weighing the amount of dissolved minerals discloses only a few grains per gallon, but this becomes impressive when it is calculated for the total volume. Adding all these loads and taking the proper averages shows that the Colorado is carrying downstream no less than 4500 million cubic feet of rock material per year.

Where does all this material come from and where does it go? For many miles upstream the canyon appears much the same and just as magnificent as at the site of the National Park. As the elevation of the river bed slowly increases, some unimportant tributaries join it. But with the first major tributary, the stream divides into two large but unequal streams, the Colorado and its tributary, the Little Colorado (Fig. 15-8).

At the junction of the rivers, two relations are noteworthy. First, the two streams meet at the same level, and at an angle that shows that the smaller stream has made the adjustment to meet the larger stream. Second, the larger stream is in the larger valley. Although both of these relations appear "natural," their significance becomes clear after some thought. These relations constitute direct evidence that the streams have cut their own valleys. The effects are in proportion to the forces at work. What else can explain the fact that the larger stream is in the larger valley, and that the two streams meet at the same level and at the proper angle? If the valleys had been merely cracks in the ground, and the streams fitted into them later, there would be no reason for this nice correspondence. More detailed and more tech-

Fig. 15-8. Conformance of the meeting of the Colorado (left branch) with the Little Colorado (right branch). Main river marking the beginning of the Grand Canyon is in the foreground. The conformance and the sizes of the three valleys is strong evidence that the streams have carved their own valleys. (U. S. Geological Survey.)

nical analysis of the relation between forces and effects leaves no doubt that the valleys have been carved by the streams now in them.

Further upstream the river bed continues to rise, sometimes more rapidly, sometimes less so. Other tributaries join the river and, with few exceptions, they meet the main stream at the same level, and the size of their valleys is appropriate to the stream size. Meanwhile, the "main" stream becomes smaller and smaller. Ultimately it becomes a brook and then a dry ravine, probably ending in a farm in upper Colorado state, or perhaps in the back yard of a home.

Geologists have followed all the tributaries and their branches and thus explored the entire drainage system of the Colorado, as can be seen from the map in Figure 15-9. The total area is nearly a quarter of a million square miles. The land over this entire area has been dissected by the river, and is still being dissected in a million and one different ways, in a million and one different places. In many places freshly exposed rock is attacked and disintegrated by water and the dissolved carbon dioxide. At every place, soil and loose ground is removed and carried downstream. At the same time the heavier particles and the larger stones grind against each other, and against the river bed. The stones themselves get rounded, and the rock is pulverized and added to the load. The valleys get deeper and wider as time goes on. The valleys grow headwards. What is now a ravine will grow into a brook. A ravine may form in a farm land in next week's storm. Every year, 500 billion cubic feet of water are at work dissecting the landscape and carrying it away. Every year these waters remove 4½ billion cubic feet of rock. A simple calculation shows that they are now reducing the land by 1 inch in about 1500 years.

What is the fate of the material carried away from the land? Again for many miles downstream from the National Park the canyon looks much the same as in the Park, but the elevation slowly drops and the valley walls widen somewhat. Ignoring for the moment the man-made

Fig. 15-9. The drainage system of the Colorado is nearly 1/4 million square miles. *(U. S. Geological Survey.)*

barrier—the Hoover Dam near Las Vegas, Nevada—the Colorado flows into California. The valley becomes very wide and the walls gradually become gentle slopes. The river has entered the flood plain and is now wide and sluggish, capable of carrying only mud and sand. The heavier rocks have been pulverized or left behind to be pulverized later. A good deal of the sediment is deposited as the river slows down on entering the flood plain.

By the time the river flows through the valley into the Gulf of California it is almost at sea level and meanders lazily, now depositing some load here, now picking it up there as the currents shift, only to redeposit it further downstream. Ultimately it enters the sea. On meeting the quiet waters of the ocean, all the remaining load is dropped quite suddenly, since motion and turbulence practically stop. Moreover most of the clay particles are precipitated chemically by the minerals present in sea water. The result is the building of the delta. The material is sorted out as it is dropped, the coarse settling out first, and progressively the finer material depositing further and further out. As the load is dropped, the river lengthens, resulting in a continuous overlap of coarse and fine material.

The extent of the deposit can be estimated by measuring the area and depth of the delta. These deposits extend to much greater depths than would at first be suspected and at every level the sediments exhibit the same sorting as that observed on the surface. Throughout the deposits *crossbedding* occurs, similar to that taking place today due to the changes in the direction of the currents. The ripple marks and mud cracks, down to the deepest sediments, are the most direct evidence that the now deep-lying sediments were deposited on the shallow waters over other ripple marks or on temporarily dried surfaces over other mud cracks. This gives rise to the idea that as the material deposits, it progressively sinks, perhaps due to its own weight. Whatever the cause of the sinking, however, there is no question that deposits several miles in depth are now being laid down by the Colorado.

Estimating the total deposit, we find it more than sufficient to

Fig. 15-10. The Colorado River at the Colorado Valley near the border of Arizona and California. The river has entered the flood plain and become sluggish. *(U. S. Geological Survey.)*

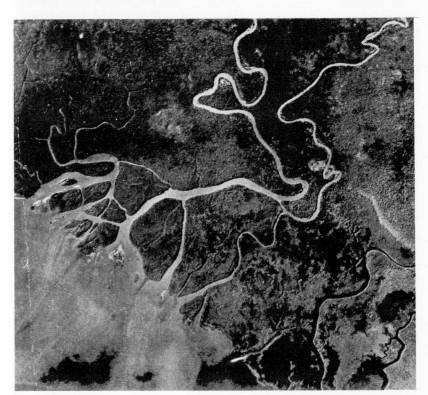

Fig. 15-11. A typical delta. *(U. S. Army.)*

account for all the material now obviously missing from the excavated land over the entire drainage system. Thus our reasoning is confirmed that the Colorado can excavate not only the gorge of its deep canyon, but its entire valley. Indeed the conclusion is inescapable that it has done so and that it will continue its destructive work until there are no high places and no irregularities left—until the entire land available to its attacks is reduced to a featureless plain, sloping only sufficiently to allow water to flow to the ocean. This final stage is called the *peneplain* stage. No other outcome is conceivable given the present forces and sufficient time.

While the reasoning has been carried out in a summary fashion for the entire valley, the same reasoning can be applied in detail to every part of the valley. At any given place it is necessary, of course, to measure the slopes, the amount of water flowing, the amount and kind of load, the kind and hardness of rock now exposed, and to examine the shape and form of the present landscape. Moreover, it is necessary to make some estimate of the form of the landscape immediately preceding the present form, from the indications now present in the region. At every place we find a correspondence between the characteristic landform now observed and the forces at work. Where the slope is steep, erosion is primarily downward, resulting in a V-shaped valley. Where the slopes are gentler, erosion is primarily sideward, resulting in a U-shaped valley with a wider bottom. Where the gradient of the bed decreases abruptly, deposition of sediment takes place. Where the velocity of the streams drops suddenly, unsorted gravel is deposited; where an already slow stream is further slowed down, finer sediments accumulate. Thus it is possible to explain in terms of the present forces, not only the formation of the valley as a whole, but to account for the smaller valleys of the tributaries, and for every ravine and every hill and gravel deposit in the entire region.

Reconstructing the History of the Valley

A most natural question arises at this point. How long did it take the Colorado to excavate its present valley? We already have the data to make a rough estimate. The Colorado is now reducing the landscape at the rate of about 1 inch in 1500 years. If the rate in the past was comparable to the present rate, the estimate is around 7 million years. The rate, of course, may not have always been the same and in fact it probably has varied considerably in the past. We may improve the estimate by analyzing in detail the rates at the various parts of the region, and by making proper allowances for changes in slope, in hardness of the rock, in the size of the river, and the like. To be on the safe side we may take the most conservative estimates in each case. But no matter how conservative we may try to be the estimates obtained remain in millions of years. Thus, we take a leap of several million years into the distant past. In this long interval of time a great many events have taken place, and the landscape must have looked quite different from what it appears today.

Is it possible to reconstruct the history of the region by identifying the events and arranging them in time sequence? To be sure many of the events have taken place long ago, and any record they may have produced has long since been eroded away. A surprising amount of evidence, however, is still present to permit the reconstruction of the history of the region. As already indicated, the present features can be explained in terms of the forces acting on the landscape immediately preceding the present. Having reconstructed the previous landscape, we may proceed to earlier and earlier events and to older and older appearances of the landscape. A few examples will illustrate the method and the reasoning.

An examination of the present Colorado valley provides the evidence that some events have taken place before others. In fact the events can be arranged in a time sequence. Some events are taking place today, while others occurred long ago. To be specific, the river as a whole is not of the same age throughout its length. At the mouth, where the delta is now depositing, the channel is young—it is being formed today. Obviously, the channel in the delta a little further upstream must have been formed in the past, and the further from the present mouth, the older the channel. The same reasoning holds true for the deposits. Further upstream the deposits in the delta are older than those nearer the mouth. Moreover, in the case of the deposits another age relation is obvious: at any given point the deposits at great depth are surely older than those near the surface. Thus, on moving upstream from the mouth, or on digging into deeper deposits at any given point, we are looking directly into the past.

At the head of the river also we find events and landforms of different ages, arranged in time sequence. The ravines, the gullies, the brooks, and the minor tributaries are recent features. A ravine may have formed last summer; a brook at an earlier time. For a brook was previously a ravine, and conversely a ravine will become a brook, and later a fair-sized tributary. Rather characteristically these young features are V-shaped, showing that erosion is predominantly down cutting. Further downstream, the valleys are older—the streams have been at work for a longer time. Thus, on traveling downstream toward the main valley we are again looking into the past. It may not be easy to tell the ages of these features in terms of years, but there is no question about their relative ages.

In the gorge itself, another time sequence is evident, almost too obvious to mention. At the site of the National Park a series of sedimentary rocks are exposed on the canyon wall. Each of these rocks is recognizable from its appearance, thickness, and other characteristics. On the rim of the canyon opposite the Park the same rocks are found and in the same sequence. There can be no doubt that the same series of rocks once extended across the gap of the canyon. There must have been a time, therefore, at which the Colorado was at the same level as the plateau. The cutting of the upper sediments is an event of long ago, and the Colorado must have occupied channels at successive levels in later times before excavating down to the present channel.

Considering these facts alone, it is possible to give a most sketchy sequence of events and delve into the distant past. There must have been a time when the mouth of the river was at the beginning of the oldest part of the delta, and the ocean extended hundreds of miles further inland from the present shore. The Colorado probably started at that time as a small stream, growing headward in the direction of the plateau. As time went on, it began to cut into the hard rocks of the plateau, beginning its canyon. As it cut deeper it developed tributaries, and these together with the main stream grew headwards, encroaching on the land area of the state of Arizona and the surrounding states. At the same time, the sediments removed from upstream were deposited to form the delta, and the river lengthened at the mouth as well. In a sequence of such events the present valley was formed. A great many details can be added and a comprehensive history of the region can be reconstructed. We can even get a glimpse of the ancient landscape before the canyon was cut. Thus, in this region we visualize a continuously evolving landscape, with features developed, only to be obliterated later. The present terrain is but a transitory phase of this evolving landscape.

World-wide Erosion and Deposition

Having established these conclusions in the Colorado valley, we may proceed to collect data and apply the same reasoning to other drainage systems. The same relations between forces and present landforms are found in the valleys of the Rio Grand, the Columbia, the Mississippi, the Hudson, and the other rivers of the American continent. In fact, the same processes are going on in all the drainage systems of all the continents. Thus, we are led to the conclusion that all the rivers of the world constitute a powerful team, conspiring to destroy the land and reduce it to sea level.

While the streams have been identified as the major agents in this conspiracy, there are other agents cooperating with them. Wind, glacial ice, ground water, and ocean waves all do their share in this destructive work. Each of these agents carves into the landscape features characteristic of its action. Each of these agents deposits landforms also characteristic of its action. Let us examine briefly the action of these agents.

The Wind. Winds blow constantly over the rock surface of the earth, at times attaining speeds of over 100 miles an hour. Depending on the velocity, winds carry a suspension of dust particles up to 0.1 mm in diameter and transport it over hundreds of miles in some instances. In a single dust storm whole states may be covered with a blanket of dust. Under the proper conditions of continued action, beds of sediments known as *loess* may be deposited hundreds of feet in thickness. A good example are the loess beds in China. The heavier particles, usually sand particles, are rolled over the surface and deposited in ridges known as sand dunes. Good examples are the sand dunes of northern Indiana, and, of course, the more extensive sand deposits in the Sahara. In arid regions, the continuous sand blasting over hard rocks produces characteristic forms such as pinacles and wind-blown caves.

Glacial Ice. Far slower than the movement of the wind or even water is the movement of ice. In the mountainous regions, where the

Fig. 15-12. Wind erosion. Note characteristic erosional and depositional features. Cave rocks near Sierra La Sal, Dry Valley, Utah. *(U. S. Geological Survey.)*

snowfall during the colder months is greater than its melting during the summer, permanent snow fields accumulate. On standing, the fluffy snowflakes become crystals of coarse ice, which under pressure fuse together into a single ice mass. Under their own weight these masses of ice descend down the valleys as gigantic tongues. During their slow and complicated movement, involving cracking, thawing, and refreezing, they engulf any loose material that may have been at the surface, and pluck it away from the rock. With pebbles and rocks as tools, the glaciers powerfully scour the bed rock itself, flattening the tools, and producing polished surfaces on the bed rock and parallel streaks in the direction of their motion. Centuries of this action change the shape of the valley into a characteristically U-shaped valley, with an amphitheaterlike head called a *cirque*. These landforms become particularly evident if the ice later disappears due to a general warming of the region.

When the glacier reaches the lower levels where the temperatures are higher, the ice melts and produces a number of characteristic depositional features. As the ice melts it drops its load unsorted. The deposit is known as *glacial till* and consists of a grand mixture ranging from fine rock powder to huge boulders. Many of the rocks and pebbles are flattened and show scratches and striations as evidence of the treatment they have received. If the ice melts at the same rate as it advances, huge mounds of material pile up in one place. This feature is called *terminal moraine*. In general, however, the ice melts either faster or slower than it advances and deposits its load over a wider area in char-

Fig. 15-13. Tongues of ice descending down mountain valleys. Worthington Glacier, Richardson Highway, Copper River, Bremer District, Alaska. *(U. S. Geological Survey.)*

acteristic gentle hills and valleys, known as *ground moraine*. Some of the depressions may be filled with water, resulting in glacial lakes.

Continential Glaciation. On realizing how characteristic the erosional and depositional features of glacial action are, a new idea emerged. Early last century the geologists were deeply puzzled when they found great heaps of boulders, mud, and gravel all mixed indiscriminately in the areas just north and south of the Alps. These deposits could not have been formed by running water, for water sorts its deposits. Nor could they have been deposited by the wind, for while the wind may under certain conditions deposit unsorted material, it could not carry the larger particles. Yet there was no other agent now evident in the region that could have deposited them.

Around 1840, Louis Agassiz, who had studied in detail the glaciers of the Alps, demonstrated that the deposits at some distance from the present glaciers were identical in all essential respects with those being deposited by glaciers at their edges today. He concluded that the glaciers extended further down in the past. He traced the glacial deposits and striations in bed rock further and further from the Alps into northern Germany and eventually over most of Europe. Considering the fact that these deposits are found over the tops of hills and mountains, he had

Fig. 15-14. Glacial striations in Clinton, Massachusetts. Evidence that this region was once covered by a sheet of ice. Direction of scratches shows movement of ice. *(U. S. Geological Survey.)*

no alternative but to conclude that the whole of Europe was once covered with an ocean of ice a mile or more thick. When he later became professor at Harvard, he found the same evidence in this country. So sure was he of his criteria, that he unhesitatingly explained the unsorted debris over most of North America as due to a continental ice sheet more than a mile thick. Detailed study confirmed his conclusions. At least four separate advances of the ice have been deciphered with intervening mild climates. Some of the most prominent features in North America—the unsorted deposits, the moraine topography, the Great

Fig. 15-15. Luray Caverns in Virginia. Stalactites hang from the ceiling and stalagmites have been built up from the floor.

Lake system, Niagara Falls, the numerous lakes in Minnesota, Wisconsin, and Michigan—can be explained in no other way (Ex. 8).

Ground Water. The action of ground water is less conspicuous but no less effective. Water is found nearly everywhere under the ground. It slowly dissolves rocks, and reacts chemically with some of them, disintegrating them and carrying away the soluble minerals. Under other conditions some of these minerals are deposited between the particles of sediments and form the cement that binds them together. In mountain regions ground water loosens the hillsides, causing landslides. It is particularly effective in eroding limestone. Limestone is calcium carbonate that is slightly soluble in waters containing carbon dioxide. As the ground water percolates through the limestone beds it dissolves away sizable caves. Within the caves some of the dissolved limestone redeposits in pillars known as stalactites and stalagmites and in other more grotesque forms. The Luray Caverns in Virginia provide good examples. As a matter of fact the surrounding area, as well as a good deal of the state of Kentucky, is hollow underground. In many places the caverns collapse and form depressions in the ground known as *sinkholes* (Ex. 9).

Shore Agents. Next to streams the most powerful agents of erosion are the waves of the ocean. Anyone who has watched waves smash against the shore during a storm must have been impressed by the power of the ocean to eat away the land. The primary cause of the waves is, of course, the wind, but their action is that of running water. Waves originate everywhere in the ocean and travel in all directions and ultimately toward the shore, either squarely on or at some angle. They vary in wavelength from a few yards to over a hundred feet. In deep waters, as we have already seen in Chapter 5 (p. 122f.), the parcel of disturbed water at any one point travels in nearly circular paths, as the waves pass. The amplitude of the motion is greatest at the surface and decreases rapidly with depth. At a depth of about half a wavelength, the motion becomes negligible so that in deep waters the bottom of the ocean is not disturbed (Fig. 15-16).

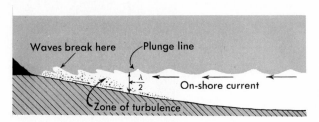

Fig. 15-16. Wave action at the shore.

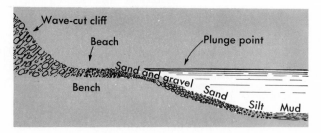

Fig. 15-17. Idealized distribution of material deposited on a shore line.

However, along the shallow shelves waves behave differently and active erosion takes place. As the waves approach a sloping coastline their type of motion changes and the waves *break* or *plunge* against the shore. This breaking takes place at the so-called *plunge line,* which is at a depth of about half a wavelength. At the plunge line, the upper part of the wave is freer to move forward, while the lower part of the wave is retarded by the friction of the shelf. As a result the water in the crests, in the upper part of the wave, piles up in front of the troughs and ultimately plunges and surges toward the shore in a violent motion, carrying with it whatever debris may be present, until the energy is spent in rising uphill or in pounding against cliffs. The returning water carries back the debris toward the ocean. The net result of this sea-saw action is to scour and erode the coast line and to carry the material and deposit it at various distances from the strand line. The coarse material is deposited in the belt between the strand line and the plunge line; the fine sand further seaward; the very fine suspension much further out (Fig. 15-17).

As a result of this action a number of typical erosional and depositional landforms develop, depending on the initial type of the coast line. If the coast line is relatively steep, cliffs develop, as well as wave-cut terraces. If the coastline is gentle, large amounts of material are removed far into the sea. If the coastline is indented, the erosion takes place faster at the promontories and slower at the bays. The result is the straightening of the coastline. In all cases, however, the sea encroaches upon the land, removing the material seaward and depositing it over a large area, which increases as more land is reduced. Given sufficient time, the waves have the competence to erode all land available to their attack, which means entire continents, to a level below the plunge line.

Summary

Contemplating the panorama of this ceaseless activity, we visualize the landscape altering continuously as the result of the relentless action of the geologic agents. Landforms are produced and destroyed. At any given time and place it is possible to explain both the erosional and depositional landforms in terms of the characteristic action of these agents. Most of these features, however, are transitory. Ultimately all the land will be worn down to a peneplain by the streams and below sea level by the waves. The only conceivable outcome is the destruction of all the land masses now exposed and the deposition of the materials in the ocean.

A number of questions arise. If these agents have been at work for a long time, why is there any land left? Is the earth so young that there has not been enough time since the "beginning"? And what was the beginning like? In the Colorado Valley we traced the "beginning" to a time when the Colorado just started to erode the Arizona plateau and to excavate the Grand Canyon some 7 million years ago. Was that the ultimate Beginning? Or was there something before that?

A clue to a possible answer comes from examining other valleys. They are now in various stages of erosion. Moreover, any estimate in terms of years reveals that they have not begun at the same time. Is there perhaps another answer? Is it possible that forces other than the gradational agents are working in the opposite direction? Are there any forces which regenerated the land in the past, and are these forces at work now, rejuvenating the land under our very eyes? We shall consider these questions in the next section.

3. THE UNSTABLE CRUST OF THE EARTH

Study of the erosional and depositional processes now going on permits us to explain the present features of the landscape as the result of the action of the geologic agents. Having understood the present, it is possible to move in both directions of time—into the past and into the future. In the immediate future we may expect gradual changes and predict the configuration of the land as time goes on. Similarly from the present configuration and the record now evident in any given region it is possible to reconstruct the appearance of the region in the immediate past and proceed to earlier and earlier configurations.

Assuming that the gradational processes are the only processes in operation, we may attempt to extrapolate to the ultimate future as well as to retrace the history to an ultimate beginning. Since the overall action of the gradational agents is unidirectional, there can be no other ultimate outcome but the complete leveling of the continents and their submergence under a universal ocean. Similarly, the ultimate beginning must have been at a time before the gradational agents had begun their destructive work. By tracing back the history of a region it should be possible to reconstruct the configuration of an "original" landscape, when the land stood highest. In the Colorado Valley the processes now observed can be traced to the time when the river had invaded the Arizona plateau, and began to cut its canyon some 7 million years ago. By similar reasoning the other drainage systems can be traced to the beginning of the erosional processes now going on. Thus, it appears possible to reconstruct the "original" landscape of all the continents and decipher the entire history of the earth on the assumption that the gradational agents are the only forces at work.

However, so sweeping an assumption is not justified. In fact, abundant evidence in the rocks indicates that the gradational processes have been interrupted many times during the long past, and probably will be interrupted again in the future. The first hint of the presence of forces working in opposite directions of the gradational agents comes from the comparison of the Colorado Valley with other regions. The drainage systems of the world are now in different stages of erosion. In some regions the leveling process is nearly complete and must have been going on for a long time. By comparison the Colorado Valley is quite young. In it erosion is mainly downcutting, and a great deal of work remains to be done. In other regions erosion has just begun, and therefore these regions are even more recent than the Grand Canyon. Any estimate in terms of years confirms the conclusions that the present erosion has begun at different times in different regions. Therefore it is not possible to extrapolate to the same time and reconstruct an "original" landscape of the entire earth. These considerations imply that there have been other forces operating that tended to elevate the land in the various regions.

On reexamining the Colorado Valley, we find convincing evidence of an upheaval. If we had been inclined to consider the Arizona plateau as part of the "original" landscape, we are soon forced to abandon the assumption. The upper surface of the plateau consists of sedimentary rocks. In the previous study of sedimentation, we have learned to recognize the characteristics of deposits. The rocks in the uppermost surface of the plateau have all the characteristics of rocks that were deposited under sea water. In no essential way do they differ from the beds now deposited in the quiet waters of the ocean at some distance from the shore. To be sure the sediments have been consolidated over the long interval of time, perhaps by pressure and the cementing action of deposited minerals. It is apparent, therefore, that at some time previous to the present erosion, the ocean extended over the rocks now standing more than a mile and a half above sea level. Either the ocean has withdrawn from the land or else the land was elevated above the ocean level. In any case there is no question that the relative level of the sea and the land have altered since the deposition of the upper strata in the plateau.

Far reaching though this conclusion may be, it is merely the beginning of new insights. Examination of the other strata now exposed in the canyon wall reveals that many other beds were deposited under sea water. Throughout the thickness of more than a mile of sediments we find several other beds that have been deposited under sea water. Moreover, from the texture and type of deposits we conclude that some were deposited near the shore, while others were in deeper waters. Coarse gravel and sands with crossbedding must have been deposited near the surface; limestones further from the shore. Apparently the coastline has encroached upon the land and receded at different times during the deposition.

Most significant of all is the fact that the beds in the column of the wall alternate between terrestrial and marine deposits. Near the bottom of the canyon wall the sediments are marine deposits. Above them the deposits are terrestrial; above these other marine deposits; and above these again terrestrial. This alternation can only mean that the region was elevated and submerged, not once, but several times in the past.

Examination of other canyon walls in other regions of this continent as well as in other continents brings out ample evidence that this situation is general over the entire globe. Again and again we find sedimentary rocks of marine origin now exposed high on land. Repeatedly we find marine deposits over terrestrial deposits and over these marine deposits again. There can be no question that the relative levels of the ocean and the continents have fluctuated many times during the geologic past. Also significant is the fact that in mountainous regions sedimentary rocks are found at the highest peaks. The rocks now making up the mountains, therefore, must have been elevated since the time when they were deposited under the sea. These far-reaching conclusions open new vistas for investigation and imply a history of the earth much longer than might have appeared from the study of the present erosional processes alone.

Recent Fluctuations of Land and Sea

While the evidence already cited is sufficient to establish the fact of crustal unrest, additional evidence from more recent events supports the conclusions even more directly. Along many of the present shores there is abundant evidence that the coasts have been elevated or depressed recently. For example in the coast of California we find a wave-cut terrace high above the present level of the Pacific. The erosion has not proceeded far enough to change the appearance, and the feature can be identified without question as a beach cut by waves similar to the one now being cut at the present sea level. Moreover, the terrace can be traced for some 300 miles. North of San Francisco it is over 300 feet above the present level of the Pacific. Southwards it dips gently, descending to sea level near Santa Barbara, and continuing below sea level for some distance. This tilting is in itself significant. By no stretch of the imagination can we visualize the surface of the Pacific Ocean tilted in this way. We can only conclude that the coastal land has been elevated and tilted to its present attitude.

On the other hand, in the Eastern seaboard we find evidence of recent submergence. A good example is the valley of the Hudson River. At its mouth in New York City, the walls of the river are the steep pillars of rock, well known as the Palisades. The bed of the river has been cut into hard rock to a considerable depth below the present sea level. The river could not have cut that deep at its present sluggish activity. It must have cut it at a time that the gradient was much greater. The river bed can be traced for about 50 miles into the Atlantic. There can be no question that the valley of the Hudson has been drowned so recently that subsequent erosion has not yet had time to alter its characteristic form.

Evidence of recent emergence or submergence is found in many regions throughout the world. Along the coast of Sweden, for example, reefs, which must have been under the surface until recently, now project above the sea. Most interesting is the rise of the coast of Norway in historic times. In some places the receding ocean has left small patches of coastal farmlands that were under the waves in medieval times. On

Fig. 15-18. Elevated coastline on the California coast. The level of the Pacific was 300 feet higher in the not too distant past on coast north of Harford. *(U. S. Geological Survey.)*

Fig. 15-19. The submerged coastline north of Portland, Maine, is evidence of recent sinking of parts of the Eastern seaboard. *(U. S. Geological Survey.)*

Fig. 15-20. Mountains consist largely of up-turned sediments, frequently of marine origin. Near view of hogback in Small Gap, 2 miles southwest of Canon City, Colorado—Morrison to left; Niobrara ridge to extreme right. (U. S. Geological Survey.)

the other side of the Atlantic, the opposite situation is found. The coast of Greenland is sinking. Old buildings and other structures formerly above high tide are now washed by the waves.

The most celebrated example of historically documented earth movements is the Temple of Jupiter Serapis, near Naples, Italy. When the Romans constructed the Temple, around 100 B.C., they obviously built it on land, overlooking the Mediterranean. During the Middle Ages the temple had disappeared below the level of the sea. In modern times it rose again. As late as the eighteenth century it was necessary to remove the marine sediments in which the pillars, still upright, were enmeshed. Even now the borings of marine mullucks can be seen high near the top of the columns. The temple is now entirely on dry land and the region appears to be still rising.

There is ample evidence that earth movements of the solid crust, known as *diastrophic* movements, are going on at present. Accurate measurements show that the coast of California is still continuing to rise, and that the Hudson Valley is at present submerging. If these movements continue, we shall have more of California and less of New York in the foreseeable future. Similarly, the British Isles are sinking rather rapidly and if the present rate continues in 40,000 years the waves will rule Britannia rather than the historical converse.

Evidence of diastrophic movements is not confined to the edges of the continents although it is most easily detected there by comparison to sea level. Far inland and everywhere on the continents there is abundant evidence of recent movement of the solid part of the earth. In the Great Lakes region, for example, we find old shore lines marking the lake levels during the Ice Age. These are now high above the present level of the Great Lakes, but more significantly they rise toward the north. Since the water surface is always level the rise and the tilting of the recent shore line can only mean that the northern part of the continent has been rising relative to the southern part. The cause is perhaps due to the relief of pressure after the melting of the overload of ice. But whatever the cause, there is no question that the tilting has been taking place.

Further evidence is found in the rocks of all ages. It has already been mentioned that the mountains consist predominantly of sediments, which are always deposited in horizontal or almost horizontal position. The sedimental beds are now found warped, contorted, and tilted, sometimes rising vertically. Almost everywhere that sediments are found, they are warped, tilted, bent, folded, contorted, and often broken and displaced from their normal position. This combined evidence led to the inevitable conclusion that terra firma, far from being stable, has been and is now in a state of slow, but continuous movement.

Earthquakes and the Earth's Interior

That the lithosphere is even now undergoing movements is evidenced most directly by the occurrence of earthquakes. Long and extensive studies have revealed that the great majority of earthquakes are caused by sudden slipping of rocks. Normally rocks are strong and brittle, capable of withstanding considerable stresses before yielding. However, continuous accumulation of forces over long periods of time results in strains beyond the strength of the rocks. At the moment the strength of the rock is exceeded, the strains are relieved by the breaking of the rock in a sudden and powerful movement. The resulting movement may be only a fraction of an inch or a few inches, although displacements of scores of feet have been observed. Repeated movements in a given region result in displacements of hundreds of feet. These displacements are called *faults,* and are common in rocks of all the ages.

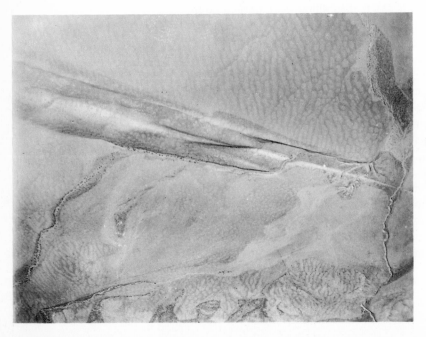

Fig. 15-21. Aerial view of San Andreas fault in the California coast. The largest displacement is due to recent earthquakes beginning with the San Francisco earthquake of 1906. Note the displacement of the stream near its mouth *(right center).* *(U. S. Geological Survey.)*

Fig. 15-22. *(right)* A seismograph designed to record the vertical vibrations. The weight is a long period pendulum and essentially motionless. The drum is firmly attached to bedrock and vibrates up and down with the bedrock.

Fig. 15-23. *(below)* A typical record of an earthquake. The primary waves arrive first and hence are the fastest; the secondary next and the destructive long waves last. The time lag in arrival increases with distance from the source.

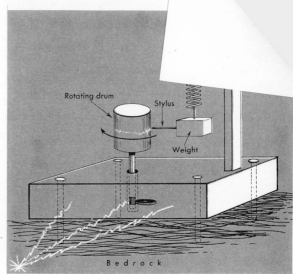

Rotating drum   Stylus

Weight

Bedrock

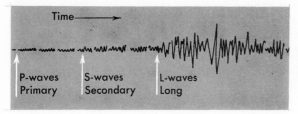

Time ───────>

P-waves   S-waves   L-waves
Primary   Secondary   Long

The earthquake phenomena not only provide direct evidence that the earth movements are now in progress, but in a sense explain the uplifts and other displacements observed in the rocks as due to accumulated stresses within the body of the earth. More significantly, a detailed study of earthquakes and the waves associated with them gives information on the interior of the earth and suggests possible origins of the forces that cause the movements.

Most earthquakes originate near the surface or within a few miles from the surface. Their destructive effects are the result of earth tremors generated during the slipping of the rocks. Although, as already mentioned, the displacements are small, the total energy released in a major earthquake is enormous. The sudden release of the strain generates vibrations in the rocks that travel within the body of the lithosphere and in the deep interior. On reaching the surface they set buildings and other structures into violent vibrations causing damage and at times wholesale destruction.

The earth tremors are recorded by instruments called *seismographs*. There are two essential parts to the instrument. One is a freely suspended heavy mass carrying a writing stylus; the other is a strip of paper on a drum of a clockwork that is firmly attached to bed rock. When the bed rock vibrates, the clockwork with the paper vibrates with it. On the other hand the heavy mass, because of its inertia and free suspension remains stationary for a long time before any motion is communicated to it. The relative motion of the stylus and paper produces a record of the tremors as a wavy line. The clockwork, of course, records the time of the arrival of the disturbance.

A great deal of information is obtained by the analysis of the record. The vibrations initiated at the site of the earthquake travel through the lithosphere and arrive at the instrument where they are recorded as a sequence of three sets of wavy lines. The first sign of the disturbance is a series of waves of small height or amplitude. Since these are the first waves to arrive they are called *primary* waves. After some time, depending on the distance of the station from the center of the earthquake, a second set of vibrations of somewhat greater amplitude arrive. These are called *secondary* waves. Some time later, a third set of waves arrive. These have the greatest amplitude by far. Sometimes the stylus goes clear off the paper. These are called *long* waves, for they have been found to have the longest wavelength.

The interpretation of the earthquake record is fairly straightforward in terms of the principles of waves studied in Chapter 5. The rocks in which the waves originate and through which they travel behave like elastic solids. Any elastic solid can vibrate in two distinct ways. In one type of vibration the particles or molecules of the solid execute a back-and-forth movement in the direction of the propagation of the disturbance. These types of waves are called *longitudinal* and are similar to sound waves in air or in water, and, in fact, they are identical with the sound waves in solids. Their speeds depend on the density and the elastic properties of the medium, which in turn depends to some extent on the pressure on the medium. In rocks near the surface of the earth the waves travel about 6 miles per second, which is quite comparable to the speed of sound in steel. In water they travel about 1 mile per second.

A rigid solid, however, can also vibrate in another way. The particles of the solid can vibrate at right angles to the movement of the disturbance. This type of motion is exemplified by vibration of a violin string in which each small segment of the wire vibrates at right angles to the length of the string. Similarly, in a solid the particles move up and down at right angles to the motion of the wave. The reason for this type of motion in a rigid solid is the fact that the particles of the solid are held with attractive forces by the neighboring particles in an equilibrium position. As they move away from their neighboring particles they are pulled back by the restoring forces; but overpassing the equilibrium point they are now pulled in the opposite direction. As a result the particles continue to vibrate. These types of vibrations are called *transverse* vibrations. It is obvious that transverse vibrations can only occur

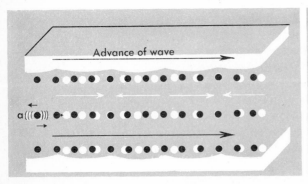
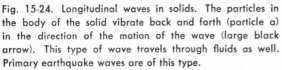

Fig. 15-24. Longitudinal waves in solids. The particles in the body of the solid vibrate back and forth (particle a) in the direction of the motion of the wave (large black arrow). This type of wave travels through fluids as well. Primary earthquake waves are of this type.

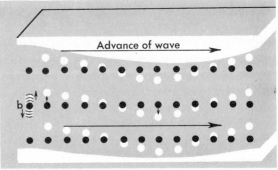

Fig. 15-25. Transverse waves in solids. The particles in the body of the solids vibrate up and down (particle b) at right angles to the motion of the wave (large black arrow). This type of wave cannot travel through fluids. Secondary earthquake waves are of this type.

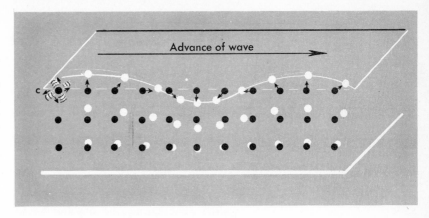

Fig. 15-26. Surface waves in solids. The particles at the surface (particle c) execute a circular motion. The disturbance dies down at depth. The long earthquake waves are of this type. Their destructiveness is due to their great amplitude.

in rigid solids; for only in solids are there restoring forces tending to pull the particles to their equilibrium positions. In fluids the displaced particles simply do not come back and the disturbance dies down. The speed of transverse waves also depends on the density of the medium and the magnitude of the restoring forces—that is, on the rigidity of the solid. In rocks near the surface of the earth they travel about 4 miles per second. They do not travel through the ocean, of course, but they do travel through the rocks at the bottom of the ocean. Since they are slower than the primary waves, they arrive at the station later and are called *secondary* earthquake waves.

In addition to these two types of waves, a third type can be generated on the *free surface* of a solid. Surface waves are in a sense a combination of longitudinal and transverse waves. Since the particles at or near the surface are attracted by forces from inside but not from outside the solid, they move freely over wide distances in circular or elliptical paths. The waves generated are similar to surface waves in water. The speeds of the waves as well as their wavelengths depend on the density of the medium and on the magnitude of the restoring forces. On surface rocks they have long wavelengths and travel with a speed of about 2 miles per second. Consequently they arrive at the station last. Incidentally the great amplitude of long waves explains their destructive effects.

The reader has probably surmised already how it is possible to measure the distance of the site of an earthquake from the station by analyzing the seismograph record. If, for example, the earthquake occurs 600 miles from the station, the primary waves, traveling at 6 miles per second, will arrive at the station 100 seconds later. The secondary waves on the other hand, traveling only 4 miles per second, will arrive 150 seconds later. Consequently a lag of 50 seconds between the primary and the secondary waves means that the earthquake took place 600 miles away. Similarly, a lag of 150 seconds means that the earthquake took place somewhere 1800 miles away. These estimates can be checked by measuring the lag between the secondary and the long waves and between the primary and the long waves, and thus a more reliable and more accurate distance may be obtained (Ex. 14).

The record from a single station gives only the distance from the

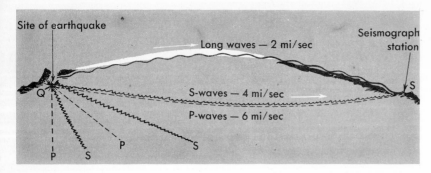

Fig. 15-27. Paths of earthquake waves from source to station. Long waves travel along the outer rock surface. Primary and secondary waves travel through the interior. Distance of the earthquake site to the station is measured by the time lag in arrival of the three types of waves.

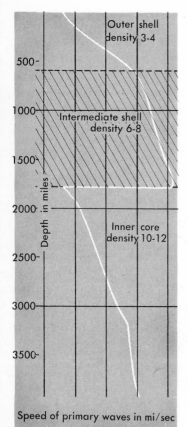

Fig. 15-28. Speed of primary waves at various depths. The discontinuities at 600 miles and 1800 miles are due to abrupt change in the type of materials and are indicative of their density and probable composition.

source. The earthquake site may be anywhere in a circle, at the determined distance from the station. However, the exact site can be located if records from three widely separated stations are compared. All that is necessary is to draw on a globe three circles, one from each station, with the appropriate distances as radii and locate the common intersection of the three circles.

Of far greater interest is the information that can be obtained about the interior and structure of the earth. This is obtained by more detailed analysis of seismograph records and their comparison with records from other stations throughout the earth. Some very general conclusions can be drawn at once. The long waves have approximately the same speed over the entire surface of the earth, indicating that the outer mantle consists of the same general type of material all over the earth. More accurate comparisons reveal that the long waves travel somewhat faster over the ocean floors than over the continents. This implies that the ocean floors consist of denser material than the continental surface. The continental surfaces consist of a veneer of sedimentary rocks, of varying thicknesses overlying a basement complex consisting of granites. The density of granites is about 2.7 grams per cubic centimeter. On the other hand, all samples of the ocean floor are basalt, which has a density of about 3.1 grams per cubic centimeter. Since seismic waves travel faster in denser material the speed is greater over the ocean floors. Conversely, by comprehensive analysis of speeds over the various parts of the globe, the general composition of the rocks over the surface of the oceans and the continents can be deduced. The ocean floors are uniformly denser than the continental surfaces. This difference in density has a bearing on the crustal unrest, as we shall see presently.

Analysis of the records of the primary and secondary waves permits us to penetrate deeper into the interior of the earth. As seen in the diagram, these waves come in a direct path from the source to the station. Owing to the curvature of the earth, the waves must travel through deeper and deeper rocks, the further the station is located from the earthquake. As expected, the average speed of these waves becomes greater when calculated for the direct distance from the source. The reason is that in part of their path they travel through deeper rocks that are under greater pressure and are also denser.

Considering the primary waves first we can follow the change in speed with deeper penetration and obtain a fair idea of the increase in density and rigidity of the rocks with depth. As already mentioned a speed of about 6 miles per second is a fair average for moderate depths. Actually, the speed is about 5 miles per second at the very surface and increases rather regularly to about $7\frac{1}{2}$ miles per second at a depth of about 600 miles. At this depth, however, an abrupt change is observed. The speed remains fairly constant, increasing only slightly below this depth. Apparently, the material is now different or at least it has markedly different density and different elastic properties. For the next 1200 miles the speed continues to increase slowly to about 8 miles per second, and then at the depth of 1800 miles from the surface, quite unexpectedly, it drops sharply to 5 miles per second. From there on the speed continues to increase moderately to the very center of the earth, attaining a speed of $6\frac{1}{2}$ miles per second. The abrupt changes of the speed at various depths reveals that the earth consists of at least three concentric shells of markedly different material—the outer zone, the intermediate zone, and the inner core (Fig. 15-29).

Even more revealing is the behavior of the secondary waves. These waves, too, increase in speed with depth down to 600 miles, and at this point again they show a marked discontinuity. They travel freely through the intermediate zone with increasing speed at greater depths. However, at the interface of the inner core, 1800 miles from the surface, something unexpected happens. The waves do not go through the inner core at all. If the station is more than 120 degrees from the earthquake, the secondary waves are not recorded at all.

The reader will remember that the secondary waves are transverse and can be transmitted only by a rigid solid. The fact that the secondary waves go through the two outer zones is convincing evidence that down to 1800 miles (almost the outer seven eighths) the earth is solid, having

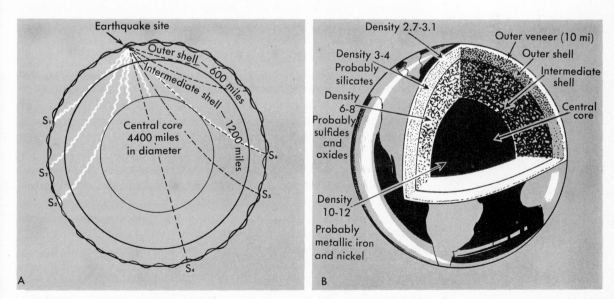

Fig. 15-29. Structure of the earth's interior. A *(left)* Analysis of the records from several stations S_1 through S_6 reveal the nature of the materials through which the waves travel. The outer seven-eighths portion behaves as an elastic solid; the central core has the properties of a fluid, since secondary waves do not go through it, and are not recorded in stations between S_3 and S_5. **B** *(right)* Model of the most probable structure, consistent with the data.

the rigidity of steel. By the same argument the inner core of the earth has the properties of a fluid—at least it is *not* an elastic solid (Ex. 13).

By a more detailed study of the changes in speed of the primary and secondary waves, it is possible to locate fairly accurately the boundaries of the three layers. In fact by more accurate analysis of the changes in speed several minor discontinuities can be located in each of the three layers, without much uncertainty. However, we can venture further than this and obtain a fair idea of the composition of the various layers by combining all the pertinent evidence. The speeds indicate the rigidity and the density of the layers. Independently, the pressure at any depth can be estimated from the weight of the overlaying layers. Moreover, the earth as a whole is 5.5 times denser than water, whereas the surface rocks on the continents are barely 2.7 times, and those on the ocean floor about 3.1 times denser than water. Taking into proper account these and other factors, such as the most probable composition of the earth as a whole, the behavior of minerals at high pressure, and the like, it is possible to make some enlightened guesses on the composition of the various layers of the earth.

The outer layer appears to be stony down to 600 miles, probably consisting of silicates of the same general nature as those at the surface. The surface rocks are granite over the continents and basalt over the oceans. However, below a certain depth, of the order of 30 to 50 miles, probably all are basaltic. Interestingly enough, a slight discontinuity in the speed of the waves is observed at this depth. Under pressure the ordinary minerals becomes denser, but also denser minerals are formed. The middle layer is more difficult to decipher. However, its density and rigidity suggest that it might consist of sulfides and oxides of iron and nickel. The inner core is an even greater puzzle. The best guess at present is that it is metallic, perhaps a mixture of iron and nickel, with a density of about 11 times that of water. It is possible, of course, that it consists of other very dense minerals, stable under the high pressures and temperatures.

Thus, the study of earthquakes not only confirms that the lithosphere is dynamic at present and explains the observed deformation of ancient rocks, but unexpectedly gives us at least a sketchy picture of the anatomy of the earth. This in turn may suggest the ultimate causes that are responsible for the crustal unrest.

Volcanic Activity

The conclusion that the main body of the earth is a rigid solid was rather unexpected for several reasons. For a long time it had been taken for granted that the earth was once molten and that it gradually cooled to its present state. According to this view only an outer skin has solidified so far, and to this day the outer layer is called the "crust." The interior was supposed to be liquid still in the process of slow cooling.

Several lines of evidence seemed to support this view. In deep wells and mines everywhere on the earth the temperature is higher than at the surface. It rises at the rate of about $1°$ C for every hundred feet of depth or about $50°$ C per mile. To be sure, only a few thousand feet have been penetrated, but if this rate continues the temperature should be about $50,000°$ C at a depth of 1000 miles, and over $200,000°$ C

Fig. 15-30. Paricutin, an active volcano in Mexico. *(Ewing Galloway.)*

at the center of the earth. If these temperatures prevail in the interior, all the materials should be in the liquid state, irrespective of the pressures (Ex. 15).

A more direct suggestion for a molten interior is provided by the volcanic activity going on at the present time in widely scattered areas. In various parts of the globe, molten rock, together with steam and other gases, issues forth. The molten rock, called *magma,* has temperatures ranging from 750° C to 1000° C and seems to be coming from depths of several miles. In the active volcanoes, the outflowing material cools somewhat and piles up in characteristic cones whose steepness depends upon the fluidity of the *lava,* as the magma is called when it reaches the surface. The fluidity in turn depends on the temperature and the composition of the molten rock. Material high in silica content of the same general composition as granitic material is viscous, while basaltic material flows more easily. If gases are present in large quantities and the material is viscous, the eruption is explosive, as in the case of Vesuvius in Italy, or Paricutin in Mexico. On the other hand, if the gaseous material is small, the temperatures are high and the material is basaltic, a more quiet outwelling takes place. A good example of the latter type are the Hawaiian volcanoes, Kilauea and Mauna Loa. In all cases large amounts of molten rock spread over large areas, which later solidify into typical igneous rocks.

The present volcanic activity is limited to relatively few places, mostly in mountain regions bordering the oceans. Most of the active volcanoes are found in the mountain ranges surrounding the Pacific. They are strung in a row from the tip of South America to Alaska and thence to the eastern seaboard of the Asiatic continent and continue to Polynesia, forming a veritable "ring of fire" around the Pacific. Since the same regions are also sites of earthquake activity, the suggestion is strong that the two phenomena are related and may have the same ultimate causes.

Volcanic activity is not confined to the present by any means. Recently extinct volcanoes, some of which may be merely dormant, are found abundantly in the regions of present activity. Moreover, ancient volcanoes are found in places where no present activity is apparent. This is not all. The roots of all mountain ranges are large masses of granite extending for hundreds of miles and to indefinite depths. The large size of the crystals is convincing evidence that the granites have cooled and solidified slowly under the insulating blanket of overlying rocks.

Moreover, almost everywhere igneous rock structures are found intruded into the sediments. These structures cut through the sediments, either across the beds as *dikes,* or between the beds as *sills.* The structural relations and the baking adjacent to the intruded igneous structures leave no doubt that the molten material was forced through cracks in the sediments and solidified later. Most significant of all, igneous rocks ultimately underlie all sedimentary rocks. Volcanic activity, therefore, has been going on throughout the geologic past, at least since the beginning of sedimentation.

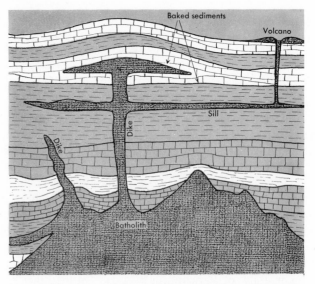

Fig. 15-31. Various types of igneous intrusions cutting into sedimentary rocks. The structural relationships and the baking at the zones of contact leave no doubt that the intruded rock was molten at the time of intrusion.

The extensive igneous activity throughout the ages, if taken at its face value, would suggest strongly that the earth has solidified from a molten state and is still molten under a thin crust. What is more natural than to suppose that the present volcanoes are cracks in the superficial rock through which molten rock emerges? What is more natural than to suppose that during the geologic past the crust was thinner and that volcanic activity was greater. This view also suggests that the mountain regions are weak zones in the crust, and that volcanic activity is responsible for pushing up the rocks causing earthquakes and the rise of mountains. Moreover, the fact that igneous rocks are found underneath all sediments suggests that the basement complex represents the "original" crust of the earth.

Unfortunately, such a simple picture can no longer be accepted. The evidence from earthquake waves is beyond dispute that the earth is solid to a depth of at least 1800 miles, which means almost the outer seven-eighth portion of the earth. Moreover, the rate of flow of the heat outward is so slow that the earth must have been solid for a long time. It becomes necessary, therefore, to reexamine the assumption of a molten interior and reinterpret the evidence that seems to support it.

The rise in temperature with depth has been measured only to 3 or 4 miles. There is no direct evidence that this rate continues to the center. To make a better estimate of internal temperatures it is necessary to consider the possible sources of the heat. The heat in the interior can only come from two sources. Either it represents the residue of the heat originally present in an incandescent state or it is being generated now by some process.

Since the discovery of radioactivity, we know that radioactive substances in the rocks at present do generate heat. A reasonable estimate of the amounts of radioactive substances suggests that they are sufficient to produce the heat now flowing outward from the interior. Consequently, it is not necessary to assume that the earth was incandescent at any time. Moreover, since the radioactive elements are chemically and physically similar to the materials found in the stony layer, they are probably found in this layer predominately. This suggests that the heat is generated mainly in the outer layer, and consequently the temperatures in the interior need not be very high. This line of reasoning leads to an estimate of about 20,000° C for the central core of the earth.

This more reasonable estimate of internal temperatures leads to an explanation of volcanic activity, without the assumption of a molten interior. Since the earth is solid, volcanic activity must be a local phenomenon. The explanation requires two distinct considerations. Assuming that the rise in temperature continues at about 50 degrees per mile to moderate depths, the temperature would be of the order of 1500° C to 2500° C at 30 to 50 miles below the surface. At these temperatures the rocks would be liquid if they were at the surface. However, at these depths the pressure of the overlying rocks, which increases by about 500 atmospheres per mile, would be sufficient to keep the rock solid.

In a local area, however, a high concentration of radioactive material may be present and the heat generated may be sufficient to melt the rock, even at the prevailing pressures. In that event, the rock melts and works its way upward, melting the rocks on the way and finally emerging through the superficial rocks and flowing out. This process would be aided if the rocks happen to be weak in that particular locality. The phenomena of volcanoes, therefore, do not necessarily imply a molten interior and indeed can *support* the idea of a solid interior.

Theories of Crustal Movement

Having established the fact that crustal movements have taken place extensively in the past and are even now going on as shown by the phenomena of earthquakes and volcanoes, we may attempt to reconstruct the course of these movements and even suggest possible causes of them. The former, the reconstruction of the sequence of events, can be done with considerable confidence from the abundant record in the rocks. It is only fair to state at the outset, however, that no satisfactory theory has so far been developed for the *causes* of crustal movement. Nevertheless, several theories have been proposed with considerable supporting evidence for some of them to merit a discussion (Ref. 15.9).

First let us bring together the relevant facts that have been established more or less firmly, indicating briefly the evidence upon which they are based. By far the greater part of the surface of the continents is covered with sedimentary rocks, indicating that at the time of sedimentation these parts of the continents were low in order to receive sediments from higher places. Many of the sediments are marine and were obviously deposited under the level of the ocean. The sediments vary in thickness, texture, and composition, and these characteristics are indicative of the conditions of sedimentation. In the present mountains, the sediments are several miles in thickness, while over the continents they are much thinner—a mile or less. The mountains, therefore, must have been the sites of extensive sedimentation and must have been adjacent to high places that served as the source of the sediments. On the other hand the present plains must have been far from the source. The continental beds are extensive and consist of fine muds and limestones. This type rock is deposited in shallow quiet seas today. Large areas of the continents must, therefore, have been submerged under shallow quiet seas.

Fig. 15-32. Profile of North America through central United States, with vertical scale exaggerated. A small rise in the level of the ocean would inundate coastal areas and a large part of the interior. By a small drop in sea level, large areas would emerge as land.

It may appear incredible at first that large areas of the continents have been under water in the past, but it is not so difficult to accept if the land-sea relations are examined more closely. The continents are not quite what the ordinary maps show. Figure 15-32 shows the present profile of North America and this is typical of the other continents. The continental mass projects above the ocean deep rather abruptly to a

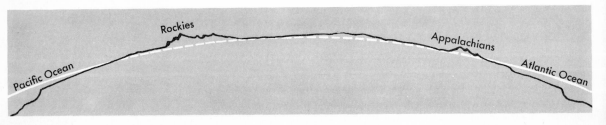

Fig. 15-33. Changes in the geography of North America by slight changes in sea level. A rise of 500 feet in sea level would result in the white area; a drop of 600 feet would result in a continent with the black outline.

height of several miles. Only the upper part of the continental mass appears above the present sea level. The ordinary maps, of course, show only the outline of the present shore. While the average height of the land is about ½ mile above sea level, large areas are only a few hundred feet in elevation. Consequently a slight rise of the ocean level relative to the land will inundate large areas of the continent. Similarly the continental mass extends beyond the present shores in practically all directions and large areas are now submerged under shallow epicontinental seas. A small drop in the ocean level would result in emergence of a large area above sea level. Therefore, small fluctuations in the level of the sea can cause considerable change in the geography (Fig. 15-33).

At the present time active sedimentation takes place in river deltas and along the ocean shores. The same general situation must have existed in the past. The greatest amounts of sediments accumulate in the river deltas. As we have already seen in the Colorado delta, the sediments sink progressively, forming beds many miles in thickness. As the material is removed from the land and is added to the sea, the level of the ocean slowly rises and inundates the lowlands. Were it not for the crustal movements, the oceans would eventually cover all the land. However, at various times the crustal movements elevate various parts of the land and sedimentation is interrupted in those places. If the uplift is general, the oceans drain off a large part of the continents, and erosion becomes more active again.

Direct evidence of repeated interruption is found in the sediments in every region. As already stated, terrestrial beds are found over marine beds, and over these marine beds again. Quite obviously the number of separate marine beds in a given region indicates the number of times the region has been under the level of the ocean.

Most revealing is the nature of the surface of contact between two series of beds. In general the beds do not fit or "conform." Quite often a bed near the bottom of the series is tilted and planed, and over this a series of level marine rocks appear. The plane between the two sets of beds is called an *unconformity*. It must represent the following sequence of events. After the deposition of the lower sediments, there must have been an uplift and subsequent erosion. How long a period this represents is not now known, but from the present rate of erosion, we conclude it must have been a long time. Nor do we know what other rocks were originally above the unconformity. However, after the upper surface of the lower sediments has been eroded it must have been submerged in order for the upper sediments to deposit.

Putting together these lines of evidence we develop a comprehensive view of the erosional cycle. We may begin with the continents

Fig. 15-34. Unconformity at the Grand Canyon. The strata below line Pu were elevated, tilted, and worn off. Then after subsidence the upper strata were deposited. Another unconformity Au is discernible below. *(U. S. Geological Survey.)*

emergent, consisting of high mountainous regions, and extensive planes and small areas of the continental shelf inundated. As active erosion proceeds, huge quantities of rock material accumulate at the mouths of the drainage systems. These areas are adjacent to the mountainous regions, for the erosion is most active in the regions of high gradients. The sediments accumulate and sink progressively, forming beds of great thickness. Elsewhere along the shores less active erosion takes place, but over wider areas. As the ocean fills in, it encroaches upon the land and inundates the areas of low elevation.

After a long period of time, for reasons we shall investigate presently, extensive crustal movements take place resulting in the elevation of the land relative to the sea. It is during these periods that the river deltas and similar regions of active deposition are folded into mountain ranges. Extensive volcanic activity is also taking place in these regions.

Causes of Crustal Movement

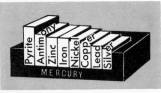

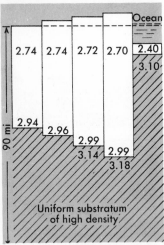

Fig. 15-35. Concept of isostasy. (Top) Blocks of different densities floating on mercury. The blocks are of unequal height but equal weight and sink to the same depth. (Bottom) More likely situation in the earth; lighter blocks in part project above average level and in part reach deeper. The figures indicate the most probable densities.

While the record of the rocks provides abundant evidence for this sequence of events, it does not point conclusively to the *causes* of the crustal movements. Two theories merit consideration. One is the *isostasy* hypothesis; the other is the hypothesis of a *shrinking earth.*

The isostasy hypothesis is based on the simple principle of floating objects. According to this hypothesis, the rocks at a depth of 30 to 50 miles are in a plastic condition. To be sure they are solid, as indicated by the speed of the earthquake waves in them. However, at the prevailing temperatures and pressures, rock will flow, given sufficient force, much like a copper wire "flows" when drawn powerfully through diamond dies.

According to this theory, the outer crust is "floating" over the plastic basement. The reader will remember that the continents consist of lighter rocks than do the ocean floors. Moreover, accurate measurements show that the force of gravity is slightly greater over the oceans than over the continents, indicating that the material is denser over the oceans than over the continents to a considerable depth. Estimates show that a continental block at a depth of about 50 miles weighs the same as an oceanic segment to the same depth (Fig. 15-36). Therefore, according to this theory the continents stick out above the ocean floors, because they consist of material which is lighter on the average. The higher continental block at 50 miles is about as heavy as the shorter oceanic block. Both float on the same level of the plastic basement.

This theory can explain, in part at least, the periodic crustal movements. At the beginning of the cycle the land is emergent and the weights of the continental and oceanic segments are fairly well balanced. As erosion proceeds and material is removed from the continents and added to the oceans, the balance is disturbed. The continental block becomes lighter than the oceanic block. If the rocks had no strength the continents would be pushed up to make up for the loss in height and the ocean floors would subside. The situation is similar to a boat loaded with sand. If sand is removed from a boat, the boat rises. However, in the case of the continents, the adjustments do not take place immediately. Owing to the strength of the rocks, the stresses accumulate over long periods of time. Ultimately, however, the strength of the rocks

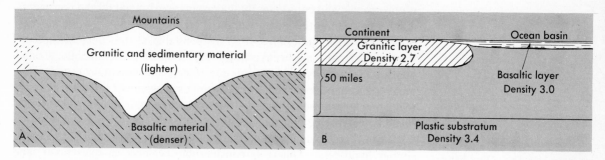

Fig. 15-36. (A) The concept of "roots of mountains." (B) Floating continents; the gravity anomalies observed at the surface are compensated for at a depth of about 50 miles.

is exceeded and a series of dynamic adjustments are initiated, resulting in the elevation of the land relative to the sea, thus beginning a new cycle.

While the theory explains the periodic rejuvenation of the land, it fails to explain the formation of the mountains during the diastrophic movements. To explain mountain building, the rather exciting hypothesis of a shrinking earth has been proposed. According to this theory the earth has been shrinking since its formation. The shrinking may be due to cooling, if the earth was ever much hotter than at present, or it may be due to the slow formation of denser mineral species under the enormous pressures at great depths. While there is great uncertainty as to the possible cause of the shrinking, there is considerable evidence that shrinking has indeed taken place. In all mountain ranges the sediments are found extensively folded. Therefore two points on opposite sides of the mountain range are much nearer today than when the sediments were lying flat. By tracing the beds it is possible to estimate the amount of crustal shrinking represented by the folds. For example, Harrisburg is no less than 86 miles nearer Pittsburgh today across the Appalachian Mountains than the rocks under them must have been when the sediments were flat. This amount of shortening of the crust corresponds to a shortening of the earth's radius by about 15 miles ($1/2\pi$ the shortening of the circumference). Since many mountain ranges are found throughout the globe, the "wrinkles" represent a considerable shortening of the radius. Even if a small fraction of the estimate has actually taken place, it is more than sufficient to account for the minor fluctuations of a few thousand feet in the level of the ocean (Exs. 19 and 20).

According to this hypothesis, whether from cooling, from the formation of denser minerals, or from some other cause, the volume occupied by the deeper layers decreases, or the pressure decreases making further compression possible. Normally, the lithosphere is strong enough to withstand deformation and no movement is apparent for long periods of time. Eventually, however, the stresses become too great for the rocks to withstand and a series of movements are initiated during which the continental and oceanic wedges move inward. Since the continental segments are lighter than the oceanic, and have become even lighter from the removal of earth material by erosion, they sink *less* than the oceanic segments. This differential movement produces two important effects. The greater sinking of the oceanic segments enlarges the capacity

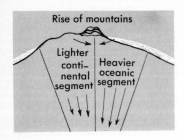

Fig. 15-37. Wedge action and mountain building. The heavier oceanic segments sink more than the lighter continental segment. The wedge action at the juncture results in the folding of weak sediments into mountains.

of the oceans, and consequently the oceans are drained off the continents. At the same time the wedge action at the edges of the continents compresses the rocks laterally. It so happens that at the edges of the continents the rocks are weakest, for they consist of sediments. Consequently the troughs of sediments are folded into mountain ranges. The great friction and local relief of pressure cause some of the rock (already at high temperature) to melt. Therefore mountain building is accompanied by extensive volcanic activity.

There are too many uncertainties at present to evaluate these and similar hypotheses. There is considerable evidence in their favor, and probably all contain a portion of the truth. However, whether these theories are correct or not should not prejudice the facts already established. There is no question that the level of the sea has fluctuated in the past, and that the lithosphere is in a dynamic state. There is no question that sedimentary rocks were deposited at low levels and many of them under the sea. There is no question that mountains have been formed from the folding of sediments deposited in deep troughs. These rocks contain the record of past events, and will yield their secrets to further inquiry. We shall take up this story in the next section.

4. DECIPHERING THE HISTORY OF THE EARTH

The exciting story of unraveling the long and complicated history of our planet may now be resumed. From the study of the erosional processes in the Grand Canyon, the history of the Colorado Valley has been traced to the beginning of the present erosion, some 7 million years ago. By similar studies, the histories of other regions may be traced and an attempt made to synthesize into a comprehensive view the evolution of the present landscape over the entire earth.

The presence, however, of sedimentary rocks in the Grand Canyon wall, and elsewhere, and the evidence of crustal movements and volcanic activity throughout the past imply previous cycles of erosion, inundation, and deposition. The long succession of such cycles imply a history of the earth that stretches back indefinitely into the vague reaches of time. A part of the record is still preserved in the sediments, but much of it has been wiped out during the intervening periods of erosion and has been confused by breaks, displacements, foldings, and alterations of the rocks. To what extent is it possible to piece together the fragmentary record and reconstruct a comprehensive history?

The reconstruction of a connected story of the history of the earth is a monumental achievement of modern geologic science. The deciphering of the past involves two rather distinct tasks. One is the interpretation of the events in a given region by untangling the fragmentary and confusing evidence now present in that region. The other is a synthesis of the evidence from the separate regions all over the earth into a comprehensive view of the whole, tracing it back into the eons of the distant past until the record disappears or becomes too meager or too confused to decipher. In this section we shall relate the evidence and the reasoning that led to the reconstruction of the story.

While the interpretation of the record is an enormously complicated task—due to the overwhelming amount of data, the fragmentary nature of the record, and the resulting confusion of the relations—the principles upon which the reasoning is based are remarkably simple.

The most fundamental guiding principle is Hutton's doctrine of *Uniformitarianism,* "The present is the key to the past." This principle is merely a restatement of the faith that the same causes that produce the geologic changes at present have been operating in the past. The effects now observed in the ancient rocks must have been produced by the same causes that produce similar effects today. Thus, if rain drop impressions are found in the rocks, a rain storm must be assumed in the ancient landscape. If extensive sand deposits with typical wind crossbedding and other characteristics are found, it must be assumed that they were deposited by the wind under desert conditions. If a rock consists of glacial till, unsorted, and contains typical scratches, it must be assumed that glaciers once stood over this region, even though the region is now in the tropics or at the equator. If marine deposits are found, and especially if they contain fossils of marine organisms, the presumption is that the ocean was at that time over this region, even though the sea coast is more than a thousand miles away today.

The second principle is equally simple, but more specific and pertains to the *relative* ages of rocks. In a series of sediments the lower strata were obviously deposited before the upper strata. Sediments are deposited in horizontal, or nearly horizontal position over rocks already there. Consequently, in a series of beds, the *upper sediments are younger than the lower sediments.* To be sure, in a given region the rocks may have been tilted or overturned, but then the evidence in the texture of the rocks and other evidence in the region will reveal the overturn. By and large, we shall not be led astray by assuming a normal sequence of deposition.

The third principle, formally called the principle of *intrusion,* is equally self-evident. Whenever an igneous intrusion such as a dike is found cutting across a sedimentary bed, it must be *younger* than the sediment. For the sediment must have been already there *before* the dike could cut through it. Similarly, if a sediment is found cracked and faulted, the faulting must have taken place after the deposition of the sediment, for the rock had to be there before it could crack. Again, if an igneous intrusion terminates in an erosional surface, the intrusion must have taken place before the erosion of that surface. Conversely, if an intrusion cuts across an erosional surface, it must have come after

Principles of Earth History

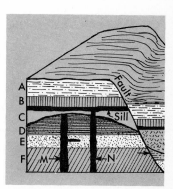

Fig. 15-38. The principle of intrusion. A feature is younger than the feature it cuts. Thus, dike M is younger than beds D but older than beds C. Dike N with the associated sill is older than the fault.

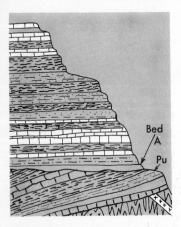

Fig. 15-39. Unconformity is a record of missing events. The mere presence of the line Pu implies a number of events between the deposition of the tilted (middle) sediments and the deposition of bed A of the upper horizontal sediments.

the erosional period that formed that surface. In general, any *structure or feature is younger than the structure or feature it cuts.*

The fourth principle is an interpretation of the significance of *unconformities,* and has already been mentioned. If a series of beds lie unconformably over another series, the presumption is obvious that an interruption has taken place between the deposition of the lower and the upper sediments. The unconformity surface indicates that a part of the record is missing. Although only a thin surface of separation, the unconformity represents a sequence of events between the deposition of the uppermost sediments of the lower set of beds and the lowermost sediments of the upper set. After deposition of the uppermost sediments of the lower set of beds, an unknown sequence of events must have taken place. These must include at least the following events: emergence with interruption of deposition, subsequent erosion, submergence, and the initiation of deposition of the next set of beds. There may have been several such sequences of events, but at least one such sequence must have taken place. Thus, by the very absence of the record of deposition, an unconformity is in itself a record of a minimum number of events in that region.

The fifth principle springs from the interpretation of the significance of fossils found in the sediments. It is formally called the principle of *life equivalency* or the principle of *organic correlation.* According to this principle, the fossils found in the rocks are the entombed remains of organisms that were alive at the time the sediments were being deposited. Consequently, the rocks are of the same age as the organisms. Moreover, *two rocks containing the same assemblage of fossils must be of the same age.* This principle is not at all self-evident, but we shall establish its validity and discuss it at greater length in the proper connection as the story unfolds (p. 569).

The Local History of a Region

The first four principles alone are sufficient to reconstruct the history of a given region from the record now present in that region. The method and the reasoning may be illustrated by applying them to the history of the Grand Canyon. The photograph of the Canyon on page 533 reveals three sequences of rocks, each separated by an unconformity marked Pa and Pu. The relations can be shown more clearly in the diagram shown in Figure 15-40. The lowermost rocks consist of a complex of igneous rocks, gneisses, and schists, the latter being metamorphosed sediments altered by diastrophism and volcanic activity. Above this complex, and separated by an unconformity, lie a series of sedimentary rocks in a tilted position. Above the latter, and again separated by an unconformity, lie the upper horizontal beds.

Direct interpretation of the record is immediately evident. Three major intervals of time are represented by the three sequences of rocks. The lowest complex are the oldest rocks. Since the schists are metamorphosed sediments, the original beds must have been deposited over still older rocks and presumably horizontally. Subsequent to the deposition, the region has been subjected to violent diastrophic movements and volcanic activity. During this interval the deposition has been interrupted and elevation with folding has taken place, perhaps several times,

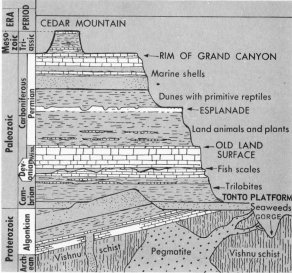

Fig. 15-40. Essentials of the geology of the Grand Canyon. (After Garrels.)

Fig. 15-41. Reconstruction of the history of the Grand Canyon. Only a small number of events are indicated. (After Noble.)

including intrusions into the schists following their folding and metamorphism. Finally, having been elevated at least once, the region was eroded to the unconformity surface Au that marks the upper boundary of the complex. All these events must have taken place prior to the formation of the erosional surface, during an indefinitely long interval of time.

The middle sediments represent another long interval of time. Following the erosion of the lower complex to the unconformity surface, the region must have again been submerged, interrupting the erosion and initiating the deposition of the middle sediments. At that time the surface must have been nearly horizontal, for beds are always deposited in approximately horizontal position. The sequence of beds now present has been deposited. Of course, the record does not show how much higher the beds extended originally. At the end of this period of deposition, another uplift, tilting, and erosion has taken place. This time the tilting is obvious from the angle between the beds and the horizontal. The final event recorded in the middle sediments is the erosion to the unconformity surface, Pu, separating them from the upper sediments.

Following the formation of the unconformity separating the middle from the upper sediments another submergence must have taken place, initiating the deposition of the upper sediments. A series of such sediments are now present but again it is not known how many more layers were deposited and removed subsequently by erosion. However, following the period or periods of deposition there has been still another uplift initiating the present erosion. The last major event in the region, still going on at present, is the digging of the Canyon and the erosion of the surface of the Arizona plateau.

Although we have gone into some detail to illustrate the method, we have related but the barest summary of the multitude of events recorded on the wall of the Grand Canyon. The three intervals represent merely the three main divisions in the book of the history of the canyon. Examination of the rocks in each series reveals several unconformities, which are barely evident in the diagram, but clearly evident in the field. Each of these minor unconformities represents a sequence of erosion, uplift, and submergence, but probably of smaller duration than the major unconformities. Moreover, the fact that a bed in a series is distinct, directly implies that the conditions of sedimentation have altered each time a new bed appears, changing the texture and thickness of the sediments. Detailed examination of the rocks brings out a wealth of information, sufficient to fill a book on the history of the Canyon (Fig. 15-41).

On the other hand, it is evident that the history is necessarily incomplete. The minor unconformities imply that a part of the record within each series is missing. The major unconformities, however, are far more serious. There is no way of knowing how many more events have taken place between the deposition of the sediments right below the unconformity and the beginning of the deposition of the sediments immediately above. Nor is there any way of estimating the length of time from the record now present in the region, for the evidence has been completely removed. Yet geologic processes were going on all the while. In fact, since during this period rocks were removed by erosion in *this* region, the material must have been deposited *somewhere else* at the same time. Nevertheless, we have exhausted the information from the record now present in this region.

Using essentially the same methods, the history of other areas can be similarly elucidated. As an example, the geology of the Chicago region may be taken (Fig. 15-42). While in the Chicago area there is no canyon wall in which the rocks are conveniently exposed to view, it is possible to determine the underlying structure from exposed rock outcrops, from quarries, and from drill holes. Interestingly enough, here also three sequences of rocks are found; a basement complex of igneous and metamorphic rocks similar to those in the Grand Canyon; an inter-

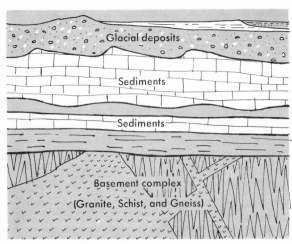

Fig. 15-42. Essentials of the geology of the Chicago region. (After Garrels.)

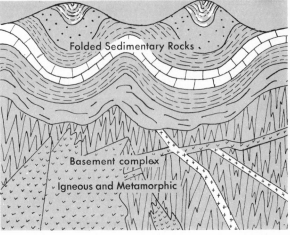

Fig. 15-43. Essentials of the geology of the Appalachian region. (After Garrels.)

mediate set of flat sediments, much thicker than in the Grand Canyon; and a superficial series of glacial debris and later deposits not represented in the Grand Canyon (Ex. 21).

Another example is the area in the central Appalachian Mountains in Pennsylvania, shown in Figure 15-43. Here also a basement complex of igneous and metamorphic rocks is found, but above them only a single series of sediments highly folded and upturned, forming the mountains. The sediments are more than 30,000 feet in thickness. There is no third major sequence above them. Similar studies have been made in other regions in North America. In each region the history can be deciphered from the record, but in each case, the record is fragmentary.

Having shown how it is possible to decipher the history of the separate regions from the record present in the region, we face the greater task of correlating the separate and admittedly incomplete chapters into a comprehensive history of the entire continent—and ultimately of the entire earth. We have in effect fragments of chapters from separate books. We do not know how these chapters fit into one another. We cannot tell, for example, whether the basement complex found in the three regions is the same set of beds deposited at the same time, nor do we know whether the thick sediments in the Appalachian Mountains are equivalent to the middle sequence in the Grand Canyon, or to the third sequence, or to neither. If the relative ages of the beds of one region and that of another could be determined, it would be possible to "intersplice" the separate records into a more comprehensive history of the continent.

Correlations

An obvious method of attack, based on the first four principles, has probably already occurred to the reader. Why not trace the beds of the Grand Canyon to those of the Chicago region and then to the Appalachians? The idea is simple and basically sound. In fact this method of *stratigraphic correlation* can be used and has been used successfully over short distances. However, the practical difficulties encountered in the field soon become insurmountable. The layers alter in texture and thickness on moving away from the canyon. Beds thin out and disappear, and other beds appear "sandwiched" between beds that are obviously continuous at the Canyon. At other places beds plunge downward into inaccessible depths, or turn upward terminating in unconformities with a complete break in the record. The same situation is found in the other regions. After a few score miles from any of the three regions, the relations become obscure, and the conclusions more and more uncertain. The uncertainties mount, and soon it becomes impossible to risk even wild guesses. Consequently, it becomes a hopeless job to connect the story of the Grand Canyon with that of the Chicago region, more than 1000 miles away, or to the Appalachians 700 miles further. Moreover, if the object is the elucidation of the history of the entire earth, the method fails completely, for there is no sequence of beds continuous from one continent to the other. Sedimentation essentially terminates at the edges of the continental shelves. Even if the beds were continuous, they would be quite inaccessible under the epicontinental seas, and entirely so under the ocean deeps.

Organic Correlation

Fig. 15-44. William "Strata" Smith. "Fossils are of the same age as the rocks in which they are entombed." *(The Bettmann Archive.)*

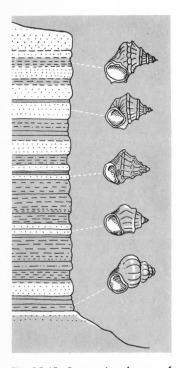

Fig. 15-45. Progressive changes of a fossil type in a series of undisturbed layers. *(After Garrels.)*

Further progress in correlation would have been difficult, if not impossible, were it not for the principle of organic correlation, already mentioned. This new and unique principle emerged from an apparently unexpected source. Around 1800 William Smith stumbled upon it almost accidentally. Smith had a meager formal education, but as a surveyor's assistant and later as a professional surveyor he was seriously preoccupied with sediments. "Strata" Smith as his friends knew him, came to know the sedimentary beds of England and Wales quite intimately. As a pastime he collected the fossils found in the rocks that he surveyed. He grew quite proficient in his hobby. He learned to recognize the fossils readily by their intricate forms and noticed that certain fossils were characteristic of the beds from which they came.

One day he visited the Reverend Richardson who had a large collection of local fossils. He amazed his learned host by picking out the unlabeled fossils from the curio cabinet and telling him precisely the rocks from which they came. Richardson was quick to see that by common sense and acute observation, Smith had stumbled upon a principle of profound significance. If the rocks can be identified by the fossils they contain, then the fossils are indicative of the relative ages of the rocks. Any two rocks containing the same assemblage of fossils must be of the same age. Rocks above these containing a different assemblage of fossils must be younger; rocks below these, containing a third assemblage of fossils, must be older. Thus, it should be possible to make a map showing all rocks of the same age, all over England, even though the rocks are not continuous, or their continuity cannot be established by direct surveying. Another map then can be drawn showing the rocks immediately younger, or immediately older, and a superposition of such maps would contain a continuous history. Richardson encouraged Smith to pursue his studies. By 1815 Smith had worked out and published a series of colored maps showing the appearance of the British Isles at successive times in the past.

The usefulness and effectiveness of this method depended upon two rather distinct but related facts concerning fossils which Smith recognized and helped establish. One is the observation that the same typical assemblage of fossils is found over and over again in widely separated areas, even though the texture of the rocks may be different. Smith traced stratigraphically continuous beds, which indeed altered. A limestone often graded into a shale and later into a sandstone, but still contained the same assemblage of fossils over the entire layer. He therefore concluded that the same assemblage of fossils indicates that the fossils are contemporaneous. Conversely, the rocks containing the same fossils must be considered of the same age, even when they cannot be traced stratigraphically.

The other observation confirms this idea, and introduces the dimension of time. Smith found that in any given locality the fossils alter from bed to bed as one goes upward. A certain fossil, typical in a given bed, shows small but progressive changes as it is traced into the beds above. Apparently the organisms developed into different forms with the passage of time. This, of course, is the idea of *evolution,* but it must be remembered that evolutionary ideas had not yet been conceived or were at best vague until Darwin gave them clarity some 60 years later. In fact the changes actually observed in organisms in successive and, hence, younger beds constitute the most direct evidence for evolution. Thus, Smith's maps implied that a given group of organisms lived at the same time and that the assemblage changes progressively with time.

Geologists in other countries soon followed Smith's example and made similar maps of their own localities. The French, who had extensively studied the beds over France and in the Alps, and had made tentative stratigraphic correlations, were delighted to find Smith's ideas applicable. They confirmed the idea that certain organisms are found widely distributed and show progressive changes in overlying and therefore younger layers. Most significantly, they found the same assemblages in rocks on the French side of the channel as on the English side, and thus were able to jump across the sea barrier and correlate the rocks of England with those of the Continent.

Correlation was facilitated by adopting a systematic naming of the rocks. The oldest sediments in Wales were called *Cambrian,* after the Roman name "Cambria" for Wales. These were the oldest rocks that contained recognizable fossils and rather surprisingly they were rich in fossils. Typical fossils in them are the trilobites (Fig. 15-46), of which many varieties were recognized. On finding the same assemblage in French rocks, the French geologists called these rocks Cambrian too, implying that they were deposited at a *time* that should be called the *Cambrian period.* The rocks below were called pre-Cambrian and again rather significantly they were invariably separated from the Cambrian sediments by an unconformity. Similarly the beds immediately above the Cambrian were called the *Ordovician* from a Roman name of a tribe living in that region. The method of naming has been continued, so that rocks of a given period are named after the locality in which they were first studied extensively.

Fig. 15-46. Cambrian trilobites. Originally found in rocks of Wales, they serve to identify as of the same age (Cambrian) the rocks in which they are found, anywhere in the world. *(American Museum of Natural History.)*

Across the ocean the American geologists, adopting Smith's principle, began to correlate the sediments of this extensive continent. They likewise found that certain typical fossils are widely distributed and that fossils show progressive changes from lower to upper sediments. Most exciting, they found in the rocks of America some of the typical fossils found in European sediments. Thus they were able to identify some rocks as Cambrian, others as Ordovician, and so on according to the rocks to which they corresponded in Europe. Since that time geologists have been engaged in fitting the rocks over the entire surface of the earth into a gigantic jig-saw puzzle. By now, the great majority of the rocks containing fossils have been correlated, although there are a few in doubt and, of course, many details are missing. The greatest uncertainties are with the oldest rocks that contain no fossils. A series of maps can now be constructed showing the successive appearance of the globe throughout a good deal of the long geologic past.

A series of maps each containing all the rocks of the same age would be the most faithful and most comprehensive representation of the history of the earth, insofar as it can be known from the record still preserved. However, for purposes of discussion a synthetic representa-

The Geologic Column

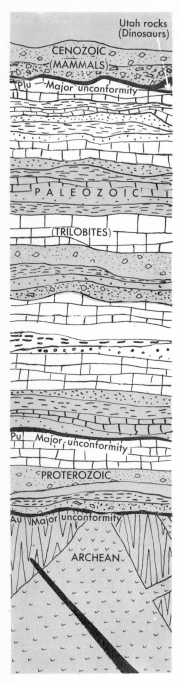

Utah rocks (Dinosaurs)

CENOZOIC (MAMMALS)

Plu—Major unconformity

P A L E O Z O I C

(TRILOBITES)

Pu Major unconformity

PROTEROZOIC

Au Major unconformity

ARCHEAN

Fig. 15-47. Composite geologic column of the rocks for the Grand Canyon, Chicago area, and the Appalachian region. Note the major unconformities Au, Pu, and Plu, separating the rocks into four series. A whole series of rocks in Utah, containing dinosaurs, are sandwiched at Plu (white arrow), resulting in five series of rocks.

tion is preferable. If we could arrange in a single diagram all the rocks now exposed on the surface of the earth in strict order from the oldest to the youngest, we would be able to see at a glance the entire history of the earth. Details would be suppressed, of course, but for that very reason, the essential relations would become clearer. Such a diagram has been constructed and is known as the *stratigraphic* column or more often as the *geologic* column. It is similar to the diagram of the Grand Canyon wall, on page 567, but it is highly synthetic containing representative rocks from all over the earth, "interspliced" in a single column.

The method of constructing the column can be illustrated by using the three regions in the United States discussed earlier. Starting in the Grand Canyon whose history we have already sketched, we find Cambrian trilobites in the lowest beds of the upper series. Consequently, the rocks below the lower unconformity are pre-Cambrian in age and all the rocks above it are of later times. In the Appalachians, we also find Cambrian trilobites, in the lowermost beds of the upper series. Consequently the two layers containing typical Cambrian trilobites are of the same age. On further search we find several other beds in the Canyon wall of the same age as certain layers in the Appalachians.

But, as the reader will recall, the Appalachians consist of over 30,000 feet of sediments, compared to about 5000 feet in the Grand Canyon. This means that the record is more extensive in the Appalachians than in the Canyon. One can, therefore, "splice" the two regions together and have a more nearly complete history of the two regions combined. This is not a simple substitution, for many layers are present in one region but not in the other. Using as markers the layers that are of the same age, we can select from one region or from the other the thickest beds, in strict order of relative age and make a composite column of the two regions.

In the Chicago area, again we find Cambrian trilobites, but this time they are in the *middle* series, in the rocks lying immediately above the basement complex. Several other layers can be correlated as of the same age with layers either in the Grand Canyon or the Appalachians. However, a few layers are not represented in either of the other regions, and some of the beds of the same age are thicker here. Consequently, we can splice these additional rocks in the proper place and thus enlarge the column. More significantly, the upper series of the Chicago area are not equivalent to the rocks in the two other regions. They do not contain trilobites but, instead, fossils of mammals. Since they lie unconformably over the trilobite rocks in the Chicago regions these must be the youngest rocks in any of the three regions and are, therefore, added to the top of the column.

Thus the composite column of the three regions consists of *four* series of rocks: the two pre-Cambrian sets, both found in the Grand Canyon; a very much enlarged series containing trilobites and a fourth series containing mammals. Continuing the correlations with other regions in this continent we proceed to enlarge the column. Rather interesting are the rocks from northwestern Colorado and Utah. A whole series of rocks containing dinosaur fossils lie uncomformably between rocks containing trilobites below, and rocks containing mammals above. This series, sandwiched in the proper place, is second from the top in the composite column (Fig. 15-47).

By continuing the process, the geologists have correlated by now the vast majority of the sediments from the entire surface of the earth. The result is a gigantic column over 100 miles in height—more than 500,000 feet of sediments. All the rocks of the same age from all over the earth are represented by a single layer. The thickness of the layer is that of the thickest layer appearing anywhere, in order to contain the maximum record of that particular time interval. Since the layers are arranged in strict sequence of age from the oldest to the youngest, the column is as continuous a history of sedimentation as is now available. Moreover, nearly all of the intrusive rocks can be inserted in the proper place of the column, since their age can be determined relative to the age of the sediments into which they intrude. The column, therefore, is the complete record of the rocks insofar as it is still preserved and can be deciphered.

The sediments themselves contain the events of deposition, but the unconformities are equally good as records of interruptions, uplifts, erosions, and inundations. The latter events are automatically dated relative to the periods of deposition. Moreover, the events of diastrophic movement, faulting and folding of rocks, mountain building, metamorphism, and volcanic activity can also be dated relative to the deposition of the sediments. Most interesting of all, the appearance, dominance, and disappearance of living forms can be located in the associated sediments in the proper height in the column and the evolution of various forms can be traced upward in successive sediments.

A glance at the column at once reveals some of the major events. Most conspicuous are four major unconformities, dividing the column into five sections. There is a suggestion of one or two more major unconformities near the bottom, but the relations are not distinct here, since the oldest rocks contain no fossils and have not yet been correlated fully and with certainty. However, the upper unconformities are distinct and unmistakable and represent world-wide breaks in the record of deposition. The reader will recall that in building the column the local unconformities are "erased" by supplying the missing record from the deposition going on in other areas during that time. What are called *major* unconformities are the breaks where the record is missing from all over the world. As yet there seem to be no rocks that bridge these gaps. These breaks imply that the emergence of the continents was world wide and that they were undergoing extensive erosion during that time. It is not clear what happened to the rocks that must have been deposited during the erosional periods. Perhaps they have been eroded afterwards, or possibly they lie in inaccessible regions under the epicontinental seas.

The world-wide unconformities provide a natural and convenient means of subdividing the geologic column into five major *sequences* of rocks. Each sequence represents an interval of geologic time called an *era,* during which the rocks were deposited. Most significantly, each sequence contains a distinct group of fossils. Accordingly, the eras have been named after the fossils most prominent in the rocks of those eras. The uppermost sequence, consisting of the most recent rocks, contains characteristically fossils of mammals, and has been called the "Age of Mammals." The next lower series contains dinosaurs, and hence the name, "Age of Dinosaurs." The third sequence from the top contains trilobites, and may be called the "Age of Trilobites." In the pre-Cambrian, the fossil record is meager, but is undoubtedly present. No generally accepted common name has been given to the pre-Cambrian eras.

The more systematic naming of the eras from the most recent to the most ancient is as follows:

> *Cenozoic,* meaning "new life" or "modern life"—the Age of Mammals.
>
> *Mesozoic,* meaning "middle life" or "medieval life"—the Age of Dinosaurs.
>
> *Paleozoic,* meaning "old life"—the Age of Trilobites.
>
> *Proterozoic,* meaning "former life" or "primitive life." This name was given after it was recognized that one-celled animals were present in these pre-Cambrian rocks (Ex. 26).
>
> *Archeozoic,* meaning "ancient life." The term was given after it was distinguished from the Proterozoic and found to contain traces of life.
>
> *Azoic,* meaning "no life," is given to an indefinitely long interval between the formation of the earth and the first appearance of life on this planet.

The systematic method of subdividing the column and the corresponding geologic time has been carried into the smaller subdivisions. Within each sequence of rocks of an era, less extensive unconformities are found which are continent wide, sometimes embracing two or more continents. These provide second-order subdivisions, called *systems of rocks,* marking the subdivisions of an era into *periods.* The Paleozoic era consists of seven such periods, the oldest being the Cambrian, as already mentioned. The remaining periods are: Ordovician, Silurian, Devonian, Mississippian, Pennsylvanian, and Permian. The Mesozoic is subdivided into three periods: the Triassic, the Jurassic, and the Cretaceous. The Cenozoic consists of only two: the Tertiary and Quaternary. Continuing the process, each period is further subdivided into *epochs, ages,* and *stages* of geologic time. Some of the major subdivisions appear in Table 15:2, which contains a comprehensive summary of the geologic past since the abundant appearance of living forms.

**Duration of Geologic Time—
Age of Rocks**

From the preceding discussion it is perhaps apparent that "geologic time" and its subdivisions are a kind of "relative" time or an "event" time. The time scale established in this way is qualitative. Neither the rock sequences are of equal thickness nor are the eras of equal length in terms of years. The same thing is true of the periods and the smaller subdivisions. Geologic time is simply a sequence of events from the oldest to the most recent. For many purposes this is sufficient and perfectly meaningful. It becomes a challenge, however, to attempt to translate this event time into the more meaningful dynamic time measured in units of standard duration such as the year.

MILLION YEARS	GEOLOGICAL UNIT OF TIME			EVENTS	LEAD-RATIO CONTROL POINTS	MAGNETITE-HELIUM RATIOS	STRONTIUM RUBIDIUM RATIOS
						(MILLION YEARS)	
0	CENOZOIC ERA	CENOZOIC PERIOD	PLIOCENE EPOCH	Man appears.		17, 15, 15, 21	
			MIOCENE EPOCH	Mammals at peak. Grazing types spread.			
			OLIGOCENE EPOCH	Mammals evolve rapidly. Great apes.		45	
			EOCENE EPOCH	Modern mammals appear.		46, 43	
			PALEOCENE EPOCH	Archaic mammals dominant.	58	53, 51, 75, 51, 50	
100	MESOZOIC ERA	CRETACEOUS PERIOD		Dinosaurs, pterodactyls, toothed birds reach peak, then disappear. Small mammals. Flowering plants and hardwood forests.		117, 120, 100, 120, 102, 132, 132	110, 150, 100
		JURASSIC PERIOD		Dinosaurs and marine reptiles dominant.			
		TRIASSIC PERIOD		Small dinosaurs. First mammals. Conifers and cycads dominate forests.		169, 158, 174, 165	
200	PALEOZOIC ERA	PERMIAN PERIOD		Continental uplift and orogeny.			
		PENNSYLVANIAN PERIOD		Reptiles and insects appear. Spore-bearing trees dominate forests.	215	200, 205, 200, 225, 215 245	
		MISSISSIPPIAN PERIOD		Climax of crinoids and bryozoans.	255	240, 245	
300		DEVONIAN PERIOD		First amphibians. Brachiopods reach climax. First forests.		240 340 365, 340	300, 280, 200, 240, 300, 540, 270, 450, 540
		SILURIAN PERIOD		Widespread coral reefs. First evidence of land life.	350	375	
400		ORDOVICIAN PERIOD		Invertebrates increase greatly. Trilobites reach peak differentiation.			
500		CAMBRIAN PERIOD		First abundant fossils. Marine life only. Trilobites and brachiopods dominant.	440		
		PRE-CAMBRIAN				550, 500, 550, 620	

TABLE 15:2

History of the earth in comparatively recent geologic times, classically worked out by the sequence of rock layers. This sequence is now supported by measuring the products of radioactive processes in the rocks. Three columns at the right give the results of such measurements. *(Scientific American Magazine,* August, 1949.)

Ever since Hutton demolished the notion of an earth only a few thousand years old, the urge was natural and irresistible to attempt to estimate the duration of time implied in the record of the rocks. That the recorded events required untold thousands of years was all too apparent. All estimates quickly ran up into millions of years, and the more events were recognized, the longer the estimates. Several methods have been used to estimate the length of the eras and their subdivisions.

One of the methods repeatedly used is based on the rate of accumulation of sediments. Extensive samplings of the various types of sediments indicate that it takes about 200 years to accumulate 1 foot of sediments at the present average rate of deposition. By the end of the nineteenth century the geologic column had grown to nearly 100 miles. Therefore, a rough estimate of time required to accumulate 500,000 feet of sediments is about 80 to 100 million years.

It was recognized, of course, that this was the roughest kind of estimate, based on a dubious "average" rate, and on the assumption that the average rate has been constant throughout the past. From all indications, however, it was a serious *underestimate*. By a more detailed analysis of the rocks for each kind of sediment such as limestone, shales, sandstones, etc., and from their proportions in the column, the estimate was increased to at least 150 to 200 million years. Furthermore, it was recognized that the present rate of deposition is much higher than it has been in the past. The continents now stand as high as they ever did, since during most of the past they were submerged receiving sediments as the record shows. Consequently, the average rate must have been much slower in the past. In addition this estimate does not take into account the intervals represented by the unconformities, during which no sediments are now available to be added to the column. From all these considerations, it was evident that the estimate of 200 million years should be multiplied by a factor ranging from 2 to 15 or more. Other methods, such as the rate of accumulation of salt in the ocean led to the same conclusions (Ex. 27). Thus, the duration of the geologic past had to be reckoned in hundreds of millions and perhaps in billions of years.

At the turn of the century, the famous British physicist Lord Kelvin applied a "physical" method for estimating the upper limit of the age of the earth. Kelvin calculated the time required for the earth to cool from an "infinitely hot" body to its present temperature and obtained the figure of 20 to 40 million years. He applied the method to the sun and obtained the figure of 40 million years as the absolute upper limit for the age of the sun itself. Even if the sun were infinitely large and infinitely hot, it could not possibly be older than 40 million years on the assumption that the source of its heat is the gravitational energy of contraction. For the age of the earth, Kelvin thought 20 million years to be the more reasonable estimate. The geologists were deeply disturbed. Having contemplated the enormity of events recorded in the sediments, they could not bear themselves to compress these events into so short a span. Yet they were unable to find a flaw in Kelvin's argument.

The discovery of radioactivity in 1897 altered the situation radically and unexpectedly. During radioactive decay heat is generated in the rocks and doubtless in the sun. Consequently neither the earth nor the sun can be considered as a simply cooling body, and hence Kelvin's calculations are not applicable. Interestingly enough, the very discovery that made Kelvin's calculations worthless gave rise to a very accurate method for the determination of the age of rocks. The reader will recall that radioactive elements decay into other elements and ultimately into stable elements. Most significantly, the rate of decay of radioactive elements is constant. It is independent of changes in pressure, temperature, chemical combination, or any other changes in the external environment. Consequently the radioactive atoms in the rocks are standard clocks and have been ticking time at a constant rate throughout the geologic past.

Rutherford was the first to suggest in 1905 that the rate of accumulation of the stable decay products may be used to estimate the age of the rocks. The method may be illustrated by using uranium and its products as an example. Uranium disintegrates into a series of radioactive elements, but the final products, lead and helium, are stable and accumulate in the rocks. The series of changes may be represented by a single equation as follows:

$$U^{238} \rightarrow Pb^{206} + 8He^4 + \text{energy}$$

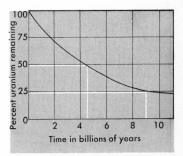

The rate of this disintegration has been measured very accurately in laboratory experiments. It is an incredibly slow rate. Out of 6.4 billion uranium atoms only one atom disintegrates per year! It takes 4.5 billion years for half of the uranium atoms to disintegrate into lead atoms. In another 4.5 billion half of the remaining half disintegrate, leaving one fourth of the original atoms still intact. At any time, always a definite fraction of those atoms still intact disintegrate per year (Ex. 28). The disintegration rate is conveniently shown in Figure 15-48.

Fig. 15-48. Percent of uranium atoms remaining after the lapse of time indicated. In 4.5 billion years half of the atoms still remain.

The method of determination of the age of minerals may be understood best by considering the simplest possible case. As soon as a pure crystal of a uranium compound is prepared lead immediately begins to accumulate in it. A pure uranium compound ordered from a chemical company will contain lead by the time it reaches us, the amount depending upon the time since the preparation of the pure crystals. By analyzing the sample chemically for the lead and uranium content, it is possible to calculate the time when the pure sample was prepared or to read it on the chart (Fig. 15-48).

In igneous rocks we find (or hope to find) an almost ideal situation similar to the above sample. At the time of crystallization of the molten rock each mineral separates into a distinct crystalline form, and the uranium minerals separate from the other materials in the rock. By crushing the rock and carefully picking the crystals of the uranium minerals and analyzing them for the lead and the uranium content, we can estimate the time since the crystallization of the minerals. The time so obtained is the age of the igneous intrusion. But from the relative ages of the intrusion and the associated sediments it is possible to assign upper and lower age limits to the sediments. Thus, in Figure 15-49, the sediments

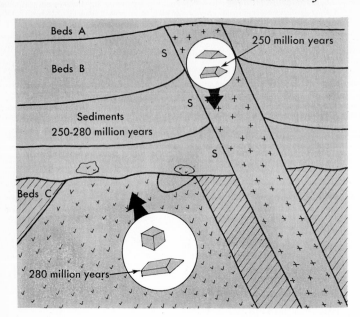

Fig. 15-49. Age of igneous intrusion from the ratios of lead atoms to uranium atoms in the minerals. Upper and lower limits of the associated sediments are found from the intrusion relationships. Thus beds B are older than 250, but younger than 280 million years.

S must be older than 250 million years but younger than 280 million years. In principle, the ages of the sediments can be pin-pointed by more extensive determinations of the ages of the associated intrusions.

In practice a number of complications are encountered which introduce many uncertainties. The crystals of the uranium minerals are not always sharp and distinct, particularly in the very ancient rocks. Besides, some of the lead may have been removed by ground water, or additional lead from other parts of the rock may have deposited in the crystal. Similarly, uranium may have been leached away or additional uranium may have deposited. Therefore, the lead to uranium ratio is not an entirely dependable index of the age of the mineral.

Fortunately, the lead produced by the decay of uranium-238 is lead-206, which is only one of the isotopes found in ordinary rock lead. By analyzing for the ratio of the isotopes of lead and comparing it to that found in ordinary lead a correction can be made, or at least serve as a signal that a correction is necessary (see p. 592). We may attempt to get another estimate by determining the helium content and obtain the helium to uranium ratio, as well as the helium to lead ratio. Moreover, the rock may contain thorium which disintegrates into lead-208. Hence the ratio of lead-208 to thorium may be used as a further check. By careful cross checking it is possible to obtain consistent and on the whole dependable results. It is significant that for the dependable determinations, there is an internal consistency. The older the rocks, as determined by their position in the stratigraphic column, the more lead they contain relative to uranium.

By extensive analysis of radioactive minerals it is found that about 60 million years have elapsed since the beginning of the Cenozoic era, about 200 million years since the beginning of the Mesozoic, and about 550 million years since the Cambrian—the beginning of abundant fossil record. The beginning of the Proterozoic may be placed at about 1200 million years ago. The beginning of the Archeozoic is much more difficult to estimate. Certain Archeozoic rocks give ages of the order of 2700 million years. These are by no means the oldest rocks known. They lie over still older rocks, or they are intruded into still older rocks. The interval between the birth of the earth and the beginning of the Archeozoic is at present hardly more than an intelligent guess. By considering the earth as a giant mineral and applying the radioactivity methods to the whole, the age of the earth is estimated between 3 and 5 billion years. This will be discussed further in Section 5.

The geologic past may be divided into pre-Cambrian and post-Cambrian. Although the pre-Cambrian represents more than five-sixths of geologic time less is known concerning it, than the succeeding time. As might be expected, knowledge becomes more definite as the events become more recent. In the following synopsis only the major physical and organic events are presented, chiefly from the record of the North American continent. Similar events occurred on the other continents at about the same time. More extensive treatment of the geologic past is found in References 15-4 and 15-5. (See also Table 15:2.)

Synopsis of Earth History

The pre-Cambrian. The Archeozoic rocks are the oldest known, and therefore underlie all other rocks. They consist largely of highly metamorphosed igneous rocks. Absence of fossil record makes correlations exceedingly difficult. The era closed with the formation of the Laurentian Mountains along the St. Lawrence, in Southeastern Canada. These mountains were completely eroded to a peneplane during the subsequent epi-Archeozoic interval.

The Proterozoic rocks overlie the Archeozoic peneplane. They are less metamorphosed, and contain a higher percentage of sedimentary rocks than the Archeozoic. In North America they were deposited in three great troughs, known as geosynclines: the *Ontarian,* the *Appalachian,* and the *Cordilleran.* The Ontarian geosyncline was a trough running generally from the Ozarks through the Great Lakes along the Canadian province of Ontario to Quebec and beyond. The Appalachian geosyncline was a great trough through the present Appalachian Mountains. The Cordilleran was a trough running in the region of the present Rockies from Mexico to the Arctic Ocean. The era closed with the formation of the Killarney Mountains, along the Canadian shield. The earliest known glaciation occurred at this time. During this era extensive deposits of iron ore took place notably in the Lake Superior region.

In all probability, life began in the Archeozoic. Primitive one-celled plants and animals were probably present in the Archeozoic. In the Proterozoic, *seaweeds, protozoans,* and *sponges* were probably present, in addition. Actual fossil record of the pre-Cambrian is very meager, but indirect evidence of the presence of the lower plants and animals is good.

The Paleozoic Era. The Paleozoic rocks are common in North America. They are predominantly sedimentary. They contain an abundance of fossils and hence correlations can be made with no difficulty. Sediments were deposited in the Appalachian and the Cordilleran geosynclines. During the several periods, shallow seas flooded first the

Fig. 15-50. Inundation of North America in Cambrian times. Marine deposits containing Cambrian trilobites are found in the dark areas now on land. Hence they were ocean troughs or geosynclines at that time.

geosynclines and then spread over the interior of the continent. The maximum submergence took place in the Ordovician, when over 60 percent of the continent was under water. The era closed with the folding of the Appalachian geosyncline forming the Appalachian Mountains. Extensive glaciation took place at this time.

The abundant record of life begins abruptly in the Cambrian. No satisfactory explanation has been offered for the sudden prolific appearance of fossils. At the beginning of the era the marine invertebrates were supreme, represented by the trilobites and brachiopods. By the Ordovician period marine vertebrates had developed. During the Silurian period land plants and land invertebrates appeared. During the Devonian the fishes became supreme, hence this period is known as the "Age of Fishes." In this period forests made their appearance, as did the first amphibians. The world's greatest coal deposits took place during the Mississippian and the Pennsylvanian. During the Pennsylvanian also the first reptiles appeared. At the close of the Permian many paleozoic forms, notably the trilobites, became extinct.

The Mesozoic Era. The Mesozoic rocks consist of terrestrial as well as marine deposits. The Cordilleran geosyncline is the main site of marine deposition. The era closed with the formation of the first generation of the Rocky Mountains.

The Mesozoic Era is properly designated as the "Age of Reptiles," for this group dwarfed into insignificance all other forms of life. Mammals made their appearance as early as the Triassic, but remained small and unimportant during the entire era. The birds appear in the Jurassic, and the flowering plants in Cretaceous. At the close of the era *all dinosaurs became extinct.*

The Cenozoic Era. During the Cenozoic Era the continent was largely emergent. In the Quaternary a great ice age occurred, of which the present is a late stage. Recent mountain building may signify the end of the Cenozoic era. It began in the late Tertiary and continued to the Quaternary. The Cordilleran Ranges were uplifted and the present Rocky Mountains rose. The process seems to be still going on.

The Cenozoic is properly designated as the "Age of Mammals." Characteristics of the era are the modernization of the plants and the invertebrates and the development of carnivorous and herbivorous mammals. Of these the horse and the elephant are the best-known representatives. Most important is the evolution of the primates, culminating in the development of man.

On looking back into the story recorded in the rocks, we recognize two major themes. One is the *recurrence* of physical events. The physical history of the earth is subrhythmic. It is a sequence of uplifts, long periods of erosion and deposition, followed by violent diastrophic movements, mountain building, and general uplifts. The other theme is the *unidirectional* development of life. The simplest forms appear in the oldest rocks, and the more and more complex forms of life appear in orderly succession in progressively younger rocks.

A number of questions arise at this point. Was life developed but once, in the dim eons of the archeozoic? Was the history of the earth subrhythmic to the beginning of the earth? So far as the record can be

Fig. 15-51. Paleozoic life. Permian reptiles and amphibians. *(Chicago Natural History Museum.)*

Fig. 15-52. Mesozoic life. This era is properly designated as the "Age of Reptiles." *(Chicago Natural History Museum.)*

Fig. 15-53. Cenozoic life. Pliocene rhinos, mastodons, and creodonts. *(Chicago Natural History Museum.)*

read the continents have always been continents and the ocean deeps have always been under water. But what was before that? Was there ever an original "crust" of the earth, and if so, is it exposed anywhere now? How did the earth form? The record is too fragmentary, and only tentative answers can be given. Some of these questions will be considered in the next section.

5. THE ORIGIN OF THE EARTH AND THE UNIVERSE

Throughout history, the questions concerning the origin of the earth and of the universe have been the most persistent and most challenging. The early views have been the visions of poets and theologians and the speculations of philosophers. In the past two centuries, with the spread of the naturalistic outlook, attempts have been made to formulate scientific hypotheses, based on evidence which has been steadily growing and becoming more and more dependable. The evidence comes from many and diverse sources, as extensive as man's field of observation of natural phenomena. However, the observations may be conveniently grouped as geological or astronomical. The deciphering of the geologic record with ever-increasing success has extended the frontier of knowledge into the remote past. Astronomical observations have related the origin of the earth to that of other celestial bodies. Human understanding has been steadily extended into the eons of greater and greater antiquity, reaching out toward a time when the earth was formed and toward an earlier time when the world came into existence. To be sure, knowledge becomes less and less certain the more ancient the events. Nevertheless, as the evidence accumulates and more is learned on how to interpret it, the ideas are gradually taking a more definite form, although they are still highly tentative.

At the present state of knowledge a number of ideas have attained a fairly definite form, and are held with varying degrees of confidence depending on the strength of the evidence in their favor. From geological and astronomical evidence it seems quite certain that the earth was formed as a separate body at some definite time in the past. It is possible to establish within reasonable limits the most probable time of this event, and hence to estimate the "age" of the earth. From observations in the solar system, it is almost certain that the earth was formed in a single event together with the other members of the sun's family. Observations in other parts of the universe suggest probable modes of formation of stars and of larger systems of stars, including galaxies. More recent observations permit us to extrapolate these ideas into the "ultimate beginning" and to entertain seriously some notions about the origin, mode of formation, and age of the entire observable universe. We shall elaborate on these ideas, citing the evidence that supports them, and evaluating the strength of the evidence in so far as that is possible in a brief account.

In 1755 the German philosopher Kant proposed the first naturalistic hypothesis for the formation of the earth and the solar system. Impressed by the prevalence of rotation in the heavenly bodies and by the common occurrence of nebulae and spiral forms in all parts of the heavens, he suggested that the solar system originated from an immense cloud of matter. According to Kant, the primeval cloud contracting by gravitational attraction, began to rotate. With continued contraction the rate of rotation increased, causing the nebula to flatten out by centrifugal force. At various parts of the flattened nebula, matter concentrated into more or less separate rings, each destined to become a planet. The bulk of the matter eventually condensed to form the sun. By a repetition of the process, the planets and their satellites were formed from the matter of each ring.

Early Theories of the
Formation of the Solar System

There are many and obvious objections to this hypothesis. Gravitational attraction alone from a single center cannot develop rotation, and diffuse material cannot condense into planets in the manner Kant postulated. For the most part, however, the hypothesis is too vague to be critically analyzed. Nevertheless, the conception is significant in that it postulates a general process for the formation of heavenly bodies and systems of stars throughout the universe. After 200 years, Kant's basic idea still offers the best hope for eventually understanding the process of formation of the bodies of the universe.

In 1796 Laplace, apparently unaware of Kant's speculations, proposed a similar hypothesis. Laplace worked out the process in greater detail, consistent with the laws of mechanics and the observations established by his time. The theory has undergone many modifications and goes by the general name of "nebular" hypothesis. According to Laplace, the original nebula was already rotating, but very slowly. As it cooled by radiation and contracted, it rotated faster and faster. This caused a flattening of the gaseous mass into a disk-shaped body, with the fastest material thrown to the outer rim. When rotation reached a certain rate, the material of the thin rim moved too fast to be held by gravitational attraction and broke off into rings that continued to rotate independently of the central mass. This material eventually became the outermost planet. Continued contraction and repetition of the process left material for the other planets at various distances. During the breakoff, rotational eddies developed in the ejected material so that the planets and their satellites were formed by a repetition of the same process on a smaller scale (Fig. 15-57).

For over a century this hypothesis was the only one seriously considered. It was elaborated and modified in the light of accumulating evidence. By the end of the nineteenth century most of the facts then known, although by no means all, seemed to be in general agreement with the theory.

Fig. 15-54. Laplace was the first to elaborate the nebular hypothesis. *(The Bettmann Archive.)*

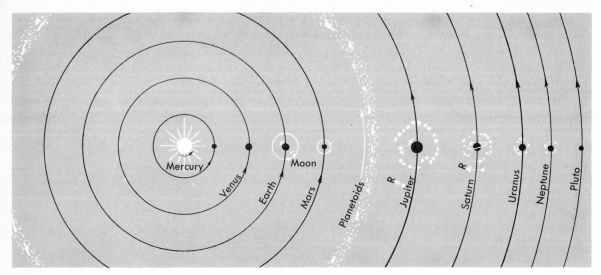

Fig. 15-55. Preponderance of east-ward motion in the solar system. The only notable exceptions are the retrograde motions of the outer satellites of Jupiter and Saturn, indicated by R.

The remarkable order observed in the solar system provided most of the evidence in favor of this theory. Practically all motion in the solar system is in the same general direction. All the planets and thousands of planetoids revolve around the sun in the same direction and in roughly the same plane. This is the plane of revolution of the earth around the sun, known as the plane of the ecliptic. The sun rotates also in the same direction, and the plane of its equator is in the plane of revolution of the planets. Moreover, the earth and all the planets (except Uranus) rotate in the same plane and in the same direction as they revolve. Further the moon and the satellites of the other planets (with a few exceptions) revolve around the parent planets in the same eastward direction and in roughly the same plane of the ecliptic. Such regularity constitutes compelling evidence that the formation of the solar system was a single event and suggests strongly that the smaller bodies within the system were also formed by the same process in the same event.

There were, however, a number of stubborn facts that were not consistent with the theory. The revolution of Uranus is almost at right angles to the plane of the ecliptic, and its satellites revolve in the same tilted plane. The satellite of Neptune, three of the remote satellites of Jupiter and the furthermost satellite of Uranus also revolve in a backward direction. Most disturbing of all, however, is the fact that the sun rotates too slowly, compared to the rate of revolution of the planets. If the sun was formed in the last stages of contraction of the rotating nebula and contains the bulk of the material, it should be spinning dizzily on its axis. Expressed technically, the outer planets have too much angular momentum, or the sun has too little to have been formed from the same nebula without the action of some outside force. There seemed no way of explaining the slowing down of the sun on sound mechanical principles.

Other objections were raised against the theory and were mounting by the end of the nineteenth century. Mathematical studies on conden-

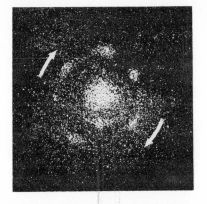

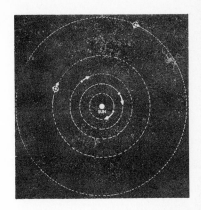

Fig. 15-56. Formation of the solar system according to Kant in 1755. *(Left)* The clotting mass of gas and dust in rotation. *(Right)* The clots grow by accretion to form planets and satellites. The remainder of the nebula contracts to form the sun. *(Yerkes Observatory.)*

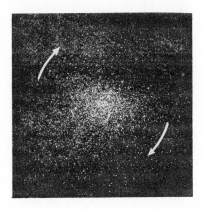

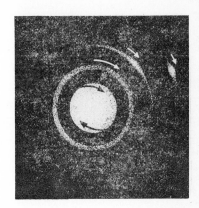

Fig. 15-57. Formation of the solar system according to Laplace in 1796. *(Left)* The rotating nebula (hot gas). *(Right)* The cooling nebula shrinks, spins faster, and is expected to leave rings of gas to condense into planets. The whole remainder forms the sun. *(Yerkes Observatory.)*

Fig. 15-58. Formation of the solar system according to the planetesimal hypothesis of Chamberlain and Moulton. *(Left)* A passing star narrowly misses the sun. Huge eruptions are expected to occur on both as they pass. *(Right)* The sun is left with a vast number of planetesimals that condensed from the erupted gases and slowly coagulate to form planets. *(Yerkes Observatory.)*

Fig. 15-59. The von Weizsäcker vortex hypothesis of 1945. *(Yerkes Observatory.)*

sation of gases showed conclusively that gaseous rings could not condense into planets. Under the conditions postulated in the nebular hypothesis, they would disperse away. Further objections came from geology. No original "crust" of the earth had been discovered. Studies in the chemical composition of the rocks indicated that the earth formed gradually by the acretion of small solid particles, similar to the meteorites falling today.

At the beginning of the present century the first rival theory, called the *planetesimal hypothesis,* was formulated by the astronomer Moulton and the geologist Chamberlin, both at the University of Chicago. Cooperating with each other, these scientists sought to develop a theory in accord with both the astronomical and the geological evidence. According to the planetesimal hypothesis, the solar system was formed as a result of a near collision of the sun with a passing star. The passing star raised enormous tides on the sun, which exploded in a series of bolts drawn in the general direction of the star. More specifically, each explosion consisted of two bolts, shot out simultaneously—a larger one on the side between the sun and the star, and a smaller one on the other side of the sun. The passing star pulled the material toward it for some distance and gave it a whirling motion. After the star receded sufficiently far (in the course of a few days or weeks), the material fell back somewhat and began to whirl around the sun. Thus, the troublesome angular momentum of the outer planets is explained by this theory, but at the price of calling on another star to do the job (Fig. 15-58).

On the process of formation of the planets after the departure of the star, this hypothesis is similar to the nebular hypothesis in general outline, but differs markedly in detail. The material in the bolts is already fairly concentrated, and is exposed to rapid cooling. Accordingly, it cooled not in a single mass all at once, but into innumerable small and solid particles, called *planetesimals.* Swarms of these particles colliding with each other formed the nuclei of planets, which grew to larger bodies by attracting other planetesimals. Some of the smaller nuclei revolved around the larger nuclei, and ultimately formed satellites. Since the passing star imparted a whirling motion in the same direction and in roughly the same plane, the regularity of the motions in the solar system follows as a consequence. According to this theory, the earth and the other planets grew rapidly in the first few hundred or thousand revolutions, and more slowly afterwards. The earth continued to grow throughout the geologic past and is even now growing by the accretion of meteorites, which are the few planetesimals still remaining.

In the first half of the present century the planetesimal hypothesis (or its variants) had all but sent into oblivion the nebular hypothesis. It explained simply and logically the troublesome angular momentum of the outer planets, which the nebular hypothesis could not do, and it explained the regularities of eastward motion in the solar system as well. It also explained the failure of finding an original crust of the earth.

However, the planetesimal hypothesis soon developed troubles of its own. The angular momentum of the outer planets was explained at the high price of calling on another star to provide it. High-powered mathematical treatment indicated that the distribution of the angular momentum, as found in the solar system, could not be accounted for by the action of only one star on the sun. Accordingly, a variant hypothesis was proposed, requiring a simultaneous near collision of the sun with *two* other stars. Other variants such as the Gaseous-Tidal Hypothesis were proposed to meet other objections. Finally, in 1939, Lyman Spitzer of Yale showed that the material raised from the sun by tidal action could not condense into planetesimals, nor into planets. The material just under the surface of the sun is at temperatures of some 10 million degrees and is kept dense only because of the high gravitational attraction of the sun. If the material is drawn from the sun by tidal force, it would expand to enormous volumes within a few minutes and could never condense. These objections raised serious doubts on all collision hypotheses.

Since 1940 we have witnessed the return to the basic idea of Kant in attempts to explain the formation of the solar system from a single mass of diffuse material. In the early 1940's the German astrophysicist, C. F. von Weizsäcker, proposed a theory that appears to remove the basic objections to the older nebular theories. According to this theory, the solar system originated from a slowly rotating diffuse cloud of gas and dust of enormous dimensions. It began to contract under gravity and flatten out, much as in Kant's hypothesis. By the time it had contracted to a size comparable to the present size of the solar system the bulk of the material at the center suddenly collapsed, forming the sun, and leaving a diffuse nebular disk rotating about the central sun. At this time the sun rotated very rapidly and contained most of the angular momentum of the original nebula.

Current Theories

At this point von Weizsäcker conceived of a mechanism for transferring angular momentum from the central sun to the outer parts of the nebula. The rapidly rotating sun, which meanwhile was getting hotter from nuclear reactions initiated in the interior, ejected masses of gaseous material into the surrounding nebula. This caused turbulence in the nebular disk, which in time broke up into a system of eddies, alternating in clockwise and counterclockwise rotation. The eddies settled down in a semipermanent pattern at definite distances from the sun, like standing waves in a swimming pool. The rotating sun fed the motion of the eddies giving them angular momentum, while at the same time the sun was losing angular motion. At this stage the system acts like a "roller bearing" device, transferring angular motion from the rotating axle toward the periphery. The whole system continued to rotate, with the same total angular momentum, but with more in the periphery, and less in the central sun (Fig. 15-59).

The theory then goes on to explain the formation of the planets and their satellites. At the regions of contact between the opposing eddies, motion decreases due to the countercurrents, and local condensation takes place forming solid particles, which may still be called *planetesimals*. In time, the small condensations grow into larger bodies, which are called "protoplanets." As these grow, their gravitational attraction also increases, and sweeps the surrounding materials even faster. Some of the smaller bodies revolve around the larger ones and a few of the more distant ones survive the mutual collision and ultimately become satellites. All the rotational motion originally present in the eddies is now contained in the growing planets and their satellites.

Von Weizsäcker developed the theory mathematically to a considerable extent. The calculations indicate that the eddies would form at about the right places, thus explaining the *spacing* of the planets according to Bode's law (Ex. 33). By taking into account the high temperatures near the sun the theory suggests a plausible explanation of the size and chemical composition of the planets. Only the heavier material remained near the sun, and hence the inner planets are smaller, contain denser materials and have no satellites. By the same action a great deal of the lighter material was repelled farther out. Hence the outer planets are very massive, contain large proportions of the light elements and are surrounded by many satellites. Most, if not all, of the known facts about the solar system seem to be explainable by the theory, or at least they are not contradicted by it. In a general sense the theory combines some of the best parts of the nebular and the planetesimal hypothesis. It is similar to the latter in explaining the formation of the earth and the planets by growth from small cold bodies. It is similar to the former by not requiring the intervention of an outside star. This last point is most interesting. It implies that the formation of the solar system is not a rare and accidental event. If the solar system can be formed by this process many stars may well have solar systems similar to our own.

After the war, von Weizsäcker's theory attracted considerable interest, especially the possibility of explaining the formation of the solar system from a single mass and still accounting for the distribution of angular momentum. Several modifications, elaborations, and extensions were offered. For example, Kuiper, of Yerkes observatory, in 1952 suggested that gravitational forces played a more important role in the formation of the eddies as well as during their condensation into planets. His calculations favor the idea that the planets were formed by condensations in the center of the eddies rather than at the "roller bearing" regions of turbulence.

Some of these theories contain sufficiently novel ideas to deserve independent names. One of the most comprehensive theories is the *dust cloud hypothesis,* proposed by Whipple of Harvard around 1948 and elaborated since. In this theory, three fairly distinct stages in the evolution of the solar system are recognized. The first stage is the formation of the original nebula into a distinct aggregate from the dispersed interstellar material of dust and gas. The second stage is the formation of the sun and the system of planets around it. The third stage is the detailed evolution of the planets after the initial establishment of the general pattern (Ref. 15-31).

Whipple's hypothesis begins with a suggestion of Spitzer that light pressure may be sufficient to drive the dust particles of interstellar space into a more compact mass. It is definitely known that the vast spaces between the stars in the galaxy contain great quantities of gas and dust particles. The total amount of interstellar material is comparable to the total mass contained in the stars, but owing to the vastness of space it is

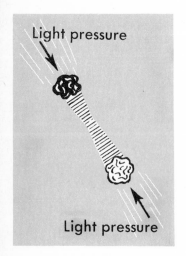

Fig. 15-60. Radiation pressure drives particles toward one another in interstellar space.

extremely diffuse—much thinner than the best vacuum that can be produced in the laboratory. The presence of dust particles is known from the reddening effect on starlight—the same effect that makes the sun appear red in a dust storm. According to Spitzer, the photons of light from the surrounding stars drive the particles toward the space between the stars. This is due to the shadow effect of one particle on the other. The particles receive more intense light from one side than from the other, and hence are driven toward each other forming a denser cloud in the space between the stars (Fig. 15-60).

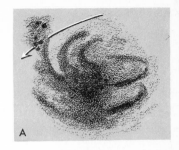

Once this process is started it gradually accelerates. The denser nebula casts a shadow on the surrounding particles and the light going through the nebula is less intense than the light coming from the stars outside the nebula. Hence more particles are driven toward the interior of the nebula. When a total mass comparable to the mass of a star has been driven into a space of some 6000 billion miles in diameter, gravitational attraction becomes perceptible, and about equal to light pressure. Consequently that part of the nebula within this volume begins to contract somewhat faster, although still very slowly for a long time. The mass so carved out by gravity from the more tenuous nebular expanse is now destined to become a star. It is interesting that extensive nebular masses are very commonly observed in interstellar space, but that nebulae of volume smaller than this are very rare. It may very well be that in these few smaller nebulae we are witnessing stars in the making. According to the dust cloud hypothesis, the sun and the solar system developed from such a nebula (Fig. 15-61).

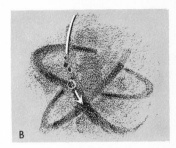

The theory then goes on to elaborate on the mechanism of the formation of the solar system during this stage. We have a nebulous mass, some 3000 times larger in diameter than the present solar system, contracting under gravity. During the contraction, the general motion is, of course, toward the center, but turbulence and eddies develop, and giant masses stream ponderously in all directions. There is no general pattern to these streams and the particular nebula destined to become the solar system has no net rotation. The angular motion of the various streams cancel each other out. However, *one of these streams,* perhaps the largest of them, is destined to form the planets. As this stream moves toward the center under gravity it accelerates. If it has any sideward motion—that is, motion other than directly toward the center (and it would be highly unlikely not to have some sideward motion)—it would *spiral* toward the center as it accelerates, rather than move directly toward it. Gaining momentum, it picks up more material and accelerates even faster. Presently, due to turbulence, the stream breaks up into "beads" all spiraling in the same general direction. Each "bead" is destined to become a planet.

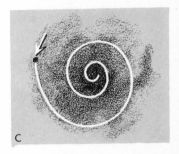

Meanwhile, the bulk of the material in the rest of the nebula, having no appreciable net angular motion, has been steadily moving toward the center, increasing the density in this region. Events happen with increasing rapidity from now on. The greater mass at the center increases the force of gravity from this region and draws larger and larger amounts of material into it. Presently the nebula collapses at the center forming a primitive sun, and the remaining material is even more rapidly drawn

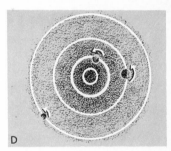

Fig. 15-61. Formation of the solar system according to the dust-cloud hypothesis. (A) In the great dust cloud streams of dust developed and moved under the cloud's gravity. (B) A major stream began to condense into protoplanets and to move toward the center of the large cloud. (C) Protoplanets continued to spiral toward the center. (D) The center collapsed into protosun. The path of the planets became more circular around the growing sun (after *Scientific American Magazine*).

590 • *Universal History*

into it. This leaves the main stream that has broken into "beads" still spiraling toward the sun, but stranded far out in space. By this time it has spiraled into a region stretching out from the sun to the present outermost reaches of the solar system. It consists of a series of "beads" still spiraling toward the sun, through a space containing some nebulous material, but much thinner than before.

The fate of the spiraling beads can now be easily predicted. It can be shown mathematically that the spiraling motion around a primitive sun will become elliptical and by collision with other material in the region it will become more and more circular. Therefore, each "bead" settles down to a nearly circular path. Out of each turbulent bead, a planet is formed. In size, each bead probably extended to the furthest satellite of that particular planet. Out of the turbulence protoplanets were formed, which grew by accretion in a manner similar to that described by the other theories. A small amount of rapidly rotating material formed the satellites. From here on the theory is not too different from the planetesimal hypothesis or from the other recent theories already discussed. This theory explains in similar fashion the gradual growth of the planets from small solid bodies, and the fact that the inner planets are small and dense, while the major planets consist of light material and have many satellites.

In the present state of our knowledge it is difficult to evaluate these theories and impossible to choose between them. All the current theories are highly tentative. None of them explain all the known facts. It may be well to point out that the rival theories are not alternate ways of explaining how things actually happened. Rather, they are alternate ways of explaining how things *might* have happened. None of the current theories can explain consistently all the known facts. For further progress we may have to wait for new principles. On the other hand, it is entirely possible that we have already stumbled upon the right path, but do not yet have sufficient facts to recognize it. We are attempting to understand the dim and ancient past from a record largely obliterated, with only minute fragments remaining. Progress is more likely to come from a more intensive study of the record and the patient gathering of more dependable facts. It is entirely possible that as the facts are slowly uncovered the true pattern will gradually emerge, obvious for all to see.

It is encouraging that a good deal of progress has been made already. The peculiarities of the solar system are now known in great detail. Study of the composition of the planets and the distribution of the elements is already bringing out new relationships. Further information is gathered from intensive study of meteorites, which are samples of matter from outer space. Study of the earliest rocks brings us closer to the beginning. Most encouraging, is the success in determining the age of the ancient rocks and of the meteorites. These studies are slow and painstaking, but they provide a more dependable avenue of approach toward illuminating the events of the ancient beginnings.

The Age of the Earth and the Solar System

In marked contrast to the uncertainty regarding the mode of formation of the solar system is the relative certainty with which its age has been determined. The geologic column provides a reasonably continuous record of the earth's history from the present to the beginning of sedimentation. The earliest rocks so far definitely identified are sediments, overlying either unaltered or metamorphosed igneous rocks. Rather significantly, the oldest sedimentary rocks are found on the continents. From all indications the continents have always been continents projecting above the ocean basins, which have always been depressions. There is no evidence of interchange between the continents and the ocean deeps, certainly not since the time of the deposition of the oldest known rocks. All the geologic changes recorded in the sediments are events subsequent to the formation of relatively stable continents, and are due to relatively minor fluctuations of the level of the ocean surface (Exs. 34, 35). Thus, the outer portion of the lithosphere has been stable and presumably solid since that time. But what was before that time? Can we get a glimpse of the conditions prior to that?

The first impulse is to assume that the igneous rocks underlying the sedimentary rocks represent the original landscape. Unfortunately, however, there is compelling evidence that the underlying igneous rocks are not older than the oldest sediments. Wherever studies have been made, the igneous rocks have been found to *intrude into the sediments above,* and the sediments, therefore, are *older* than the igneous rocks below. Yet the sedimentary rocks cannot be the oldest rocks ever formed on the surface of the earth. The very *first* sediments must have been deposited over pre-existing rocks, and the sedimentary material must have been derived from earlier, nonsedimentary rocks. Were these rocks the "original crust" of the earth?

Although an "original" crust of the earth has not been definitely identified anywhere, there is a strong suggestion that such a crust once existed. Igneous rocks underlie everywhere the thin veneer of sedimentary rocks, forming a continuous igneous structure over the entire outer portion of the lithosphere. More relevant evidence comes from earthquake waves. The earth has the structure of concentric zones, with each layer fairly sharp, and increasing in density toward the center. Such a stratification can take place only from a fluid or at least a "plastic" condition. Moreover, the speeds of earthquake waves through the body of the earth correspond to speeds in typical igneous material. These facts constitute strong evidence that the earth consists predominantly of igneous rocks and has passed through a molten, or at least a "semimolten," condition. If this is so, the failure to find an original crust is not so difficult to understand. It is possible, of course, that parts of the original crust are now exposed to view but have not yet been recognized as such. It is more likely, however, that such a crust, if it ever existed, has been melted and remelted and altered beyond recognition by subsequent volcanic and diastrophic activity. Consequently, the oldest rocks that can now be identified, are sedimentary.

Having reconstructed the primordial conditions as far back as the record can be deciphered at present, we may now investigate the problems regarding the age of the earth. The most reliable age determinations are provided by the radioactivity method. The essential idea has been already discussed in Section 4, page 577. Uranium disintegrates into

TABLE 15:3
Naturally Occurring Radioactive Isotopes

Radioactive Isotope	Stable Decay Products	Half-Life (in millions of years)
Uranium-238	Lead-206, Helium-4	4,510
Uranium-235	Lead-207, Helium-4	710
Thorium-232	Lead-208, Helium-4	13,900
Potassium-40	Calcium-40, Argon-40	1,310
Rubidium-87	Strontium-87	50,000

lead at a constant rate. By analyzing a mineral and determining the ratio of lead to uranium, the time since the crystallization of the mineral can be calculated, and from this the age of the associated rocks can be deduced. Altogether five radioactive isotopes have lifetimes sufficiently long to be of value in estimating the age of the most ancient rocks. These isotopes together with their half lives and their stable decay products are given in Table 15-3. The reader will note that the first three decay into lead, but each into a different isotope. In principle any one of the five radioactive isotopes can be used. By determining the ratio of the respective decay product to the parent radioactive isotope, the age of the mineral can be readily calculated, on the assumption that no change in the amount of the radioactive isotope or the product has taken place since the formation of the mineral.

In any given rock, of course, we can never be sure that contamination or removal of the radioactive isotopes or their products has not taken place during the enormous span of time since the formation of the mineral. An obvious way of reducing the uncertainty immediately suggests itself. *If* two or more radioactive isotopes and their decay products are present in the same rock, *and if* the separate measurements give the same figure for the age of the rock, then the result may be accepted with considerable confidence, approaching certainty if all five radioisotopes are present. Unfortunately, all five radio isotopes rarely are present and the results rarely agree. In rocks containing uranium, however, at least two radioactive isotopes with their products are always present—namely, U-238 with its decay product Pb-206, and U-235 with its decay product Pb-207. If no contamination or loss has taken place, the ratio Pb-206 to U-238 should check perfectly with the ratio Pb-207 to U-235. Moreover, since natural uranium always contains the two isotopes with the same ratio (140 parts of U-238 to 1 part of U-235), the ratio of Pb-207 to Pb-206 should check the other two ratios if all the lead came from uranium and no loss has taken place. If in a given rock these three ratios give the same age, there is a strong indication that this particular rock has the age determined. Moreover, uranium-bearing rocks almost always contain thorium and a further check may be made by taking the ratio of its decay product Pb-208 to the parent isotope Th-232.

Incidentally, a fifth ratio is available—namely, the ratio of He to all the radioisotopes U-238, U-235 and Th-232. This ratio is not so

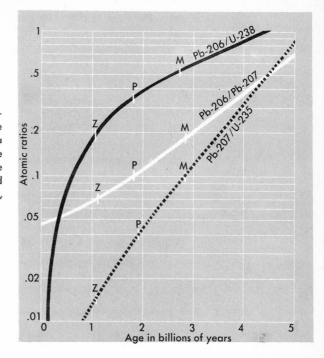

Fig. 15-62. Change of atomic ratios with time. Estimates are considered reliable if all three ratios give the same age. Monazite sands in southern Rhodesia give the three ratios (marked M), corresponding to the age of 2.7 billion years. A zircon sample from granite in Halibuston County, Ontario, gave the ratios marked Z; a pegmatite from Beaver Lodge Lake, Saskatchewan, gave the ratios P. (After Harrison Brown.)

reliable, since helium being a gas may have escaped from the rocks, but it provides a check for a *minimum* age of the rock.

The *minimum* age of the earth can be reliably estimated from the age of the oldest rocks on its surface. The oldest rocks whose age has been reliably determined so far are certain monazites from Southern Rhodesia. These rocks contain uranium and lead as well as thorium. Fortunately, nearly all the lead in these particular rocks is *radiogenic;* that is, it comes from the radioactive decay. It consists almost entirely of lead-206, lead-207, and lead-208, which are the decay products of U-238, U-235, and Th-232, respectively. Independent determinations of the ratio Pb-206 to U-238, and Pb-207 to U-235 give the same figure for the age for this rock. It is 2.7 billion years. A third determination of the ratio of Pb-206 to Pb-207 checks the results almost perfectly (Fig. 15-62). The other ratios agree fairly well with these results. Therefore the earth must at least be as old as the rocks of Southern Rhodesia. Since these sediments are not the oldest rocks by any means, the earth must be considerably older than this. Other estimates, although not quite so dependable, place the *minimum* age of the earth at about *3.2 billion years* (Ex. 36).

An *upper limit* of the age of the earth can be reliably estimated by an extension of the radioactivity method. This requires a more sophisticated discussion of radioactivity. That the age of the earth is not infinite follows without question from the very fact that radioactive elements are now present on the earth. These elements are unstable, and although they have long lifetimes they could not have existed on the earth forever. Uranium-235, with a half life of only 700 million years, is still on the earth. It would have become undetectable if it had

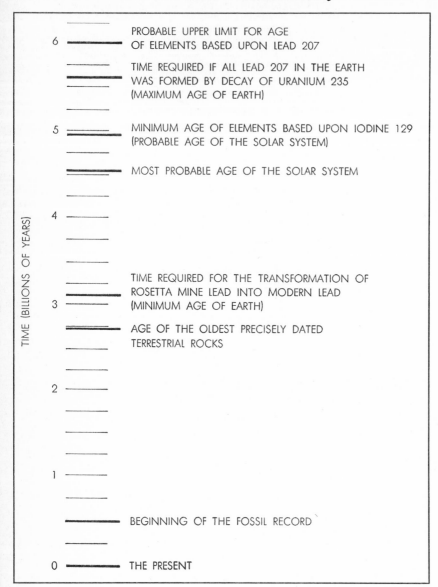

Fig. 15-63. Summary of present knowledge of the age of the solar system and the elements based on the study of the ratios of elements in rocks and meteorites, according to Harrison Brown. (*Scientific American Magazine*, April, 1957.)

been decaying for more than a score of lifetimes or so. There are, however, good estimates of the total amounts of uranium and lead on the earth. Even if all the lead-207 came from the decay of U-235, the process could not have been going on for more than *5.6 billion years*. This is the *absolute upper limit* for the age of the earth. It is the maximum possible time since the earth formed as a separate body. However, we have reasons to suspect that some of the lead-207 was formed prior to the formation of the earth and was incorporated in the material that formed the earth. The earth, therefore, must be younger than 5.6 billion years.

To narrow down further the margin between the upper and lower limits of the age of the earth it is necessary to consider in greater detail the isotopic composition of lead. Ordinary lead found in lead mines consists of four isotopes with atomic weights of 204, 206, 207, and 208. The last three are radiogenic, but Pb-204 is not produced by any known process from the decay of any other element. Presumably this isotope was formed originally at the same time all the elements were formed by a process yet unknown, sometime before the formation of the solar system. The elements synthesized in that process constituted the material out of which the solar system was formed. The Pb-204 isotope, therefore, can be used as an index of "original" lead. We have strong reasons to believe that during the synthesis of the elements all the isotopes of a given element were produced in about the same proportions (p. 597). In any event, there is no question that during the geologic past the amounts of the radiogenic isotopes of lead had been increasing from radioactive decay. Consequently, the *proportion* of Pb-204 has been constantly *decreasing*. In uranium-bearing rocks we expect and do find a smaller ratio of Pb-204 to Pb-206, and the older the rock the smaller the ratio, provided no mixing has taken place. Incidentally, the presence of Pb-204 in the uranium minerals is a good indication of contamination with rock lead and provides a means for correction. Complete absence of Pb-204 indicates no contamination.

It is more significant, however, to consider what happens to "ordinary" rock lead found throughout the earth, outside the uranium-bearing rocks. The geologic processes mix the radiogenic lead with the lead already present in the rocks. Consequently, as time goes on the lead that separates as lead minerals contains a smaller proportion of lead-204. As a result there has been a continuous evolution of the isotopic composition of lead. The older samples of rock lead contain a *higher* proportion of Pb-204 and the proportion decreases as time goes on. In present-day lead—for example, the lead minerals currently deposited in the red clays of the Pacific—the ratio of Pb-204 to Pb-206 is 1:18.95. In older samples of rock lead the ratio is higher. The highest ratio yet found on the earth comes from the Rosetta Mine of South Africa with a ratio of 1:12.65. On calculation, this lead must be 3.1 billion years old. Therefore the earth is at least as old as this. The search proceeds, but in view of the geologic processes continuously going on,

Fig. 15-64. An iron meteorite. The ratios of radiogenic lead to uranium indicate ages of 2 to 3 billion years. *(Yerkes Observatory.)*

it is unlikely that a sample of more primitive lead will be found that escaped mixing with radiogenic lead subsequently produced.

Fortunately, there is one source of "fossil" samples of lead that in all probability have escaped mixing. These are to be found in meteorites. From all indication these unannounced visitors from outer space come from within the solar system. They consist of stony or metallic materials, which must have crystallized long ago, probably at about the time of formation of the solar system. According to the favored view, they are fragments of a planet originally situated between Mars and Jupiter, which either did not form completely or broke up into the meteorites and the planetoids. The meteorites often contain small quantities of uranium, radiogenic lead, as well as rock lead. From the ratio of radiogenic lead to uranium the ages of meteorites are estimated at 2 or 3 billion years, thus confirming the age determinations of the rocks on the earth. Most significant is the composition of the rock lead, which contains Pb-204, in these meteorites. A small sample of rock lead separated from the sulfide phase of a meteorite from the meteor crater in Arizona gives a ratio of Pb-204 to Pb-206 as 1:9.41. This is the highest ratio yet determined, placing the age of the meteorite at 4.5 billion years. If this is the "original" lead at the time of formation of the solar system, then the event must have taken place about 4.5 billion years ago. This is the best estimate we have at present for the age of the earth and the solar system (Ref. 15-19).

An interesting confirmation of the age of the solar system comes from a totally independent method—by estimating the age of the moon. This has been worked out in great detail by Sir George Darwin, son of the famous proponent of the theory of evolution. Very accurate checks on the length of the day show conclusively that the day is lengthening by about one second in 100,000 years. Darwin determined this by comparing the exact time of eclipses in the past as predicted by the present length of the day, and as they are recorded as far back as Babylonian times. Even though the rate of lengthening is exceedingly small, the lag in time adds up day by day, so that in the course of centuries it becomes several hours (Ex. 37). The lengthening of the day is due to a gradual slowing down of the rotation of the earth. Undoubtedly, the slowing down is caused by the tidal action of the moon on the earth and the resulting friction. The moon attracts the rotating tidal bulge and slows the earth down. By Newton's laws of motion the earth's tidal bulge attracts the moon and speeds it up. Consequently, the moon moves further into a larger orbit around the earth, and the lunar month lengthens at the same time the day lengthens.

Darwin considered the problem in the reverse sense. In the past the moon must have been nearer the earth, and the length of the lunar month shorter, just as the day was shorter. He calculated that when the day and the lunar month were equal, both were about 4 hours in length, and the moon revolved about 8000 miles from the center of the earth. Darwin then made the daring proposal that prior to that the moon was actually in contact with the earth and a part of it. Since the earth-moon system had all the angular momentum it now has, the moon separated from the earth due to the rapid rotation, aided perhaps by

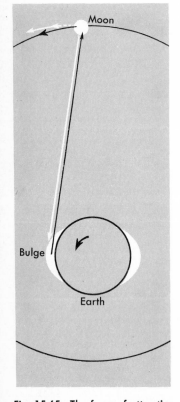

Fig. 15-65. The force of attraction of the moon for the tidal bulge slows down the earth. The opposite force of attraction of the bulge on the moon speeds up the moon.

the sun's tidal forces. A more amazing proposal followed—that the moon came from the region that is now the Pacific Ocean. It is still more amazing that the density of the moon is that of granite, and precisely the amount of granite now absent from the basin of the Pacific is equal to the mass of the moon. Making the best estimate from the rate of slowing down of the earth since that time, Darwin calculated that the event took place some 4 billion years ago. There is considerable uncertainty in this figure, due to the possibility of the earth's being molten during the early stages resulting in greater friction, but the agreement with the more dependable age estimates from radioactivity is indeed remarkable. Other methods, although much less reliable, nevertheless give the same order of magnitude for the time of the birth of the solar system. If a sample of the moon's surface becomes available from space explorations in the near future, it should be possible to check these figures by analyzing the minerals on the moon.

The concordance of evidence on the age of the solar system and the plausibility of the theories concerning its formation have encouraged scientists to venture into the larger questions of the age and origin of the galaxies and of the entire universe. Evidence is gathering from many sources pointing to some tentative hypotheses to be seriously considered. Although these ventures can be regarded only as bold leaps into the great unknown, a number of facts have been well established which undoubtedly have some bearing on the questions concerning the "beginning of things."

The Age and Origin of the Universe

It is rather significant that a number of independent estimates of age of the bodies in the universe converge on a figure somewhere between 5 and 8 billion years. The age of the solar system has been narrowed down to around 4½ billion years by three different estimates— the age of the earth, the age of meteorites, and the age of the moon. Other methods (not here considered) although less reliable point to the same figure.

Radioactivity permits us to go one step further and consider the age of the materials out of which the solar system was formed. The reasoning leading to an upper limit to the age of the solar system (p. 593) is applicable to the age of the chemical elements as well. Since the radioactive elements are still present, they could not have existed forever. We do not yet know where or how the elements were synthesized, but we have a good idea of the time of the synthesis. From the composition of the earth, the meteorites, and the planets we have fairly reliable estimates of the abundance of the various isotopes of uranium, lead, and other elements in the solar system. From the rate of decay we can calculate the abundances at any time in the past. Even if all Pb-207 came from U-235, the process of decay of U-235 could not have started more than about 6.5 billion years ago. However, we can do a little better than that. The internal consistency of the abundance of the various isotopes and other reasoning from nuclear physics suggest strongly that at the time of the synthesis, the isotopes of the heavy elements were produced in approximately equal amounts. Therefore, the amount of Pb-207 originally produced was about equal to that of the

E2 NGC 221 (M 32)

E7 NGC 3115

NGC 4449

Fig. 15-66. Elliptical galaxies (E$_2$ and E$_7$) and irregular galaxy *(bottom). (Mount Wilson and Palomar Observatories.)*

stable isotope Pb-204. Making the correction, we estimate 6 billion years as the most probable age of the elements now found in the solar system. Consideration of the other isotopes points to a similar figure. Since the solar system is a part of the galaxy, this is the lowest limit of age of our galaxy.

It is rather remarkable that the evidence from distant galaxies led to a similar figure. In the distant galaxies we look directly into the past and see the galaxies as they appeared when they emitted the light now received on the earth. The most distant galaxes now photographed with the 200-inch telescope are 2 billion light years away, and must have existed this long ago in the shape we now observe them. Radio telescopes receive signals from invisible objects twice as far and perhaps a little further. From the rate of weakening of the radio signals and the change in the wavelength, it appears unlikely that objects more than 7 or 8 billion light years will be observed or even be observable in principle. These are the oldest objects that can be observed in principle. We are tempted to say, the oldest objects that exist, since it makes little sense to speak of objects as "existing," but being *unobservable in principle* (Ex. 39).

The evidence bearing most directly on the age of the galaxies comes from the red shift observed in their spectra. This phenomenon has been discussed in Chapter 14, page 514. The shift of the spectral lines toward the red indicates that the spirals are receding from our galaxy. The greater the distance of the galaxies, the greater the red shift, and hence the greater the speed of recession. The most distant galaxy for which the red shift has been reliably measured so far is 1.1 billion light years away, receding with a speed of 38,000 miles per second. This is one-fifth the speed of light. If this spiral has been receding at this speed in the past, then it was next to our galaxy 5.5 billion years ago. Moreover, since the galaxies are now moving away with speeds in proportion to their distances, *all* the galaxies were next to our galaxy about 5.5 billion years ago. In other words all the galaxies were in the same big lump at that time. Was this the beginning of the Universe?

Further evidence on the age of the galaxies and their evolution is obtained from the examination of their forms and a more detailed analysis of their structure and contents. More than a billion galaxies are now within reach of modern telescopes. They come in all varieties of form, but may be classified as irregular, elliptical (or globular), and spiral. Only about 3 percent are irregular. These consist of unevenly spaced stars and great quantities of gas and dust. A good example are the Magellanic Clouds. About 20 percent of the galaxies are elliptical. These are nearly spherical in shape and consist of red giant stars with very little or no cloud material.

By far the great majority of the galaxies, however, are spirals, ranging in shape from slightly flattened spherical objects to very thin disks. Our own galaxy is a spiral about 80,000 light years in diameter and about 10,000 light years in thickness. A typical spiral consists of a dense concentration of stars near the center, with spiral arms winding about it. Measurement of the Doppler shift leaves no doubt that they are rotating, with the arms trailing. Rather significantly, in the central region there is little or no cloud material, and the stars are typical red giants. On the other hand, the arms contain blue giants and great quantities of dust and gas. Surrounding the spiral are hundreds of globular clusters, outlining an overall spherical form. The stars in the clusters are also typical red giants.

The appearances of these forms alone, particularly the spiral form with their unmistakable rotation suggest the course of their evolution, just as they did to Kant two centuries ago. The forms in each class grade imperceptibly into one another and the suggestion is strong that the different forms represent different stages in their evolution. Accordingly, a theory has been proposed very similar to the dust cloud hypothesis for the formation of the solar system, but on a much vaster scale. Actually we are in a better position to confirm the hypothesis in the case of the spirals than in the case of the solar system. We can observe numerous spirals, but only one solar system. Moreover, we know something about the types of stars found in different parts of the galaxies from observation in our own galaxy and in nearby galaxies. As discussed on page 509, the red giants in the galactic center and in the globular clusters are very old stars, in the last stages of their evolution. On the other hand the stars found in the arms of the spirals are typical blue giants. These are young stars. At the rate at which they are shining, they must have been formed very recently. They could not have been radiating at the present rate for more than a few tens of millions of years. Most probably they were formed from the dust and gas found only in the spiral arms. Very significantly, the blue giants are absent from the center of the spiral galaxies, from the globular clusters, and from the elliptical galaxies—precisely from the places in which nebulous material is also absent.

According to one of the current theories, the earliest stage of the galaxies was irregular, consisting primarily of gas, perhaps only hydrogen, the simplest of the elements. The majority of them had some rotation and these were destined to evolve into spirals. Contracting under gravity, a nebula began to flatten out, assuming the spiral form, with the arms trailing. At the central regions, the gaseous hydrogen began to condense into stars, resulting in thinning out of the space between the stars. These stars began to gravitate around their common center of gravity. Nuclear reactions were initiated in the interior of the stars, and the stars proceeded in their individual evolution along a path suggested in Chapter 14, page 499. By now the stars in the central region of the galaxy have evolved to the red-giant stage.

The material left out at right angles to the plane of rotation has undergone a similar evolution. This material formed the red giants, which clustered in compact but widely separated systems. These are the globular clusters, marking the outline of the original nebula. In the evolution of the red giants, helium is synthesized from hydrogen. It is estimated that something like 6 to 8 billion years is required to reach this stage, and consequently the red giants are the oldest stars in the galaxy.

Meanwhile, the gaseous material has been concentrating in the

Sa NGC 4594

Sb NGC 2841

Sc NGC 5457 (M101)

Fig. 15-67. Spiral galaxies in the last stages of development. In the earlier stages they develop from irregular galaxies. *(Mount Wilson and Palomar Observatories.)*

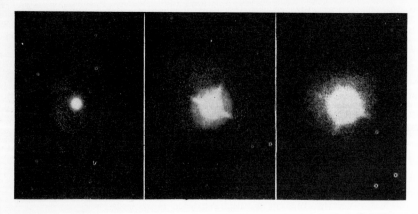

Fig. 15-68. Expanding nebulosity around Nova Aquilae, Nov. 3, 1918. *(Left)* July 20, 1922; *(center)* Sept. 3, 1926; *(right)* Aug. 14, 1931. *(Mount Wilson Observatory.)*

plane of the spiral by mutual gravitational attraction. Some red giants were formed in the early stages, and there are a few red giants which can be identified as the oldest stars in the spiral arms. However, the abundant material resulted in the formation of larger stars and more rapid evolution by some of them in this region. Some of the stars, having gone beyond the red-giant stage, exploded into novas filling the interstellar space with large quantities of gas and dust. Out of this interstellar material, other stars were formed, and presumably some are still being formed today. This theory explains the presence of "population I" stars in the galaxy with a predominance of young blue supergiants in the spiral arms (Ref. 15-18).

According to this theory, the elliptical galaxies, constituting about 20 percent of the total, are not in the line of descent of the spiral. The irregular protogalaxy from which they were formed had little or no rotation. Consequently, red giants were formed from the beginning in all parts of the nebula. These gravitated around their common center of gravity, forming a system similar to the globular clusters, but on a much vaster scale. It is significant that the elliptical spirals consist of red giants with little or no gas or dust, and have no net rotation.

The theory has a considerable appeal because of its simplicity and reasonableness. It explains the great variety of forms observed among the galaxies. It is consistent with a great many observations in our own galaxy and in the nearby galaxies. It incorporates the theory of evolution of the stars in the main sequence, and explains the distribution of stars of population II, of which red giants are representative, and population I, of which the blue giants and the sun are representative (see p. 499).

The plausibility of the theory is further enhanced, because it provides the framework for a theory of the synthesis of the elements. According to a favored theory, the elements were (and still are) synthesized inside the stars of the main sequence during their evolution through the various stages. The primordial material is hydrogen and the first generation stars consist entirely of this element. When a star grows sufficiently to form a hot and dense core of hydrogen, thermonuclear reactions begin converting the hydrogen into helium. By the time most of the hydrogen is gone, the helium core has become denser and very hot. The rise in temperature causes the star to expand and cool at the outer regions, becoming a red giant. Meanwhile in the hot core, perhaps at a temperature of 100,000,000 degrees, helium is slowly being transformed into the heavier elements. The synthesis continues up to iron-56, which is one of the most stable elements in the periodic system (see page 429). The elements beyond iron cannot be synthesized with the materials now present in the core. The star slowly cools and contracts, getting hotter. Due to instability from various causes, some of the stars explode flaring up into extremely brilliant stars called *novas*. In the explosion they belch into interstellar space large quantities of the heavier elements up to iron.

Out of this material a star of the "second generation" is formed. The material consists of the heavy elements (up to iron), but also of great quantities of hydrogen from interstellar space. In due time, thermonuclear reactions begin at the center of the new star, but since hydrogen and helium are now present, neutrons are produced, which react with the iron forming the heavier elements including the radioactive elements. This star in turn goes through the various stages, and ultimately may explode as a nova, throwing into space the material which contains some radioactive elements. If this theory is correct, the radioactive elements in the material from which the solar system was formed were synthesized in the interior of a "second-generation star" and our sun is a "third-generation" star.

We are now approaching the end of our story. All lines of inquiry into the most distant past converge on the same event. The age of the solar system, the age of the elements, the age of the red giants, the age of the galaxies, the recession of the galaxies, all point irresistibly to a cosmic event that took place some 7 or 8 billion years ago. We have traced back to the time when the primitive galaxies were close to one another, perhaps "touching," but rushing out with tremendous speeds in all directions as if from the same point. Can we take the final step and say that they started from the same "point" at the same time and that this was the "beginning of the world"?

In the late 1920's the Belgian Jesuit Georges Lemaitre, arguing mainly from the recession of the spirals, carried the idea to its logical conclusion. He imagined that in the beginning the whole universe consisted of a single gigantic "atom" containing all the matter and all the energy now present in it. It was a superradioactive atom and highly unstable. Consequently, it underwent a tremendous explosion, throwing into space in all directions gigantic fragments, which in time disintegrated into smaller fragments. Fragments having the mass of a galaxy separated from one another and these in time decayed into smaller and smaller "atoms" until the stable atoms of the ordinary elements were formed. Out of this material the galaxies, the stars, and the planets evolved.

This is merely one of the theories of modern speculation. Lemaitre's conception has been modified in many ways. Recently, George Gamow modernized the theory and developed an alternate hypothesis for the formation of the elements in the "first 5 minutes" of this explosion. Other speculations have appeared recently. One theory conceives the universe as "pulsating." It assumes that prior to the "explosion" the galaxies were falling into one another by gravity, and "bounced back" after the mutual impact. They are now slowing down and when they eventually stop, they will reconverge and repeat the performance. Another theory proposed by Hoyle assumes the continuous creation of matter.

We hesitate to evaluate these theories or even to discuss them further. There is so little convincing evidence for any of the theories at present. We have already piled up uncertainty upon uncertainty on the theories concerning the origin of the solar system, the galaxies, and the elements. To venture beyond them is at present too premature. There are many large questions still open. Is the universe finite or infinite? Is space Euclidian for four-dimensional? Is space "curved"? Did the universe have a beginning, or has it existed forever? Until some of these questions are answered with some confidence, it is too premature to speak of an "ultimate" Beginning.

Meanwhile, research is continuing on all fronts and evidence is gathering. Many of the theories of more limited scope will be confirmed, modified, or replaced by better theories. The 200-inch telescope is already bringing a wealth of information. The question whether the universe is finite or infinite may be settled in our day. Nuclear physics is making great strides in uncovering the structure of matter. Hydrogen may not be the "primordial" material. Recent nuclear research has discovered a host of particles—about 30 in number—intermediate in mass between the electron and the proton. They are positive, negative, and neutral. Some are even heavier than the proton (Ex. 13.4). Negative protons, the "antiprotons," have been produced in the accelerating machines. What all this means is not yet clear. Equally exciting and within grasp is the possibility of landing on the moon, and examining its fossil surface and the meteorites on it. Interplanetary travel may not be further off, and interstellar travel now appears as a distinct possibility.

As we conclude this treatise we realize that most of the basic questions remain unanswered. We have to wait for research to collect the evidence for further progress. These questions may never be answered by science with finality, but judging from the past performance, better and better answers should be forthcoming. The wonder is not so much that our knowledge is so limited, but that so much has been learned in so short a time.

NOTES AND EXERCISES

1. The sun is a gigantic heat engine, driving the circulation of the atmosphere. The sun is ultimately responsible for the erosional processes on the earth. Elaborate on these statements.

2. What chemical elements and compounds are of geologic importance in the atmosphere? In the hydrosphere? In the lithosphere?

3. Distinguish between a mineral and a rock. Give several examples of each. Distinguish, further, between sedimentary, igneous, and metamorphic rocks. For each type of rock give the characteristics observable in the rock; give their mode of formation.

4. The Colorado River has carved its own gorge and, indeed, its own valley over the entire drainage system. Summarize the evidence for this conclusion.

5. Suppose you stand on the shore near the delta of the Colorado. How recent are the deposits near the surface? In what two directions would you look for older and older deposits? Explain each.

6. Name the major geologic agents. Describe the mode of action of each. Mention some of the erosional and depositional landforms characteristic of the action of each agent.

7. Suppose you find a hill of gravel. What geologic agents could not have formed it as a depositional feature? Why not?

8. Numerous lakes are found in Wisconsin and in the surrounding states. Could these have been formed by running water? Could they have been formed by any agent now present in the region? What is the evidence that they have been formed by glacial ice? How does the evidence of the deposits in the region confirm this idea?

9. What geologic agent is responsible for the formation of caves and sink holes in Kentucky?

Carbon dioxide dissolves in water to form carbonic acid.

$$CO_2 + H_2O \longrightarrow H_2CO_3$$

Limestone (calcium carbonate, $CaCO_3$) is relatively insoluble in water. However, it reacts with carbonic acid to form the relatively soluble calcium bicarbonate.

$$CaCO_3 + H_2CO_3 \longrightarrow Ca(HCO_3)_2$$

In terms of these reactions explain the formation of caves. Explain the formation of stalactites.

10. Gradation tends to level the surface of the earth. What is the evidence that forces in the past have offset this tendency and that these forces are still at work?

11. What is the evidence that a large part of North America—for example, the Grand Canyon region—has been under the ocean? What is the evidence that it has been under water several times in the past?

12. Consider the three types of earthquake waves: primary, secondary, and long. What is the approximate speed of each type in miles per second near the earth's surface? Which of these vary in average speed with distance from the source? What *two* reasons explain their variation? What is the order of arrival at a station?

13. What type of vibration is associated with each type of earthquake wave? Which of these travel through solids? Through liquids?

What information about the structure of the earth is obtained from the long waves? From the primary? From the secondary?

Summarizing the information, what is the evidence that the outer seven-eighths portion of the earth is solid? That the inner core is "fluid"? What is the evidence for the zoning of the earth?

14. The primary waves from an earthquake arrived in the seismograph station in Denver at 7h, 10m, 0s. The secondary waves arrived at 7h, 11m, 40s. What is the time lag between the two waves? How far is the earthquake from Denver? When did the earthquake take place?

The same earthquake was recorded in Los Angeles, but with a time lag of 50 seconds. How far is the earthquake from Los Angeles?

Drawing on a map these distances, locate the possible locations of the earthquake. What is necessary to locate the earthquake definitely?

What is the approximate time of arrival of the long waves in Denver? How can this estimate be improved using Figure 15-29.

15. What is the evidence of internal sources of energy in the earth. Is the earth losing heat into space from the interior? Is the interior necessarily getting colder? What are the probable sources of the earth's internal energy? What is the best estimate of the temperature at 100 miles below the surface? At the center of the earth?

16. Why is volcanic activity no longer considered evidence that the earth is molten below a few miles? How is volcanic activity explained at present?

17. What is an unconformity? What sequence of events does it imply?

18. Describe and evaluate the isostasy hypothesis. At what depth does "plastic" flow take place? What is the evidence that the oceanic segments are denser than the continental segments?

19. What is the evidence that the earth may be shrinking? What are the possible causes of this shrinkage? Why are the geosynclines considered "zones or weakness" in the rocks? What is the evidence that the mountains are formed by the folding of geosynclines?

20. Imagine the earth to be perfectly smooth and an *unstretchable* wire girdling the earth fitting perfectly—that is, forming a circumference. Suppose you increase the length of the wire by 6 feet. Would you expect the wire now to be sensibly looser? Would you be able to put a ring the thickness of cardboard around the earth between the earth and the wire? How thick a ring would fit between the wire and the earth?

21. Interpreting Figure 15-42, write a sequence of events in the Chicago region similar to the one done in the text on the Grand Canyon.

22. Write a sequence of events in North America, using the composite column, Figure 15-47.

23. In correlating rocks, certain fossils are found most useful, and are called "index fossils." What do you suppose are the characteristics of "index fossils"? Wide or narrow geographical distribution? Wide or narrow vertical distribution? Abundant or rare? Is it surprising that microscopic organisms have been found most useful? Why?

24. A critic accuses the geologists of circular argument: "The geologists say that certain rocks are mesozoic because they contain mesozoic fossils, and then turn around and say that the fossils are mesozoic because they are found in mesozoic rocks."

Is the criticism justified? Defend your answer.

25. What is the ultimate basis of division of geologic time into eras? In the absence of measurement of the age of rocks in terms of years, what is the evidence that trilobites flourished and became extinct before the appearance of dinosaurs? That dinosaurs became extinct before the appearance of mammals such as the horse?

26. The sudden appearance of abundant records of life in the Cambrian has long been a puzzle to geologists and paleontologists. At one time it was thought that life was created during the long period represented by the pre-Cambrian unconformity. When fossils of single-celled animals and plants were found in earlier rocks, it was thought that they represented life that became extinct, and that the present forms of life were created anew, just before the Cambrian. Hence, "Proterozoic," meaning former life. On the theories of the creation of life on the planet see Ref. 15.16.

27. *The Age of the Ocean.* The ocean contains 1.6×10^{16} tons of salt. At the present time the rivers of the world bring into the ocean 1.6×10^{8} tons of salt per year. What is the age of the ocean on the assumption that the rate has been constant throughout the past and that the ocean started as fresh water? Are these assumptions justified? Why? Why not? Why is the age so determined most probably an underestimate?

28. An igneous rock contains a uranium mineral. On analysis the atomic ratio of Pb^{206} to U^{238} is 0.20. Using Figure 15-62, estimate the age of the mineral. What assumptions are necessary for this estimate? How would you proceed to check on these assumptions? (See also p. 592.) How is the age of the mineral related to the age of the rock containing the mineral? What assumptions are necessary?

29. In Fig. 15-49 if the minerals in dike X are 280 million years old and those in dike Y are 250 million years old, what can you say about the age of beds B? Beds C? Beds A?

30. Suppose we make a movie one hour long for the entire history of the earth. Taking the age of the earth as 3.6 billion years, what length of geologic time would each second of showing time represent? If there are 16 frames to the second, what time interval would each frame represent? If the movie started at 11:00 A.M., at what time would the beginning of the Cambrian be shown? How many minutes is the paleozoic era? The mesozoic? The cenozoic? The existence of man on the planet? The beginning of civilization?

31. What is the evidence that the solar system was formed in a single event? List the significant observations, both geological and astronomical, which any theory of the formation of the solar system should explain.

32. Which of the facts in Exercise 31 are explained by the nebular hypothesis? Which cannot be explained by this hypothesis? Repeat for the planetesimal hypothesis; for the hypothesis of von Weizsäcker. Repeat for the dust cloud hypothesis. Compare the four hypotheses. Which do you favor?

33. In 1772 the German astronomer J. C. Bode noticed that the distance of the planets could be obtained in astronomical units by adding 0.4 to the series 0, 0.3, 0.6, 0.9, 1.2. . . . Find the distances of the planets as predicted by Bode's law. Compare them with the actual distances. How good is the agreement? Which of the four hypotheses of the formation of the solar system explain Bode's law?

34. There is a continuous record of marine organisms since the beginning of the Cambrian, 550 million years ago. What is the maximum range in the temperature of the ocean since that time?

35. The oldest sedimentary rocks so far dated are 2.7 billion years old. What conditions are necessary for the deposition of sedimentary rocks? What does this imply about the range of temperatures on the surface of the earth at that time? What can you say about the temperature of the sun during the past 2.7 billion years?

36. What is the *minimum* age of the earth? How is it estimated? What is the *maximum* age of the earth? How is it estimated? What is the best estimate for the age of the earth and the solar system? How is it obtained?

37. Sir George Darwin estimated the age of the moon from the rate of lengthening of the day. Suppose the length of the day is measured today accurately to 0.0001 second and is taken as the "standard day." Now suppose further that tomorrow, for some unknown reason, the day lengthens by 0.001 second but remains constant in the future. How much later than predicted would future events take place? If predicted to take place in 30 days? In a year? In 100 years? In 1000 years? In 10,000 years? Would the discrepancy be detectable? How much larger would be the discrepancy if the day lengthened by 0.001 second once a century?

38. In what sense is our sun considered a "third generation" star? What is the evidence that the materials forming the sun must have come from the explosion of a "second generation" star? What elements are synthesized in a "second generation" star? In a "first generation" star?

39. If Hubble's velocity-distance law holds for the distant nebulae, why is it impossible to observe nebulae more distant than about 7 or 8 billion light years? What would be the radius of the observable universe? Could there be a universe outside the "observable" universe? Clarify the meaning of your terms.

40. Enumerate the lines of evidence pointing to 7 or 8 billion years as the age of the universe. Are all lines converging on the same figure? Is there any evidence in contradiction to these figures?

APPENDIX

A. MATHEMATICS

This appendix is a summary of the mathematical background necessary to follow the text discussion readily. As mentioned in the preface, the treatment in this book is nonmathematical in the sense that it does not require complex symbolism, involved techniques of mathematical manipulation, or higher mathematics beyond simple algebra. Nevertheless, since number is the language of science, the discussion is analytical and quantitative. For the most part, the reasoning employs arithmetic, everyday geometry, a few simple ideas from algebra, and one or two concepts from trigonometry.

The reader has doubtless been exposed to the elementary mathematical ideas and techniques encountered in this book even though he may not have great facility with them. They are summarized here as a refresher and for ready reference. This summary is in no way a substitute for a full treatment of elementary mathematics. A few remarks, however, are added to provide further insight into some of the most common concepts and operations.

It is presupposed that the reader is familiar with the four fundamental operations of arithmetic—namely, *addition, subtraction, multiplication,* and *division;* and that he understands the meaning of *term, sum, difference, factor, multiplicand, multiplier, product, dividend, divisor,* and *quotient.*

The multiplication sign is either $\times$ or $\cdot$. Thus $3 \times 2 = 3 \cdot 2 = 3$ *times* $2 = 6$.

Arithmetic

607

The division sign ÷ or /, the latter indicating a fraction.

Fractions. A fraction is a number that may be considered as an indicated division. The *numerator* (on top) is divided by the *denominator* (on the bottom). Thus $\frac{1}{4}$, $\frac{3}{8}$, $\frac{12}{5}$.

In a *proper* fraction, the numerator is smaller than the denominator and the value of the fraction is less than 1. Thus, $\frac{3}{4}$ is less than 1.

In an *improper* fraction, the numerator is larger than the denominator. Thus $\frac{12}{5}$ is larger than 1.

Improper fractions may be expressed as *mixed numbers* and vice versa. Thus $\frac{12}{5} = 2\frac{2}{5}$; $6\frac{1}{2} = \frac{13}{2}$.

An *integer,* or *whole number,* may be considered as a fraction with 1 as the denominator. Thus: $3 = \frac{3}{1}$; $428 = \frac{428}{1}$.

Reciprocals. The reciprocal of a fraction is the inverse of the fraction; that is, it is the fraction "upside down." Thus, the reciprocal of $\frac{2}{3}$ is $\frac{3}{2}$; the reciprocal of 12 is the inverse of $\frac{12}{1}$, which is $\frac{1}{12}$.

Since division is the inverse of multiplication, dividing by a fraction is the same as multiplying by the reciprocal of the fraction. Thus, $25 \div \frac{3}{2} = 25 \times \frac{2}{3}$. Similarly, $25 \times \frac{1}{2} = 25 \div 2 = \frac{25}{2}$.

The value of the fraction is unchanged if both the numerator and denominator are multiplied by the same number. Thus,

$$\frac{3}{2} = \frac{3 \times 5}{2 \times 5} = \frac{15}{10}$$

Similarly, the value of a fraction is unchanged if both numerator and denominator are divided by the same number. Thus,

$$\frac{8}{12} = \frac{8/4}{12/4} = \frac{2}{3}$$

The familiar "cancelling" is an application of this rule.

However, adding (or subtracting) the same number to numerator and denominator *does* alter the value of the fraction. Thus $\frac{2}{3}$ is *not* equal to $\frac{2+5}{3+5} = \frac{7}{8}$.

$\frac{2}{3} \neq \frac{2+5}{3+5}$. The sign $\neq$ is read "is not equal to."

Percentage. Percent is the fractional part of a number expressed in "parts per hundred." Thus, $\frac{3}{4}$ of a group means 3 out of 4, or 75 out of a 100 or 75 percent; similarly, 30 percent of 20 means $(30/100) \times 20 = .03 \times 20 = 6$.

Decimals. Decimals are special fractions in which the denominator is some power of 10. Thus, $0.1 = \frac{1}{10}$; $0.03 = \frac{3}{100}$ or $\frac{3}{10^2}$; $325.2 = 325\frac{2}{10}$; $25.42 = 25\frac{42}{100}$.

Moving the decimal point one place to the right multiplies the number by 10; two places to the right multiplies the number by 10×10 or 100; n places to the right multiplies the number by 10^n (that is, $10 \times 10 \times 10 \ldots n$ times). Moving the decimal point one place to the left *divides* the number by 10; n places to the left divides the number by 10^n.

Powers—Exponents. When a number appears as a factor more than one time, the multiplication can be expressed more efficiently in *exponential* form or *power* form. The *base* is the number which appears as the factor and the *exponent* is the number of times the base multiplies itself. Thus, $2 \times 2 \times 2 \times 2 \times 2 = 2^5$, where 2 is the base and 5 is the exponent (or power). Similarly, $10 \times 10 \times 10 = 10^3$. Conversely, 5^4 means $5 \times 5 \times 5 \times 5 = 625$.

2^5 is read "two to the fifth power" or simply "two to the fifth."

The second power is often called "square." Thus 7^2 may be read as "seven to the second," but is more often read "seven squared." The reason for this terminology is that the area of a square is the length of the side multiplied by itself.

The third power is often called "cube." Thus, 7^3 is read "seven cubed" as well as "seven to the third." The reason for this terminology is that the volume of a cube is the length of the side multiplied by itself three times.

If the number appears as a factor only once, the exponent 1 is understood. Thus, $10 = 10^1$.

Multiplication. The definition of exponents permits the efficient multiplication of exponentials.

Since $4^5 = 4 \times 4 \times 4 \times 4 \times 4$, and $4^3 = 4 \times 4 \times 4$, it follows that $4^5 \times 4^3 = (4 \times 4 \times 4 \times 4 \times 4) \times (4 \times 4 \times 4) = 4^8$.

The same answer results by adding the exponents: $4^5 \times 4^3 = 4^{5+3} = 4^8$.

This leads to the *multiplication rule: To multiply numbers expressed as powers of the same base, add the exponents.* In general,

$$a^n \times a^m = a^{n+m}$$

Division. Similarly, division of exponentials may be carried out efficiently:

$$4^5 \div 4^3 = \frac{4 \times 4 \times 4 \times 4 \times 4}{4 \times 4 \times 4} = 4 \times 4 = 4^2$$

This leads to the *division rule: To divide numbers expressed as powers of the same base, subtract the exponent of the denominator from the exponent of the numerator.* In general,

$$a^n \div a^m = \frac{a^n}{a^m} = a^{m-n}$$

Negative exponents. The idea of exponents has been extended to negative powers. Applying the rule for the division of 4^3 by 4^5 yields

$$\frac{4^3}{4^5} = 4^{3-5} = 4^{-2}$$

In terms of the original definition of exponents, 4^{-2} is meaningless. However, by carrying out the division in the extended form,

$$\frac{4^3}{4^5} = \frac{4 \times 4 \times 4}{4 \times 4 \times 4 \times 4 \times 4} = \frac{1}{4 \times 4} = \frac{1}{4^2}$$

Therefore, for the sake of consistency, 4^{-2} is set equal to $\frac{1}{4^2}$.

From this follows the *definition* of negative exponents: *A number to a negative exponent is the reciprocal of the number to the positive exponent.* That is,

$$a^{-n} = \frac{1}{a^n}$$

Thus, $10^{-2} = \frac{1}{10^2} = \frac{1}{100}$; $\frac{1}{10^3} = 10^{-3}$; likewise, $\frac{1}{10^{-5}} = 10^5$

As a consequence of this definition, any exponential may be moved from the numerator to the denominator (or vice versa) by changing the *sign* of the exponent.

Zero as an exponent. Another consequence of the rule for division of powers is the definition of zero as an exponent.

The division rule for 4^3 divided by 4^3 yields

$$4^3 \div 4^3 = \frac{4^3}{4^3} = 4^{3-3} = 4^0$$

Thus far, 4^0 is meaningless. However, $\frac{4^3}{4^3} = 1$ (any number divided by itself is 1). Therefore for the sake of consistency, 4^0 is set equal to 1; that is, $4^0 = 1$. In general, $N^0 = 1$.

That is, any number, N, to the zeroth power is equal to 1, since in all cases N^0 means that the number to some power has been divided by the *same number* to the *same power*.

Raising to a power. To raise a number already in power form to another power, multiply the exponents. Thus,

$$(4^5)^3 = 4^5 \times 4^5 \times 4^5 = 4^{5 \times 3} = 4^{15}$$

Roots. The expression $\sqrt{25}$ means to find the number that when multiplied by itself will give 25. The number is obviously 5, since $5^2 = 25$. The expression $\sqrt{25}$ is read "the square root of 25."

Similarly, the expression $\sqrt[3]{64}$ means to find a number that multiplied by itself three times will give 64. The number is obviously 4, since $4^3 = 4 \times 4 \times 4 = 64$. The expression $\sqrt[3]{64}$ is read "the cube root of 64." More generally, $\sqrt[n]{N}$ means the nth root of N.

Very few numbers have roots that are whole numbers or that can be obtained by inspection. There are several methods for calculating roots, but these will not be discussed here. Since high accuracy is not required for most purposes (see "Approximations," below), the roots may be approximated by trial and error.

Thus, $\sqrt{30}$ must lie between 5 and 6, since $5^2 = 25$ and $6^2 = 36$. Further, since 30 lies about halfway between 25 and 36, a good guess for the $\sqrt{30}$ is about 5.5. Squaring 5.5 gives 30.25, which is close to 30. If higher accuracy is desired, a second or third guess may be tried.

Roots of Exponentials. Certain roots of exponentials may be obtained more simply by a further extension of the concept of exponents.

The expression $\sqrt{4^6}$ means to find a number that when multiplied by itself will give 4^6. The answer is obviously 4^3, since $4^3 \times 4^3 = 4^6$.

Similarly, $\sqrt[3]{4^{24}} = 4^8$, since $4^8 \times 4^8 \times 4^8 = 4^{24}$. In general, $\sqrt[n]{a^m} = a^{m/n}$.

This can be stated as a rule: To obtain the nth root of an exponential, divide the exponent by n.

This extension leads to an alternate expression of roots. Thus, $\sqrt{2} = 2^{1/2}$, since $2^{1/2} \times 2^{1/2} = 2^{1/2 + 1/2} = 2^1 = 2$.

Similarly, $\sqrt[3]{10} = 10^{1/3}$

The most important application of exponents is the handling of very large or very small numbers encountered in science. This is done by expressing the numbers in the efficient notation of powers of 10.

Scientific Notation

Powers of 10. From the definitions of exponents, it is clear that all multiples of 10 can be expressed as powers of 10. Thus, $100 = 10 \times 10 = 10^2$; $1000 = 10 \times 10 \times 10 = 10^3$.

Similarly, $\dfrac{1}{100} = \dfrac{1}{10 \times 10} = \dfrac{1}{10^2} = 10^{-2}$;

$\dfrac{1}{1000} = \dfrac{1}{10 \times 10 \times 10} = \dfrac{1}{10^3} = 10^{-3}$.

Moreover, multiples or submultiples of 10 have common names (such as thousand, million, billion) that are familiar and meaningful. The following table is a partial list.

1,000,000,000,000	=	10^{12}	one trillion
1,000,000,000	=	10^9	one billion
1,000,000	=	10^6	one million
1,000	=	10^3	one thousand
100	=	10^2	one hundred
10	=	10^1	ten
1	=	10^0	one
0.1	=	10^{-1}	one tenth
0.01	=	10^{-2}	one one-hundredth
0.001	=	10^{-3}	one one-thousandth
0.000,001	=	10^{-6}	one one-millionth
0.000,000,001	=	10^{-9}	one one-billionth

For numbers greater than 1, the exponent is positive and is equal to the number of zeros following the 1. For numbers smaller than 1, the exponent is negative and is equal to the number of places 1 is to the right of the decimal point.

Very large or very small numbers can be read *meaningfully,* by expressing them as products of appropriate powers to ten.

Thus, 10^{12} may be read as "one trillion." However, if expressed as $10^3 \times 10^9$ (to which it is equal), it is read "one thousand-billion." Similarly, if expressed as $10^6 \times 10^6$, it is read as "one million-million."

Similarly, 10^{-15} expressed as $10^{-6} \times 10^{-9}$ is read as "one one-millionth of a billionth"; expressed as $10^{-3} \times 10^{-12}$ it is read as "one one-thousandth of a billionth."

Other numbers. Any number can be expressed as the product of a number and a power of 10. Thus, 4256 may be expressed as

$$425.6 \times 10$$

or $\qquad 42.56 \times 100 = 42.56 \times 10^2$

or $\qquad 4.256 \times 100 = 4.256 \times 10^3$

Moving the decimal point to the left divides the number by 10; hence to restore the value, the number is multiplied by a power of 10 equal to the number of places the decimal point has been moved to the left.

In decimals smaller than 1, the decimal point is moved to the right, and the resulting number is multiplied by a negative power of 10 equal to the number of places the decimal point has been moved to the left. Thus,

$$0.000342 = 3.42 \times \frac{1}{10,000} = 3.42 \times \frac{1}{10^4} = 3.42 \times 10^{-4}$$

Usually, the decimal point is moved so that the first number lies between 1 and 10. However, this is a matter of choice, and at times the decimal point is moved so that the resulting expression can be read simply and meaningfully. Thus the speed of light, 30,000,000,000 cm per sec, can be expressed as 3×10^{10} cm per sec. But if expressed as 30×10^9 cm per sec, it can be read as "30 billion centimeters per second."

Manipulating very large or very small numbers. The scientific notation makes possible the convenient handling of multiplication or division of very unwieldy numbers.

Example 1: Suppose it is desired to calculate the distance light travels in a year, given the speed of light and the number of seconds in a year.

speed of light = 30,000,000,000 cm per sec = 3×10^{10} cm per sec
one year = 31,500,000 sec = 3.15×10^7 sec

Therefore, the required distance = $(3 \times 10^{10}) \times (3.15 \times 10^7) = (3 \times 3.15) \times (10^{10} \times 10^7) = 9.45 \times 10^{17}$ cm.

Further, if this is expressed as 945×10^{15} or, better, as $945 \times (10^6 \times 10^9)$ cm, it may be read as "945 million-billion centimeters."

Example 2: To find the time required for light to come from the sun to the earth, given the distance of the sun and the speed of light

distance of the sun = 93,000,000 mi = 9.3×10^7 mi
speed of light = 186,000 mi per sec = 1.86×10^5 cm per sec

$$\text{time} = \frac{\text{distance}}{\text{speed}} = \frac{9.3 \times 10^7}{1.86 \times 10^5} = \left(\frac{9.3}{1.86}\right) \times \left(\frac{10^7}{10^5}\right)$$
$$= 5 \times 10^2 = 500 \text{ sec}$$

Example 3: What is the weight of 2,000,000,000,000,000 hydrogen atoms if each weighs 0.000,000,000,000,000,000,000,001,66 gram?

weight = $(2 \times 10^{15}) \times (1.66 \times 10^{-24}) = 3.72 \times 10^{-9}$ g
(to be read as "3.72 billionths of a gram")

Approximations

Despite the fact that science is an exact discipline, much of its mathematical reasoning can be carried out with approximate numerical values. In fact, the scientist often deliberately rounds off numbers, uses rough estimates of numbers, and makes mental estimates of complicated mathematical expressions. The loss of exactness is more than compensated by the meaningfulness of the numbers and by the ease with which the answers are obtained. Moreover, the use of round numbers introduces a simplicity that permits placing the emphasis on the reasoning involved in the discussion.

Accuracy of data. All scientific data derived from measurement have a limited accuracy because of errors inherent in the method of measurement. The accuracy is indicated by the number of *significant* figures. Thus, the statement that the polar diameter of the earth is 7926.68 miles indicates that it is known accurately to six significant figures (with some uncertainty in the sixth figure). The accuracy of most measurements does not exceed three or four significant figures. For most purposes, however, accuracy of six or even four significant figures is not necessary, and consequently the numbers are rounded off.

Rounding off. To round off a number, select the significant figure to which the accuracy is desired. Then (a) if the next digit is less than 5, replace all succeeding digits by zeros and at the same time drop the decimals; (b) if the next digit is 5 or greater, increase the significant figure by one and replace the succeeding digits by zeros.

The method is illustrated in the following successive steps in rounding off the polar diameter of the earth.

7926.7	to five significant figures
7927	to four significant figures
7930	to three significant figures
7900	to two significant figures
8000	to one significant figure

Approximate calculations. The rounding off of numbers and the scientific notation make possible the quick estimate of answers and avoid tedious calculations. The following examples will illustrate the method.

Example 1: Suppose it is desired to compare the diameter of the earth with that of the moon. Given:

diameter of the earth (polar) = 7927.68 mi
diameter of the moon = 2159.9 mi

The desired answer requires the division of 7927.68 by 2159.9. By long division the answer is 3.6704.

The scientist, however, usually proceeds in another way. He rounds off the diameter of the earth to 8000 miles; that of the moon to 2000 miles; and quickly gives the answer as "nearly 4." While this is not "exact," it is sufficiently accurate for most purposes and for a meaningful comparison of the size of the two bodies.

Example 2: To find the time required for a radar signal to go to the moon and be reflected back. Given:

speed of light = 186,000 mi per sec = 1.9×10^5 cm per sec
distance of the moon = 240,000 mi = 2.4×10^5 mi

$$\text{time for double journey} = \frac{2 \times (2.4 \times 10^5)}{1.9 \times 10^5} = \frac{4.8}{1.9} \doteq 2\frac{1}{2} \text{ sec}$$

The sign $\doteq$ is read "is approximately equal to."

Order of magnitude. Quite often, even less accuracy than one significant figure is sufficient for rough estimates. Thus, distance to the sun may be taken as "about" 100 million miles; the speed of light is $\frac{1}{5}$ of a million miles per second. Similarly, in comparing the diameter of the earth (8000 miles) to that of the sun (864,000 miles), the former can be taken as of "the order of" 10 thousand miles and the latter as of "the order of" 1 million miles. These numbers, while "inexact," are nevertheless quantitative and are useful in making meaningful comparisons.

Numbers indicating only order of magnitude are indicated by $\sim$. Thus, if d is the diameter of the water molecule, the expression $d \sim 10^{-8}$ cm is read as follows: The diameter of the water molecule is "of the order of one one-hundred millionths of a centimeter."

Algebra   Algebra is essentially generalized arithmetic. The generalization is achieved largely by the device of using letters and other symbols instead of numbers. The symbolism facilitates carrying out the operations and permits the emphasis to be placed on relations.

Symbolism. Any letter can be used as the symbol of any number, known or unknown. Usually, the first letters of the alphabet stand for known quantities and the last (x, y, or z) for unknowns. In order to suggest the meaning of the symbol, the letter is often the initial of the quantity symbolized. Thus, h may stand for *h*eight; A for *a*rea; W for *w*eight. In any given discussion the meaning of the symbols should be clearly stated.

Subscripts. A further aid to symbolism is the use of subscripts on the symbols. This helps differentiate the symbols and avoids the introduction of many different symbols in a given discussion. Thus, while d may stand for diameter, d_1 may stand for the diameter of the first body and d_2 for the diameter of the second body; alternately d_1 may stand for the diameter of a balloon at the first temperature and d_2 the diameter at the second temperature. Similarly, d_e may stand for the diameter of the earth and d_s the diameter of the sun. In any given discussion the meaning of the subscripts should be clearly stated or unmistakenly implied.

Another efficient method of symbolism is the use of primes. Thus V may stand for the original volume and V' the new volume: V' is read "V-prime"; V'' is read "V-double prime."

Equations. The central part of algebra is the equation. It is a statement that the quantity represented by a combination of symbols on the left is equal to the quantity represented by a combination of symbols on the right.

Thus
$$3v = 4 \times 24$$
where v may represent the velocity of a body.

Solving equations. The *fact* of *equality* is not destroyed by *any operation* performed on one side of the equation, provided that the *same* or *equivalent operation* is performed on the other side. All operations for "solving" equations are consequences of this principle.

Thus, in the equation above, dividing both sides by 3 gives
$$v = 4 \times 8 = 32$$

The operations usually performed in solving equations are the following:

Adding the same number:
$$\begin{array}{rcl} x - 2 &=& 14 \\ + 2 &=& +2 \\ \hline x &=& 16 \end{array} \quad \text{or} \quad \begin{array}{rcl} x - a &=& 14 \\ + a &=& +a \\ \hline x &=& 14 + a \end{array}$$

Subtracting the same number:
$$\begin{array}{rcl} y + 7 &=& 28 \\ - 7 &=& -7 \\ \hline y &=& 21 \end{array} \quad \text{or} \quad \begin{array}{rcl} y + 3c &=& 28c \\ - 3c &=& -3c \\ \hline y &=& 25c \end{array}$$

Multiplying by the same number:

$$\frac{x}{5} = 20 \qquad \text{or} \qquad \frac{x}{a} = 20$$

$$\frac{x}{5} \times 5 = 20 \times 5 \qquad\qquad \frac{x}{a} \times a = 20 \times a$$

$$x = 100 \qquad\qquad\qquad x = 20a$$

Dividing by the same number: $\qquad 3x = 12 \qquad \text{or} \qquad ax = 12$

$$\frac{3x}{3} = \frac{12}{3} \qquad\qquad \frac{ax}{a} = \frac{12}{a}$$

$$x = 4 \qquad\qquad\qquad x = \frac{12}{a}$$

Squaring both sides: $\qquad c = 3 \times 10^{10} \qquad \text{or} \qquad \sqrt{x} = 10$

$$c^2 = 9 \times 10^{20} \qquad\qquad x = 100$$

Extracting the square root of both sides:

$$x^2 = 25 \times 10^{10} \qquad \text{or} \qquad U_1^2 = 16U_2^2$$

$$x = 5 \times 10^5 \qquad\qquad U = 4U_2$$

Geometry

Most of the concepts of elementary geometry are common experience. The reader is advised to look them up if he does not know them.

The following is a list of common concepts:

Plane figures: triangle, square, rectangle, parallelogram, circle, ellipse, parabola, hyperbola.

Solid figures: cube, sphere, rectangular, parallelepiped ("box").

In addition, the reader should know the following relations:

Plane figures. The *perimeter* of a plane figure is the sum of the sides.

The area of a square is the square of the side: $A = s^2$.

The area of a triangle is ½ the base times the height: $A = \frac{1}{2} bh$.

Solid figures. The volume of a rectangular box is the length times the width times the height: $V = lwh$.

The volume of a cube is the length of the side cubed: $V = s^3$.

Circles. The diameter is twice the radius: $d = 2r$.

The ratio of the length of the circumference, C, to the diameter, d, is π; that is $\frac{C}{d} = \pi$. Hence, $C = \pi d$.

The numerical value of π is 3.1416. That is, the circumference of a circle is a little more than 3 times the diameter.

The area of a circle is π times the square of the radius: $A = \pi r^2$.

Spheres. The area of a sphere: $A = 4\pi r^2$.

The volume of a sphere: $V = \frac{4}{3} \pi r^3$ or $V = \frac{1}{6} \pi d^3$.

Angular measure. A circle is divided into 360 degrees. A right angle is 90 degrees.

One degree is divided into 60 minutes (60′) and each minute into 60 seconds (60″).

Angles and arcs are measured in the same units. Thus an *angle* of 45 degrees formed by the radii from the center cuts an *arc* of 45 degrees on the circumference.

Proportionality

One of the most powerful tools in quantitative thinking is the concept of proportionality and the related concepts of ratio, proportion, and variation. These are some of the most neglected concepts in arithmetic.

Ratio. A ratio may be defined simply as a fraction indicating one number divided by another. Thus, the ratio of 5 to 3 is $\frac{5}{3}$. As such, it may be handled as any other fraction.

However, "ratio" implies *comparison*. The ratio of 5 to 3 implies how many times 5 is as large as 3. To emphasize its comparative nature, the ratio of 5 to 3 is designated as 5:3.

Proportion. A proportion is a statement of the equality of two ratios. Thus, since the ratio of 5 to 3 is equal to the ratio of 10 to 6, the fact of equality can be stated as an ordinary equation:

$$\frac{5}{3} = \frac{10}{6}$$

To emphasize that the quantities are *compared* and *what* quantities are compared, however, the proportion is also written as 5:3::10:6. It is read "5 is to 3 as 10 is to 6."

The reader should develop facility in interpreting either form and in translating one form into the other.

Two additional forms of expressing proportions implicitly will be developed in the discussion of the more inclusive idea of *proportionality*.

Proportionality. Much of the quantitative thinking and experimenting in science is concerned with establishing a relation between one quantity and another quantity and ultimately expressing it as the equality of ratios. This leads to the concept of proportionality.

Everyday experience offers numerous instances in which one quantity depends upon another quantity. Thus, the height of a child depends on his age; the brightness of a light depends on its distance from the observer; the length of the circumference of a circle is related to the length of the diameter (or of the radius); the area of a circle is also related to the length of the diameter; the average temperature of a locality is related to the latitude.

In the majority of cases, the relation between the first quantity and the second is not a simple one. In many cases, however, simple relations do exist and can be expressed in *simple* mathematical forms. Several types of relations will be considered.

Direct proportionality. In one of the simplest types of relation, the first quantity increases or decreases (that is, *varies*) in direct ratio to the second quantity. A good example is the relation of the length of the circumference to the length of the diameter. In a comparison of any two circles, if the diameter of the second circle is 1.7456 times as long as that of the first, the circumference of the second circle is also 1.7456 times that of the first. If a circular wave expands so that the diameter increases by 30 percent, the circumference also increases by 30 percent. The circumference is said to be *directly proportional* to the diameter (or to *vary directly* as the diameter). Direct proportionality is expressed as follows:

$$C \propto d$$

which is read as "C is proportional to d."

The proportionality expression can be transformed into an ordinary equation:

$$C = k \times d$$

where k is the proportionality constant. The value of k in this instance has been shown to be π.

From either of the above expressions it is clear that the ratio of the circumferences of any two circles, C_1/C_2, is the same as the ratio of the diameters, d_1/d_2. As shown above, the equality of these ratios can be expressed as a proportion.

Another example will clarify further the meaning of the proportionality constant. In buying a commodity, say sugar, the total money to be paid, M, is proportional to the weight bought, w:

$$M \propto w$$

That is, buying twice as much sugar will cost twice as much money; buying one half as much sugar will cost one half as much; etc.

In order to find the actual bill in dollars, however, the price is needed. The proportionality expression is transformed into the equation

$$M = p \times w$$

where p is the price and is the *proportionality constant*. It represents "money per pound."

Every proportionality constant is of the general nature of a "price," in that it represents the number that transforms the proportionality expression into an ordinary equation.

Directly proportional to the square.   The area of a square depends on the length of the side. However, *doubling* the side does not double the area, but increases it to four times; *tripling* the side increases the area to *nine* times. The area is said to be *proportional to the square* of the side:

$$A \propto s^2$$

When transformed into an ordinary equation, this becomes

$$A = ks^2$$

where k is a constant depending on the units chosen for the measurement.

Similarly, areas of circles are proportional to the square of diameters:

$$A \propto d^2$$

or

$$A = kd^2$$

where k is $\pi/4$.

In all cases of similar geometric figures, the areas are proportional to the square of corresponding lines.

Directly proportional to the cube.   The volume of a cube is directly proportional to the *cube* of the side:

$$V \propto s^3$$

or

$$V = ks^3$$

Similarly, the volume of a sphere is directly proportional to the cube of the diameter:

$$V \propto d^3$$

$$V = kd^3 = \frac{1}{6} \pi d^3$$

In general, volumes of *solids* vary directly as the *cubes* of corresponding lines.

Inversely proportional. In some instances, increase in one quantity results in a proportional *decrease* in the other quantity. Thus, for a given distance, *doubling* the (average) speed decreases the time of travel to *one half*. Speed is *inversely proportional* to the time.

$$v \propto \frac{1}{t}$$

or

$$v = \frac{k}{t}$$

where k is a constant depending on the distance under consideration and the units chosen for the measurements.

Inversely proportional to the square. Nature provides some interesting cases in which the value of a quantity *decreases* as the square of another quantity *increases*. The best example is the brightness of a light source, which *decreases* as the square of the distance from the source *increases:*

$$B \propto \frac{1}{d^2}$$

$$B = \frac{k}{d^2}$$

Doubling the distance decreases the brightness to *one fourth; tripling* the distance decreases the brightness to *one ninth*. This type of proportionality is called "inverse-square" proportionality.

These ideas may be extended to more complicated types of proportionality, but need not be considered here.

Trigonometry   Trigonometry is the study of triangles and the ratios between sides and angles. Only two ideas will be considered here—namely, the concepts of *tangent* and *sine*.

Tangent. When the sun is shining on a flat landscape, it is obvious that the taller trees cast the longer shadows. More precisely, the shadows are *directly proportional* to the heights (at any given time of the day).

Expressed geometrically, the trees form similar triangles, $A_1B_1C_1$, $A_2B_2C_2$, etc., in which the corresponding sides are proportional.

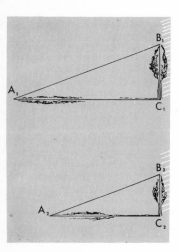

Two types of proportion may be immediately set up, for tree 1 and tree 2:

$$\frac{\text{height } 1}{\text{height } 2} = \frac{\text{shadow } 1}{\text{shadow } 2} \quad \text{or} \quad \frac{B_1C_1}{B_2C_2} = \frac{A_1C_1}{A_2C_2}$$

and

$$\frac{\text{height } 1}{\text{shadow } 1} = \frac{\text{height } 2}{\text{shadow } 2} \quad \text{or} \quad \frac{B_1C_1}{A_1B_1} = \frac{B_2C_2}{A_2C_2}$$

Thus the ratios of the *height* to *shadow* are the same for all trees, for a given angle elevation of the sun (that is, for the same angle A). Hence, by measuring the ratios of height to shadow for one tree, the height of any other tree can be calculated from the length of its shadow (and vice versa).

The ratio of *height:shadow* is defined as the tangent of angle A. That is,

$$\tan A = \frac{BC}{AC} = \frac{\text{height}}{\text{shadow}}$$

The tangents of all angles have been calculated and appear in tables of many books in mathematics and science.

Example: A tree casts a shadow of 84 feet. The angle of elevation of the sun is 17 degrees. What is the height of the tree?

From the tables: tan 17° = 0.30573

therefore

$$\frac{\text{height}}{\text{shadow}} = \tan 17° = 0.30573 \text{ or } 0.31 \text{ (approx)}$$

and therefore

height = shadow × 0.31 = 84 × .31 = 26 ft (approx)

Sine. The ratio *BC* to *AB* is likewise constant for a given angle. It is defined as the sine of angle *A*:

$$\sin A = \frac{BC}{AB}$$

In the diagram, *BC/AB* is the ratio of the height of the tree to the direct line from the top of the tree to the tip of the shadow.

For any given angle, four additional ratios are constant, but these need not be discussed here.

B. NUMERICAL DATA

1 meter (m) = 39.37 inches (a little over a yard)   **Metric System**
1 centimeter (cm) = 0.01 meter = 0.39 inch (⅖ inch)
1 kilometer (km) = 1000 meters = 0.62 mile (⅝ mile)
1 cubic centimeter (cc) (volume of a cube 1 cm on the side) = 1/28.3
    fluid ounces
1 liter (1) = 1000 cubic centimeters (very nearly) = 1.06 quarts (a little
    over 1 quart)
1 gram (g) = weight of 1 cc of water (very nearly)
1 kilogram (kg) = 1000 grams = 2.2 pounds
1 metric ton = 1000 kilograms = 2200 pounds

1 yard = 3 feet = 36 inches = 91.4 cm   **British System**
1 mile = 5280 feet = 1.6 km
1 pound = 16 ounces = 453.4 g
1 ton = 2000 pounds = 907 kg

Angstrom unit (Å) = 10^{-8} cm = of the order of magnitude of the diam-   **Interrelationships of Some**
    eter of atoms   **Commonly Used Units**
Astronomical unit (AU) = 93,000,000 mi = 149,000,000 km = dis-
    tance from earth to sun
Light year (LY) = 6×10^{12} mi = 9.6×10^{12} km = distance light
    travels in a year
calorie (cal) = 4.18 joules = 4.18×10^7 ergs

kilowatt hour (kwh) = 3,600,000 joules

atmosphere (atm) = 14.7 lb per in.^{2} = 1.003 kg per cm^2 = 10^6 dynes per cm^2

electron volt (ev) = 1.6 × 10^{-19} joules = 1.6 × 10^{-12} ergs

atomic mass unit (AMU) = 931 Mev

1 gram = 9 × 10^{20} ergs = 9 × 10^{13} joules = 2.15 × 10^{13} calories

Important Physical Quantities

Diameter of the earth (average) = 7918 mi = 12,542 km

Distance to the moon (average) = 239,000 mi = 380,000 km

Distance to the sun = 93,000,000 mi = 149,000,000 km

F.P. of water = 0° C = 273° A = 32° F

B.P. of water = 100° C = 373° A = 212° F

Velocity of light = 3 × 10^{10} cm per sec = 180,000 mi per sec

Avogadro's number = 6 × 10^{23} (number of hydrogen atoms in 1 gram of hydrogen)

Charge on the electron = 4.8 × 10^{-10} esu = 1.6 × 10^{-19} coulombs

Faraday = 96,500 coulombs = 3 × 10^{14} esu = 6 × 10^{23} electrons

Weight of hydrogen atom = 1.66 × 10^{-24} g

Weight of electron = 9.1 × 10^{-28} g = 1/1838 weight of the hydrogen atom

REFERENCES FOR FURTHER READING

REFERENCES FOR CHAPTER 1

1.1 Conant, J. B., *Modern Science and Modern Man*. New York: Columbia Univ. Press, 1952. BOOKS
Explores the philosophical implications of modern physics and modern chemistry.

1.2 Hogben, L., *Science for the Citizen*. New York: W. W. Norton and Co., Inc., 1957.
Written for the layman so that he may understand the development of the sciences in the background of society.

1.3 Jaffe, B., *Chemistry Creates a New World*. New York: Thomas Y. Crowell Co., 1957.
An enthusiastic account of the progress being made in modern chemistry.

1.4 Jeans, J., *The Growth of Physical Science* (2d ed.). New York: Cambridge Univ. Press, 1951.
Begins with the Babylonian system of counting and ends with today's mystery of subatomic structure.

1.5 Margenau, H., *The Nature of Physical Reality*. New York: McGraw-Hill Book Co., Inc., 1950.
Philosophical. A physicist analyzes the nature of scientific knowledge and the reality beyond the senses.

1.6 Russell, B., *The Scientific Outlook*. Chicago: The Free Press, 1931.
A leading philosopher discusses the place of man, his ethics and religion in a world of matter and force.

1.7 Shapley, H., Rapport, S., and Wright, H., *A Treasury of Science* (4th ed.). New York: Harper & Bros., 1959.
A general survey of the three worlds of science: the physical world, the world of life, and the world of man.

1.8 Standen, A., *Science is a Sacred Cow*. New York: E. P. Dutton and Co., Inc., 1950.
A needed lesson on the value of seeing things in an unprejudiced light.

1.9 Sullivan, J. W. N., *The Limitations of Science*. New York: The Viking Press, 1933.
The power, kinds of knowledge, and limitations of modern science (also paperback).

1.10 Untermeyer, L., *Makers of the Modern World*. New York: Simon and Schuster, Inc., 1955.

> Contains biographies of 92 moderns—including artists, inventors, philosophers, composers, scientists, and statesmen—who have greatly influenced twentieth-century thought and culture.

1.11 Whitehead, A. N., *Science and the Modern World*. New York: New American Library of World Literature, 1948.

> Eight lectures at Harvard on the influence of science on Western culture.

ANTHOLOGY

1.12 Feigl, H. and Broderick, M., *Readings in the Philosophy of Science*. New York: Appleton-Century-Crofts, Inc., 1953.

> A collection of original papers on the nature of science and the scientific method. For advanced readers. See especially:
>
> (a) Bridgman, P. W., "The Logic of Modern Physics," pp. 34-46.
>
> (b) Poincare, H., "Non-Euclidean Geometries and the Non-Euclidean World," pp. 171-180.
>
> (c) Schlich, M., "Are Natural Laws Conventions," pp. 181-188.
>
> (d) Campbell, N. R., "The Structure of Theories," pp. 288-308.
>
> (e) Einstein, A., "The Laws of Science and the Laws of Ethics," pp. 779-780.

ARTICLES in *Scientific American*

1.13 Barnard, C. I., "A National Science Policy," **197,** No. 5, pp. 45-49 (1957).

> The National Science Foundation shows that science is neglected in the U. S.

REFERENCES FOR CHAPTER 2

BOOKS

2.1 Baker, R. H., *When Stars Come Out* (Rev. ed.). New York: The Viking Press, 1954.

> A guide to the heavens, written to explain many phenomena.

2.2 Beet, E. A., *The Sky and its Mysteries*. London: G. Bell and Sons, Ltd., 1952.

> A preliminary treatment that combines history and astrophysics.

2.3 Branley, F. M., *Mars*. New York: Thomas Y. Crowell Co., 1955.

> Discusses Mars, the planet in the solar system most like the Earth. Accurate, clear descriptions.

2.4 Jones, H. S., *Life on Other Worlds*. New York: The Macmillan Co., 1940.

> Presents the evidence, summarized from present-day astronomy, on the question of whether life exists on other worlds.

2.5 Kuiper, G. P., *The Atmospheres of the Earth and Planets*. Chicago: Univ. of Chicago Press, 1951.

> A collection of papers on a symposium by authorities in astronomy, geology, chemistry, and physics. For reference and the advanced reader.

2.6 Ley, W. and von Braun, W., *The Exploration of Mars*. New York: The Viking Press, 1956.

A scientist's explanation of a proposed voyage to Mars. Excellent color illustrations and diagrams.

2.7 Nicolson, M. H., *Voyages to the Moon*. New York: The Macmillan Co., 1948.

A collection of stories of cosmic voyages from the literature of two centuries.

2.8 Pickering, J. S., *1001 Questions Answered About Astronomy*. New York: Dodd, Mead and Co., Inc., 1958.

Common questions about the universe and its components answered by a staff member of the famous Hayden Planetarium in New York.

2.9 Skilling, W. T. and Richardson, R. S., *A Brief Text in Astronomy* (Rev. ed.). New York: Henry Holt and Co., Inc., 1959.

For general background or as a stimulus to further study.

2.10 Watson, F. G., *Between the Planets* (Rev. ed.). Cambridge, Mass.: Harvard Univ. Press, 1956.

An interesting and well-illustrated source book for the amateur astronomer, including the story of the asteroids, comets, meteors, and meteorites which traverse our solar system.

2.11 Whipple, F. L., *Earth, Moon and the Planets*. New York: McGraw-Hill Book Co., Inc., 1941.

An outstanding astronomer makes the subject understandable to the general reader.

2.12 Zim, H. S. and Baker, R. H., *Stars: A Guide to the Constellations, Sun, Moon, Planets and Other Features of the Heavens*. New York: Simon and Schuster, Inc., 1956.

A small pocket book for the novice, the amateur, or anyone who wants to enjoy the wonders of the heavens.

2.13 Cohen, M. R. and Drabkin, I. E., *A Source Book in Greek Science*. New York: McGraw-Hill Book Co., Inc., 1948.   **ANTHOLOGIES**

A collection of original papers on the nature of science and the scientific method. See especially:
   (a) Aristotle, "The Theory of Concentric Spheres," pp. 101f. "The Rotation of the Earth on its Axis," pp. 105f. "The Shape and Size of the Earth," pp. 143f.
   (b) Eratosthenes, "Measurement of the Circumference of the Earth," pp. 149f.
   (c) Aristarchus, "The Heliocentric Hypothesis," pp. 107f.
   (d) Ptolemy, C., "The Heavens Rotate as a Sphere," pp. 122f.

2.14 Shapley, H. and Howarth, H. E., *Source Book in Astronomy*. New York: McGraw-Hill Book Co., Inc., 1929.

A collection of original papers on the nature of science and the scientific method. See especially:
   (a) Copernicus, N., "A Theory That the Moon Moves Around the Sun," pp. 1-13.
   (b) Kepler, J., "The Discovery of the Laws of Planetary Motion," pp. 30-40.
   (c) Galilei, Galileo, "Discovery of Jupiter's Satellites," pp. 49-52.
   (d) Newton, I., "Law of Gravitation," pp. 77-79. "The System of the World," pp. 79-88.

ARTICLES
in *Scientific American*

2.15 Beals, C. S., "Fossil Meteorite Craters," **199,** No. 1, pp. 32-39 (1958).
Craters up to 500 million years old have now been found by aerial photography.

2.16 Chapman, S., "The Earth in the Sun's Atmosphere," **201,** No. 4, pp. 64-71 (1959).
The extremely rarefied, superheated gas of the corona may surround the earth.

2.17 Newell, H. E., "The Satellite Project," **193,** No. 6, pp. 20-33 (1955).

2.18 Newgard, J. J. and Levoy, M., "Nuclear Rockets," **200,** No. 5, pp. 46-51 (1959).
With chemical fuels near their limits, rocket engineers turn to nuclear reactions.

2.19 Rice, F. O., "The Chemistry of Jupiter, **194,** No. 6, pp. 119-128 (1956).

2.20 Sciama, D., "Inertia," **196,** No. 2, pp. 99-109 (1957).
Newton thought it was an intrinsic property of matter; a modern theory disagrees.

REFERENCES FOR CHAPTER 3

BOOKS

3.1 Bachman, C. H., *Physics.* New York: John Wiley and Sons, Inc., 1955.
Modern physics for the nonacademic student.

3.2 Coleman, J. A., *Relativity for the Layman.* New York: William-Frederick Press, 1954.
Relativity, the theory "understood by only 12 men," is clearly explained.

3.3 Galilei, G., *Two New Sciences.* New York: The Macmillan Co., 1914 (paperback).
A translation of the original work. The concept of acceleration is developed in the "Third Day." Excerpt also in Ref. 3.10(a).

3.4 Lemon, H. B., *From Galileo to the Nuclear Age.* Chicago: Univ. of Chicago Press, 1946.
A textbook of the basic principles of physics for the nonscience student, presented in an interesting manner.

3.5 Levinger, E. E., *Galileo.* New York: Julian Messner, Inc., 1952.
The trials, defeats, and victories of one of the great pioneers of science. This tells of Galileo's great discoveries and inventions and the greater problem he faced in trying to open the eyes of the world.

3.6 Lieber, L. R., *The Einstein Theory of Relativity.* New York: Rinehart and Co., Inc., 1945.
Einstein's relativity presented in a comparatively elementary manner with simplified mathematical terms.

3.7 Newton, I., *Mathematical Principles of Natural Philosophy.* Chicago: Univ. of Chicago Press, 1947.
Original work unabridged. Book 3 contains the System of the World. Excerpt also in Ref. 3.10(b).

3.8 Semat, H., *Physics in the Modern World.* New York: Rinehart and Co., Inc., 1949.

College physics introduced to the novice with simplicity and thoroughness. All basic fields are amply discussed.

3.9 Sullivan, J. W. N., *Isaac Newton*. New York: The Macmillan Co., 1938.

A spirited evaluation of the life and genius of Newton.

3.10 Feigl, H. and Brodbeck, M., *Readings in the Philosophy of Science.* New York: Appleton-Century-Crofts, Inc., 1953.

ANTHOLOGIES

See especially:

(a) Russell, B., "On the Notion of Cause, with Applications to the Free-Will Problem," pp. 387-407.

3.11 Moulton, F. R. and Schifferes, J. J., *The Autobiography of Science.* Garden City, N. Y.: Doubleday and Co., Inc., 1945.

Collection of original papers. See especially:

(a) Galilei, Galileo, "Two New Sciences" (brief excerpt), pp. 77-86.

(b) Newton, I., "Principia: On Laws of Motion," pp. 171-194.

(c) Fahrenheit, D., "The First Mercury Thermometer," pp. 206-208.

(d) Thompson, B. (Count Rumford), "Heat is a Form of Motion: An Experiment in Boring Cannon," pp. 240-245.

(e) Joule, J. P., "On Matter, Living Force, and Heat," pp. 293-299.

(f) Thomson, W. (Lord Kelvin), "If Nature Could Run Backward," pp. 467-468.

(g) Einstein, A., "The Theory of Relativity," pp. 520-535.

3.12 Ginzburg, V. L., "Artificial Satellites and Relativity," **200,** No. 5, pp. 149-160 (1959).

ARTICLES
in *Scientific American*

A Soviet physicist relates how satellites could be used to test Einstein's theory.

3.13 Mengel, J. T. and Herget, P., "Tracking Satellites by Radio," **198,** No. 1, pp. 23-29 (1958).

An account of how radio is used to determine the orbits of artificial satellites.

3.14 Van Allen, J. A., "The Artificial Satellite," **195,** No. 5, pp. 41-47 (1956).

REFERENCES FOR CHAPTER 4

4.1 Bachman, C. H., *Physics.* New York: John Wiley and Sons, Inc., 1955.

Modern physics for the nonacademic student.

BOOKS

4.2 Bragg, W. L., *Electricity.* London: G. Bell and Sons, 1936.

Written for the general reader by a Nobel Prize winner. Clear and interesting account of a wide range of electrical phenomena.

4.3 Lemon, H. B., *From Galileo to the Nuclear Age.* Chicago: Univ. of Chicago Press, 1946.

A textbook for the nonacademic student. The subject of electricity is discussed clearly in Chs. 25, 26, and 27.

4.4 McDougal, W., *Fundamentals of Electricity*. American Tech. Soc., 1954.

An introduction to electricity useful for the beginning and intermediate student alike. Abundant diagrams and clear definitions.

4.5 Millikan, R. A., *Electrons + and −*. Chicago: Univ. of Chicago Press, 1947.

Excellently written but requires moderate background. Discusses the early Nobel Prize winning experiment on the measurement of the electronic charge (Chs. 3 and 4) and brings the knowledge up to date.

4.6 Semat, H., *Physics in the Modern World*. New York: Rinehart and Co., Inc., 1949.

College physics introduced to the novice with simplicity and thoroughness. All basic fields are amply discussed.

4.7 Skilling, H. H., *Exploring Electricity*. New York: Ronald Press Co., 1948.

The history of the electron from early experiments in Babylonia to the first atomic explosion in New Mexico; included are experiments of Faraday, Ampère, and Ohm.

ANTHOLOGIES   **4.8** Magie, W. F., *Source Book in Physics*. New York: McGraw-Hill Book Co., Inc., 1935.

Excerpts from original papers.

   (a) Gilbert, W., "On Magnetism and Electricity," pp. 387-393.

   (b) Franklin, B., "The One Fluid Theory of Electricity," pp. 400-403.

   (c) Coulomb, C., "Law of Electric Force—Law of Magnetic Force," pp. 408-420.

   (d) Galvani, L., "On Animal Electricity," pp. 420-427.

   (e) Volta, A., "On Electricity," pp. 427-431.

   (f) Oersted, H. C., "Action of Currents on Magnets," pp. 436-441.

   (g) Ampère, A. M., "Actions Between Currents," pp. 446-460.

   (h) Faraday, M., "Electrical Experiments," pp. 472-511.

4.9 Moulton, F. R. and Schifferes, J. J., *The Autobiography of Science*. Garden City, N. Y.: Doubleday and Co., Inc., 1945.

Brief excerpts by Gilbert and Faraday included in 4.8 (a) and (h) above.

ARTICLE
in *Scientific American*   **4.10** Elsasser, W. M., "The Earth as a Dynamo," **198**, No. 5, pp. 44-63 (1958).

The magnetism of the earth may be caused by electric currents in the earth's core.

REFERENCES FOR CHAPTER 5

BOOKS   **5.1** Bachman, C. H., *Physics*. New York: John Wiley and Sons, Inc., 1955.

Modern physics for the nonacademic student.

5.2 Birren, F., *New Horizons in Color*. New York: Reinhold Publishing Corp., 1955.
> Will give the reader a greater appreciation and understanding of color in its relationship to science.

5.3 Bragg, W., *The Universe of Light*. New York: The Macmillan Co., 1934.
> A very readable book by a Nobel Prize winner. The electromagnetic spectrum and the evidence for the wave and particle nature of radiation are discussed in Chs. VII and IX.

5.4 Holton, G., *Introduction to Concepts and Theories in Physical Science*. Reading, Mass.: Addison Wesley Publishing Co., Inc., 1952.
> The photoelectric effect and the quantum theory are presented in Ch. 23.

5.5 Lemon, H. S., *From Galileo to the Nuclear Age*. Chicago: Univ. of Chicago Press, 1946.
> Textbook for nonacademic students and the general reader. Excellent discussion of light and wave phenomena in Part V, Chs. 35 through 39.

5.6 Semat, H., *Physics in the Modern World*. New York: Rinehart and Co., Inc., 1949.
> College physics introduced to the novice with simplicity and thoroughness. All basic fields are amply discussed.

5.7 Magie, W. F., *Source Book in Physics*. New York: McGraw-Hill Book Co., Inc., 1935. **ANTHOLOGY**
> Excerpts from original papers.
> > (a) Huygens, C., "Principle." "Reflection of Light." "Refraction of Light," pp. 283-289.
> > (b) Grimaldi, F. M., "Diffraction of Light," pp. 294-298.
> > (c) Newton, I., "Dispersion of Light." "The Nature of Light," pp. 298-308.
> > (d) Young, T., "Interference of Light," pp. 308-315.
> > (e) Fresnel, A. J., "Diffraction of Light," pp. 318-324.
> > (f) Roemer, O., "The Velocity of Light," pp. 335-337.
> > (g) Bradley, J., "The Velocity of Light," pp. 337-340.
> > (h) Fizeau, A. H. L., "The Velocity of Light," pp. 340-342.
> > (i) Michelson, A. A. and Morley, E. W., "The Michelson-Morley Experiment," pp. 369-377.
> > (j) Maxwell, C., "A Dynamical Theory of Electromagnetic Field," pp. 528-538.

5.8 Kline, M., "The Straight Line," **194,** No. 3, pp. 104-115 (1956). **ARTICLES** in *Scientific American*
> If you think you learned all about it in high school, you are in for a surprise.

5.9 Rush, J. H., "The Speed of Light," **193,** No. 2, pp. 62-67 (1955).

REFERENCES FOR CHAPTER 6

6.1 Asimov, I., *Only a Trillion: Speculations and Explorations on the Marvels of Science*. New York: Abelard-Schuman, Ltd., 1957. **BOOKS**
> An absorbing excursion into the realms of the exceedingly large and the exceptionally small.

6.2 Boeke, K., *Cosmic View: The Universe in 40 Jumps.* New York: The John Day Co., Inc., 1957.

A "journey outward through space to the edge of infinity, then through decreasing scales of size to the atom's nucleus—in a series of drawings each seen from a point ten times farther or ten times closer than the previous."

6.3 Born, M., *The Restless Universe.* Dover Publications, Inc., 1951.

Covers the basic matter of the universe from molecules to mesons.

6.4 Lucretius, *On the Nature of the Universe.* Penguin Books, 1951 (paperback).

The classic poem, "On the Nature of Things," translated in prose from the Latin. "In reality there are only atoms and void."

6.5 Melson, A. G., *From Atomos to Atom.* Pittsburgh: Duquesne Univ. Press, 1952.

A scholarly treatment of the evolution of the concepts of the Democritan *atoms* and the Aristotelian *minima.* The problem of Parmenides, sketched in Ex. 8, is found on pp. 13f. For the advanced reader.

6.6 Pauling, L., *General Chemistry.* San Francisco: W. H. Freeman and Co., 1958.

A standard textbook of college chemistry. Many of the fundamental concepts presented in the above discussion are found in Chs. 1 and 2.

6.7 Selwood, P. W., *General Chemistry.* New York: Henry Holt and Co., Inc., 1959.

A standard textbook in college chemistry. Atomism and atomic structure are presented in Chs. 1 and 2.

ARTICLES
in *Scientific American*

6.8 Editors, "Democritus on the Atom," **181,** No. 5, pp. 48-50 (Nov. 1949).

6.9 Kirkpatrick, P., "X-ray Microscope," **180,** No. 3, pp. 44f. (March 1949).

6.10 Melnick, J. J., "Viruses Within Cells," **189,** No. 6, pp. 38-41 (Dec. 1953).

These giant molecules are visible with the electron microscope.

6.11 Müller, E. W., "A New Microscope," **186,** No. 5, pp. 48-63 (May 1952).

6.12 Müller, E. W., "Atoms Visualized," **196,** No. 6, pp. 113-125 (June 1957).

A field ion microscope makes pictures of the atoms in a crystal by means of ions.

6.13 Pauling, L. and Corey, R. B., "The Structure of Protein Molecules," **191,** No. 1, pp. 51f. (July 1954).

6.14 Schroedinger, E., "What is Matter?" **191,** No. 3, pp. 58f. (Sept. 1954).

REFERENCES FOR CHAPTER 7

BOOKS

7.1 Gamow, G., *The Birth and Death of the Sun.* Penguin Books, 1940 (paperback).

Written for the layman. Molecules and molecular motion are discussed on pp. 19-28.

7.2   Lemon, H. B., *From Galileo to the Nuclear Age.* Chicago: Univ. of Chicago Press, 1946.

>   Textbook for the nonacademic student. The kinetic molecular theory is presented in Ch. 18.

7.3   Selwood, P. W., *General Chemistry.* New York: Henry Holt and Co., Inc., 1959.

>   Standard textbook in college chemistry. The states of matter and gas laws are discussed in Ch. 5; the molecular theory and crystal structure in Ch. 6; solutions in Ch. 12.

7.4   Magie, W. F., *Source Book in Physics.* New York: McGraw-Hill Book Co., Inc., 1935.   ANTHOLOGIES

>   Excerpts from original papers.
>   (a) Boyle, R., "The Force of the Spring of Air," pp. 84-92.
>   (b) Gay-Lussac, "The Expansion of Gases by Heat," pp. 165-172.
>   (c) Kelvin, "An Absolute Scale of Temperature," pp. 236-242.
>   (d) Maxwell, C., "The Distribution of Molecular Velocities," pp. 258-261.

7.5   Leicester, H. M. and Klickstein, H. S., *Source Book in Chemistry.* New York: McGraw-Hill Book Co., Inc., 1952.

>   Excerpt from original paper.
>   (a) Avogadro, L. R. A. C., "Hypothesis of Atoms and Molecules," pp. 232-238.

7.6   Alder, B. J. and Wainwright, T. E., "Molecular Motions," **201,** No. 4, pp. 113-127 (1959).   ARTICLES in *Scientific American*

>   Studies of particle motion, aided by computers, elucidate the structure of matter.

7.7   Cullity, B. D., "Diffusion in Metals," **196,** No. 5, pp. 103-111 (1957).

>   The wandering of atoms in solid crystals produces important metallurgical effects.

7.8   Editors, "Giant Molecules," the entire September issue (11 articles) devoted to molecules, **197,** No. 3 (1957).

REFERENCES FOR CHAPTER 8

8.1   Boyle, R., *The Sceptical Chymist.* New York: E. P. Dutton and Co., Inc., 1911.   BOOKS

>   A classic of scientific literature which challenges the theory of Aristotle that all substances are composed of earth, air, fire, and water. Its present value lies in the acuteness of Boyle's reasoning, his sound philosophy, his broad views, and his clarity of expression.

8.2   Hutton, K., *Chemistry: The Conquest of Materials.* Penguin Books, 1957 (paperback).

>   Written for the layman. Part I deals with the theories of atoms and molecules in a simplified manner.

8.3   Leicester, H. M., *The Historical Background of Chemistry.* New York: John Wiley and Sons, Inc., 1956.

>   Covers fully the often neglected Greek, Chinese, and Arabic

periods. The spread of atomic theories in the seventeenth century is discussed in Ch. XII; the laws of atomic combinations in Ch. XVI.

8.4 Tilden, W. A., *Famous Chemists*. Baltimore: George Routledge and Sons, 1921.

A very readable account of the character, work, and significance of John Dalton.

8.5 Timm, J. A., *General Chemistry* (3d ed.). New York: McGraw-Hill Book Co., Inc., 1956.

Standard textbook in college chemistry. Atoms and molecules are discussed in Ch. 3; atomic and molecular weights in Ch. 6; chemical symbolism in Ch. 7.

ANTHOLOGY **8.6** Leicester, H. M. and Klickstein, H. S., *Source Book in Chemistry*. New York: McGraw-Hill Book Co., Inc., 1952.

Excerpts from original papers.

(a) Boyle, R., "Arguments Against the Four Elements; Definition of an Element," pp. 34-42.

(b) Dalton, J., "The Atomic Theory," pp. 208-220.

(c) Avogadro, A., "Hypothesis of Atoms and Molecules," pp. 231-238.

(d) Cannizgaro, S., "Sketch of a Course of Chemical Philosophy," pp. 406-417.

(The classic paper that established the method of determination of atomic and molecular weights. Remarkably modern presentation.)

(e) Berzelius, J. J., "Chemical Symbols and Formulas," pp. 262-264.

REFERENCES FOR CHAPTER 9

BOOKS **9.1** Conant, J. B., *On Understanding Science*. Mentor Books, 1951.

The significance of Lavoisier's work on combustion and the overthrow of the Phlogiston theory are discussed in Ch. 3.

9.2 Faraday, M., *The Chemical History of a Candle*. New York: Thomas Y. Crowell Co., 1957.

The famous lectures delivered to an audience of young people at the Royal Institution in London, Christmas 1860. Remarkable integration of the chemistry of combustion up to that time.

9.3 Leicester, H. M., *The Historical Background of Chemistry*. New York: John Wiley and Sons, Inc., 1956.

Lavoisier and the foundation of modern chemistry are discussed in Ch. XV.

9.4 Pauling, L., *College Chemistry* (2d ed.). San Francisco: W. H. Freeman and Co., 1955.

Standard textbook in college chemistry. Descriptive and theoretical chemistry, presented in a well-integrated and lucid manner. Combustion and acids-bases are discussed in Ch. 5.

9.5 Timm, J. A., *General Chemistry* (3d ed.). New York: McGraw-Hill Book Co., Inc., 1956.

Good coverage of major concepts in chemistry. Oxidation and reduction are discussed in Chs. 12, 14, and 15; acids and bases in Ch. 23.

9.6 Leicester, H. M. and Klickstein, H. S., *Source Book in Chemistry.*   ANTHOLOGY
New York: McGraw-Hill Book Co., Inc., 1952.
> Excerpts from original papers.
> (a) Boyle, R., "Experiments in Combustion," pp. 43-47.
> (b) Stahl, G. E., "The Phlogiston Theory," pp. 58-61.
> (c) Priestley, J., "Of Dephlogisticated Air," pp. 112-122.
> (d) Lavoisier, A., "On Combustion in General," pp. 168-174.
> (e) Arrhenius, S., "On the Disassociation of Substances Dissolved in Water," pp. 483-490.

9.7 Burbidge, G. and Hoyle, F., "Anti-matter," **198,** No. 4, pp. 34-39   **ARTICLES**
(1958).   in *Scientific American*
9.8 Durveen, D. I., "Lavoisier," **194,** No. 5, pp. 84-96 (1956).
> He initiated the chemical revolution; the French Revolution cost him his head.

9.9 Arrhenius, S., "Theory of Electrolytic Dissociation," *Journal of the*   **ARTICLE**
American Chemical Society, **34,** pp. 353-364 (1912).
> The Willard Gibbs Award lecture, delivered in Chicago, May 12, 1911.

REFERENCES FOR CHAPTER 10

10.1 Asimov, I., *Building Blocks of the Universe.* New York: Abelard-   BOOKS
Schuman, Ltd., 1957.
> Winner of the 1958 Best Science Book for Youth award, this study of the elements is outstanding for its clarity and scholarship. It discusses "how they were discovered, who discovered them, how they got their names, what their uses are, and what their dangers are."

10.2 Asimov, I., *The World of Carbon.* New York: Abelard-Schuman, Ltd., 1958.
> Outstanding for its clarity and accuracy, this is an excellent introduction to a complex subject.

10.3 Davis, H. M., *The Chemical Elements.* Science Service, 1959 (paperback).
> Revisions by G. T. Seaborg, discoverer of most of the transuranium elements. Contains all the elements 1-102.

10.4 Mendeléeff, Dmitri I., *Principles of Chemistry* (5th ed.). Translated by G. Kamensky. New York: Longmans, Green and Co., 1891.
> The famous Faraday lecture delivered in London on June 4, 1889, appears in the appendix of Vol. 2, pp. 435-454.

10.5 Meyer, J. S., *The Elements: Builders of the Universe.* Cleveland: World Publishing Co., 1957.
> A layman's survey of the history, properties, and uses of the 102 known elements.

10.6 Weeks, M. E., *Discovery of the Elements* (6th ed.). Journal of Chemical Education, 1956.

"The chemical elements, those primeval building materials from which Nature has constructed all her various forms, have been discovered, one by one, through the ages, by patient searchers in many lands." This is a readable and well-documented account.

ANTHOLOGY   **10.7** Leicester, Henry M. and Klickstein, Herbert S., *A Source Book in Chemistry*. New York: McGraw-Hill Book Co., Inc., 1952.

Excerpts from original papers.

(a) Dobereiner, Johann W., "An Attempt to Group Elementary Substances According to Their Analogies," pp. 268-272.

(b) Mendeléeff, Dmitri I., "The Relation Between the Properties and Atomic Weights of the Elements," pp. 438-439. "A Natural System of the Elements and Its Use on Predicting the Properties of Undiscovered Elements," pp. 439-444.

ARTICLE   **10.8** Ghiorso, A. and Seaborg, G. T., "The Newest Elements," **195**, in *Scientific American*   No. 6, pp. 66-80 (Dec. 1956).

The number of elements is now 102—more are anticipated.

REFERENCES FOR CHAPTER 11

BOOKS   **11.1** Asimov, I., *Inside the Atom* (Rev. ed.). New York: Abelard-Schuman, Ltd., 1958.

A view of the atom from the inside with nontechnical explanations of atomic particles.

11.2 Lemon, H. B., *From Galileo to the Nuclear Age*. Chicago: Univ. of Chicago Press, 1946.

Textbook for the nonacademic student. The material discussed in our Ch. 11 is more extensively covered in Chs. 28, 29, 31, 32, 33, and 34.

11.3 Rutherford, E., Chaldwick, J. and Ellis, C. D., *Radiations From Radioactive Substances*. New York: Cambridge Univ. Press, 1930.

An elegant presentation of the modern theory. Read especially Chs. I, II, and VIII. For the advanced reader.

ANTHOLOGIES   **11.4** Magie, W. F., *A Source Book in Physics*. New York: McGraw-Hill Book Co., Inc., 1935.

(a) Faraday, M., "The Laws of Electrolysis," pp. 492-498.

(b) Crookes, W., "The Cathode Discharge," pp. 563-576.

(c) Goldstein, "The Canal Rays," pp. 576-578.

(d) Thomson, J. J., "The Electron," pp. 583-597.

(e) Roentgen, W. K., "X-rays," pp. 600-610.

(f) Becquerel, H., "The Radiation from Uranium," pp. 610-613.

(g) Curie, P. and M. S., "Polonium. Radium," pp. 613-616.

11.5 *Encyclopaedia Britannica.* Many good articles are found in recent editions.

11.6 da C. Andrade, E. N., *The Birth of the Nuclear Atom,* **195,** No. 5, pp. 93-107 (1956).

> Rutherford was unaware that his discovery of the nucleus would change the world.

ARTICLE
in *Scientific American*

11.7 Rutherford, E., "The Scattering of α and β Particles by Matter and the Structure of Matter," *Philosophical Magazine,* **21,** pp. 669-688 (1911).

> The famous paper in which the theory was proposed.

11.8 Aston, F. W., "Isotopes and Atomic Weights," *Nature,* **105,** pp. 617-619 (1920).

MAGAZINE ARTICLES

REFERENCES FOR CHAPTER 12

12.1 Asimov, I., *Inside the Atom* (Rev. ed.). New York: Abelard-Schuman, Ltd., 1958.

> A view of the atom from the inside with nontechnical explanations of atomic particles. The atomic future is explored.

BOOKS

12.2 Bohr, N., *Atomic Physics and Human Knowledge.* New York: John Wiley and Sons, Inc., 1958.

> A series of essays from 1932 to 1957 regarding the philosophic implications of the quantum theories. The essay on "Atoms and Human Knowledge" (1955) is quite understandable (pp. 83-93).

12.3 Heisenberg, W., *Physics and Philosophy—The Revolution in Modern Science.* New York: Harper & Bros., 1958.

> For the general reader with some philosophic and scientific background.

12.4 Pauling, L., *General Chemistry.* San Francisco: W. H. Freeman and Co., 1953.

> A standard textbook in college chemistry. The discussion of the quantum theory and molecular substance in Ch. 8 is somewhat advanced but still understandable. Ionic valence is treated in Ch. 9; electron sharing in Ch. 10; oxidation-reduction in Ch. 11; acids and bases in Ch. 21.

12.5 Selwood, P. W., *General Chemistry.* New York: Henry Holt and Co., Inc., 1959.

> A standard textbook in college chemistry. Considerably simpler than Pauling (Ref. 12.4). Atomic structure is discussed in Ch. 2; atomic combinations in Ch. 3; acids and bases in Ch. 13.

12.6 Thomsen, G., *The Atom* (5th ed.). New York: Oxford Univ. Press, 1956.

> Opens the world of the atom to the layman with ease and simplicity. Physical characteristics of the atom as well as its relation to chemistry are discussed.

12.7 DeBenedetti, S., "Mesonic Atoms," **195,** No. 4, pp. 93-102 (Oct. 1956).

ARTICLES
in *Scientific American*

12.8 Darrow, K. K., "The Quantum Theory," **186,** No. 3, pp. 47-54 (March 1952).

12.9 Nier, A. O., Co., "The Mass Spectrometer," **188,** No. 3, pp. 68-74 (March 1953).

REFERENCES FOR CHAPTER 13

BOOKS

13.1 Asimov, I., *Inside the Atom* (Rev. ed.). New York: Abelard-Schuman, Ltd., 1958.
> A view of the atom from the inside with nontechnical explanations of atomic particles. The atomic future is explored.

13.2 Coleman, J. A., *Relativity for the Layman.* New York: William-Frederick Press, 1954.
> Relativity, the theory "understood by only 12 men," is clearly explained.

13.3 Fermi, L., *Atoms in the Family.* Chicago: Univ. of Chicago Press, 1954.
> The absorbing story of Enrico Fermi, one of the leaders in the Manhattan Project, who piloted the first self-sustaining chain reaction as well as many other projects which led to the successful explosion of the first atomic bomb.

13.4 Gamow, G., *Mr. Tompkins in Wonderland.* New York: Cambridge Univ. Press, 1940.
> An excellent introduction to recently discovered physical laws. Explains relativity, and quantum theory, by placing man in a dream universe of very small relative size.

13.5 Gamow, G., *Mr. Tompkins Explores the Atom.* New York: Cambridge Univ. Press, 1944.
> Mr. Tompkins, searching for a perfect gambling system, finds molecular motion, intricacies of the electron, and the cyclotron. An added section relates the lectures from which the bank clerk's dreams have sprung.

13.6 Glasstone, S., *Sourcebook on Atomic Energy* (2d ed.). New York: D. Van Nostrand Co., Inc., 1958.
> A new edition of a very popular and authoritative reference work on atomic energy, atomic theory, and atomic science, sponsored by the U. S. Atomic Energy Commission.

13.7 Hughes, D. J., *On Nuclear Energy.* Cambridge, Mass.: Harvard Univ. Press, 1957.
> Nuclear energy applied to peacetime use. Insight is given into the atom and its parts. Atomic reactions are explained.

13.8 Jones, G. O., *et al., Atoms and the Universe.* New York: Charles Scribner's Sons, 1956.
> A comprehensive account of the atom and its importance to man and the universe. The discussion of the energy, mass, and composition of matter assumes much previous knowledge of the subject.

13.9 Smyth, H. D., *Atomic Energy for Military Purposes.* Princeton: Princeton Univ. Press, 1945.
> The first official report describing the efforts and accomplishments of the Manhattan District Project. Quite readable.

13.10 Bethe, H. A., "The Hydrogen Bomb," **182**, No. 4, pp. 18-23 (1950).

13.11 Bethe, H. A., "What Holds the Nucleus Together," **189**, No. 3, pp. 58-63 (1953).

13.12 Burbidge, G. and Hoyle, F., "Anti-matter," **198**, No. 4, pp. 34-39 (1958).

13.13 Courant, E. D., "A One Hundred Billion Volt Accelerator, **188**, No. 5, pp. 40-45 (1953).

13.14 DeBenedetti, S., "Mesonic Atoms," **195**, No. 4, pp. 93-104 (1956).

13.15 Flagg, J. F. and Zerboski, E. L., "The Atomic Pile Chemistry," **187**, No. 1, pp. 62-67 (1952).

13.16 Gell-Mam, M. and Rosenbaum, E. P., "Elementary Particles," **197**, No. 1, pp. 72-88 (1957).

13.17 Hahn, O., "The Discovery of Fission," **198**, No. 2, pp. 76-84 (1958).

13.18 Hofstadter, R., "The Atomic Nucleus, **195**, No. 1, pp. 55-71 (1956).

13.19 Johnson, G. and Brown, H., "Non-Military Nuclear Explosions," **199**, No. 6, pp. 29-35 (1958).

13.20 Kamen, M., "Tracers," **180**, No. 2, pp. 30-41 (1949).

13.21 Mayer, M. G., "The Structure of the Nucleus," **184**, No. 3, pp. 22-34 (1951).

13.22 Morrison, P., "The Neutrino," **194**, No. 1, pp. 58-79 (1956).

13.23 Morrison, P. and E. "The Neutron," **185**, No. 4, pp. 44-53 (1951).

13.24 Oppenheimer, J. R., "The Age of Science: 1900-1950," **183**, No. 3 pp. 20-23 (1950).

13.25 Platzman, R. L., "What Is Ionizing Radiation," **201**, No. 3, pp. 74-83 (1959).

13.26 Post, F. R., "Fusion Power," **197**, No. 6, pp. 73-84 (1957).

13.27 Schumar, J. R., "Reactor Fuel Elements," **200**, No. 2, pp. 37-43 (1959).

13.28 Segre, E. and Wiegand, C. E., "The Antiproton," **194**, No. 6, pp. 37-41 (1956).

13.29 Smith, L., "The Bevatron," **184**, No. 2, pp. 20-25 (1951).

13.30 Spitzer, L., Jr., "The Stellarator," **199**, No. 4, pp. 28-35 (1958).

13.31 Weisskopf, V. F. and Rosenbaum, E. P., "A Model of the Nucleus," **193**, No. 6, pp. 84-91 (1955).

13.32 Wilson, R. R., "Particle Accelerators," **198**, No. 3, pp. 64-76 (1958).

ARTICLES

in *Scientific American*

REFERENCES FOR CHAPTER 14

14.1 Abetti, G., *The Sun.* New York: The Macmillan Co., 1957.

A comprehensive treatment of modern solar knowledge for the inquiring layman and the student of astronomy or astrophysics.

14.2 Bok, B. J., *The Astronomer's Universe.* New York: Cambridge Univ. Press, 1958.

An account of recent developments that have given new tools and methods to astronomers and have facilitated a rapid increase in our knowledge of the universe.

14.3 Bok, B. J. and P. F., *The Milky Way* (3d ed.). Cambridge, Mass.: Harvard Univ. Press, 1957.

An introduction to radio astronomy, the stars, and changes occurring in our own galaxy.

BOOKS

14.4 Fath, E. A., *The Elements of Astronomy* (5th Ed.). New York: McGraw-Hill Book Co., Inc., 1955.

> An introduction to astronomy, requiring a knowledge of simple mathematics and plane geometry.

14.5 Gamow, G., *The Birth and Death of the Sun*. New York: The Viking Press, 1940 (paperback).

> Interestingly written for the general reader.

14.6 Pickering, J. S., *1001 Questions Answered About Astronomy*. New York: Dodd, Mead and Co., Inc., 1958.

> Common questions about the universe and its components answered by a staff member of the famous Hayden Planetarium in New York City.

14.7 Skilling, W. T. and Richardson, R. S., *A Brief Text in Astronomy* (Rev. ed.). New York: Henry Holt and Co., Inc., 1959.

> For general background or as a stimulus to further study. A larger standard text is also available by the same authors (Holt, 1947).

14.8 Thiel, R., *And There was Light: The Discovery of the Universe*. New York: Alfred A. Knopf, Inc., 1957.

> Adventure and discovery in the world of astronomy, from the star-gazing astrologers of Babylon and China to the astrophysicists of today.

14.9 Vaucouleurs, G. de, *Discovery of the Universe*. New York: The Macmillan Co., 1957.

> Describes both the evolution of man's ideas of the universe and the development of modern astronomical concepts.

14.10 Scientific American, *The New Astronomy*. New York: Simon and Schuster, Inc., 1955 (paperback).

> A series of recent articles reprinted from *Scientific American*.

14.11 Scientific American, *The Universe*. New York: Simon and Schuster, Inc., 1957 (paperback).

> A series of recent articles reprinted from *Scientific American*.

ANTHOLOGY

14.12 Heath, T. L., *Greek Astronomy*. New York: E. P. Dutton and Co., Inc., 1932.

> A translation of the most important manuscripts in Greek astronomical thought, with extensive commentary.
> (a) Aristarchus, "Sizes and Distances of the Sun and Moon," pp. 100-104.
> (b) Archimedes, "Sand-Reckoner," pp. 105-109.

ARTICLES
in *Scientific American*

14.13 Bok, B. J., "The Arms of the Galaxy," **201,** No. 6, pp. 92-104 (1959).

14.14 Burbidge, M. and G., "Stellar Populations," **199,** No. 4, pp. 43-50 (1958).

14.15 Friedman, H., "Rocket Astronomy," **200,** No. 6, pp. 52-59 (1959).

14.16 Kroft, R. R., "Pulsating Stars and Cosmic Distance," **201,** No. 1, pp. 48-55 (1959).

14.17 Lovell, A. B. C., "Radio Stars," **188,** No. 1, pp. 17-21 (1953).

14.18 Marshak, R. E., "The Energy of the Stars," **182,** No. 1, pp. 42-45 (1950).

14.19 Payne-Gaposchkin, C. H., "Why Are Galaxies Spiral?" **189,** No. 3, pp. 89-99 (1955).

14.20 Vaucouleurs, G. de, "The Clouds of Magellan," **194,** No. 4, pp. 52-75 (1956).

14.21 Westerhout, G., "The Radio Galaxy," **201,** No. 2, pp. 44-51 (1959).

REFERENCES FOR CHAPTER 15

15.1 Ames, G. and Wyler, R., *The Earth's Story*. Creative Educational Society, Inc., 1957.   B O O K S

"Provides many of the basic data of geology in an interesting and provocative way...."

15.2 Barnett, L., *The Universe and Dr. Einstein* (Rev. ed.). New York: William Sloane Associates, 1957.

The universe unfolded through the work of Albert Einstein; matter from macrocosm to microcosm is excellently explained.

15.3 Carrington, R., *The Story of Our Earth*. New York: Harper & Bros., 1956.

Evolution, from the origin of the earth to the appearance of civilized man.

15.4 Croneis, C. and Krumbein, W. C., *Down to Earth*. Chicago: Univ. of Chicago Press, 1936.

Presents geology, one of the sciences least known and understood by the layman, in a highly interesting manner.

15.5 Dunbar, C. O., *Historical Geology*. New York: John Wiley and Sons, Inc., 1949.

Discusses fossils, origin of the earth, and geological periods; included is an introduction to plants and animals.

15.6 Gamow, G., *Biography of the Earth; Its Past, Present and Future*. New York: The Viking Press, 1941 (paperback).

Interestingly written for the general reader.

15.7 Gamow, G., *The Creation of the Universe*. New York: The Viking Press, 1952.

Discusses the theory of the formation of the universe from the explosion of a primordial "atom."

15.8 Garrels, R. M., *A Textbook of Geology*. New York: Harper & Bros., 1951.

Interestingly written for the serious but nonscience major.

15.9 Hapgood, C. H. and Campbell, J. R., *Earth's Shifting Crust*. Pantheon Books, Inc., 1958.

A commentary on contemporary geophysical research. The author is interested particularly in his postulate that the earth's crust shifts in response to the pressure of the polar ice cap.

15.10 Hoyle, F., *The Nature of the Universe*. New York: Harper & Bros., 1950 (paperback).

Discusses the origin and future of the earth, planets, and stars. For the general reader.

15.11 Lobeck, A. K., *Geomorphology*. New York: McGraw-Hill Book Co., Inc., 1939.

An attractively illustrated approach to the study of landscapes.

15.12 Moore R., *The Earth We Live On*. New York: Alfred A. Knopf, Inc., 1956.

> The advance of geology as a science and the accomplishments of eminent personalities who have been pioneers in man's quest for knowledge; answers many ancient questions about the origin of the earth.

15.13 Payne-Gaposchkin, C., *Stars in the Making*. Cambridge, Mass.: Harvard Univ. Press, 1952.

> A unique presentation of the evolution of the universe; excellent photographs.

15.14 Pfeiffer, J., *The Changing Universe*. New York: Random House, Inc., 1956.

> A description of radio astronomy, which is exploring a new universe by interpreting the "voices" and "noises" from outer space.

15.15 Shuler, E. W., *Rocks and Rivers*. New York: Ronald Press Co., 1945.

> Strikingly illustrated, with appeal for any age group.

15.16 Swinnerton, H. H., *The Earth Beneath Us*. Boston: Little, Brown and Co., 1955.

> Various theories about the origin of our world, the forming of the elements, physiognomy of the earth, and first appearances of life.

15.17 Scientific American, *The Planet Earth*. New York: Simon and Schuster, Inc., 1957.

> A series of recent articles reprinted from *Scientific American*.

ARTICLES in *Scientific American*

15.18 Blaauw, A., "Young Stars," **194**, No. 2, pp. 36-41, (1956).

15.19 Brown, H., "The Age of the Solar System," **196**, No. 2, pp. 71-82 (1957).

15.20 Bucher, W. H., "The Crust of the Earth," **182**, No. 5, pp. 32-41 (1950).

15.21 Bullen, K. E., "The Interior of the Earth," **193**, No. 3, pp. 56-66 (1955).

15.22 Deevey, E. S., Jr., "Radio Carbon Dating," **186**, No. 2, pp. 24-28 (1952).

15.23 Ewen, H. I., "Radio Waves from Interstellar Hydrogen," **189**, No. 6, pp. 42-46 (1953).

15.24 Fisher, R. L. and Revelle, R., "The Trenches of the Pacific," **193**, No. 5, pp. 36-41 (1955).

15.25 Fowler, W. A., "The Origin of the Elements," **194**, No. 3, pp. 82-91 (1956).

15.26 Gray, G., "A Larger and Older Universe," **188**, No. 6, pp. 56-66 (1953).

15.27 Kraus, J. D., "Radio Telescopes," **192**, No. 3, pp. 36-43 (1955).

15.28 Oliver, J., "Long Earthquake Waves," **200**, No. 3, pp. 131-143 (1959).

15.29 Opik, E. J., "Climate and the Changing Sun," **198**, No. 6, pp. 85-95 (1958).

15.30 Urey, H. C., "The Origin of the Earth," **187**, No. 4, pp. 53-60 (1952).

15.31 Whipple, F. L., "The Dust Cloud Hypothesis," **78**, No. 5, pp. 34-45 (1948).

INDEX